ELEMENTARY
ALGEBRA

ELEMENTARY
ALGEBRA

EUGENE D. NICHOLS

DEPARTMENT OF MATHEMATICS EDUCATION
Florida State University

HOLT, RINEHART AND WINSTON, INC.   1966
New York · Chicago · San Francisco · Toronto · London

Preface

This is an introductory course in modern algebra. It is intended for beginning college students who have not had an algebra course in high school or for those students who have had a strictly traditional high school algebra course.

The following are a few of the important features of *Elementary Algebra:*

The basic concepts of sets are introduced in the first chapter and used throughout the book. This approach provides an elegant way of expressing many mathematical relations and helps clarify and unify other algebraic concepts. Of course, this chapter on sets may be used as a reference or a review by students who have already studied sets.

Throughout, there is emphasis on reasoning, discovery, and justification of algebraic processes through basic properties. The *why* and *how* of mathematical processes are given serious attention. The idea of proof as the basis of mathematics is introduced gradually and carefully.

The exposition of new topics is complete and clear. This encourages students to discover mathematical truths and patterns for themselves. The careful presentation will help students develop the ability to read mathematical discourses.

Many learning aids are included to help students with different levels of understanding: a vocabulary list, chapter review exercises, a chapter test and a summary of properties and theorems at the end of each chapter. Cumulative review exercises are included at the ends of chapters 4, 8, 11, and 14. References for students' additional reading are also included at the end of each chapter. A glossary of mathematical terms used in the book and a complete index are found at the end of the text.

The author wishes to acknowledge his indebtedness to Wagner G. Collins of Robbinsdale, Minnesota; E. Henry Garland of Tallahassee, Florida, for his many suggestions concerning content and pedagogy; and Miss Mary Clyde Johnson for typing the manuscript.

Tallahassee, Florida   E. D. N.
December 1965

Contents

SYMBOL LIST

ϵ	is an element of	2
{ }	set	3
ϕ	empty set	3
$\subseteq$	is a subset of	10
$\forall$	for every	10
$\subset$	is a proper subset of	11
$\cup$	union	16
$\cap$	intersection	17
$\overline{A}$	complement of set A	22
$\leq$	is less than or equal to	59
$\geq$	is greater than or equal to	59
$\lvert {}^-5 \rvert$	absolute value of negative 5	61
$0.\overline{12}$	repeating decimal	66
$\{x \mid x = 3\}$	the set of all x such that $x = 3$	182
(x, y)	ordered number pair	276
x^n	the nth power of x	313
$\sqrt[n]{x}$	nth root of x	326
$U \times U$	cross product set where $x \,\epsilon\, U$ and $y \,\epsilon\, U$	395
A'	inverse of function A	405
$\doteq$	is approximately equal to	428

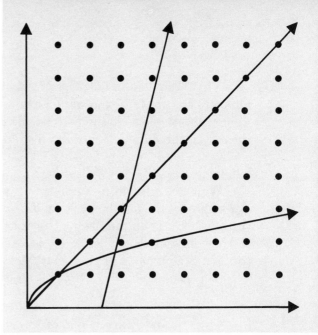

CHAPTER 1

Sets

INTRODUCTION

In everyday conversation we often speak of collections of things or objects. For example, you might need to refer to a collection of books in the library of your school, or of the pencils in your desk, or of the students in your school, or of the boys and girls in the United States less than 17 years of age. Each of these groups of objects is a *set*. We will agree to think of a *set* as a collection of objects. A description will be given enabling us to tell whether or not an object belongs to a given set.

Consider the following:
    A: the set consisting of the numbers 1, 5, 10, 20
    B: the set consisting of the students in this class
    C: the set of all desks in this room

Now consider three other sets.
    D: the set of all natural numbers, that is, 1, 2, 3, 4, 5, . . .
    E: the set of all even natural numbers, that is, 2, 4, 6, 8, . . .
    F: the set of all odd natural numbers, that is 1, 3, 5, 7, . . .

1

The three dots in each case on page 1 indicate that each sequence of numbers continues in the same pattern. It should be easy for you to see the pattern in each case and to decide how to continue. For example, for the set D, the number following 5 would be 6, then 7, and so on. For the set E, 10 would follow 8, then 12, and so on. Name the four numbers following 12 in E. Name the four numbers following 7 in F.

We shall refer to a member of a set as being an element of the set. For example, the number 5 is an *element* or *member* of the set A; however, the number 3 is not an element of this set. If there is a girl by the name of Mary in your class, then Mary is an *element* of the set B. We can express the same thought by saying that Mary *belongs* to the set B. The Greek letter ϵ is used to indicate that an object belongs to a particular set.

If G is the set of all girls in this room
and Mary is one of the girls in this room, then

Mary ϵ G

which is read: Mary is a member of G

If N is the set of all natural numbers, then

107 ϵ N

means: 107 is a member of the set of all natural numbers

To say that Jane is *not* an element of set G
we draw a diagonal line through the symbol ϵ and write

Jane $\notin$ G

The number 5 belongs to or is a member of the set D. The number 2,035,717 is also an element of this set. Explain. Is the number 2,035,717 a member of set E? F? How many elements are there in the set A? B? C? D? E? F?

From your answers to the preceding question you will see a difference between the sets A, B, C and the sets D, E, F. Can you describe this difference?

Sets such as A, B, and C are called "finite sets," and sets such as D, E, and F are called "infinite sets." Can you explain the reason for choosing the words "finite" and "infinite" to describe these sets?

It is awkward to write "the set of numbers 1, 2, 3" every time we want to indicate that we are speaking of the *set of these numbers*, rather than the *numbers themselves*. To simplify writing, we shall use braces within which we shall list the members of the set.

$$\{1, 2, 3\}$$

means

the set consisting of the numbers 1, 2, 3

$$\{Johnny, Susie\}$$

means

the set consisting of Johnny and Susie

Since it is impossible to list all members of an infinite set, we list several members of the set and then write three dots. The dots indicate that the pattern established by the first few elements of the set continues indefinitely. It is important, however, to list enough members so that the reader will get the pattern and know how to continue in case he wants to list more members. For example, to describe a set as $\{1, \ldots\}$ is not enough to show what set is intended; but the description of the set $\{1, 3, 5, 7, 9, \ldots\}$ is sufficient to indicate that the set of all odd natural numbers is intended.

There is one set which we have not yet mentioned. It is the one which contains no members, and is called the *empty* or *null* set. We use the symbol "ϕ" to refer to the *empty set*.

EXERCISES

1. Give three examples of finite sets.

2. Give three examples of infinite sets.

3. Would you be able to count, given sufficient time and patience, the elements of any finite set? Explain your answer.

4. Would you be able to count, given sufficient time and patience, the elements of any infinite set? Explain your answer.

5. List the first five members of the set of all natural numbers divisible by

    a. 3   **b.** 5   **c.** 10   **d.** 12   **e.** 13   **f.** 15

[HINT: We say that 35 *is divisible by* 5 because the quotient $35 \div 5 = 7$ is a *natural* number.]

6. List the elements of the following sets.

    a. The natural numbers less than 6
    b. The schools in your athletic conference
    c. The months of the year
    d. Your teachers this semester

    e. The months whose names start with the letter D
    f. The natural numbers less than 9 and greater than 6
    g. The odd natural numbers less than 20
    h. The planets of the solar system
    i. The seasons of the year
    j. The odd natural numbers less than 20 which are divisible by 5
    k. The natural numbers between 50 and 100 which are divisible by 6

7. Is each natural number in the answer for problem **6k** divisible by both 2 and 3, that is, is each number which is divisible by 6 divisible by 2 and also divisible by 3?

8. What do the three sets described below have in common? [HINT: First list their elements.]

The natural numbers less than 7 which are also greater than 5
The odd natural numbers less than 20 which are also divisible by 7
The states of the United States entirely surrounded by water

9. Each of the following two phrases describes the empty set.

    The set of all polar bears whose natural habitat is Africa
    The set of all girls on your school's football squad

Give three phrases each describing the empty set.

10. Let T be the set of natural numbers divisible by 3. Label each statement as either true or false.

a. $39 \in T$	**d.** $237 \in T$	**g.** $522 \notin T$
b. $17 \notin T$	**e.** $112 \in T$	**h.** $92,322 \in T$
c. $117 \notin T$	**f.** $10,001 \in T$	**i.** $92,321 \in T$

11. Let S be the set of natural numbers divisible by 9. Label each statement as either true or false.

a. $81 \notin S$	**c.** $207 \in S$	**e.** $34,560 \notin S$
b. $89 \in S$	**d.** $88,092 \in S$	**f.** $88,776 \in S$

Numbers and numerals

Perhaps you ponder at times such questions as "How many numbers *five* are there?" The answer is: there is only *one* number five. Yet the number five has many names. When we want to refer to the number five we may use any one of many names such as

$$5 \qquad \tfrac{10}{2} \qquad 3+2 \qquad V \qquad \text{five} \qquad 2\tfrac{1}{2} \times 2$$

Is there an end to the list of different names for the number five that we might write?

As you recall from previous study a name of a number is called a *numeral*. In algebra, we write and talk mostly about numbers. Occasionally, however, we do refer to numerals. For example, we may say

The numeral 5 is larger than the numeral 5

We may also say: The numeral V is a Roman numeral for the number five.

Sometimes it is a little awkward to be careful about distinguishing between numbers and numerals. For example, when saying "Give an example of a two-digit number divisible by 7," we are somewhat careless. It is because, when saying "a two-digit number," we really mean a two-digit numeral, since we tell the number of digits by looking at a symbol. For example, "43" has two digits, "4" and "3". To be quite careful, we would have to rephrase the statement above to read something like this

Give an example of a two-digit numeral
which names a number divisible by 7

At times in this book, we shall allow ourselves the luxury of avoiding the awkwardness due to the distinction between number and numeral. We shall use the less careful language, provided we are rather sure that it will not confuse you.

In the example above, we talked about the *divisibility* of a number by 7. Also in problem **5** we said that 35 is divisible by 5 because the quotient $35 \div 5 = 7$ is a natural number. We state the following general definition.

■ *Definition of x Is Divisible By y* For natural numbers x and y, *x is divisible by y* means the quotient $x \div y$ is a natural number. In such cases, we will say that y is a *divisor* of x.

For example, 6 has four divisors: 1, 2, 3, and 6. The number 6 divided by each of the divisors results in a quotient which is a natural number.

It is interesting to classify all natural numbers into different sets according to the number of divisors they have. The definitions below accomplish this for us.

■ *Definition of Prime Number* A natural number which has exactly two divisors is called a *prime number*.

■ *Definition of Composite Number* A natural number which has more than two divisors is called a *composite number*.

For example, 6 is a composite number because it has more than two divisors; 7 is a prime number because it has exactly two divisors, 1 and 7.

EXERCISES

1. Each set of five names below contains four names for the same number. Identify the one name which does not fit with the other four.

    a. $\frac{18}{2}$ IX $2\frac{1}{2} \times 4$ $4\frac{1}{2} \times 2$ $99 \div 11$

RECALL: 3^2 (read: three squared or three to the second power) means 3×3.

              2^3 (read: two cubed or two to the third power) means $2 \times 2 \times 2$.

              2^4 (read: two to the fourth power) means $2 \times 2 \times 2 \times 2$.

    b. 2^4 4^2 $\frac{32}{2}$ $\frac{48}{2}$ $29 - 13$

RECALL: $\sqrt{16}$ (read: the square root of sixteen) is 4 because $4 \times 4 = 16$.

              $\sqrt[3]{27}$ (read: the cube root of twenty-seven) is 3 because $3 \times 3 \times 3 = 27$.

    c. $\sqrt{64}$ $\sqrt{24}$ $2 \times \sqrt{16}$ $4 \div \frac{1}{2}$ VIII

    d. $\frac{1}{2}$ $\sqrt{\frac{1}{4}}$ $\frac{1}{4} + \frac{1}{4}$ $\sqrt{2}$ .5

    e. .25 $\frac{1}{4}$ $\sqrt{\frac{1}{2}}$ $\sqrt{\frac{1}{16}}$ $\frac{1}{8} + \frac{1}{8}$

RECALL: 24_{five} means 2 fives $+$ 4 ones, which is fourteen.

    f. 21_{seven} 30_{five} 15_{ten} 32_{six} 13_{twelve}

2. In the set of natural numbers, there is only one number which is *neither* prime *nor* composite. What number is it?

3. There is only one prime number which is also an even number. What number is it?

4. Write a brief argument showing that any even number greater than 2 is not a prime number.

5. List the first ten members of the set of prime numbers.

6. Let P be the set of prime natural numbers less than 11. Label the following statements as true or false.

    a. $6 \in P$ **d.** $7 \in P$ **g.** $1 \notin P$

    b. $9 \notin P$ **e.** $5 \notin P$ **h.** $0 \in P$

    c. $3 \in P$ **f.** $13 \in P$ **i.** $11 \in P$

Matching sets

Consider the following two sets.

$$\{1, 2, 3\} \qquad \{100, 101, 102\}$$

The elements of the first set are the numbers 1, 2, 3, and the elements of the second set are the numbers 100, 101, 102. We can attempt to pair up the elements of one set with the elements of the other in the following way.

$$
\begin{array}{lll}
1 \longleftrightarrow 100 & 1 \longleftrightarrow 100 & 2 \longleftrightarrow 100 \\
3 \longleftrightarrow 101 \text{ or} & 2 \longleftrightarrow 101 \text{ or} & 1 \longleftrightarrow 101 \text{ and so on.} \\
2 \longleftrightarrow 102 & 3 \longleftrightarrow 102 & 3 \longleftrightarrow 102
\end{array}
$$

In how many different ways can the elements of these two sets be matched?

Note that each time you pair or match the elements of the two sets above, no elements are left over in either set. For each element in the first set, there is a corresponding element in the second set; and for each element in the second set, there is a corresponding element in the first set. When the elements of two sets can be matched in this way, the relationship is called a *one-to-one correspondence* between the two sets. When a one-to-one correspondence exists between two sets, they are called *matching sets*.

Is it possible to establish a one-to-one correspondence between the two following sets? Why or why not?

$$\{1, 2, 3, 4\} \qquad \{17, 19, 21, 23, 25\}$$

You probably found that it is only necessary to be able to count in order to tell whether or not two finite sets are matching sets. What about infinite sets?

Let A be the set of *all* natural numbers and B the set of all *even* natural numbers. We display in writing only parts of infinite sets and then indicate by three dots that not all of the set is described.

$$A: \{1, 2, 3, 4, 5, 6, 7, 8, \ldots\}$$
$$B: \{2, 4, 6, 8, 10, 12, 14, 16, \ldots\}$$

Is it possible to establish a one-to-one correspondence between sets A and B? Let us try.

$$
\begin{array}{l}
A: \{1, 2, 3, 4, \ 5, \ 6, \ 7, \ 8, \ldots\} \\
\quad\ \updownarrow \updownarrow \updownarrow \updownarrow \ \updownarrow \ \updownarrow \ \ \updownarrow \ \ \updownarrow \\
B: \{2, 4, 6, 8, 10, 12, 14, 16, \ldots\}
\end{array}
$$

The double-headed arrows above show some elements of set A paired with some elements of B and vice versa. Now, you should observe that it is possible to know how to continue this process of pairing as far as you please. In this pairing, which element of B is paired with a given element of A? What element of B would be matched with the element 201 of A? With 1024 of A? 3,000,001 of A? We can, therefore, conclude that the set of all natural numbers and the set of even natural numbers are matching sets.

Let us consider another pair of infinite sets.

$$X: \{1, 2, 3, 4, 5, 6, 7, 8, \ldots\}$$
$$Y: \{100, 101, 102, 103, 104, 105, 106, 107, \ldots\}$$

The set X is the set of all natural numbers and the set Y is the set of natural numbers which are greater than 99. Both sets are infinite sets. Why? Are X and Y matching sets? To answer this question, we display one way of establishing a one-to-one correspondence between these two sets.

$$X: \{\ 1,\quad 2,\quad 3,\quad 4,\quad 5,\quad 6,\quad 7,\quad 8, \ldots\}$$
$$\updownarrow \quad \updownarrow \quad \updownarrow \quad \updownarrow \quad \updownarrow \quad \updownarrow \quad \updownarrow \quad \updownarrow$$
$$Y: \{100, 101, 102, 103, 104, 105, 106, 107, \ldots\}$$

Thus, the number 1 in the set X is paired with the number 100 in the set Y; 2 with 101; and so on. What number in Y would be paired with 20 in X? With 100 in X? With 1007 in X? What number in X would be matched with 107 in Y? With 200 in Y? With 1075 in Y?

Let us match two finite sets.

$$A: \{\tfrac{1}{2}, \tfrac{1}{3}, \tfrac{1}{4}, \tfrac{1}{5}, \tfrac{1}{6}\} \qquad\qquad A: \{\tfrac{1}{2}, \tfrac{1}{3}, \tfrac{1}{4}, \tfrac{1}{5}, \tfrac{1}{6}\}$$
$$\updownarrow \ \updownarrow \ \updownarrow \ \updownarrow \ \updownarrow \qquad \text{or} \qquad \updownarrow \ \updownarrow \ \updownarrow \ \updownarrow \ \updownarrow$$
$$B: \{2, 3, 4, 5, 6\} \qquad\qquad B: \{3, 4, 5, 6, 2\}$$

or in some other way. In either case we have established that A and B are matching sets by showing a one-to-one correspondence between the members of the two sets.

EXERCISES

1. Are the following pairs of sets matching sets?
   a. $S:$ {2, 3, 4, 5, 6}
      $T:$ {Mike, Bob, Hal, Leroy, Ed, Bill}
   b. $C:$ {Scranton, Florida, California}
      $D:$ {St. Paul, Chicago, Denver, Vermont}
   c. $G:$ {1, 3, 5, 7, 9, ...}
      $H:$ {2, 4, 6, 8, 10}

2. Give examples of three pairs of *finite* sets such that the two sets in each pair are matching sets.

3. Give examples of three pairs of finite sets such that *no* two sets in a pair are matching sets.

4. Give examples of three pairs of *infinite* sets such that the two sets in each pair are matching sets.

5. For each pair of sets, a one-to-one correspondence is shown. Describe the one-to-one correspondence between the elements of A and those of B.

Example:

$$A: \{1, 2, 3, 4, \ldots\}$$
$$\updownarrow \ \updownarrow \ \updownarrow \ \updownarrow$$
$$B: \{1, 4, 9, 16, \ldots\}$$

Description: Each element of A is matched with its square ($1^2 = 1$; $2^2 = 4$; $3^2 = 9$; and so on).

a. $A: \{\frac{1}{2}, \frac{1}{3}, \frac{1}{4}, \frac{1}{5}, \ldots\}$
$\updownarrow \ \updownarrow \ \updownarrow \ \updownarrow$
$B: \{2, 3, 4, 5, \ldots\}$

b. $A: \{\frac{1}{2}, \frac{1}{3}, \frac{1}{4}, \frac{1}{5}, \ldots\}$
$\updownarrow \ \updownarrow \ \updownarrow \ \updownarrow$
$B: \{3, 4, 5, 6, \ldots\}$

c. $A: \{\frac{1}{4}, \frac{1}{6}, \frac{1}{8}, \frac{1}{10}, \ldots\}$
$\updownarrow \ \updownarrow \ \updownarrow \ \updownarrow$
$B: \{3, 5, 7, 9, \ldots\}$

d. $A: \{1, 2, 3, 4, \ldots\}$
$\updownarrow \ \updownarrow \ \updownarrow \ \updownarrow$
$B: \{1, 8, 27, 64, \ldots\}$

e. $A: \{\frac{1}{2}, \frac{1}{3}, \frac{1}{4}, \frac{1}{5}, \ldots\}$
$\updownarrow \ \updownarrow \ \updownarrow \ \updownarrow$
$B: \{\frac{1}{4}, \frac{1}{9}, \frac{1}{16}, \frac{1}{25}, \ldots\}$

f. $A: \{1, 2, 3, 4, \ldots\}$
$\updownarrow \ \updownarrow \ \updownarrow \ \updownarrow$
$B: \{2, 5, 8, 11, \ldots\}$

g. $A: \{\frac{1}{2}, \frac{1}{4}, \frac{1}{8}, \frac{1}{16}, \ldots\}$
$\updownarrow \ \updownarrow \ \updownarrow \ \updownarrow$
$B: \{\frac{3}{4}, \frac{3}{8}, \frac{3}{16}, \frac{3}{32}, \ldots\}$

h. $A: \{1, 2, 3, 4, 5, \ldots\}$
$\updownarrow \ \updownarrow \ \updownarrow \ \updownarrow \ \updownarrow$
$B: \{2, 3, 5, 7, 11, \ldots\}$

i. $A: \{1, 2, 3, 4, 5, \ldots\}$
$\updownarrow \ \updownarrow \ \updownarrow \ \updownarrow \ \updownarrow$
$B: \{2, 8, 18, 32, 50, \ldots\}$

j. $A: \{1, 2, 3, 4, 5, \ldots\}$
$\updownarrow \ \updownarrow \ \updownarrow \ \updownarrow \ \updownarrow$
$B: \{3, 9, 19, 33, 51, \ldots\}$

k. $A: \{1, 2, 3, 4, 5, \ldots\}$
$\updownarrow \ \updownarrow \ \updownarrow \ \updownarrow \ \updownarrow$
$B: \{3, 10, 29, 66, 127, \ldots\}$

l. $A: \{\frac{1}{2}, \frac{3}{4}, \frac{5}{6}, \frac{7}{8}, \ldots\}$
$\updownarrow \ \updownarrow \ \updownarrow \ \updownarrow$
$B: \{3, 7, 11, 15, \ldots\}$

Subsets and equality

Frequently we choose one set and use its elements to form other sets.

■ *Definition of Universal Set* The larger set from which we choose members to form new sets is called the *universe* or *universal set*. Sets formed from elements of the universe are called subsets of the universe.

For example, you may want to consider your mathematics class to be the universal set under discussion. Next, you might want to refer to the set of boys and the set of girls in this class. Let C stand for the set of all students in this class, G for the set of all girls in this class, and B for the set of all boys in this class.

■   *Definition of Subset* G is a *subset* of C (written $G \subseteq C$) means that every element of G is also an element of C.

Thus, for the example above, $B \subseteq C$ means that the set of boys in the class is a subset of the set of all students in the class.

Sometimes we want to make statements which are true for *all* sets. To do this, we use such phrases as "for all sets X" or "for every set X," or "for each set X." To save space, we abbreviate each of these phrases with a single symbol "$\forall_x$". Thus, the statement

$$\forall_x \; X \subseteq X$$

is read: for every set X, X is a subset of X. In other words, *every set is a subset of itself*. Explain why this is true.

Since the empty set, ϕ, has no elements, it is difficult to verify what might be true about ϕ. We, therefore, make certain agreements so as to minimize the number of exceptions to the agreements we have already made.

■
$$\forall_x \; \phi \subseteq X$$

Thus, we agree that the empty set is a subset of every set.

■   If a set M *is not a subset* of set N, that is, there is at least one element in M which is not in N, we write $M \nsubseteq N$, which is read: M is not a subset of N.

If we agree for the moment to consider this mathematics class as the universe, then we can form various subsets of this universe. We could have the subset E which would contain those students in the class wearing glasses. Another subset of the universe might be F, the set of all varsity football players in this mathematics class.

If it should happen that this class would consist of boys only, then "the set of members in this mathematics class" and "the set of boys in this mathematics class" would describe exactly the same set. In other words, the set of members in this mathematics class would be the same as the set of boys in this mathematics class.

■ *Definition of Equal Sets* If set A and set B are two names for one set, we say that sets A and B are *equal* and write $A = B$.

For example, if $A = \{1, 2, 3\}$ and $B = \{1+2, 1+1, 1\}$, then $A = B$. Explain.

We stated above that every set is a subset of itself: $\forall_x X \subseteq X$. It is also true that $\forall_x X = X$. The symbol $\subseteq$ is a combination of two symbols: $\subset$ and $=$.

■ *Definition of Proper Subset* Whenever we want to say that a set X is a subset of Y, but $X \neq Y$, we write $X \subset Y$ which is read: X is a *proper subset* of Y, and $X \not\subset Y$ means X is *not* a proper subset of Y

For example, $\{1, 2\}$ is a proper subset of $\{1, 2, 3\}$. Why? But, $\{1, 2\ 3\}$ is *not* a proper subset of $\{1+2, 1+1, 1\}$. Why? We shall agree that $\forall_{x = \phi} \phi \subset X$; that is, the empty set is a *proper* subset of every nonempty set.

EXERCISES

1. **a.** Give examples of two sets A and B such that A is a subset of B and B is not a subset of A.
   b. Give examples of two sets C and D such that C is not a subset of D and D is not a subset of C.
   c. Give examples of sets E and F such that E is a subset of F and F is a subset of E. (Do you end up with two different sets E and F?)

2. On the basis of problem **1c**, complete the following statement.
   $\forall_A \forall_B$, if $A \subseteq B$ and $B \subseteq A$, then ___?___.
   ($\forall_A \forall_B$ is read: for every set A and for every set B.)

3. List the members of your household as a set H. Form three different subsets of H.

4. Given the following sets
   $E = \{1, 3, 4, 6\}$ $G = \{1, 6\}$ $H = \{1, 3, 4, 6, 8, 9\}$
   Label each statement as either true or false.

a. $E \subseteq G$	**d.** $G \subset H$	**g.** $H \subset H$	**j.** $\phi \subset H$	**m.** $H \not\subseteq H$
b. $H \subseteq E$	**e.** $H \subseteq G$	**h.** $\phi \subseteq E$	**k.** $E \not\subset H$	**n.** $G \not\subseteq H$
c. $G \subseteq H$	**f.** $H \subseteq H$	**i.** $\phi \subseteq G$	**l.** $E \not\subseteq G$	**o.** $G \not\subset G$

5. Let the universal set U be the set of those states of the United States which are located west of the Mississippi River.

    a. If P is the set of the states (chosen from U) touching the Pacific Ocean, label each of the following as either true or false.

        i. $P \subseteq U$ *ii.* $P \subset U$ *iii.* $P = U$

    b. If C is the set of the states (chosen from U) touching the border of Canada, label each of the following as either true or false.

        i. $C \subseteq U$ *ii.* $C \subset U$ *iii.* $C = U$ *iv.* $C \subset P$

    c. If T is the set of the states (chosen from U) directly adjoining the Mississippi River, label each of the following as either true or false.

        i. $T \subset U$ *ii.* $T \subset C$ *iii.* $T \subset P$

6. Regroup the following list of sets into groups of equal sets. (If a base of a numeral is not given, assume that it is ten.)

    a. $\{1, 2, 3, 4, \ldots\}$ **f.** $\{10_{\text{two}}, 10_{\text{three}}, 10_{\text{four}}\}$

    b. $\{2, 4, 6, 8, \ldots\}$ **g.** $\{.25, .5\}$

    c. $\{1, 3, 5, 7, \ldots\}$ **h.** $\{4, 3, 2\}$

    d. the set of all natural numbers   **i.** $\{10_{\text{two}}, 11_{\text{two}}, 100_{\text{two}}\}$

    e. $\{\frac{1}{2}, \frac{1}{4}\}$ **j.** $\{\frac{1}{4} + \frac{1}{4}, \frac{1}{8} + \frac{1}{8}\}$

    k. the set of all even natural numbers

    l. the set of all odd natural numbers

    m. the set of all natural numbers which are divisible by 2

    n. the set of all natural numbers which are not divisible by 2

Disjoint sets and Venn diagrams

Given two sets, they are related in one of two ways. Either they have no elements in common or they have one or more elements in common.

◼   *Definition of Disjoint Sets*   If two sets have *no* elements in common, then they are called *disjoint sets*.

Consider, for example, the following two subsets of the set of natural numbers N.

$$A = \text{the set of all natural numbers between 25 and 37}$$
$$\text{not including 25 and 37}$$

$$B = \text{the set of all natural numbers less than 32}$$

Sets A and B have some elements in common. For example, $30 \in A$ and $30 \in B$. Answer the following questions concerning sets A and B.

How many elements are there in set A?

How many elements are there in set B?

How many elements are common to sets A and B?

Name several elements common to sets A and B.

Name several elements which belong to A but not to B.

Name several elements which belong to B but not to A.

The relationship between sets A and B described above may be portrayed in the following manner.

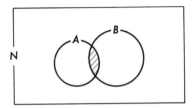

Fig. 1

In figure 1, we designate the points within circle A to be the elements of set A. The points within circle B represent the elements of set B. The elements of both A and B are contained in set N, the set of all natural numbers, which is represented by the interior of rectangle N. The shaded part represents the elements which belong to *both* A and B.

Pictorial representations of a set and its subsets like that in figure 1 are called Venn diagrams.[1]

Now consider the following two sets.

G = the set of all natural numbers less than 20

D = the set of all natural numbers between 10 and 17, not including 10 and 17

What can you say about every element of D as far as its membership in the set G is concerned? Figure 2 shows the relationship between the sets G and D.

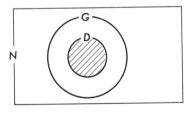

Fig. 2

---

[1] The eighteenth-century Swiss mathematician Euler introduced the idea of using circles in this way. Venn, a British logician of the nineteenth century, introduced further refinements to the idea. Therefore, these diagrams are referred to as Euler circles or Venn diagrams.

Consider another pair of sets.

E = the set of all natural numbers less than 12
F = the set of all natural numbers between 50 and 100

Is figure 3 a correct representation of the relationship between these two sets? Sets E and F described above are disjoint sets. What about sets G and D?

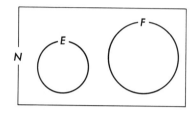

Fig. 3

EXERCISES

1. In this problem, the universal set U is the set of all natural numbers and zero. A and B are subsets of U. In each instance, tell whether or not
i. $A \subseteq B$ *ii.* $A \subset B$ *iii.* $A = B$ *iv.* A and B are disjoint sets.

a. $A = \{1, 2, 3\}$; $B = \{1, 2, 3, 4, 5\}$
b. $A = \{0, 1\}$; $B = \{0\}$ [HINT: The set consisting of the number 0 is not the empty set, because it has one element in it, namely the number 0.]
c. $A = \{1, 4, 6\}$; $B = \{1, 6, 7\}$
d. A is the set of all natural numbers divisible by 10.
   B is the set of all natural numbers.
e. A is the set of all natural numbers less than 100.
   B is the set of all natural numbers greater than 55.
f. $A = \{1, 2\}$; $B = \{1, 2\}$
g. $A = \{0\}$; $B = \{0\}$
h. $A = \phi$; $B = \{0\}$
i. $A = \phi$; $B = \phi$

2. In this problem, let U be the universal set. In each case state whether or not

i. $A \subseteq B$ *ii.* $A \subset B$ *iii.* $A = B$ *iv.* A and B are disjoint sets.

Example: $U = \{4, 6, 8, 10, 12\}$
       $A = \{4\}$ $B = \{4, 6\}$
       i. $A \subseteq B$ *ii.* $A \subset B$ *iii.* $A \neq B$ *iv.* not disjoint

a. $U = \{0, 1, 2, 3, 4, 5\}$
   $A = \{1, 3, 4, 5\}$ $B = \{1, 4, 5\}$
b. $U = \{\frac{1}{2}, \frac{1}{3}, \frac{1}{4}\}$
   $A = \{.5\}$ $B = \{.5, .25\}$
c. $U = \{0, 1\}$
   $A = \{0\}$ $B = \phi$
d. $U = \{$Arizona, California, New Mexico, Oregon$\}$
   $A = \{$Arizona, California$\}$ $B = \{$Oregon, California, Arizona$\}$
e. $U = \{$New York, Los Angeles, Chicago, New Orleans$\}$
   $A = \{$Los Angeles, Chicago$\}$ $B = \{$Chicago$\}$
f. $U = \{1, 2, 3, 4, 5, 6, 7, 8, 9\}$
   $A = \{1, 3, 7, 9\}$ $B = \{3, 7, 8, 9\}$
g. $U = $ the set of all natural numbers less than 20
   $A = $ the set of natural numbers less than 9
   $B = $ the set of natural numbers greater than 5 and less than 8
h. $U = $ the set of all natural numbers
   $A = $ the set of all even natural numbers
   $B = $ the set of all odd natural numbers

3. **a.** Suppose you know that $5 \, \epsilon \, X$ and $5 \, \epsilon \, Y$, where X and Y are some sets. Are you justified in concluding that $X \subseteq Y$? $Y \subseteq X$? X and Y are not disjoint?

   b. Suppose you know that sets M and P have three common elements. Give one conclusion you are justified in drawing from this fact.

4. Let U, the universal set, be the set of all natural numbers. Using the interior of a rectangle to represent U, draw a Venn diagram showing the correct relationships between the following sets.

$$U = \{1, 2, 3, 4, \ldots\}$$
$A = \{4\}$ $B = \{6, 5, 4\}$ $C = \{5\}$ $D = \{10\}$

Operations with sets

You are already familiar with at least four operations with numbers: addition, subtraction, multiplication, and division. Each of these is called a *binary* operation because each requires a pair of numbers. Examine the meaning of the word "binary" in your dictionary.

To show, for example, that addition does require a pair of numbers, all you need to do is to take the following simple example.

Add 3 and 5

which can be written as $3 + 5$.

It is obvious that if you said "add 3" it would not be clear what is to be done. You must name a second number before addition can be performed. The same is true for subtraction, multiplication, and division. Each of these operations requires a pair of numbers before it can be carried out. Now we will learn to perform operations with sets.

Consider the following two sets.

$$A = \{1, 5, 7, 16\} \qquad B = \{7, 16, 21\}$$

We shall obtain a third set, C, by combining the elements of the set A with the elements of the set B. Thus, $C = \{1, 5, 7, 16, 21\}$.

The set C is called the *union* of sets A and B.

We will use the following notation for the operation of union

$$A \cup B = C, \text{ or } \{1, 5, 7, 16\} \cup \{7, 16, 21\} = \{1, 5, 7, 16, 21\}$$

Another example is worked out for you below. Study it.

$$X = \{5, 10, 15\} \qquad Y = \{7, 9, 11, 13\}$$
$$\{5, 10, 15\} \cup \{7, 9, 11, 13\} = \{5, 7, 9, 10, 11, 13, 15\}$$

Note one interesting difference between the pairs of sets A and B, and X and Y. Sets A and B have elements which are common to both, sets, whereas the sets X and Y have no common elements. That is, sets X and Y are disjoint sets, whereas sets A and B are not disjoint sets.

Note that the set $X = \{5, 10, 15\}$ has three elements. The set $Y = \{7, 9, 11, 13\}$ has four elements. The union of the two sets, $X \cup Y = \{5, 7, 9, 10, 11, 13, 15\}$, has seven elements. What is the relationship between the numbers 3, 4, and 7?

Now, observe the set $A = \{1, 5, 7, 16\}$. It has four elements. The set $B = \{7, 16, 21\}$ has three elements. The union, $A \cup B = \{1, 5, 7, 16, 21\}$, has five elements.

Draw a conclusion concerning the number of the elements in the union of two disjoint sets; in the union of two sets which are not disjoint sets.

■ *Definition of Union* The *union* of any pair of sets X and Y is a set consisting of all the elements which belong to X or Y.

The word "or" is being used here in a sense which may be different from the sense to which you are accustomed. The phrase: is a member of X *or* Y may imply any one or all three of the following:

a is a member of X
a is a member of Y
a is a member of both X and Y

Assigned such meaning, the word "or" is referred to as being "inclusive or" rather than "exclusive or." That is, the sentence "*a* is a member of *X* or *Y*" is true if *a* belongs only to *X*, only to *Y*, or to both *X* and *Y*.

Let us now obtain a third set from the sets *A* and *B* in a different way. We will take this third set to be the set of only those elements which are in *both A* and *B*.

We had $A = \{1, 5, 7, 16\}$ and $B = \{7, 16, 21\}$ The only elements which are in both *A* and *B* are 7 and 16. The set *D*, then, consisting of elements belonging to both *A* and *B* is $D = \{7, 16\}$.

The set $D = \{7, 16\}$ is the *intersection* of sets $A = \{1, 5, 7, 16\}$ and $B = \{7, 16, 21\}$. *A* intersection *B* equals *D* is written as

$$A \cap B = D$$

The symbol for the operation of intersection is $\cap$.

■ *Definition of Intersection*   The *intersection* of a pair of sets is the set consisting of only those elements which are common to both sets.

Sets $X = \{5, 10, 15\}$ and $Y = \{7, 9, 11, 13\}$ do not have any common elements. Therefore, their intersection is the empty set; thus $\{5, 10, 15\} \cap \{7, 9, 11, 13\} = \phi$.

Observe that it takes a pair of sets to perform the operations of union and intersection. Therefore, *union and intersection are binary operations*.

Given any pair of sets, there is a set which is their union. Also, given any pair of sets, there is a set which is their intersection.

EXERCISES

1. Name the set which is the intersection of each pair of sets below.

   a. *A:* all natural numbers
   B: all odd natural numbers

   b. *A:* all natural numbers
   B: all even natural numbers

   c. *A:* all odd natural numbers
   B: all even natural numbers

   d. *A:* all natural numbers
   B: all prime natural numbers

   e. *A:* all students in your school
   B: all students in your school enrolled in mathematics courses

   f. *A:* all students in your school over 15 years of age
   B: all students in your school under 15 years of age

2. Name the set which is the union of each pair of sets in problem **1.**
3. Give an example of a pair of finite disjoint sets.
4. Give an example of a pair of infinite disjoint sets.

5. Give an example of a pair of finite sets which are not disjoint.

6. Give an example of a pair of infinite sets which are not disjoint.

7. Find the intersection of each pair of sets in problems **3-6**.

8. Find the union of each pair of sets in problems **3-6**.

9. Explain why the intersection of the empty set with any set is the empty set. This may be stated as follows:

$$\forall_A \ A \cap \phi = \phi; \text{ therefore, } \phi \cap \phi = \phi$$

10. Explain why the union of the empty set with any set is that set. This may be stated as follows:

$$\forall_A \ A \cup \phi = A; \text{ therefore, } \phi \cup \phi = \phi$$

11. Let $A = \{1, 3, 5\}$, $B = \{3, 5, 7, 9\}$, and $C = \{4, 6, 8, 10\}$. Find

a. $A \cup B$ **c.** $A \cup C$ **e.** $B \cup C$

b. $A \cap B$ **d.** $A \cap C$ **f.** $B \cap C$

g. $(A \cup B) \cup C$ [HINT: Parentheses here mean that you first find the set $A \cup B$, then you find the union of the resulting set with C.]

h. $A \cup (B \cup C)$ **k.** $A \cup (B \cap C)$

i. $(A \cap B) \cap C$ **l.** $(A \cup B) \cap (A \cup C)$

j. $A \cap (B \cap C)$ **m.** $A \cap (B \cup C)$

12. Given any set A, do the indicated operation.

a. $A \cup A$ **e.** $(A \cup A) \cap A$

b. $A \cap A$ **f.** $(A \cap A) \cup A$

c. $(A \cup A) \cup A$ **g.** $A \cup \phi$

d. $(A \cap A) \cap A$ **h.** $A \cap \phi$

Counting the subsets of a finite set

When studying various sets, it is good practice to specify the universe from which the elements of sets are selected. For example, we may agree that for the purposes of our study for this particular moment, we shall select the elements of our sets from the set of natural numbers: $\{1, 2, 3, 4, \ldots\}$. That is, the set of natural numbers is, at this time, the universal set or the universe. Thus

$$U = \{1, 2, 3, 4, \ldots\}$$

Of course, there is no limit to the number of subsets we can get from the set of natural numbers.

For example, the set $A = \{1\}$ is a subset of U. So is $B = \{3, 7, 10\}$. Both A and B are subsets of U. Why? Thus, $A \subseteq U$ and $B \subseteq U$. Name a few more subsets of U, where U is the set of all natural numbers.

Now consider the universe L, where $L = \{1, 2\}$; that is, the only members in the universe are the numbers 1 and 2. Let us form all possible subsets of L. In doing this, we must remember that the empty set is a subset of every set. Furthermore, we must remember that every set is a subset of itself. Now, we are ready to list all subsets of $L = \{1, 2\}$.

$$\phi \qquad \{1\} \qquad \{1, 2\}$$
$$\{2\}$$

Thus, the set $L = \{1, 2\}$ has *two* elements and *four* subsets.

Now, take the universe $K = \{1, 2, 3\}$. Form all possible subsets of K.

$$\phi \qquad \{1\} \qquad \{1, 2\} \qquad \{1, 2, 3\}$$
$$\{2\} \qquad \{1, 3\}$$
$$\{3\} \qquad \{2, 3\}$$

Thus, the set K has *three* elements and *eight* subsets.

Now, take the universe $T = \{1, 2, 3, 4\}$. Form all possible subsets of T.

$$\phi \quad \{1\} \quad \{1, 2\} \quad \{1, 2, 3\} \qquad \{1, 2, 3, 4\}$$
$$\{2\} \quad \{1, 3\} \quad \{1, 2, 4\}$$
$$\{3\} \quad \{1, 4\} \quad \{1, 3, 4\}$$
$$\{4\} \quad \{2, 3\} \quad \{2, 3, 4\}$$
$$\{2, 4\}$$
$$\{3, 4\}$$

Thus, the set T has *four* elements and *sixteen* subsets

Let us tabulate our results:

Number of elements in a set	Number of all possible subsets
2	$4 = 2 \cdot 2$
3	$8 = 2 \cdot 2 \cdot 2$
4	$16 = 2 \cdot 2 \cdot 2 \cdot 2$

If you carefully examine this table, you should see a pattern. This pattern tells you the relationship between the number of elements in the universal set and the number of all possible subsets. According to this pattern, there should be $2 \cdot 2 \cdot 2 \cdot 2 \cdot 2$ or 32 subsets that can be formed from a universal set with *five* elements. Work it out, listing all the subsets, and see whether or not you obtain 32 subsets. According to this pattern, how many subsets does a set with six elements have? A set with seven elements? What about a set with one element? To fit into the pattern, a set with one element would have to have two subsets. Let us check.

Let $A = \{5\}$. The subsets of A are ϕ and $\{5\}$. Thus, $A = \{5\}$ has two subsets.

EXERCISES

Given $A = \{\frac{1}{2}, \frac{1}{3}, \frac{1}{4}, \frac{1}{5}\}$ and $B = \{\frac{1}{4}, \frac{1}{5}, \frac{1}{6}, \frac{1}{7}, \frac{1}{8}\}$

1. Form all subsets of A. How many subsets are there?
2. How many subsets of set B are there?
3. Determine $A \cup B$.
4. How many subsets may be formed from $A \cup B$?
5. Determine $A \cap B$.
6. **a.** Form all subsets of $A \cap B$. How many are there?
   b. How many of these are proper subsets of $A \cap B$?
   c. How many of these are proper non-empty subsets of $A \cap B$?

Subsets of infinite sets

You have learned how to predict the number of subsets that can be obtained from a given finite set. What about subsets of infinite sets? First of all, since there is no end to the number of elements in an infinite set, there is no end to the number of subsets one can obtain. This is easily seen by considering only those subsets which have one element. For example, take the set of all natural numbers $\{1, 2, 3, 4, 5, 6, \ldots\}$. Some subsets are

$$\{1\}, \{2\}, \{3\}, \{4\}, \{5\}, \{6\}, \text{ and so on}$$

Each of these subsets has only one element, and there is no end to the number of these subsets.

There is at least one interesting thing about subsets of infinite sets which you already might have observed in the discussion of matching sets. We saw that given any finite set, say $A = \{5, 7, 10\}$, and deleting at least one element of it, say 5, we obtain a subset $B = \{7, 10\}$ which cannot be matched with the original set A. This is because the set A has more elements than the set B.

Let us now see whether the same is true for infinite sets. In the set of all natural numbers $N = \{1, 2, 3, 4, 5, \ldots\}$, let us delete the number 1. We obtain the set $K = \{2, 3, 4, 5, 6, \ldots\}$ such that $K \subset N$, because every member of K is also a member of N and $K \neq N$.

Is it possible to establish a one-to-one correspondence between the set N and its subset K? The answer is "yes." Here it is.

$$N: \{ \ 1, \ 2, \ 3, \ 4, \ 5, \ 6, \ \ldots \ \}$$
$$\updownarrow \ \updownarrow \ \updownarrow \ \updownarrow \ \updownarrow \ \updownarrow$$
$$K: \{ \ 2, \ 3, \ 4, \ 5, \ 6, \ 7, \ \ldots \ \}$$

That is, to every number which is a member of the set N, we assign a number, the next greater natural number, which is a member of K. Do you see that *every* member of N has a "mate" in K? That every member of K has a "mate" in N? Thus we found a way of establishing a one-to-one correspondence between the set of all natural numbers and its proper subset, all natural numbers except 1.

You should now be ready to state some conclusions. They will be contained in the answers to the following questions.

If X is a finite set and Y is a proper subset of X, can X and Y be matching sets?

If W is an infinite set and Z is a proper subset of W, can W and Z be matching sets?

EXERCISES

1. Let the universal set be the set of all natural numbers, $U = \{1, 2, 3, 4, 5, 6, \ldots\}$.

   a. Show one way of establishing a one-to-one correspondence between U and the set of all natural numbers greater than 100.
   b. Is it possible to establish a one-to-one correspondence between U and the set of all even numbers? If your answer is yes, show one way of doing it. If your answer is no, explain.
   c. Is it possible to establish a one-to-one correspondence between U and the set of all natural numbers less than 1001? If your answer is yes, show one way of doing it. If your answer is no, explain.

2. Let $U_1 = \{1, 2, 3, 4, 5, \ldots\}$
   $U_2 = \{1, 3, 5, 7, 9, \ldots\}$
   $U_3 = \{100, 101, 102, 103, 104, 105, \ldots\}$

   Find

a. $U_1 \cup U_2$	d. $U_1 \cap U_2$	g. $(U_1 \cup U_2) \cup U_3$
b. $U_1 \cup U_3$	e. $U_1 \cap U_3$	h. $(U_1 \cap U_2) \cap U_3$
c. $U_2 \cup U_3$	f. $U_2 \cap U_3$	i. $(U_1 \cup U_2) \cap U_3$

THE THEORY OF SETS

The ideas of sets were developed toward the end of the nineteenth-century. George Boole (1815–1864) and Georg Cantor (1845–1918) are two mathematicians credited with the development of these ideas. You may have heard people speak of "Boolean Algebra," that is, the algebra of sets. It is so called in honor of Boole, who was the first to introduce these ideas. Cantor is considered to be the founder of set theory.

Complement of a set

Take the universe to be the set $U = \{1, 2, 3, 4, 5, 6, 7, 8, 9, 10\}$, that is, the natural numbers from 1 through 10. Now take a subset of U, say $A = \{5, 6, 7\}$. We will consider the set of elements remaining in U after the set A has been formed. This set is $B = \{1, 2, 3, 4, 8, 9, 10\}$. You will note two things about A and B. First, they are disjoint; that is

$$A \cap B = \phi$$

Second, the union of A and B gives us the universe; that is

$$A \cup B = U = \{1, 2, 3, 4, 5, 6, 7, 8, 9, 10\}$$

The set B is called the *complement* of the set A
We will use the symbol $\overline{A}$ for the complement of A

We state two generalizations concerning the complement of a set. Explain them.

■ $\forall_A A \cap \overline{A} = \phi$ and $\forall_A A \cup \overline{A} = U$

Using our previous way of representing relationships between sets pictorially, we show this in the following Venn diagram.

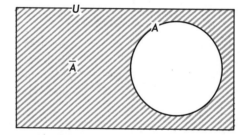

If the interior of the rectangle represents the universe and the interior of the circle the set A, then $\overline{A}$, the complement of A, is represented by the shaded portion. The Venn diagram makes it easy to see that a set and its complement are always disjoint sets and that the union of a set and its complement is the universe.

EXERCISES

1.   Let $U = \{1, 2, 3, 4, 5, 6, 7, 8\}$. Determine $\overline{A}$ from the given set A.

Example: $A = \{1, 2, 6\}$
$\overline{A}$ is the set of elements in U other than the elements of A. Therefore, $\overline{A} = \{3, 4, 5, 7, 8\}$.

   a. $A = \{2, 4, 6, 8\}$ **b.** $A = \{1, 3, 5, 7\}$ **c.** $A = \{1, 8\}$

2. Let $U = \{1, 2, 3, 4, 5, 6, 7\}$, $A = \{1, 2\}$, and $B = \{2, 4, 5\}$.
Determine the following sets.

a. $\overline{A}$	**g.** $\overline{A} \cup \overline{B}$
b. $\overline{B}$	**h.** $\overline{A} \cap A$
c. $A \cap B$	**i.** $\overline{B} \cap B$
d. $\overline{A \cap B}$	**j.** $\overline{A} \cap B$
e. $\overline{A} \cap \overline{B}$	**k.** $A \cap \overline{B}$
f. $\overline{A \cup B}$	**l.** $\overline{A} \cup B$

3. Let $U = \{0, 1, 2\}$, and $A = \{0\}$.
Label each statement as either true or false.

a. $\overline{A} = U$	**d.** $\overline{A} \cap U = \{1, 2\}$
b. $A \cup U = \{1, 2\}$	**e.** $\overline{A} = \{1, 2\}$
c. $A \cap U = \phi$	**f.** $\overline{U} = \{0\}$

4. $U = \{1, 3, 5, 7, 9, 11\}$, $A = \{1, 5\}$, $B = \{7, 9, 11\}$, $C = \{3, 7, 9, 11\}$,
and $D = \{1, 11\}$.   Determine the following sets.

a. $\overline{B}$	**i.** $U \cap \overline{C}$
b. $\overline{C}$	**j.** $D \cap \phi$
c. $\overline{D}$	**k.** $\overline{B} \cap \phi$
d. $\overline{A}$	**l.** $\overline{U \cap A}$
e. $A \cup U$	**m** $D \cup B$
f. $A \cap U$	**n.** $\overline{D} \cap \overline{B}$
g. $\overline{A} \cap U$	**o.** $\overline{U}$
h. $C \cap \overline{D}$	

5. Let $U =$ the set of all natural numbers. Describe in words the complement of each of the following sets.

Example: $X = \{1, 2\}$
$\overline{X}$: the set of all natural numbers greater than 2

a. $A = \{1, 2, 3\}$
b. $B = \{100, 101, 102, 103, \ldots\}$
c. $C = \{17, 18, 19, 20, \ldots, 58, 59, 60\}$
d. $D = \{2, 4, 6, 8, 10, \ldots\}$
e. $E = \{1, 3, 5, 7, 9, 11, \ldots\}$
f. $F = \{2, 3, 5, 7, 11, 13, 17, 19, 23, \ldots\}$
g. $G = \{7, 14, 21, 28, 35, 42\}$
h. $H = \{10, 20, 30, 40, \ldots, 210\}$
i. $I = \{1000, 900, 800, \ldots, 100\}$
j. $J = \{1, 4, 7, 10, 13, 16, \ldots\}$

Example   Given a universal set U containing six elements and two subsets A and B. A contains three elements, and B contains four elements. $B \cap A$ contains two elements. How many elements are there in each of the following sets?

a. $\overline{A}$ **b.** $\overline{B}$ **c.** $\overline{A} \cup B$ **d.** $\overline{B \cap A}$ **e.** $\overline{A \cup B}$

How to Solve: For the purpose of making a pictorial representation the six elements of U are named 1, 2, 3, 4, 5, and 6; or, $U = \{1, 2, 3, 4, 5, 6\}$.

$B \cap A$ contains two elements. We draw A and B so that they have two elements in common. $B \cap A = \{2, 3\}$, so $B \cap A$ contains two elements.

$\overline{A}$ consists of all elements in U which are not in A. Therefore, $\overline{A} = \{4, 5, 6\}$, or $\overline{A}$ contains three elements.

$\overline{B}$ is the set of all elements in U that are not in B. Therefore, $\overline{B} = \{1, 6\}$, or $\overline{B}$ contains two elements.

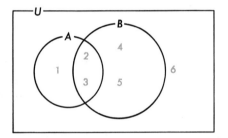

$\overline{A}$ contains three elements and B contains four elements, but $\overline{A} \cup B$ does not necessarily contain seven elements. Remember $\overline{A} = \{4, 5, 6\}$, $B = \{2, 3, 4, 5\}$. Since 4 and 5 are common to both $\overline{A}$ and B, $\overline{A} \cup B = \{2, 3, 4, 5, 6\}$, or $\overline{A} \cup B$ contains five elements.

$\overline{B} = \{1, 6\}$, $\overline{A} = \{4, 5, 6\}$; so $\overline{B} \cap \overline{A} = \{6\}$ or $\overline{B} \cap \overline{A}$ contains one element.

$A = \{1, 2, 3\}$, $B = \{2, 3, 4, 5\}$, $A \cup B = \{1, 2, 3, 4, 5\}$. The elements in $\overline{A \cup B}$ are all of the elements in U that are not in $A \cup B$. Therefore, $\overline{A \cup B} = \{6\}$, or $\overline{A \cup B}$ contains one element.

6. Given a universal set U containing thirteen elements and two subsets C and D; C contains four elements and D contains seven elements; $C \cap D$ contains two elements.

Indicate how many elements there are in the following sets. (Venn diagrams will prove helpful.)

a. $C \cup D$	**d.** $\overline{C} \cup D$	**g.** $\overline{C \cap D}$
b. $\overline{C}$	**e.** $D \cup C$	**h.** $\overline{C} \cup \overline{D}$
c. $\overline{D}$	**f.** $C \cap \overline{D}$	**i.** $C \cap \overline{D}$

7. Given a universal set U containing nine elements and three subsets G, F, and K; G contains four elements, F contains six elements, K contains two elements, $G \cup F$ contains seven elements, $K \cap F$ contains one element and $G \cap K$ contains two elements.

How many elements are there in each of the following sets?

a. $G \cap F$	**e.** $\overline{F \cap G}$	**h.** $\overline{K}$
b. $\overline{G} \cap F$	**f.** $K \cup F$	**i.** $\overline{K} \cap \overline{G}$
c. $\overline{F} \cap G$	**g.** $G \cup K$	**j.** $\overline{K \cup G}$
d. $\overline{F} \cup \overline{G}$		

VOCABULARY

Use each of the following correctly in a sentence. Numerals in parentheses refer to the pages where these words were used. If you are not sure of the meaning of any word, turn to the indicated page and refresh your memory.

binary (15)	matching sets (7)
Boolean Algebra (21)	numeral (5)
complement (22)	member (2)
composite number (5)	natural number (3)
disjoint sets (12)	null set (3)
divisible (5)	one-to-one correspondence (7)
divisor (3)	prime number (5)
element (2)	proper subset (11)
empty set (3)	set (1)
Euler circles (13)	subset (10)
finite set (2)	union (16)
infinite set (2)	universe (9)
intersection (17)	Venn diagram (13)

DEFINITIONS

■ *Definition of x Is Divisible By y* For natural numbers x and y, *x is divisible by y* means the quotient $x \div y$ is a natural number. In such cases we say that y is a *divisor* of x.

■ *Definition of Prime Number* A natural number which has exactly two divisors is called a *prime number*.

■ *Definition of Composite Number* A natural number which has more than two divisors is called a *composite* number.

■ *Definition of Universal Set* The larger set from which we choose members to form new sets is called the *universe* or *universal set*. Sets formed from elements of the universe are called subsets of the universe.

■ *Definition of Subset* G is a subset of C (written $G \subseteq C$) means that every element of G is also an element of C.

■ *Definition of Equal Sets* If set A and set B are two names for one set, we say that sets A and B are *equal* and write $A = B$.

■ *Definition of Proper Subset* Whenever we want to say that a set X is a subset of Y but $X \neq Y$, we write $X \subset Y$, which is read: X is a proper subset of Y; and $X \not\subset Y$ means X is not a proper subset of Y.

■ *Definition of Disjoint Sets* If two sets have *no* elements in common, then they are called *disjoint sets*.

■ *Definition of Union* The *union* of any pair of sets X and Y is a set consisting of all elements which belong to X or Y.

■ *Definition of Intersection* The *intersection* of a pair of sets is the set consisting of only those elements which are common to both sets.

REVIEW EXERCISES

1. Let P be the set of prime numbers less than 100. Label each statement as either true or false.

    a. The number 2 is the only even number such that $2 \in P$.
    b. $P \subset T$, where T is the set of all prime numbers less than 200.

    c. $101 \in P$ **e.** $\{2, 11, 21\} \subset P$ **g.** $81 \notin P$
    d. $169 \in P$ **f.** $\{37, 41, 43\} \not\subset P$ **h.** $13 \notin P$

2. Label each statement as either true or false.

    a. The set of even natural numbers and the set of prime numbers are disjoint sets.
    b. The set of even natural numbers and the set of odd natural numbers are matching sets.
    c. If U = the set of natural numbers and $A = U$, then $\overline{A} = \phi$.
    d. Every set with four elements has 16 subsets.
    e. $\{1, 3, \frac{1}{2}\} \cap \{\frac{1}{4}, \frac{1}{2}\} = \{1\}$
    f. $\forall_X X \cap X = \phi$
    g. $\forall_Y Y \cap \phi = Y$
    h. $\forall_M M \cup \phi = M$
    i. If $A = \{0, \frac{1}{2}, \frac{1}{4}\}$ and $B = \{0, \frac{1}{3}, \frac{1}{9}\}$, then $A \cap B = \phi$
    j. $\{\frac{1}{2}, \frac{1}{3}, \frac{1}{4}\} \subset \{\frac{1}{2}, \frac{1}{4}, \frac{1}{8}, \frac{1}{16}\}$

3.   **a.** How many subsets of $\{10, 15, 20, 25\}$ have exactly one element? Two elements? Three elements? Four elements? Five elements? No elements?

    b. List the elements of the set described by "all natural numbers less than 17 and greater than 11."

    c. Which of the following phrases describe the empty set?

        i. the set of all natural numbers greater than 15 and less than 16
        ii. the set of all fractions greater than $\frac{1}{2}$ and less than $\frac{1}{3}$
        iii. the set of all prime numbers less than 3
        iv. the set of all odd natural numbers greater than 21 and less than 23
        v. the set of all voters in the United States less than 19 years of age

4. Draw and shade Venn diagrams to verify the truth of each of the following statements for any two sets A and B, that are subsets of some universe U.

    a. $U \cap A = A$ **c.** $A \cap \overline{A} = \phi$ **e.** $\overline{A \cap B} = \overline{A} \cup \overline{B}$
    b. $A \cup \overline{A} = U$ **d.** $\overline{A \cup B} = \overline{A} \cap \overline{B}$ **f.** $\overline{\overline{A}} = A$

5. If the sets A, B, and C are as pictured in the figure below, name the elements of each of the following:

a. $C \cap B$ **f.** $A \cup (B \cup C)$ **k.** $(A \cap B) \cap C$
b. $A \cap B$ **g.** $\overline{A}$ **l.** $\overline{(A \cap B)} \cap C$
c. $B \cap C$ **h.** $\overline{B}$ **m.** $A \cap (B \cap C)$
d. $A \cup B$ **i.** $\overline{C}$ **n.** $\overline{(A \cup B)} \cap C$
e. $(A \cup B) \cup C$ **j.** $\overline{(A \cup B)} \cup C$

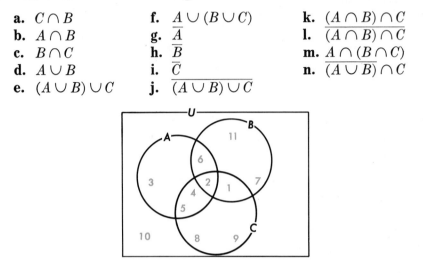

6. Which of the following describes correctly what is pictured in the Venn diagram in the figure below?

   i. $A \subset B$ *iv.* $(A \cap B) \subset A$
  ii. $A \cap B = \phi$ *v.* $A \cup B = A$
 iii. $(A \cup B) \subset A$

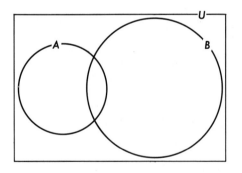

CHAPTER TEST

1. Define

    a. matching sets   **d.** union of A and B
    b. A is a subset of B **e.** disjoint sets
    c. intersection of X and Y **f.** complement of a set

2. a. $A = \{1, 7, 13, 41, 67\}$ $B = \{41, \frac{1}{2} + \frac{1}{2}, 6 + 7, 7, 70 - 3\}$
Are A and B matching sets? Explain.
b. Give an example of one pair of infinite sets which are matching.

3. For each pair of sets tell whether the set A is a subset of B.

a. $A = \{0, 1, 2\}$ $B = \{0, 1, 2, 3, 4, 5\}$
b. $A = \{5, 6, 7\}$ $B = \{6, 7\}$
c. $A = \{2, 4, 6, \ldots\}$ $B = \{1, 2, 3\}$
d. $A = \{1, 3, 5, \ldots\}$ $B = \{1, 2, 3, \ldots\}$
e. $A = \{\text{all prime numbers}\}$ $B = \{1, 2, 3, \ldots\}$

4. For each pair of sets tell whether the set X is a proper subset of Y.

a. $X = \{2, 4, 6, \ldots\}$ $Y = \{1, 2, 3, \ldots\}$
b. $X = \{1, 3, 5, \ldots\}$ $Y = \{1, 2, 3, \ldots\}$
c. $X = \{\text{all prime numbers}\}$ $Y = \{1, 2, 3, \ldots\}$
d. $X = \{1, 2, 3, \ldots\}$ $Y = \{1, 2, 3, \ldots\}$
e. $X = \{10, 11, 12\}$ $Y = \{1, 2, 3, \ldots\}$
f. $X = \{1, 2, 3, \ldots, 98, 99, 100\}$ $Y = \{1, 2, 3, \ldots, 198, 199, 200\}$
g. $X = \{1, 2, 3\}$ $Y = \{1, 2, 3, 4\}$
h. $X = \phi$ $Y = \{0\}$

5. Find both the intersection and the union of each pair of sets.

a. $A = \{5, 6, 7, 8, 9\}$ $B = \{7, 8, 9, 10\}$
b. $C = \{1, 3, 5, \ldots\}$ $D = \{2, 4, 6, \ldots\}$
c. E = all students in your school over 16 years of age
F = all students in your school under 16 years of age

6. Determine whether or not each of the following statements is true for all sets A.

a. $A \cap \phi = \phi$ **b.** $A \cup \phi = \phi$

7. If the universal set is the set of natural numbers, give the complement of each of the following sets.

a. $A = \{1, 2, 3, 4, 5\}$ **b.** $B = \{1, 3, 5, \ldots\}$ **c.** $C = \{5, 10, 15, \ldots\}$

8. List the elements of the following sets.

a. natural numbers less than 11 and greater than 7
b. even natural numbers less than 13
c. prime natural numbers less than 12

9. Suppose $A = \{0, 1, 2\}$. List *all* subsets of A. How many subsets did you form?

10. Given the universal set U and subsets C, F, and G.

$U = \{1, 2, 3, 4, 5, 6, 7, 8\}$
$C = \{2, 6, 7, 8\}$ $F = \{1, 2, 4, 6\}$ $G = \{1, 2, 3, 5, 8\}$

List the elements of each of the following sets.

a. $C \cap F$ **d.** $(C \cup F) \cap G$ **g.** $U \cup C$
b. $F \cup G$ **e.** $\overline{G \cap F}$ **h.** $C \cup \overline{C}$
c. $\overline{C}$ **f.** $U \cap F$ **i.** $\overline{F} \cap \overline{G}$

11. List the elements of the set of

 a. all composite numbers less than 15
 b. all prime numbers less than 15

12. How many natural numbers are neither prime or composite?

13. How many even natural numbers are also prime numbers?

14. Which of the following numerals name the number five?

 a. $\sqrt{25}$ **b.** 10_{five} **c.** 11_{four} **d.** 21_{three} **e.** $\sqrt[3]{15}$

BIBLIOGRAPHY

Glenn, W. H., and Johnson, D. A. *Sets, Sentences, and Operations*. St. Louis, Missouri: Webster Publishing Company, 1960. pp. 1-34.

Gray, James F. *Sets, Relations, and Functions*. New York: Holt, Rinehart and Winston, Inc., 1962.

Kelly, John L. *Introduction to Modern Algebra*. New York: D. Van Nostrand Company, Inc., 1960. pp. 36-76.

The National Council of Teachers of Mathematics. *The Mathematics Student* Journal. Washington, D. C.

Nichols, Eugene D.; Kalin, Robert; and Garland, Henry. *Introduction to Sets* (A Programmed Unit). New York: Holt, Rinehart and Winston, Inc., 1962.

Rademacher, H., and Toeplitz, O. *The Enjoyment of Mathematics*. Princeton: Princeton University Press, 1957. pp. 34-42.

School Mathematics Study Group. *First Course in Algebra*. New Haven: Yale University Press, 1961. pp. 1-6.

The University of Chicago, The College Mathematics Staff. *Concepts and Structure of Mathematics*. Chicago: The University of Chicago Press, 1954. pp. 116-160.

Woodward, E. J., and McClennan, R. *Elementary Concepts of Sets*. New York: Holt, Rinehart and Winston, Inc., 1959.

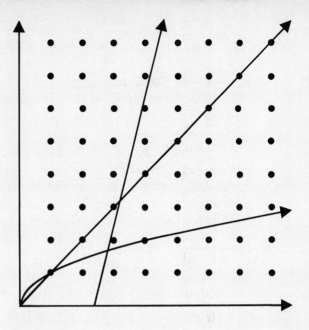

CHAPTER 2

Properties of Operations— Numbers of Ordinary Arithmetic

SYMBOLS FOR GROUPING

A story is told about an employee who was out traveling for his employer. His task was to investigate the merit of buying certain stock on a stock market. He found the price rather high; therefore, he decided to wire his employer before deciding whether or not to buy the stock. The return wire read as follows:

NO PRICE TOO HIGH

The employee went ahead and bought the stock not knowing, of course, that his employer intended to say

NO, PRICE TOO HIGH

The punctuation symbol **,** was of crucial importance in that case.

In the English language, as in other languages, we use punctuation marks such as the comma and period in order to make clear statements. Punctuation marks are very important. The preceding example illustrates this point.

In mathematics, there are similar situations in which it is necessary to use mathematical punctuation symbols such as ( ) parentheses, [ ] brackets, and { } braces. These symbols are often necessary to make clear what is to be done in mathematics problems. Consider, for example, the following arithmetic problem: Give the simplest name for $2 + 3 \times 7$.

There are two ways that one might do this simplification

$$i. \quad 2 + 3 \times 7 = 5 \times 7 = 35$$
$$\text{or} \quad ii. \quad 2 + 3 \times 7 = 2 + 21 = 23$$

Obviously, both ways cannot be intended, because 35 is not equal to 23. The expression $2 + 3 \times 7$ *must* have only one meaning. It is customary to use parentheses, which are mathematical punctuation marks, to make the meaning of such phrases clear.

We shall agree that one should perform the operation inside the parentheses first. Thus, we use parentheses to indicate that certain operations are to be performed first. Thus

$$(2 + 3) \times 7 = 5 \times 7 = 35$$
$$2 + (3 \times 7) = 2 + 21 = 23$$

You will find that, for convenience and brevity, parentheses are frequently omitted in some expressions. In this case, it is necessary for us to reach some kind of an agreement on the unique meaning of $2 + 3 \times 7$. AGREEMENT: Whenever addition, subtraction, multiplication, and division are involved in a problem and there are no parentheses to guide us, we shall perform the multiplication and division first, then the addition and subtraction.

According to this agreement

$$2 + 3 \times 7 = 2 + 21 = 23$$

Similarly

$$2 + 6 \div 3 = 2 + 2 = 4$$
$$\tfrac{1}{2} \times 7 - 16 \div 8 = 3\tfrac{1}{2} - 2 = 1\tfrac{1}{2}$$
$$3 \times 5 - 2 \times 3 + 7 \times 11 = 15 - 6 + 77 = 9 + 77 = 86$$

Whenever divisions and multiplications are indicated, these two operations are performed in the order they occur, from left to right.

Example: $\begin{aligned}3 \times 4 \div 2 \div 3 \times 2 &= 12 \div 2 \div 3 \times 2 \\ &= 6 \div 3 \times 2 \\ &= 2 \times 2 \\ &= 4\end{aligned}$

When additions and subtractions appear, we perform these operations as they occur, from left to right.

Example: $\begin{aligned}10 - 8 + 4 + 6 - 3 + 5 &= 2 + 4 + 6 - 3 + 5 \\ &= 6 + 6 - 3 + 5 \\ &= 12 - 3 + 5 \\ &= 9 + 5 \\ &= 14\end{aligned}$

We will use various ways of expressing the product of a pair of numbers. Instead of writing 3×4, we may also indicate this product by $3 \cdot 4$, $(3)4$, $3(4)$, or $(3)(4)$.

EXERCISES

For each of the following, find the simplest name.

Examples:

$i.$ $\begin{aligned}7 \cdot (\tfrac{1}{2} - \tfrac{1}{3}) &= 7 \cdot (\tfrac{3}{6} - \tfrac{2}{6}) \\ &= 7 \cdot \tfrac{1}{6} \\ &= \tfrac{7}{6}\end{aligned}$

$ii.$ $\begin{aligned}\tfrac{1}{2} \times [\tfrac{1}{3} \times (.7 - \tfrac{1}{2})] &= \tfrac{1}{2} \times [\tfrac{1}{3} \times (.7 - .5)] \\ &= \tfrac{1}{2} \times [\tfrac{1}{3} \times .2] \\ &= \tfrac{1}{2} \times [\tfrac{1}{3} \times \tfrac{1}{5}] \\ &= \tfrac{1}{2} \times [\tfrac{1}{15}] \\ &= \tfrac{1}{30}\end{aligned}$

$iii.$ $\begin{aligned}\{[7 + (6 \cdot 3)] \cdot 2\} \cdot 5 &= \{[7 + 18] \cdot 2\} \cdot 5 \\ &= \{25 \cdot 2\} \cdot 5 \\ &= 50 \cdot 5 \\ &= 250\end{aligned}$

1. $5 \cdot (\tfrac{2}{5} - \tfrac{1}{5})$
2. $2 \cdot (\tfrac{5}{7} - \tfrac{2}{7})$
3. $\tfrac{1}{2} \cdot (\tfrac{2}{3} - \tfrac{1}{3})$
4. $.5 \times (.3 - .1)$
5. $50 \times (.2 - .1)$
6. $(17 - 13) \times (20 + 5)$
7. $(\tfrac{3}{5} - .2) \times (.6 - \tfrac{1}{2})$
8. $3 \cdot [4 \cdot (7 - 5)]$
9. $5 \cdot [3 \cdot (2 + 7)]$

10. $5 \cdot (7 + 2 - 8) + 3 \cdot \tfrac{1}{2}$
11. $1737 + 14.75 + 13.6$
12. $14.75 + 1737 + 13.6$
13. $1737 + 13.6 + 14.75$
14. $.675 \times 10$
15. $10 \times .675$
16. $(15.7 + 198.5) + 3.6$
17. $15.7 + (198.5 + 3.6)$
18. $(6.2 \times 3) \times 2$

19. $6.2 \times (3 \times 2)$
20. $(3 \times 6.2) \times 2$
21. $5 \cdot (6 + 7)$
22. $5 \cdot 6 + 5 \cdot 7$

23. $(11 + 12) \cdot 10$
24. $11 \cdot 10 + 12 \cdot 10$
25. $3 \times [(4 \cdot 6) + (7 \cdot 9)]$
26. $\{[4(3) + 14] \div 13\} + 4 \cdot 7$

BASIC PROPERTIES OF ADDITION AND MULTIPLICATION

For the present, we shall assume that the universal set is the set of all numbers of ordinary arithmetic. This is the set of numbers with which you have been working in the elementary school grades.

Each group of examples below is intended to illustrate an important property of some operation on numbers. Study each group, then give two more examples which fit the particular pattern.

$$2 + 7 = 9 \text{ and } 7 + 2 = 9, \text{ therefore } 2 + 7 = 7 + 2$$

$$\tfrac{1}{2} + 3 = 3\tfrac{1}{2} \text{ and } 3 + \tfrac{1}{2} = 3\tfrac{1}{2}, \text{ therefore } \tfrac{1}{2} + 3 = 3 + \tfrac{1}{2}$$

$$\tfrac{3}{2} + \tfrac{7}{2} = 5 \text{ and } \tfrac{7}{2} + \tfrac{3}{2} = 5, \text{ therefore } \tfrac{3}{2} + \tfrac{7}{2} = \tfrac{7}{2} + \tfrac{3}{2}$$

$$.7 + 1.2 = 1.9 \text{ and } 1.2 + .7 = 1.9, \text{ therefore } .7 + 1.2 = 1.2 + .7$$

The pattern or property suggested by the examples above is called

THE COMMUTATIVE PROPERTY OF ADDITION [CPA]

What does the word "commutative" suggest to you? Look it up in a dictionary.

To say, in an abbreviated form, that the commutative property of addition is true for *every* number x and *every* number y in the agreed on universal set, we write

■ CPA: $\forall_x \forall_y \, x + y = y + x$

RECALL: The symbol "$\forall$" is an abbreviation for "for every."

$$3 \cdot 24 = 72 \text{ and } 24 \cdot 3 = 72, \text{ therefore } 3 \cdot 24 = 24 \cdot 3$$

$$\tfrac{1}{2} \cdot 17 = 8\tfrac{1}{2} \text{ and } 17 \cdot \tfrac{1}{2} = 8\tfrac{1}{2}, \text{ therefore } \tfrac{1}{2} \cdot 17 = 17 \cdot \tfrac{1}{2}$$

$$\tfrac{2}{3} \times \tfrac{4}{5} = \tfrac{8}{15} \text{ and } \tfrac{4}{5} \times \tfrac{2}{3} = \tfrac{8}{15}, \text{ therefore } \tfrac{2}{3} \times \tfrac{4}{5} = \tfrac{4}{5} \times \tfrac{2}{3}$$

$$.36 \times 1.6 = .576 \text{ and } 1.6 \times .36 = .576, \text{ therefore } .36 \times 1.6 = 1.6 \times .36$$

Is this last pattern on the preceding page clear to you? Give two more examples of your own that fit this pattern. The property suggested by the examples above is called

THE COMMUTATIVE PROPERTY OF MULTIPLICATION [CPM]

CPM is stated in an abbreviated form as follows:

■   CPM: $\forall_x \, \forall_y \, x \cdot y = y \cdot x$

We frequently omit the dot in "$x \cdot y$" and write "xy" to indicate the product of x and y. We can show the product of a and b in the following ways: $a \cdot b$, $a \times b$, ab. Show $a \cdot (b + c)$ in two more ways.

From CPA and CPM, you will notice that commutativity is a property of operations on numbers. The operations of addition and multiplication have this property. What about subtraction? Is $5 - 2 = 2 - 5$? Of course not. And what about division? Is $4 \div 8 = 8 \div 4$? The answer is "no," since $4 \div 8$ is equal to $\frac{1}{2}$ and $8 \div 4$ is equal to 2 and $\frac{1}{2} \neq 2$ (read: $\frac{1}{2}$ is not equal to 2).

We therefore say that multiplication and addition are *commutative operations*. On the other hand, division and subtraction are *non-commutative* operations.

$$(3 + 16) + 34 = 19 + 34 = 53, \text{ and}$$
$$3 + (16 + 34) = 3 + 50 = 53; \text{ therefore}$$
$$(3 + 16) + 34 = 3 + (16 + 34)$$
$$(.13 + .3) + 1.9 = .43 + 1.9 = 2.33, \text{ and}$$
$$.13 + (.3 + 1.9) = .13 + 2.2 = 2.33; \text{ therefore}$$
$$(.13 + .3) + 1.9 = .13 + (.3 + 1.9)$$

Give two more examples of your own to show that you understand this pattern. This property is called

THE ASSOCIATIVE PROPERTY OF ADDITION [APA]

■   APA: $\forall_x \, \forall_y \, \forall_z \, (x + y) + z = x + (y + z)$

The choice of the word *associative* is quite sensible here. This can be seen by observing what is involved in this property. Examine, for example, $(3 + 16) + 34 = 3 + (16 + 34)$. On the left side of the equality sign, 16 is grouped, or *associated*, with 3. On the right side of the equality sign, 16 is associated with 34. Thus, the associative property of addition tells us that 16 can be associated with either 3 or 34 in these expressions and the answer will be the same. We agree that if parentheses are omitted, as in $3 + 5 + 7$, it will mean $(3 + 5) + 7$.

$$(13 \cdot 8) \cdot 4 = 104 \cdot 4 = 416, \text{ and}$$
$$13 \cdot (8 \cdot 4) = 13 \cdot 32 = 416; \text{ therefore}$$
$$(13 \cdot 8) \cdot 4 = 13 \cdot (8 \cdot 4)$$

$$(\tfrac{1}{7} \cdot \tfrac{2}{3}) \cdot \tfrac{1}{2} = \tfrac{2}{21} \cdot \tfrac{1}{2} = \tfrac{1}{21}, \text{ and}$$
$$\tfrac{1}{7} \cdot (\tfrac{2}{3} \cdot \tfrac{1}{2}) = \tfrac{1}{7} \cdot \tfrac{1}{3} = \tfrac{1}{21}; \text{ therefore}$$
$$(\tfrac{1}{7} \cdot \tfrac{2}{3}) \cdot \tfrac{1}{2} = \tfrac{1}{7} \cdot (\tfrac{2}{3} \cdot \tfrac{1}{2})$$

Give two more examples of your own that follow the same pattern.

Do you see a similarity between this property and the associative property of addition? You should not have any difficulty guessing that the name for this property is

THE ASSOCIATIVE PROPERTY OF MULTIPLICATION [APM]

■   APM: $\forall_x \forall_y \forall_z (xy)z = x(yz)$

IMPORTANT AGREEMENT: By now, you should have observed that a letter, say x, may occur more than once in an equation. In case we are told to replace x by a numeral, say 3, then we are to replace every x in that equation by 3.

As in the case of commutativity, associativity is a property of an operation on numbers. You have seen that the operations of addition and multiplication are associative. As with addition, we shall agree that if parentheses are omitted, as in $2 \cdot 3 \cdot 4$, it will mean $(2 \cdot 3) \cdot 4$.

To check subtraction and division for associativity, let us take an example for each operation. Is $(10 - 5) - 4 = 10 - (5 - 4)$? To decide on the answer, we simplify each side separately as shown below.

$$(10 - 5) - 4 = 5 - 4 = 1$$
$$10 - (5 - 4) = 10 - 1 = 9$$
$$\text{and } 1 \neq 9$$
$$\text{Thus, } (10 - 5) - 4 \neq 10 - (5 - 4)$$

Is one example sufficient to prove that the operation of subtraction is not associative?

Consider the operation of division. Is $(12 \div 6) \div 3 = 12 \div (6 \div 3)$?

$$(12 \div 6) \div 3 = 2 \div 3 = \tfrac{2}{3}$$
$$12 \div (6 \div 3) = 12 \div 2 = 6$$
$$\text{and } \tfrac{2}{3} \neq 6$$
$$\text{Thus, } (12 \div 6) \div 3 \neq 12 \div (6 \div 3)$$

We can therefore conclude that neither subtraction nor division is an associative operation.

EXERCISES

1. In each exercise below, some property is illustrated. Name the property.

Examples: $3 + 4 = 4 + 3$ The property illustrated is CPA.
$(7 \times 6) \times 2 = 7 \times (6 \times 2)$ APM is illustrated.

a. $19 + 35 = 35 + 19$ e. $6 \times 998 = 998 \times 6$
b. $\frac{1}{2} + 30 = 30 + \frac{1}{2}$ f. $(1 \cdot 3) \cdot 5 = 1 \cdot (3 \cdot 5)$
c. $(6 + 7) + 9 = 6 + (7 + 9)$ g. $(0 \cdot 2) \cdot 13 = 0 \cdot (2 \cdot 13)$
d. $3 \times \frac{1}{3} = \frac{1}{3} \times 3$ h. $(1 \cdot 2) + 3 = (2 \cdot 1) + 3$

i. $(3 + 5) \times (4 \times 10) = (5 + 3) \times (4 \times 10)$
j. $(1 \times 17) \times (6 + 11) = (17 \times 1) \times (6 + 11)$

2. The commutative and associative properties of addition and multiplication can be used to good advantage in simplifying numerical expressions. Study the examples below and then find a way of grouping to simplify the computations as much as possible.

Examples: *i.* $(12 + 19) + 1 = 12 + (19 + 1)$
$= 12 + 20$
$= 32$

ii. $(\frac{2}{5} \times 4.7) \times 25 = (4.7 \times \frac{2}{5}) \times 25$
$= 4.7 \times (\frac{2}{5} \times 25)$
$= 4.7 \times 10$
$= 47$

a. $(56 + 97) + 3$ h. $(870 + 869) + 130$
b. $(178 + 987) + 13$ i. $(3.2 + 9.9) + .1$
c. $(159 + 1999) + 1$ j. $(\frac{1}{4} + \frac{3}{2}) + \frac{1}{2}$
d. $(998 + 376) + 2$ k. $(\frac{3}{7} + \frac{1}{3}) + \frac{4}{7}$
e. $(901 + 455) + 99$ l. $(\frac{1}{9} + \frac{1}{2}) + \frac{8}{9}$
f. $(37 \times 20) \times \frac{1}{2}$ m. $(\frac{8}{7} \times \frac{6}{11}) \times \frac{7}{8}$
g. $(100 \times \frac{1}{16}) \times 8$ n. $(25 \times 73) \times 4$

CLOSURE

Let us consider the set of natural numbers as our universal set. If we add a pair of natural numbers, the sum is always a natural number. For example, $1 + 21 = 22$, $179 + 382 = 561$, $5 + 5 = 10$, and so on. We would face an impossible task if we should decide to search for a pair of natural numbers whose sum is not a natural number. The name for this property is *closure*. Thus, the set of natural numbers is said to be *closed* under the operation of *addition*.

What about the operation of multiplication? Given a pair of natural numbers, is the product always a natural number? Perhaps you already answered "yes"; you are right. Again we would have an impossible task to find an example where this is not true. Therefore, the set of natural numbers is said to be *closed* under the operation of *multiplication*.

Let us now examine the operation of subtraction. For example, $7 - 3 = 4$; but $3 - 7 = ?$ has no answer among the natural numbers. One example for which an answer does not exist among the natural numbers is sufficient to conclude that the set of natural numbers is *not closed* under the operation of *subtraction*.

You may already be familiar with the set of integers, that is, the union of the set of positive whole numbers, negative whole numbers, and zero. The set of integers *is* closed under subtraction, because for every pair of integers, there exists an integer which is their difference.

Let us now investigate closure under division. For example, $10 \div 5 = 2$; but $5 \div 10 = ?$ has no answer among natural numbers. Thus, the set of natural numbers is *not closed* under the operation of *division*. Is the set of integers closed under division? Prove your answer.

We conclude that the set of natural numbers is closed under addition and multiplication. It is *not* closed under subtraction and division.

If we use N for the set of natural numbers, then the closure property of N under addition may be stated as follows:

■   ClPA: $\forall_{a \, \epsilon \, N} \, \forall_{b \, \epsilon \, N} \, (a + b) \, \epsilon \, N$

State, similarly, the closure property of the set of natural numbers under multiplication.

EXERCISES

For each exercise determine whether the given set of numbers seems to be closed under the given operations.

Example: Set: all odd natural numbers; operations: **a.** addition
                b. multiplication

How to Solve: **a.** Is the sum of a pair of odd natural numbers an odd natural number? Let us try.
$$3 + 5 = 8$$

Answer: No, the set of odd natural numbers is not closed under addition.

b. The question here is: Is the product of a pair of odd natural numbers an odd natural number? Let us try a few.

$$5 \times 5 = 25$$
$$7 \times 11 = 77$$
$$9 \times 7 = 63$$

Answer: There seems to be no reason to suspect that the product of a pair of odd numbers is not an odd number (later you will be able to prove it). Therefore we say that the set of odd natural numbers *seems* to be closed under multiplication.

1. Set: all even natural numbers; operations: **a.** addition   **b.** multiplication

2. Set: all natural numbers divisible by 3; operations: **a.** addition **b.** multiplication

3. Set: all natural numbers divisible by 4; operations: **a.** addition **b.** multiplication

4. Set: all even natural numbers; operation: take half of the sum of a pair of numbers

5. Set: all natural numbers divisible by 5; operation: divide by 10

6. Set: all natural numbers divisible by 3; operation: take half of the product of a pair of numbers

7. Set: all natural numbers divisible by 9; operation: take one-third of the sum of a pair of numbers

8. Set: $\{.1, .01, .001, .0001, \ldots\}$; operations: **a.** multiplication **b.** division

9. Set: $\{1, 2\}$; operations: **a.** multiplication **b.** addition

10. Set: $\{\frac{1}{2}, 1, 2\}$; operations: **a.** multiplication **b.** division

11. Set: $\{\frac{1}{2}, \frac{1}{4}, \frac{1}{8}, \frac{1}{16}, \frac{1}{32}, \ldots\}$; operations: **a.** addition **b.** multiplication

12. Set: $\{\frac{1}{3}, \frac{1}{9}, \frac{1}{27}, \frac{1}{81}, \ldots\}$; operation: multiply by $\frac{1}{3}$

13. Set: $\{0, 1\}$; operations: **a.** addition; **b.** multiplication; **c.** subtraction

14. Set: $\{1, \frac{1}{5}, \frac{1}{25}, \frac{1}{125}, \ldots\}$; operation: multiply by $\frac{1}{5}$

15. Set: $\{1, 4, 9, 16, 25, 36, 49, 64, \ldots\}$; operation: multiply the number by itself

16. Set: all prime numbers; operations: **a.** addition   **b.** multiplication

17. Set: $\{0, \frac{1}{2}, 1\}$; operation: multiplication

18. Set: $\{0\}$; operation: addition

More about addition and multiplication

Suppose a man is selling tickets for a benefit at $3 each. If he sells seventeen tickets the first day and four tickets the next, what are the total receipts?

We could arrange our computation in the following manner

$$3 \times (17 + 4) = 3 \times 21 = 63$$

That is, knowing the total number of tickets sold (21) and the price of each ticket ($3), we find the total receipts to be $63.

But he could also write it as follows:

$$(3 \times 17) + (3 \times 4) = 51 + 12 = 63$$

The product of three and seventeen indicates the receipts for the first day, and the product of three and four indicates the receipts for the second day. Their sum is the total intake.

We see, then, that $3 \times (17 + 4) = (3 \times 17) + (3 \times 4)$.

A simple property of "=" permits us to say that, if $3 \times (17 + 4) = (3 \times 17) + (3 \times 4)$, then $(3 \times 17) + (3 \times 4) = 3 \times (17 + 4)$. This property is

■ $\forall_x \forall_y$, if $x = y$, then $y = x$

It is called Symmetric Property of Equality.

EXERCISES

1.   Work each of the following in the two ways shown in the example and determine whether or not the results are the same.

Example: $4 \times (3 + 5) = 4 \times 8 = 32$
$4 \times (3 + 5) = (4 \times 3) + (4 \times 5) = 12 + 20 = 32$

a. $6 \times (7 + 4)$

b. $8 \times (5 + 7)$

c. $\frac{2}{3} \times (6 + 9)$

d. $\frac{1}{3} \times (.6 + 9)$

e. $\frac{3}{5} \times (\frac{1}{2} + \frac{1}{3})$

f. $31 \times (11 + 12)$

g. $\frac{4}{7} \times (\frac{1}{3} + \frac{1}{2})$

h. $1.5 \times (1.5 + 1.5)$

i. $1 \times (17 + 99)$

j. $3.3 \times (.5 + .4)$

k. $.05 \times (100 + 200)$

l. $.005 \times (1000 + 2000)$

m. $0 \times (21 + 36)$

n. $\frac{1}{3} \times (\frac{1}{3} + \frac{1}{3})$

o. $25 \times (0 + 1)$

p. $.1 \times (.01 + .001)$

2.   Give replacements for x, y, and z to obtain true statements.

a. $5 \times (6 + 9) = (y \times 6) + (y \times 9)$
b. $3 \times (x + 6) = (3 \times 5) + (3 \times 6)$
c. $z \times (4 + 11) = (5 \times 4) + (5 \times 11)$
d. $(\frac{1}{2} \cdot \frac{3}{4}) + (\frac{1}{2} \cdot \frac{3}{10}) = .5 \cdot (.75 + z)$

THE DISTRIBUTIVE PROPERTY

The property which we explored in the previous section is called

THE DISTRIBUTIVE PROPERTY OF MULTIPLICATION
OVER ADDITION [DPMA].

To state this property, we write

■   DPMA: $\forall_x \forall_y \forall_z \, x(y + z) = (xy) + (xz)$

This property tells us that multiplication is distributive with respect to addition. For example, 17 may replace x, 5 may replace y, and 6 may replace z, to yield

$$17 \cdot (5 + 6) = (17 \cdot 5) + (17 \cdot 6)$$

Simplify both sides and see whether you get the same answer.

We now summarize the properties of operations on numbers which we have observed thus far

i. addition is commutative and associative
ii. multiplication is commutative and associative
iii. multiplication is distributive with respect to addition

It is appropriate to ask whether or not some other operation is distributive with respect to addition or with respect to any other operation. Let us try some pairs of operations with which you are familiar.

First, let us introduce other symbols to be used in a way similar to the way we have used the symbols x, y, and z. We agreed that we could replace each letter by a numeral. For example, $x + y + z$ becomes $6 + \frac{4}{5} + .76$ when x is replaced by 6, y is replaced by $\frac{4}{5}$, and z is replaced by .76.

The new symbols, let us say $\oplus$ and $\odot$, will be used with the intent of having them replaced by symbols for operations: $+$, $-$, $\div$, $\times$.

Now we are in a position to write the equation

$$x \oplus (y \odot z) = (x \oplus y) \odot (x \oplus z)$$

where the letters x, y, and z are replaceable by numerals, and the symbols $\oplus$ and $\odot$ are replaceable by symbols for operations.

We already know that replacing $\oplus$ by $\times$ and $\odot$ by $+$ will always give us true statements no matter what numerals go in place of x, y and z. Let us now try another replacement. Put $+$ in place of $\oplus$ and $+$ in place of $\odot$. Does the pattern

$$x + (y + z) = (x + y) + (x + z)$$

yield true statements no matter what numerals are put in place of x, y and z? Let us test this.

Is $2 + (5 + 7) = (2 + 5) + (2 + 7)$ a true statement?
$$2 + (5 + 7) = 2 + 12 = 14$$
$$\text{and} \quad (2 + 5) + (2 + 7) = 7 + 9 = 16$$

Since $14 \neq 16$, the statement is false, and we conclude that the operation of addition is not distributive with respect to itself. Is one example sufficient to prove this?

The answer to the preceding question is "yes." It is sufficient to show one exception in order to prove that a statement is false. This is known as a *counter-example*. Can you think of an operation which is distributive with respect to itself?

EXERCISES

1. When the symmetric property of equality is applied to the statement $\frac{1}{2} + \frac{1}{3} = 1 - \frac{1}{6}$, the statement $1 - \frac{1}{6} = \frac{1}{2} + \frac{1}{3}$ is obtained. Write the statement which is obtained from $3 \times (89 + 46) = (3 \times 89) + (3 \times 46)$ when the symmetric property of equality is applied to it.

2. For each expression, write the equation which involves the given expression as either an example of the distributive property or as a consequence of the distributive and symmetric properties.

Examples:
$$5 \cdot (7 + 8) = (5 \cdot 7) + (5 \cdot 8)$$
$$(3 \cdot 92) + (3 \cdot 64) = 3 \cdot (92 + 64)$$

a. $16 \cdot (3 + 5)$

b. $\frac{1}{3} \cdot (7 + 3)$

c. $(.5 \times 6) + (.5 \times 7)$

d. $(.08 \times \frac{1}{2}) + (.08 \times .3)$

e. $\frac{1}{2} \cdot (\frac{1}{3} + \frac{1}{4})$

f. $33 \cdot (\frac{1}{3} + \frac{1}{11})$

g. $(42 \times \frac{1}{2}) + (42 \times 7)$

h. $.1 \times (.7 + .5)$

i. $.02 \times (.02 + .03)$

j. $(5 \times 7) + (5 \times 13)$

k. $(11 \times 12) + (11 \times 16)$

l. $(\frac{3}{4})(\frac{5}{6}) + (\frac{3}{4})(\frac{7}{6})$

m. $(7 \times 20) + (7 \times 13)$

n. $(37 \times 46) + (37 \times 4)$

o. $25 \times (25 + 25)$

p. $(\frac{1}{2} \cdot 0) + (\frac{1}{2} \cdot 1)$

3.   Work out two examples for each case to check whether or not each of the following statements is true.

Statement.   Multiplication is distributive with respect to multiplication.

Examples: i. $3 \times (4 \times 5) = (3 \times 4) \times (3 \times 5)$

$\qquad$ 3×20 $\quad|\quad$ 12×15

$\qquad$ 60 $\qquad\quad \neq 180$

$\qquad$ ii. $\frac{1}{2} \times (\frac{2}{3} \times \frac{4}{7}) = (\frac{1}{2} \times \frac{2}{3}) \times (\frac{1}{2} \times \frac{4}{7})$

$\qquad\quad$ $\frac{1}{2} \times \frac{8}{21}$ $\qquad|\qquad$ $\frac{2}{6} \times \frac{4}{14}$

$\qquad\qquad$ $\frac{8}{42}$ $\qquad\qquad|\qquad$ $\frac{1}{3} \times \frac{2}{7}$

$\qquad\qquad$ $\frac{4}{21}$ $\qquad\quad \neq \qquad \frac{2}{21}$

$\qquad$ The statement is false.

a.   Division is distributive with respect to multiplication.
b.   Division is distributive with respect to subtraction.
c.   Multiplication is distributive with respect to subtraction.
d.   Multiplication is distributive with respect to division.
e.   Addition is distributive with respect to multiplication.
f.   Addition is distributive with respect to division.
g.   Addition is distributive with respect to subtraction.
h.   Subtraction is distributive with respect to subtraction.
i.   Subtraction is distributive with respect to multiplication.

SPECIAL PROPERTIES OF ONE AND ZERO

In the four groups of examples below, each group is intended to suggest a certain pattern or property. Try to discover these properties. Supply two more examples which fit each pattern. After you have discovered the pattern for each case, see the statements and names of the properties below.

$165 \cdot 1 = 165$	$39 \div 1 = 39$	$79 + 0 = 79$	$135 \cdot 0 = 0$
$0 \cdot 1 = 0$	$0 \div 1 = 0$	$0 + 0 = 0$	$0 \cdot 0 = 0$
$\frac{4}{7} \cdot 1 = \frac{4}{7}$	$\frac{13}{17} \div 1 = \frac{13}{17}$	$\frac{12}{19} + 0 = \frac{12}{19}$	$\frac{2}{7} \cdot 0 = 0$
$1.67 \times 1 = 1.67$	$3.5 \div 1 = 3.5$	$17.6 + 0 = 17.6$	$6.75 \times 0 = 0$
.	.	.	.
.	.	.	.
.	.	.	.

Before reading on, try to express these properties in your own words.

▓　*Property* of *One* for *Multiplication* [P1M]
$\forall_x x \cdot 1 = x$

▓　*Property* of *One* for *Division* [P1D]
$\forall_x x \div 1 = x$

▓　*Property* of *Zero* for *Addition* [PZA]
$\forall_x x + 0 = x$

▓　*Property* of *Zero* for *Multiplication* [PZM]
$\forall_x x \cdot 0 = 0$

Can you suggest some other patterns that might be familiar from your previous study of mathematics?

EXERCISES

1.　From what we know already, we can prove that

$$\forall_x 1 \cdot x = x$$

Proof　　　$1 \cdot x = x \cdot 1$　by reason of CPM
　　　　　　　$= x$　　　by reason of P1M

Now, you prove each of the following:

　　a. $\forall_x 0 + x = x$　**b.** $\forall_x 0 \cdot x = 0$　**c.** $\forall_a \forall_b \forall_c (a + b)c = ac + bc$

2.　In each example below, name the property involved in going from one step to the next.

Examples:　　*i.* $3 \cdot (4 \cdot 7) \overset{(1)}{=} 3 \cdot (7 \cdot 4)$
　　　　　　　　　　$\overset{(2)}{=} (3 \cdot 7) \cdot 4$

　　　　　(1) CPM (Point out the specific place where this property was used.)
　　　　　(2) APM (Point out the specific place where this property was used.)

　　　ii. $[(5 + 0) + (6 \cdot 0)] \times 1 \overset{(1)}{=} [5 + (6 \cdot 0)] \times 1$
　　　　　　　　　　　　　　　　$\overset{(2)}{=} [5 + 0] \times 1$
　　　　　　　　　　　　　　　　$\overset{(3)}{=} [5] \times 1$
　　　　　　　　　　　　　　　　$\overset{(4)}{=} 5$

　　　　　(1) PZA
　　　　　(2) PZM
　　　　　(3) PZA
　　　　　(4) P1M

iii. $(2+7) + \frac{1}{3} + 13 \cdot 0 + 23 \cdot 1$

$\overset{(1)}{=} (7+2) + \frac{1}{3} + 13 \cdot 0 + 23 \cdot 1$

$\overset{(2)}{=} 7 + (2 + \frac{1}{3}) + 13 \cdot 0 + 23$

$\overset{(3)}{=} 7 + (\frac{1}{3} + 2) + 0 + 23$

(1) CPA

(2) APA and P1M

(3) CPA and PZM (In each case point out the specific place at which the property you named was used.)

a. $3 + 7 \overset{(1)}{=} 7 + 3$

b. $(3 + \frac{1}{2}) + \frac{1}{3} \overset{(1)}{=} 3 + (\frac{1}{2} + \frac{1}{3})$

c. $4 \cdot 125 \overset{(1)}{=} 125 \cdot 4$

d. $(\frac{1}{2} \cdot \frac{1}{4}) \cdot \frac{1}{7} \overset{(1)}{=} \frac{1}{2} \cdot (\frac{1}{4} \cdot \frac{1}{7})$

e. $(3 \cdot 5) \cdot 7 \overset{(1)}{=} (5 \cdot 3) \cdot 7$

f. $(10 + 3) + 27 \overset{(1)}{=} (3 + 10) + 27$

g. $(\frac{2}{7} + \frac{3}{4}) + \frac{1}{2} \overset{(1)}{=} \frac{2}{7} + (\frac{3}{4} + \frac{1}{2})$

h. $3 \cdot 0 + (\frac{1}{2} \cdot \frac{1}{3}) \cdot \frac{1}{4} \overset{(1)}{=} 0 + (\frac{1}{2} \cdot \frac{1}{3}) \cdot \frac{1}{4}$

$\overset{(2)}{=} (\frac{1}{2} \cdot \frac{1}{3}) \cdot \frac{1}{4} + 0$

$\overset{(3)}{=} (\frac{1}{2} \cdot \frac{1}{3}) \cdot \frac{1}{4}$

$\overset{(4)}{=} \frac{1}{2} \cdot (\frac{1}{3} \cdot \frac{1}{4})$

i. $[6(5 + 8)] + 0 \overset{(1)}{=} [6(8 + 5)] + 0$

$\overset{(2)}{=} [6(8) + 6(5)] + 0$

$\overset{(3)}{=} 6(8) + 6(5)$

j. $3 \cdot (1 + 4) + 4 \cdot 7 \overset{(1)}{=} (3 \cdot 1) + (3 \cdot 4) + 4 \cdot 7$

$\overset{(2)}{=} 3 + (3 \cdot 4) + 4 \cdot 7$

$\overset{(3)}{=} 3 + (4 \cdot 3) + (4 \cdot 7)$

$\overset{(4)}{=} 3 + 4(3 + 7)$

k. $5 \cdot [(3 + 9) + 7] \overset{(1)}{=} 5 \cdot [(9 + 3) + 7]$

$\overset{(2)}{=} 5 \cdot [9 + (3 + 7)]$

$\overset{(3)}{=} 5 \cdot (9) + 5 \cdot (3 + 7)$

l. $5[(3 + 4) + 6] \overset{(1)}{=} 5[3 + (4 + 6)]$

$\overset{(2)}{=} 5[(4 + 6) + 3]$

$\overset{(3)}{=} 5(4 + 6) + 5(3)$

$\overset{(4)}{=} 5(4) + 5(6) + 5(3)$

m. $1 \times [6 \times 3 + 6 \times 7] \overset{(1)}{=} 1 \times [6(3 + 7)]$

$\overset{(2)}{=} [6(3 + 7)] \times 1$

$\overset{(3)}{=} 6(3 + 7)$

INVERSE OPERATIONS

From your study of arithmetic you know that the most frequently used operations are addition, subtraction, multiplication, and division. The operations of addition and subtraction are closely related to each other. To see this relation, observe the following examples.

$$5 - 2 = 3 \qquad \text{and} \qquad 3 + 2 = 5$$
$$17 - 3 = 14 \qquad \text{and} \qquad 14 + 3 = 17$$
$$3.5 - .7 = 2.8 \qquad \text{and} \qquad 2.8 + .7 = 3.5$$
$$\tfrac{1}{3} - \tfrac{1}{4} = \tfrac{1}{12} \qquad \text{and} \qquad \tfrac{1}{12} + \tfrac{1}{4} = \tfrac{1}{3}$$

From these examples you can see that every subtraction problem can be changed to a related addition problem. Actually, if you did not know how to subtract, you could still find answers to subtraction problems. For instance, the example $17 - 9 = ?$ would be changed to $? + 9 = 17$. Now, you need to answer the question, "9 added to what number gives 17?" In this case you will have no difficulty in giving the answer immediately. In more difficult problems, you might need to try a few numbers before finding the one which will work.

To generalize the relation which exists between addition and subtraction, we resort to letters.

■ $\forall_x \, \forall_{y \le x} \forall_z \; x - y = z$ is equivalent to $z + y = x$

Why must we state that y is less than or equal to x?

We say that subtraction is the *inverse* operation of addition.

There is a similar relation between the operations of multiplication and division. Observe the examples below to see what this relation is.

$$16 \div 2 = 8 \text{ or } \tfrac{16}{2} = 8 \qquad \text{and} \qquad 8 \cdot 2 = 16$$
$$34 \div 4 = 8\tfrac{1}{2} \text{ or } \tfrac{34}{4} = 8\tfrac{1}{2} \qquad \text{and} \qquad 8\tfrac{1}{2} \cdot 4 = 34$$
$$\tfrac{1}{2} \div \tfrac{1}{3} = \tfrac{3}{2} \text{ or } \frac{\tfrac{1}{2}}{\tfrac{1}{3}} = \tfrac{3}{2} \qquad \text{and} \qquad \tfrac{3}{2} \cdot \tfrac{1}{3} = \tfrac{1}{2}$$
$$.5 \div 3 = \tfrac{1}{6} \text{ or } \tfrac{.5}{3} = \tfrac{1}{6} \qquad \text{and} \qquad \tfrac{1}{6} \cdot 3 = .5$$

From these examples you can see that a division problem can be changed to a related multiplication problem. For instance, the answer to the first example, "What is the answer when 16 is divided by 2?" is the same as the answer to the question, "What number multiplied by 2 gives 16?" Formulate for yourself questions to fit second, third, and fourth examples.

Using letters, we can portray the relation between multiplication and division as follows:

■ $\forall_x \, \forall_{y \,=\, 0} \, \forall_z \quad x \div y = z$ is equivalent to $z \cdot y = x$

Why do we state that y is not to be replaced by 0?

We say that division is the *inverse* operation of multiplication.

You will note that there is a similarity between the two preceding statements containing letters. The only difference is in the operation signs. Now, using $\odot$ and $\oplus$ to stand for operations, we can write a generalization for two operations which are inverses of each other.

"$\odot$ and $\oplus$ are inverses" means
$$x \odot y = z \text{ is equivalent to } z \oplus y = x$$

You should replace the letters x, y, and z above by numerals and the symbols $\odot$ and $\oplus$ by operation symbols to see what pairs of operations have the inverse relation.

EXERCISES

1.   Change each of the following subtraction problems to a related addition problem, and solve it.

Example:
$$\tfrac{1}{2} - \tfrac{1}{3} = x$$
$$x + \tfrac{1}{3} = \tfrac{1}{2}$$
$$x + \tfrac{2}{6} = \tfrac{3}{6}$$
$$\tfrac{1}{6} + \tfrac{2}{6} = \tfrac{3}{6}$$
Therefore, $\tfrac{1}{6}$ in place of x makes the statement true.
$$\tfrac{1}{2} - \tfrac{1}{3} = \tfrac{1}{6}$$

a. $17 - 12 = x$
b. $25 - 5 = y$
c. $13 - .5 = z$
d. $.73 - .03 = a$
e. $998 - 97 = m$

f. $21\tfrac{3}{4} - 19\tfrac{1}{4} = p$
g. $\tfrac{3}{4} - \tfrac{1}{2} = n$
h. $\tfrac{3}{7} - \tfrac{1}{3} = u$
i. $14 - t = 5$
j. $111 - c = 11$

k. $r - 73 = 71$
l. $\tfrac{1}{2} - s = \tfrac{1}{4}$
m. $.75 - x = .03$
n. $g - .99 = .02$
o. $h - \tfrac{3}{7} = \tfrac{1}{5}$

2.   Change each of the following division problems to a related multiplication problem, and solve it. Three of them have no answer! Find these.

Examples: *i.* $48 \div 6 = x$
$$x \cdot 6 = 48$$
$$8 \cdot 6 = 48$$
Therefore, 8 in place of x makes the statement true.
$$48 \div 6 = 8$$

ii. $\frac{8}{9} \div \frac{2}{3} = m$

$m \cdot \frac{2}{3} = \frac{8}{9}$

$\frac{4}{3} \cdot \frac{2}{3} = \frac{8}{9}$

Therefore, $\frac{4}{3}$ in place of m makes the statement true.

$\frac{8}{9} \div \frac{2}{3} = \frac{4}{3}$

a. $40 \div 8 = x$

b. $625 \div 25 = m$

c. $56 \div 7 = n$

d. $156 \div 13 = p$

e. $.5 \div 1 = q$

f. $.3 \div .1 = s$

g. $\frac{1}{4} \div \frac{1}{2} = n$

h. $\frac{9}{32} \div \frac{3}{4} = r$

i. $280 \div y = 35$

j. $165 \div t = 5$

k. $u \div 11 = 133$

l. $a \div \frac{3}{7} = \frac{2}{5}$

m. $\frac{3}{2} \div c = \frac{1}{2}$

n. $q \div 1.2 = 14.7$

o. $101 \div r = \frac{1}{2}$

p. $0 \div 2 = x$

q. $3 \div 0 = y$

r. $\frac{0}{7} = n$

s. $\frac{11}{0} = p$

t. $15 \div t = 0$

3. Let us invent two new operations: *alphation* and *betation*. All you know about these two operations is that each is the inverse of the other. The symbol for alphation is α and the symbol for betation is β. Change each of the alphation problems below to a related betation problem.

Example: $7 \alpha 3 = 10\frac{1}{2}$

The related betation problem is $10\frac{1}{2} \beta 3 = 7$

a. $2 \alpha 2 = 2$

b. $3 \alpha 4 = 6$

c. $12 \alpha 5 = 30$

d. $\frac{1}{2} \alpha \frac{1}{3} = \frac{1}{12}$

e. $.1 \alpha .02 = .001$

f. $50 \alpha 10 = 250$

g. $\frac{2}{3} \alpha \frac{1}{3} = \frac{1}{9}$

h. $10 \alpha .01 = .05$

i. $500 \alpha 300 = 75000$

j. $\frac{1}{3} \alpha \frac{1}{4} = \frac{1}{24}$

4. Look carefully at your answers in exercise **3.** Can you tell how the operations of alphation and betation are related to operations with which you are familiar? That is, change the expressions below to expressions involving multiplication and division.

$$x \alpha y \qquad\qquad\qquad x \beta y$$

From word phrases to mathematical phrases

We find many occasions in mathematics to solve problems. Frequently problems are stated in words. Here is a very simple problem.

Three more than twice a number is 4. What is the number?

Sometimes we can obtain an answer to a problem like this very quickly without having to do any work on paper. At other times the problems may be more involved and we need to do some writing to get the answer.

Usually, the first thing to do is to write a mathematical phrase which depicts what is stated in words. Let us do that for the problem above.

We use x to refer to the number mentioned in the problem. Then we

write $\qquad\qquad$ $2x$ $\quad$ for $\quad$ *twice a number*

and $\qquad\qquad$ $2x + 3$ $\quad$ for $\quad$ *three more than twice a number*

We obtain the equation

$$2x + 3 = 4$$

which describes what was stated above in words.

EXERCISES

For each word phrase, write the mathematical phrase. Do not compute the answer.

Examples: $\qquad$ *i.* 2 less than 3 times n $\qquad$ $3n - 2$

$\qquad\qquad$ *ii.* Four times the sum of a and b $\qquad$ $4(a + b)$

1. the sum of 3 and 25
2. the sum of 12 and y
3. 5 more than m
4. the sum of $4x$ and $5y$
5. $9t$ increased by $4s$
6. 5 times the sum of $2x$ and $3y$
7. 9 subtracted from x
8. n subtracted from 12
9. 3 less than 10
10. x less than 12
11. t less than $3x$

12. 15 decreased by 3
13. x decreased by 5
14. 9 decreased by $6t$
15. $7s$ decreased by $2m$
16. 5 times the sum of 6 and x
17. the sum of $2x$ and $3y$ multiplied by 4
18. 20 divided by x
19. $3t$ divided by 7
20. $4x$ divided by the sum of a and b
21. the sum of x and y divided by n

PROPERTIES

▪ *Closure Property of Addition* $\quad$ [ClPA]
$\quad$ $\forall_{x \, \epsilon \, N} \, \forall_{y \, \epsilon \, N} \quad (x + y) \, \epsilon \, N$

▪ *Closure Property of Multiplication* $\quad$ [ClPM]
$\quad$ $\forall_{x \, \epsilon \, N} \, \forall_{y \, \epsilon \, N} \quad (xy) \, \epsilon \, N$

▪ *Commutative Property of Addition* $\quad$ [CPA]
$\quad$ $\forall_{x} \, \forall_{y} \, x + y = y + x$

■ *Commutative Property of Multiplication*   [CPM]
$\forall_x \forall_y \, xy = yx$

■ *Associative Property of Addition*   [APA]
$\forall_x \forall_y \forall_z \, (x + y) + z = x + (y + z)$

■ *Associative Property of Multiplication*   [APM]
$\forall_x \forall_y \forall_z \, (xy)z = x(yz)$

■ *Distributive Property of Multiplication over Addition*   [DPMA]
$\forall_x \forall_y \forall_z \, x(y + z) = (xy) + (xz)$

■ *Symmetric Property of Equality*
$\forall_x \forall_y$, if $x = y$, then $y = x$

■ *Property of One for Multiplication*   [P1M]
$\forall_x \, x \cdot 1 = x$

■ *Property of one for Division*   [P1D]
$\forall_x \, x \div 1 = x$

■ *Property of Zero for Addition*   [PZA]
$\forall_x \, x + 0 = x$

■ *Property of Zero for Multiplication*   [PZM]
$\forall_x \, x \cdot 0 = 0$

VOCABULARY

Use each of the following correctly in a sentence. Numerals in the parentheses refer to pages where these words were used. If you are not sure of the meaning of any word, turn to the indicated page and refresh your memory.

associative (35)

braces (32)

brackets (32)

closure (37)

commutative (34)

commutative operation (35)

counter-example (42)

distributive (41)

inverse operations (46)

mathematical phrase (48)

non-commutative operations (35)

parentheses (32)

punctuation symbols (31)

symmetric property of equality (40)

word phrase (48)

REVIEW EXERCISES

1. Simplify each of the following:

a. $4[13(5 + 7)]$

b. $7\{[6(9) - 8] \div 23\}$

c. $\frac{1}{2}[(\frac{1}{2} - \frac{1}{3}) \div \frac{1}{6}]$

d. $(5.1 - 1.3)(5.1 + 1.3)$

e. $1.0\{[1.1(1.1 + 1.1) + 1.1]1.1\}$

f. $3 + 7 \times 4$

g. $12 \div 4 \times 2 \div 6$

h. $21 - 2 \cdot 3 \cdot 3$

i. $5 \cdot 0 + 4 - 2 \cdot 2$

j. $17 + 2 - 6 - 2 + 4$

2. Name the property or properties used in going from one step to the next.

a. $[2 \cdot 0 + 3(4 + 6)] \times 7 \overset{(1)}{=} [0 + 3(4 + 6)] \times 7$
$\overset{(2)}{=} [3(4 + 6)] \times 7$
$\overset{(3)}{=} 7 \times [3(4 + 6)]$
$\overset{(4)}{=} 7[3(4) + 3(6)]$

b. $13 \times [(4 \times 7) \times 11] \overset{(1)}{=} 13 \times [4 \times (7 \times 11)]$
$\overset{(2)}{=} 13 \times [(7 \times 11) \times 4]$
$\overset{(3)}{=} 13 \times [7 \times (11 \times 4)]$
$\overset{(4)}{=} [7 \times (11 \times 4)] \times 13$
$\overset{(5)}{=} [(7 \times 11) \times 4] \times 13$

c. $7[(5 + 3) + 6] \overset{(1)}{=} 7[(3 + 5) + 6]$
$\overset{(2)}{=} 7[3 + (5 + 6)]$
$\overset{(3)}{=} 7(3) + 7(5 + 6)$

3. Replace the letters with numerals to obtain true statements.   In some cases there is more than one such replacement, and in one case there is none!

a. $43 + 7 = 7 + x$

b. $6 \cdot m = m \cdot 6$

c. $7 \cdot (6 + n) = 7 \cdot 6 + 7 \cdot 13$

d. $y + (3 + z) = (y + 3) + z$

e. $2 \cdot 7 + 2 \cdot p = 2 \cdot (m + p)$

f. $(3 \times 10) \times 13 = 3 \times (r \times 13)$

g. $13 \times (11 + 7) = 13 \times a + 13 \times b$

h. $u \times (6 + s) = (6 + s) \times u$

i. $4 \cdot 5 + 17 = 17 + 4 \cdot s$

j. $\frac{4}{3} - \frac{4}{5} = t$

k. $a - 13 = 39$

l. $\frac{2}{3} \div \frac{1}{4} = h$

m. $\frac{1}{5} \div x = \frac{1}{20}$

n. $\frac{5}{0} = v$

o. $\frac{0}{6} = t$

p. $\frac{0}{x} = 0$

4. For each problem determine whether the given set of numbers is closed under the given operations.

a. Set: $\{\frac{1}{2}, 0\}$; operations: *i.* addition *ii.* multiplication

b. Set: all numbers between 0 and 1; operations: *i.* addition *ii.* subtraction *iii.* multiplication *iv.* division

c. Set: {1, 10, 100, 1000, 10000, . . .}; operations: *i.* multiplication *ii.* division

d. Set: all even natural numbers; operation: average a pair of numbers

e. Set: {. . ., 16, 8, 4, 2, 1, $\frac{1}{2}$, $\frac{1}{4}$, $\frac{1}{8}$, . . .}; operations: *i.* addition *ii.* multiplication

5. Using the fact that subtraction is the inverse of addition, write a related addition statement for each subtraction statement.

a. $10 - 3 = 7$

b. $9.6 - 3.8 = 5.8$

c. $\frac{3}{5} - \frac{1}{2} = \frac{1}{10}$

d. $x - y = z$

6. Using the fact that division is the inverse of multiplication, write a related multiplication statement for each division statement.

a. $51 \div 3 = 17$

b. $121.8 \div 2.1 = 58$

c. $\frac{3}{4} \div \frac{7}{5} = \frac{15}{28}$

d. $x \div y = z$, $(y \neq 0)$

7. Which of the following two statements shows that $\odot$ is an inverse of $\oplus$?

a. If $a \odot b = c$, then $a \oplus c = b$. **b.** If $a \odot b = c$, then $c \oplus b = a$.

8. For each word phrase, write the mathematical phrase.

a. $3m$ increased by $5t$

b. the sum of x and $2y$

c. the product of 5 and $2x + y$

d. $3s$ divided by $4m$

e. $2m$ decreased by 5

f. $5n$ decreased by $4x$

g. 3 decreased by $(a + b)$

h. x less than 10

CHAPTER TEST

1. Write the simplest numeral for each of the following:

a. $6 \cdot (3 + 5 \cdot 6 - 2)$

b. $[5(2) + 11] \div 3$

c. $4 \times \{78 - [5 \cdot 4 + (15 \div 3)] \times 3\} \cdot 2$

2. Name the property illustrated by each of the following:

a. $3\frac{1}{3} + 7 = 7 + 3\frac{1}{3}$

b. $(2 \cdot 4) \cdot 15 = 2 \cdot (4 \cdot 15)$

c. $(3 + 7) + 11 = 3 + (7 + 11)$

d. $6 \cdot 7 + 6 \cdot 11 = 6(7 + 11)$

e. $(3 \cdot 7) \cdot 2\frac{1}{3} = 2\frac{1}{3} \cdot (3 \cdot 7)$

f. $5 \cdot (6 + 13) = 5 \cdot 6 + 5 \cdot 13$

g. $(13 + 79) + 0 = 13 + 79$

h. $(.6 \times 39) \times 1 = .6 \times 39$

i. $6[(5+7)+9] = 6[9+(5+7)]$ **k.** $(4 \times 13) \times 0 = 0$

j. $5+(6 \cdot 7+6 \cdot 11) = 5+6(7+11)$ **l.** $(12 \div 3) \div 1 = 12 \div 3$

3. In the following exercises, the letters x, y, and z hold places for numerals. Give replacements for x, y, and z to obtain true statements. In one case there is no such replacement! In some cases there are several.

a. $13 \times (x+4) = 13 \times 11 + 13 \times 4$ **g.** $\frac{0}{5} = x$

b. $y \times (6+z) = 7\frac{1}{2} \times 6 + 7\frac{1}{2} \times 17$ **h.** $113 \div z = 22.6$

c. $4\frac{1}{2} \times (x+y) = 4\frac{1}{2} \times 9 + 4\frac{1}{2} \times 2\frac{1}{3}$ **i.** $y - \frac{2}{9} = \frac{3}{5}$

d. $(7 \cdot z) \cdot 3\frac{1}{2} = 7 \cdot (5 \cdot 3\frac{1}{2})$ **j.** $\frac{6}{0} = y$

e. $x + \frac{1}{4} = \frac{1}{3}$ **k.** $x + (7+6) = (7+6) + x$

f. $11 - y = 4\frac{1}{4}$ **l.** $(3+y) \div 1 = 3+y$

m. $17\frac{1}{3} + 6\frac{1}{2} \times 2\frac{1}{2} + 6\frac{1}{2} \times 4\frac{1}{4} = 17\frac{1}{3} + z(2\frac{1}{2} + 4\frac{1}{4})$

n. $5 \cdot x + 10 \cdot y = (x + 2 \cdot y) \cdot 5$

o. $3(x+y+z) = 3 \cdot x + 3 \cdot y + 3 \cdot z$

4. Answer the following questions and give an example to illustrate a "yes" answer and give a counter-example to support a "no" answer.

a. Is multiplication distributive over subtraction?

b. Is subtraction distributive over division?

c. Is subtraction associative?

5. Name the property involved in going from one statement to the next.

a. $1 \times [7 \times 6 + 7 \times 11] \overset{(1)}{=} 1 \times [7 \times (6+11)]$
$$\overset{(2)}{=} [7 \times (6+11)] \times 1$$
$$\overset{(3)}{=} 7 \times (6+11)$$

b. $(3 + 5\frac{1}{2}) \cdot 5 + 9 \cdot 6 \overset{(1)}{=} 9 \cdot 6 + (3 + 5\frac{1}{2}) \cdot 5$
$$\overset{(2)}{=} 9 \cdot 6 + 5 \cdot (3 + 5\frac{1}{2})$$
$$\overset{(3)}{=} 9 \cdot 6 + (5 \cdot 3 + 5 \cdot 5\frac{1}{2})$$

6. Tell whether every replacement of x, y, and z produces a true statement, if the universal set is the set of ordinary numbers of arithmetic.

a. If $x - y = z$, then $z + y = x$.   **b.** If $x \div y = z$, then $y = x \cdot z$.

7. Suppose that $\odot$ and $\oplus$ are inverse operations. Label each statement as either true or false:

a. If $\frac{1}{3} \odot \frac{1}{2} = \frac{5}{6}$, then $\frac{5}{6} \oplus \frac{1}{3} = \frac{1}{2}$.   **b.** If $\frac{3}{8} \oplus \frac{1}{3} = \frac{3}{4}$, then $\frac{3}{4} \odot \frac{1}{3} = \frac{3}{8}$.

8. Is the set of all odd natural numbers closed under

a. addition?   **b.** subtraction?   **c.** multiplication?   **d.** division?

9.   For each word phrase, write the mathematical phrase.

   a. 5 increased by x
   b. y increased by $3t$
   c. the product of $(3x + y)$ and $(2t + 1)$
   d. $3s$ decreased by 4
   e. $4n$ divided by $(x - y)$
   f. $(2 - a)$ multiplied by 10

BIBLIOGRAPHY

Adler, Irving. *Magic House of Numbers*. New York: The John Day Company, 1957.

Adler, Irving. *The New Mathematics*. New York: The John Day Company, 1958. pp. 13-124

Ball, W. W. R., and Coxeter, H. S. M. *Mathematical Recreations and Essays*. London: Macmillan, 1942.

Bakst, Aaron. *Mathematics: Its Magic and Mastery*. New York: Van Nostrand, 1941.

Dantzig, Tobias. *Number, The Language of Science*. New York: Macmillan, 1954.

Dubisch, Roy. *The Nature of Number*. New York: Ronald Press Co., 1952.

Friend, J. N. *Numbers: Fun and Facts*. New York: Charles Scribner's Sons, 1954.

Gardner, Martin. *Mathematical Puzzles & Diversions*. New York: Simon and Schuster, 1959.

Gilles, William F. *The Magic and Oddities of Numbers*. New York: Vantage Press, 1953.

Pedoe, Dan. *The Gentle Art of Mathematics*. New York: The Macmillan Company, 1959.

Reid, C. *From Zero to Infinity*. New York: Thomas Y. Crowell Co., 1960 (2nd rev. ed.).

Ringenberg, Lawrence A. *A Portrait of 2*. Washington, D.C.: National Council of Teachers of Mathematics, 1956.

Sawyer, W. W. *Mathematician's Delight*. Baltimore: Penguin Books, 1956. Chapter 5.

Smith, D. E. *Number Stories of Long Ago*. Washington, D.C.: National Council of Teachers of Mathematics, 1955.

Smith, D. E., and Ginsberg, J. *Numbers and Numerals*. Washington, D.C.: National Council of Teachers of Mathematics, 1956.

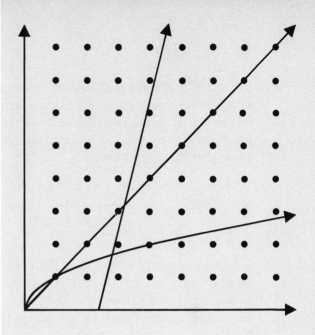

CHAPTER 3

Rational and Irrational Numbers — Operation of Addition

THE NUMBER LINE

From your previous experience, you know what a straight line is. Now that you know about sets, we will consider a line to be a set of points. To be sure, for a set of points to be a straight line they have to be arranged in a certain way. Here is a picture of a straight line.

The arrows on both ends suggest that there is no end to this set of points. We can extend the picture in either direction and all the points thus included will be on the line.

It is *convenient* to assign numbers to the points on a line so that we can refer to the points by the use of numbers. To do this, we choose one point and assign to it the number 0. Then we mark off equal distances to the left and right of the point corresponding to the number 0 and assign numbers to them, as in the picture below. It is not necessary to have a line in a horizontal position; but we shall agree to place it in this position for convenience, so that we can refer to points as being to the *left* or to the *right* of a given point.

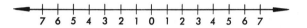

Now you will notice that there are two points corresponding to each number (except 0). Thus, if you should want to call your friend's attention to the point corresponding to, say, the number 4, he would not know which point you intended. We would like to have only one point for each number. Conversely, each point should have only one number associated with it. When this is accomplished, we say that we have a *one-to-one correspondence* between points on the *number line* and the numbers.

In order to establish a one-to-one correspondence between the points on the number line and the numbers, we will have to make a distinction between the points to the left of the point corresponding to 0 and those to its right. Let us put letters of identification above the points on the line, and agree to write the number names below the line preceded by the *raised symbol* + for the points to the right of zero and by the *raised symbol* − for the points to the left of zero.

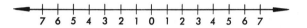

Now there is only one point corresponding to a given number. For example, point N corresponds to the number $^+1$ (*positive 1*) and H corresponds to the number $^-5$ (*negative 5*). Conversely, there is only one number corresponding to a given point. For example, the number $^-2$ (negative 2) corresponds to the point K and the number $^+7$ (positive 7) corresponds to the point D.

We call the numbers of this kind *directed numbers*. By means of directed numbers, we can answer not only the question "how many?" but also the question "in what direction?"

For example, instead of saying "5 degrees above zero" we may say "$^+5$ degrees" (positive 5 degrees); or, instead of saying "17 degrees below zero" we may say "$^-17$ degrees" (negative 17 degrees).

Having directed numbers, we are now in a position to discuss more fully a one-to-one correspondence between the points on the number line and the new numbers.

negative direction · · · · · · · positive direction

J E H C L K F A N P M I B G D

−7 −6 −5 −4 −3 −2 −1 0 +1 +2 +3 +4 +5 +6 +7

We must understand that the choice of the direction to the right to be the positive direction is quite arbitrary. We could choose the direction to the left as the positive direction; we could even choose to picture the line in a vertical position, or slanted in some other direction. But once a direction is chosen as positive, the opposite direction must be the negative direction.

You will note that the symbols "+" and "−" are now used to mean either of two different things; "+" may mean either to add or that a positive number is used. Explain the two meanings of the symbol "−."

For example: $^+3 - {}^-4$ means "subtract negative four from positive three."

To make this distinction quite clear, you noticed that we are elevating the symbols "+" and "−" whenever they are used to indicate a positive or a negative number, respectively. To indicate addition or subtraction, the symbols will not be elevated.

EXERCISES

Think of five situations in which the idea of a direction and its opposite can be used. Then choose one of the directions to be positive and the opposite direction to be negative. Describe a specific case in words, then restate it using directed numbers.

Example: Situation: business transactions in which gain or loss may take place
Directions: gain—positive, loss—negative
A case: a gain of 5 dollars, a loss of $12\frac{1}{2}$ dollars
Directed numbers: $^+5$ dollars, $^-12\frac{1}{2}$ dollars

INTEGERS

In the first chapter you worked with the natural numbers. You are so used to these numbers that it does not take much thought on your part to tell which one of two given natural numbers is greater.

For example, of the two numbers 195 and 375, 375 is greater than 195.

Now we have a set of numbers which consists of positive whole numbers $+1$, $+2$, $+3$, $+4$, $+5$, $+6$, and so on, negative whole numbers -1, -2, -3, -4, -5, -6, and so on, and the number 0. We say that all of these numbers make up the set of numbers called the *integers*. Thus, the set of all integers, I, is the union of the set of positive integers, I_P, the set of negative integers, I_N, and the set whose only member is 0.

$$I = I_P \cup I_N \cup \{0\}$$

Given any two integers we shall need to know which of the two is the greater. Study the examples below and find out how we compare two integers.

Example: Suppose the two integers to be compared are -5 and $+1$. We locate the two points corresponding to the two numbers: point H corresponds to -5, point N corresponds to $+1$. Point N is to the *right of* the point H, and we say that $+1$ is greater than -5.

Is $+6$ greater than $+2$? Which point corresponds to $+6$? To $+2$? Is G to the right of P? Is -3 greater than -5? Why?

We shall use the symbol ">" to mean *is greater than*, and the symbol "<" to mean *is less than*. Thus $+1 > -5$ is read "positive one is greater than negative five." We can also write $-5 < +1$, which is read "negative five is less than positive one."

You see that the number line comes in very handy when you want to compare two numbers. Of course, it would be impractical to have a picture of a line long enough to locate on it points, very far apart, but once you get the principle well in mind, you should have no trouble telling which one of two given numbers is the greater.

Use the picture of the number line above to verify each of the following. One of the statements is false. Find it!

$-6 < -5$	$-1 > -5$	$0 > -1$	$0 < +1$
$0 < +6$	$+7 < -7$	$-5 > -7$	$+1 > -1$

Does it follow from the agreement on how to compare integers that any positive integer is greater than any negative integer? Is every positive integer greater than 0? Is every negative integer less than 0?

Having the two symbols of inequality, "<" and ">," we can obtain two more symbols: " ≮," which means *is not less than*, and " ≯," which means *is not greater than*.

Examine each of the statements below. One is false. Find it!

$$^-3 ≮ ^-5 \qquad ^-1 ≯ ^+3 \qquad ^-1 ≮ 0$$
$$0 ≯ ^+7 \qquad ^+2 ≮ ^+2 \qquad ^+25 ≯ ^+100$$

You can easily guess that the symbol "≠" means *is not equal to*. For example, $^+3 ≠ {}^+4$, $^+6 + {}^+3 ≠ {}^+6 + {}^+7$ are true statements, while $^+6 ≠ {}^+6$ is a false statement.

We can obtain two more symbols by combining "<" with " =" and ">" with " =".

The two symbols thus obtained are "≤" (read "is less than *or* equal to,") and "≥" (read "is greater than *or* equal to.") For example, $^+5 ≤ {}^+7$ (read "positive five is less than or equal to positive seven") and $^+3 ≥ {}^+3$ (read "positive three is greater than or equal to positive three") are true statements.

Note that each statement above consists of two parts. For example, the first statement has the parts

    i. positive five is less than positive seven

    ii. positive five is equal to positive seven

The two parts are connected by the word *or*. We shall agree to consider the whole statement true if either one of the parts is true. Also, the whole statement is true if both parts are true. If both parts are false, the entire statement is false. Thus, $^+4 ≥ {}^+7$ (read: positive four is greater than or equal to positive seven) is false, because "positive four is greater than positive seven" is false and "positive four is equal to positive seven" is false.

EXERCISES

1. List the letters **a** through **p** on your paper; then write true for each true statement and false for each false statement.

a. $^-5 ≠ {}^+5$

b. $0 < {}^-17$

c. $^-8 > {}^+11$

d. $^-7 ≯ {}^+8$

e. $^-1 ≮ {}^+1$

f. $^-10 ≮ {}^-15$

g. $^+5 ≤ {}^+7$

h. $^+6 ≥ {}^+8$

i. $^-3 ≤ {}^-3$

j. $^-2 ≥ {}^-2$

k. $^-100 ≤ {}^+100$

l. $0 ≯ 0$

m. $0 < {}^-1150$

n. $0 > {}^+25$

o. $^+10 ≮ {}^+10$

p. $^-1 ≯ 0$

2.   Use the set $U = \{^-2, ^-1, 0, ^+1, ^+2\}$ as the universal set from which to obtain the replacements for x. Give all replacements for x which will produce true statements in each of the following:

a. $x > {}^+1$	**d.** $x \neq 0$	**g.** $x \geq {}^+2$	**j.** $x < {}^+2$
b. $x < 0$	**e.** $x \leq {}^-2$	**h.** $x > {}^+2$	**k.** $x \leq {}^+2$
c. $x \leq {}^-1$	**f.** $x < {}^-2$	**i.** $x \neq {}^-2$	**l.** $x \geq {}^-2$

3.   Using the set $U = \{^-2, ^-1, 0, ^+1, ^+2\}$, for each statement tell whether it is true or false. Explanation: "$\{x \mid x > {}^+1\}$" means "the set of all x belonging to U such that x is greater than ${}^+1$."

a. $\{x \mid x > {}^+1\} = \{x \mid x \geq {}^+2\}$ 　　　 **e.** $\{x \mid x > {}^-2\} = \{x \mid x < {}^+2\}$

b. $\{x \mid x < 0\} = \{x \mid x \leq 0\}$ 　　　 **f.** $\{x \mid x \neq 0\} \subseteq U$

c. $\{x \mid x > {}^-2\} = \{x \mid x > {}^-1\}$ 　　　 **g.** $\{x \mid x > {}^-2\} \subseteq \{x \mid x \leq {}^+2\}$

d. $\{x \mid x \leq {}^+2\} = \{x \mid x \geq {}^-2\}$ 　　　 **h.** $\{x \mid x \neq 0\} \nsubseteq \{x \mid x < {}^+2\}$

4.   True or false?

Examples: 　　*i.* $0 = {}^-1$ *or* ${}^+3 < {}^+4$
　　　　　　　　　True, because one of the two statements, ${}^+3 < {}^+4$, is true.

　　　　　　ii. $0 = {}^-1$ *or* ${}^+3 > {}^+4$
　　　　　　　　　False, because each of the two statements: $0 = {}^-1$, ${}^+3 > {}^+4$, is false.

　　　　　　iii. ${}^-1 < 0$ *or* ${}^+1 > 0$
　　　　　　　　　True, because each of the two statements: ${}^-1 < 0$, ${}^+1 > 0$, is true.

　　　　　　iv. $0 = {}^-1$ *and* ${}^+3 < {}^+4$
　　　　　　　　　False, because one of the two statements, $0 = {}^-1$, is false.

　　　　　　v. $0 = {}^-1$ *and* ${}^+3 > {}^+4$
　　　　　　　　　False, because each of the two statements: $0 = {}^-1$, ${}^+3 > {}^+4$, is false.

　　　　　　vi. ${}^-1 < 0$ *and* ${}^+1 > 0$
　　　　　　　　　True, because each of the two statements: ${}^-1 < 0$, ${}^+1 > 0$, is true.

a. ${}^+3 = {}^+4$ or ${}^+7 < {}^+9$ 　　　 **g.** ${}^-9 \leq {}^-8$ or ${}^-12 > {}^-3$

b. ${}^-5 < {}^+3$ and ${}^+9 \neq {}^-7$ 　　　 **h.** $0 < {}^+3$ and ${}^+4 \leq {}^+4$

c. ${}^-13 \leq {}^+4$ or ${}^+5 \leq {}^+5$ 　　　 **i.** ${}^+7 \nless {}^+6$ or ${}^-15 > {}^-19$

d. ${}^+6 > {}^+2$ and ${}^-6 < {}^+3$ 　　　 **j.** ${}^+3 < {}^+4$ and ${}^+1 \leq {}^+2$

e. ${}^+6 \neq {}^+5$ or ${}^-3 = {}^+3$ 　　　 **k.** ${}^-9 \ngtr {}^+3$ or ${}^-7 \neq {}^-6$

f. ${}^-11 < {}^+9$ and ${}^+1 < {}^+2$ 　　　 **l.** ${}^+4 > {}^+12$ and ${}^-6 < {}^-7$

5. True or false?

    a. If x is negative and y is positive, then $x > y$
    b. if x is negative and y is positive, then $x \neq y$
    c. if x is negative and y is positive, then $x \nless y$
    d. if x is positive, then $x > 0$
    e. if x is negative, then $x > 0$

Absolute value

Look at the pairs of numbers listed below.

$$+5, \; ^-5$$
$$^-3, \; ^+3$$
$$^+100, \; ^-100$$
$$^-17, \; ^+17$$
$$0, \; 0$$

Think of two more number pairs which would fit this pattern.

In each pair above, we have a number and its *opposite*.

$$^-5 \text{ is the opposite of } \quad ^+5$$
$$^+3 \text{ is the opposite of } \quad ^-3$$
$$^-100 \text{ is the opposite of } ^+100$$
$$^+17 \text{ is the opposite of } \; ^-17$$
$$0 \text{ is the opposite of } \quad 0$$

Did you notice that the opposite of a positive number is a negative number and the opposite of a negative number is a positive number? Is zero the only number which is its own opposite?

It is frequently useful to associate with each directed number its *absolute value*. For example, the absolute value of $^-5$ is $^+5$, the absolute value of $^-7$ is $^+7$, the absolute value of $^+3$ is $^+3$, the absolute value of $^+5$ is $^+5$, and the absolute value of 0 is 0.

Thus, the absolute value of a positive number is the number itself, whereas the absolute value of a negative number is its opposite, which is a positive number. To abbreviate *the absolute value of x*, we write $|x|$, for example

$|^-5| = {}^+5$ (read: the absolute value of negative five is positive five)
$|^+5| = {}^+5$ (read: the absolute value of positive five is positive five)
$|^+3| = {}^+3$ (read: the absolute value of positive three is positive three)
$|0| = 0$ (read: the absolute value of zero is zero)

In general,

$$\forall_{x \geq 0} \; |x| = x$$
$$\forall_{x < 0} \; |x| = \text{the opposite of } x$$

EXERCISES

1.   True or false?

a. $^-2 \neq {}^+2$

b. $|^-2| \neq |^+2|$

c. $^-7 > {}^+8$

d. $|^-7| > {}^+8$

e. $|^+17| < 0$

f. $|^-21| < |^+20|$

g. $|0| > {}^-2$

h. $^-3 \not> {}^-5$

i. $^-1 < |^-17|$

j. $^-3 > {}^-256$

k. $|^-10| \neq |^+10|$

l. $|^-156| = |^+156|$

m. $0 < |^-1137|$

n. $|^+11| > |^+2|$

o. $|^-211| \not< |^+10|$

p. $|^-100| \not> |^+100|$

q. $|^-337| < |^-2|$

r. $0 \neq |0|$

s. $|^-1| < |^-100|$

t. $|^-2| \not> |^+2|$

2.   True or false?   For each false statement, give a counter-example. The universal set is the set of integers.

a. $\forall_{x>y}$ $|x| > |y|$

b. $\forall_{x \neq y}$ $|x| \neq |y|$

c. $\forall_{x<y}$ $|x| < |y|$

d. $\forall_{x=y}$ $|x| = |y|$

e. $\forall_{x \leq y}$ $|x| \leq |y|$

f. $\forall_{x \geq y}$ $|x| \geq |y|$

g. $\forall_{x \leq -2}$ $|x| \geq {}^+2$

h. $\forall_{x \geq +2}$ $|x| \geq {}^+2$

i. $\forall_{x \leq 0}$ $|x| \leq 0$

j. $\forall_{x \geq 0}$ $|x| \geq 0$

Addition of integers

We cannot use numbers to good advantage unless we at least know how to add, subtract, multiply, and divide them.

We shall first learn to add directed numbers. For this, we shall use the number line.

We shall imagine making moves along the number line. A move to the right will be described by a positive number and a move to the left by a negative number. Study the following examples.

A move from A to M is described by $^+3$ (Explain why.)

A move from N to B is described by $^+4$

A move from C to F is described by $^+3$

A move from E to B is described by $^+11$

A move from A to C is described by $^-4$

A move from L to E is described by $^-3$

A move from B to I is described by $^-1$

A move from M to H is described by $^-8$

Using an integer, describe a move from J to D. From D to J. From J to A. From D to A.

We now use the idea of moves in adding directed numbers. Suppose we have the following problem

$$^+2 + {}^+3 = ?$$

Study the picture below until you understand what has been done.

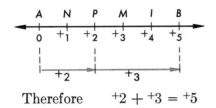

Therefore $^+2 + {}^+3 = {}^+5$

Study each of the problems and pictures below to see how their answers are obtained.

Examples: i. $^-1 + {}^-4 = ?$

Therefore $^-1 + {}^-4 = {}^-5$

ii. $^+3 + {}^-1 = ?$

Therefore $^+3 + {}^-1 = {}^+2$

iii. $^+2 + {}^-5 = ?$

Therefore $^+2 + {}^-5 = {}^-3$

EXERCISES

1. Find the sum in each of the following, using the number line as in the examples above. Make a picture of the moves for each problem.

a. $^+1 + {}^+5$	**h.** $^-2 + {}^-4$	**o.** $^-2 + {}^+6$
b. $^+3 + {}^+3$	**i.** $^-1 + {}^+7$	**p.** $^+6 + {}^-2$
c. $0 + {}^+5$	**j.** $^-7 + {}^+2$	**q.** $0 + {}^-7$
d. $0 + {}^+7$	**k.** $^+3 + {}^-4$	**r.** $^-7 + 0$
e. $0 + {}^-5$	**l.** $^-4 + {}^+3$	**s.** $^-8 + {}^-1$
f. $0 + {}^-3$	**m.** $^-4 + {}^-7$	**t.** $^-1 + {}^-8$
g. $^-1 + {}^-2$	**n.** $^-7 + {}^-4$	

2. Study your answers in exercise **1.** Can you discover a pattern which will help you to get answers to addition problems without the use of the number line?

Can you find answers to the following without the use of the number line? Try it!

a. $^-19 + {}^+13$	**f.** $^+42 + {}^+38$	**k.** $^+105 + {}^-205$
b. $^+91 + {}^-47$	**g.** $^-41 + {}^-32$	**l.** $^-366 + {}^-42$
c. $^-16 + {}^-19$	**h.** $^+176 + {}^+133$	**m.** $^-378 + {}^-112$
d. $^-16 + {}^+42$	**i.** $^+573 + {}^+335$	**n.** $^-85 + {}^+12$
e. $^+37 + {}^-13$	**j.** $^+13 + {}^-173$	**o.** $^-105 + {}^+15$

3. Replace the letters with numerals to obtain true statements.

Example: $^+3 + x = {}^-4$

On the number line we would go seven units to the left from $^+3$ to reach $^-4$. Therefore, if x is replaced by $^-7$, we obtain a true statement: $^+3 + {}^-7 = {}^-4$

a. $n + {}^+3 = {}^+7$	**f.** $^-13 + t = {}^+22$	**k.** $w + {}^-5 = {}^-10$
b. $^+5 + m = {}^-3$	**g.** $s + {}^+12 = {}^-3$	**l.** $c + {}^-9 = {}^-9$
c. $^-6 + {}^+14 = p$	**h.** $^+13 + {}^-7 = v$	**m.** $^+11 + r = 0$
d. $y + {}^-9 = {}^-13$	**i.** $^-19 + k = {}^-11$	**n.** $^-4 + s = {}^-4$
e. $^+7 + x = {}^+2$	**j.** $z + {}^+12 = {}^+3$	**o.** $0 + x = 0$

4. True or false?

a. $|{}^+2| + |{}^-3| < {}^-3 + {}^+2$	**e.** $^-3 + {}^+2 < |{}^-5|$
b. $^+4 + {}^-8 \neq {}^-4$	**f.** $|{}^-5| + {}^-5 \neq 0$
c. $^+6 + {}^-3 > {}^-2$	**g.** $(|{}^+6| + {}^-5) + {}^-1 \not< {}^+2$
d. $^+6 + |{}^-5| > {}^+11$	**h.** $|{}^-3| + |{}^-2| \not< {}^-3 + {}^-2$

5. True or false? For each false statement, give one counter-example. The universal set is the set of integers.

   a. $\forall_{x>0} \ \forall_{y>0} \ (x + y) > 0$
   b. $\forall_{x<0} \ \forall_{y<0} \ (x + y) < 0$
   c. $\forall_x \ x + 0 = x$
   d. $\forall_{x>0} \ \forall_{y<0} \ (x + y) < 0$
   e. $\forall_{x>0} \ \forall_{y<0} \ (x + y) > 0$
   f. $\forall_{x>0} \ \forall_{y<0}$, if $|x| > |y|$, then $(x + y) < 0$
   g. $\forall_{x>0} \ \forall_{y<0}$, if $|x| > |y|$, then $(x + y) > 0$
   h. $\forall_{x>0} \ \forall_{y<0}$, if $|x| < |y|$, then $(x + y) < 0$
   i. $\forall_{x>0} \ \forall_{y<0}$, if $|x| < |y|$, then $(x + y) > 0$
   j. $\forall_{x>0} \ \forall_{y<0}$, if $|x| = |y|$, then $(x + y) = 0$

RATIONAL NUMBERS

Let us return to a picture of the number line.

You recall that there is a one-to-one correspondence between some points on the number line and the integers. So far we have paid attention only to integers and their associated points. But you know that there are many more points on the number line. Let us enlarge the portion of the number line between the points A and N.

We could go on marking more points because there is always at least one more point between any two that we marked. For example, to find a point between A and X, you could take 0 and $+\frac{1}{10}$ and find a number between the two. For example, $+\frac{1}{20}$ will do because $0 < +\frac{1}{20} < +\frac{1}{10}$. We agree that $0 < +\frac{1}{20} < +\frac{1}{10}$ is an abbreviation for $0 < +\frac{1}{20}$ and $+\frac{1}{20} < +\frac{1}{10}$. Can you devise a method which will never fail to give you a number which is between two given numbers?

Numbers such as those described above are called *rational numbers*.

Each rational number has a name which can be expressed in the form

$$\frac{^+a}{b} \text{ or } \frac{^-a}{b} \text{ or } \frac{0}{b}$$

where a and b can be replaced by names for natural numbers. Let us make two replacements to obtain some non-zero rational numbers.

$$3 \text{ for } a, 7 \text{ for } b: {}^+\tfrac{3}{7}, {}^-\tfrac{3}{7}$$
$$4 \text{ for } a, 1 \text{ for } b: {}^+\tfrac{4}{1}, {}^-\tfrac{4}{1}$$

A simpler name for ${}^+\tfrac{4}{1}$ is ${}^+4$; a simpler name for ${}^-\tfrac{4}{1}$ is ${}^-4$.

Any natural number replacement for b in $\dfrac{0}{b}$ results in 0. For example,

$$\tfrac{0}{2} = 0; \quad \tfrac{0}{25} = 0; \quad \tfrac{0}{596} = 0$$

Do rational numbers remind you of fractions? You should notice that the set of rational numbers includes the integers. Thus, *the set of integers is a subset of the set of rational numbers.*

On the number line below there are marked a few points which correspond to some of the rational numbers.

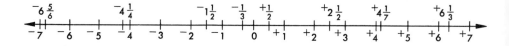

You will recall from arithmetic that each rational number has a decimal name. For example

$$^+\tfrac{1}{2} = {}^+.5 \qquad ^+2\tfrac{1}{2} = {}^+2.5 \qquad ^-4\tfrac{1}{4} = {}^-4.25$$

Some rational numbers have more complicated decimal names than those above.

To find a decimal name for $\tfrac{1}{3}$, we divide 1 by 3.

$$
\begin{array}{r}
0.333\ldots \\
3\,\overline{\smash{\big)}\,1.000} \\
\underline{9} \\
10 \\
\underline{9} \\
10 \\
\underline{9} \\
1
\end{array}
$$

We see that $\tfrac{1}{3} = .333\ldots$. We shall write $.\overline{3}$, the meaning of the bar being that 3 is repeated on and on without end. Thus, $\tfrac{1}{3} = .\overline{3}$.

Divide 31 by 99 to verify that $\tfrac{31}{99} = .\overline{31}$. The bar over 31 means that 31 repeats on and on, that is, $.\overline{31} = .313131\ldots$.

From these examples you see that a rational number may be represented in the form of a decimal which either ends (*terminating decimal*), or is a *repeating decimal;* that is, it has a block of one or more digits which repeat on and on in the same pattern.

Rational numbers are added according to the same patterns that integers are added. The examples below are for your study.

Examples:

$$\frac{^+1}{3} + \frac{^-1}{6} = \frac{^+2}{6} + \frac{^-1}{6} = \frac{^+1}{6}$$

$$\frac{^+1}{8} + \frac{^-3}{4} = \frac{^+1}{8} + \frac{^-6}{8} = \frac{^-5}{8}$$

$$\frac{^-1}{4} + \frac{^-7}{12} = \frac{^-3}{12} + \frac{^-7}{12} = \frac{^-10}{12} = \frac{^-5}{6}$$

$$^+3.12 + {^-1.08} = {^+2.04}$$

$$^-12.7 + {^+9.8} = {^-2.9}$$

EXERCISES

1. How many points which correspond to rational numbers on the number line are there between the points corresponding to 0 and $^+1$?

2. What replacements would you make in $\frac{a}{b}$ to obtain all positive integers?

3. What replacements would you make in $\frac{^-a}{b}$ to obtain all negative integers?

4. Give five different replacements for a and for b in $\frac{a}{b}$, each resulting in 0.

5. For each of the following rational numbers give a decimal and state whether it is a terminating or a repeating decimal.

Example: $\frac{3}{8}$

```
  0.375
8 ⟌ 3.000
  2 4
  ———
   60
   56
   ——
   40
   40
   ——
    0
```

The decimal name for $\frac{3}{8}$ is a terminating decimal, namely .375.

Example: $\dfrac{1}{7}$

$$
\begin{array}{r}
0.142857 \\
7\,\overline{)\,1.000000} \\
7 \\
\overline{30} \\
28 \\
\overline{20} \\
14 \\
\overline{60} \\
56 \\
\overline{40} \\
35 \\
\overline{50} \\
49 \\
\overline{1}
\end{array}
$$
← from here on we have repetition

The decimal name for $\frac{1}{7}$ is a repeating decimal, namely $.\overline{142857}$.

a. $\frac{5}{8}$ **e.** $\frac{1}{6}$ **i.** $\frac{5}{6}$ **m.** $\frac{8}{9}$

b. $\frac{4}{9}$ **f.** $\frac{7}{9}$ **j.** $\frac{4}{15}$ **n.** $\frac{3}{11}$

c. $\frac{2}{3}$ **g.** $\frac{6}{11}$ **k.** $\frac{2}{15}$ **o.** $\frac{5}{9}$

d. $\frac{3}{8}$ **h.** $\frac{2}{11}$ **l.** $\frac{6}{17}$ **p.** $\frac{5}{18}$

6. Find the sums.

a. $^+\frac{1}{2} + {}^+\frac{1}{5}$ **h.** $^-\frac{29}{7} + {}^+\frac{29}{7}$ **o.** $^+20.6 + {}^-28.9$

b. $^+\frac{2}{3} + {}^-\frac{1}{9}$ **i.** $^+1.9 + {}^+12.6$ **p.** $^-1.2 + {}^-13.9$

c. $^+\frac{7}{8} + {}^-\frac{1}{2}$ **j.** $^+3.9 + {}^-2.6$ **q.** $^-7.9 + {}^+2.8$

d. $^-\frac{4}{5} + {}^-\frac{7}{15}$ **k.** $^+10.3 + {}^-20.6$ **r.** $^-100.1 + {}^+99.3$

e. $^+\frac{4}{7} + {}^-\frac{1}{14}$ **l.** $^-7.12 + {}^-8.13$ **s.** $^-17.6 + {}^+117.6$

f. $^-\frac{1}{3} + {}^-\frac{5}{4}$ **m.** $^-3.9 + {}^+9.1$ **t.** $^-261.5 + {}^+261.5$

g. $^+\frac{2}{9} + {}^-\frac{7}{3}$ **n.** $^+12.1 + {}^-14.0$ **u.** $^+199.69 + {}^-199.69$

Repeating decimal numerals

It is easy to conclude that every terminating decimal names a rational number. Given a terminating decimal, it is easy to find a name of the form $\dfrac{a}{b}$.

$$.175 = \frac{175}{1000} \qquad .16507 = \frac{16{,}507}{100{,}000}$$

■ In general $.n_1 n_2 \ldots n_k = \dfrac{n_1 n_2 \ldots n_k}{\underbrace{10 \times 10 \times \ldots \times 10}_{\text{10 used } k \text{ times}}}$

where each of $n_1, n_2, \ldots, n_k$ is replaceable by the digits from 0 through 9.

Does a repeating decimal name a rational number? Let us develop a way of finding names of the form $\frac{a}{b}$ for numbers given by repeating decimals. Follow each step.

Given $.\overline{7}$, we write $n = .\overline{7}$
Since $.\overline{7} = .777 \ldots$, 10 times $.\overline{7}$ is equal to $7.\overline{7}$
Thus, $10n = 7.777 \ldots$
$n = .777 \ldots$

Now, if $a = b$ and $c = d$
then $a - c = b - d$

Knowing that $10n - n = 10 \cdot n - 1 \cdot n = (10 - 1)n = 9n$, we have

$$10n = 7.777 \ldots$$
$$n = .777 \ldots$$
$$\overline{10n - n = 7}$$
$$9n = 7$$
$$n = \tfrac{7}{9}$$

Therefore, $.\overline{7} = \tfrac{7}{9}$. Divide 7 by 9 to verify this.

We now carry out the work in finding a name of the form $\frac{a}{b}$ for $.\overline{135}$.

Study each step

$$1000n = 135.135135 \ldots$$
$$n = .135135 \ldots$$
$$\overline{1000n - n = 135}$$
$$999n = 135$$
$$n = \tfrac{135}{999}$$

Therefore, $.\overline{135} = \tfrac{135}{999}$. Divide 135 by 999 to verify this.

A Challenge to You We can generalize the procedure above to show that there is a name of the form $\frac{a}{b}$ for each repeating decimal. Study each step below.

Each repeating decimal is of the form

$$.\overline{n_1 n_2 \ldots n_k}$$

We are ignoring the whole number parts, since we know that every whole number w has a name of the form $\frac{w}{1}$.

Since we will be multiplying by multiples of 10, we observe the following abbreviation.

$$10 \times 10 = 10^2 \text{ (read: ten to the second power)}$$
$$10 \times 10 \times 10 = 10^3 \text{ (read: ten to the third power)}$$
$$10 \times 10 \times 10 \times 10 = 10^4 \text{ (read: ten to the fourth power)}$$
$$10 \times 10 \times 10 \times \ldots \times 10 = 10^k \text{ (read: ten to the } k\text{th power)}$$

Now returning to the problem

$$10^k \cdot x = n_1 n_2 \ldots n_k . n_1 n_2 \ldots n_k \ldots$$
$$x = \qquad\qquad .n_1 n_2 \ldots n_k \ldots$$
$$\overline{ }$$
$$10^k \cdot x - x = n_1 n_2 \ldots n_k$$
$$(10^k - 1)x = n_1 n_2 \ldots n_k$$
$$x = \frac{n_1 n_2 \ldots n_k}{10^k - 1}$$

Now observe that $n_1 n_2 \ldots n_k$ is a k-digit numeral naming a natural number and $10^k - 1$ is also a natural number. Thus, x is given in the form $\frac{a}{b}$, where a and b are natural numbers.

EXERCISES

1. Give an example of a repeating decimal in which a block of

   a. two digits repeats. **b.** three digits repeats. **c.** five digits repeats.

2. For each number, determine a name of the form $\frac{a}{b}$, where a and b are natural numbers.

Examples: *i.* $2.35 = 2 + \frac{35}{100}$
$$= \frac{200}{100} + \frac{35}{100}$$
$$= \frac{235}{100}$$
$$= \frac{47}{20}$$

ii. $.6\overline{3}$
   Let $n = .633\ldots$
   Then $10n = 6.333\ldots$
   $10n - n = 6.3\overline{3} - .6\overline{3}$
   $9n = 5.7$
   $n = \frac{5.7}{9} = \frac{57}{90} = \frac{19}{30}$
   Thus, $.6\overline{3} = \frac{19}{30}$

a. .7	**j.** 1.3	**s.** $2\frac{3}{4}$
b. 2.97	**k.** $2\frac{1}{6}$	**t.** .125
c. $.8\overline{3}$	**l.** .875	**u.** $3.\overline{2}$
d. $.1\overline{6}$	**m.** $.\overline{4}$	**v.** 1.36
e. $2.\overline{3}$	**n.** $3\frac{1}{9}$	**w.** $2.\overline{6}$
f. 3.17	**o.** 7.06	**x.** $.\overline{307692}$
g. 5.9	**p.** $.\overline{7}$	**y.** $2.1\overline{8}$
h. $.\overline{1}$	**q.** .365	**z.** $3.1\overline{2}$
i. $4.\overline{6}$	**r.** $1\frac{2}{9}$	**a'.** $4.2\overline{7}$

IRRATIONAL NUMBERS

You observed that between any two rational numbers there is another rational number. You should see that this is true no matter how close the two rational numbers are. For example, consider the rational numbers $\frac{2}{37}$ and $\frac{2}{38}$. To find a number which is between the two, we can simply find the average (arithmetic mean) of the two numbers.

$$\frac{\frac{2}{37} + \frac{2}{38}}{2} = \frac{\frac{76}{1406} + \frac{74}{1406}}{2} = \frac{\frac{150}{1406}}{2} = \frac{75}{1406}$$

To see that $\frac{75}{1406}$ is indeed between $\frac{2}{37}$ and $\frac{2}{38}$, all you need to do is to observe that $\frac{2}{37}$ is the same as $\frac{76}{1406}$ and $\frac{2}{38}$ is the same as $\frac{74}{1406}$. Now it is easy to see that

$$\frac{74}{1406} < \frac{75}{1406} < \frac{76}{1406}$$

Since between any two rational numbers, there is another rational number, the set of rational numbers is called *dense*. In fact, it might appear to you that every point on the number line has a rational number associated with it, but this is not so.

Let us consider a number which, when multiplied by itself, gives 2. Multiplying a number by itself is called "squaring the number." For example, $3^2 = 9$ is read "three squared equals nine" or "the square of three is nine." You will see later that in the set of directed numbers there are two numbers whose square is positive nine; they are $^+3$ and $^-3$.

The positive number that makes the statement $x^2 = 2$ true is $^+\sqrt{2}$. We will keep in mind that we are dealing with a positive number, and omit the raised $+$ sign to simplify writing. Thus, we have
$$(\sqrt{2})^2 = \sqrt{2} \times \sqrt{2} = 2.$$

In the following discussion we shall make use of the fact that

$\forall_{a>0} \, \forall_{b>0} \, \forall_{c>0}$, if $a < b < c$, then $a^2 < b^2 < c^2$
also $\forall_{a>0} \, \forall_{b>0} \, \forall_{c>0}$, if $a^2 < b^2 < c^2$, then $a < b < c$

Note that
$1.4 < \sqrt{2} < 1.5$, since $(1.4)^2 = 1.96$ and $(1.5)^2 = 2.25$ and
$$1.96 < 2 < 2.25.$$
$1.41 < \sqrt{2} < 1.42$, since $(1.41)^2 = 1.9881$ and $(1.42)^2 = 2.0164$ and
$$1.9881 < 2 < 2.0164.$$
$1.414 < \sqrt{2} < 1.415$, since $(1.414)^2 = 1.999396$ and $(1.415)^2 = 2.002225$
$$\text{and } 1.999396 < 2 < 2.002225.$$

Continuing on, we can find rational numbers that are as close to $\sqrt{2}$ as we please; but we can never find a rational number that is equal to $\sqrt{2}$.

We can devise a method for finding rational numbers which are very close to $\sqrt{2}$. We start with 1 as a trial divisor of 2.

$$\begin{array}{r} 2 \\ \hline 1\,|\overline{2} \\ 2 \\ \hline 0 \end{array}$$

$1 < \sqrt{2}$ and $2 > \sqrt{2}$, thus, $1 < \sqrt{2} < 2$; so we choose a trial divisor between 1 and 2, say the average of 1 and 2, which is 1.5.

$$\begin{array}{r} 1.3 \\ \hline 1.5\,|\overline{2.00} \\ 1\,5 \\ \hline 50 \\ 45 \\ \hline 5 \end{array}$$

$1.3 < \sqrt{2} < 1.5$ so we choose a trial divisor between 1.3 and 1.5, the average of 1.3 and 1.5, which is 1.4.

$$\begin{array}{r} 1.42 \\ \hline 1.4\,|\overline{2.000} \\ 1\,4 \\ \hline 60 \\ 56 \\ \hline 40 \\ 28 \\ \hline 12 \end{array}$$

$1.4 < \sqrt{2} < 1.42$ so we choose a trial divisor between 1.4 and 1.42, the average of 1.4 and 1.42, which is 1.41. (How do we know that $\sqrt{2}$ is 1.4, correct to the nearest tenth?)

$$\begin{array}{r} 1.418 \\ \hline 1.41\,|\overline{2.00000} \\ 1\,41 \\ \hline 590 \\ 564 \\ \hline 260 \\ 141 \\ \hline 1190 \\ 1128 \\ \hline 62 \end{array}$$

$1.41 < \sqrt{2} < 1.418$, so we choose the next trial divisor, the average of 1.41 and 1.418, which is 1.414.

$$\begin{array}{r} 1.4144 \\ \hline 1.414\,|\overline{2.0000000} \\ 1\,414 \\ \hline 5860 \\ 5656 \\ \hline 2040 \\ 1414 \\ \hline 6260 \\ 5656 \\ \hline 6040 \\ 5656 \\ \hline 384 \end{array}$$

$1.414 < \sqrt{2} < 1.4144$, so we know that $\sqrt{2}$ is 1.414 correct to the nearest .001. Why?

This process may be continued as far as we please to obtain *rational approximations* which are as close to $\sqrt{2}$ as we want to make them. But no rational number is equal to $\sqrt{2}$.

Continuing a few more times, we find that to seven decimal places $\sqrt{2}$ is 1.4142135. To check to see how close the number 1.4142135 is to $\sqrt{2}$, we multiply it by itself.

$$1.4142135 \times 1.4142135 = 1.99999982358225$$

The result differs from 2 by

$$.00000017641775$$

which is a very small number! The square of each successive estimate is closer to 2.

Since no rational number is equal to $\sqrt{2}$, $\sqrt{2}$ has no name of the form $\frac{a}{b}$, where a and b are natural numbers. A number which is not a rational number is called an *irrational number*.

EXERCISES

1. Find the rational number midway between

    a. $\frac{1}{2}$ and $\frac{6}{4}$
    b. $\frac{5}{8}$ and $\frac{4}{16}$
    c. $\frac{28}{37}$ and $\frac{13}{74}$
    d. 4.17 and 4.96
    e. $\frac{11}{2}$ and $\frac{5}{6}$
    f. 2.19 and 1.11
    g. 3.12 and 3.76

2. The table on page 449 supplies squares and approximations of square roots, correct to the nearest .001, of numbers from 1 through 100. Record the positive square root of each of the following numbers from the table. Each of these numbers has a whole number for its square root.

Example: 9216; $\sqrt{9216} = 96$

    a. 2401   **c.** 4489   **e.** 1225   **g.** 576
    b. 8836   **d.** 2809   **f.** 6084   **h.** 4761

3. Compute an approximation of the positive square root. In each case, carry out the computations to four decimal places and round off to three decimal places; if the fourth place is less than 5, just drop the fourth decimal place). Compare your result with that given in the table on page 449.

Example: Approximate $\sqrt{3}$ correct to the nearest .001. Choose 2 as the first trial divisor of 3.

$$
\begin{array}{r}
1.5 \\
2\,\overline{\,|3.0\,} \\
\underline{2} \\
10 \\
\underline{10} \\
0
\end{array}
$$

therefore, $1.5 < \sqrt{3} < 2$

Choose a rational number between 1.5 and 2, say 1.8, as the next trial divisor.

$$
\begin{array}{r}
1.66 \\
1.8\,\overline{\,|3.000\,} \\
\underline{1\ 8} \\
1\ 20 \\
\underline{1\ 08} \\
120 \\
\underline{108} \\
12
\end{array}
$$

therefore, $1.66 < \sqrt{3} < 1.8$

Choose a number between 1.66 and 1.8, say 1.7, as the next trial divisor.

$$
\begin{array}{r}
1.76 \\
1.7\,\overline{\,|3.00\,} \\
\underline{1\ 7} \\
1\ 30 \\
\underline{1\ 19} \\
110 \\
\underline{102} \\
8
\end{array}
$$

therefore, $1.7 < \sqrt{3} < 1.76$

Choose a number between 1.7 and 1.76, say 1.73, as the next trial divisor.

$$
\begin{array}{r}
1.734 \\
1.73\,\overline{\,|3.00000\,} \\
\underline{1\ 73} \\
1\ 270 \\
\underline{1\ 211} \\
590 \\
\underline{519} \\
710 \\
\underline{692} \\
18
\end{array}
$$

therefore, $1.73 < \sqrt{3} < 1.734$

Choose a number between 1.73 and 1.734, say 1.732, as the next trial divisor.

```
               1.7321
    1.732│3.0000000
          1 732
          1 2680
          1 2124
            5560
            5196
            3640
            3464
            1760
            1732
              28
```

therefore, $1.732 < \sqrt{3} < 1.7321$

Hence, the $\sqrt{3}$ is within .0001 of 1.732 or 1.732 is $\sqrt{3}$, correct to three decimal places.

$$1.732 \times 1.732 = 2.999824$$

a. $\sqrt{5}$ **b.** $\sqrt{19}$ **c.** $\sqrt{27}$

REAL NUMBERS AND THE NUMBER LINE

We have discovered that, in addition to rational numbers, there are also irrational numbers. For example, $\sqrt{2}$ is an irrational number. We shall now show that there is a point on the number line which corresponds to $\sqrt{2}$. Thus, we shall show that there are points on the number line in addition to those corresponding to the rational numbers.

To do this, we need to recall a property of right triangles. Consider, for example, the right triangle whose sides have lengths of 3″, 4″, and 5″. Note that $3^2 + 4^2 = 5^2$. This is an illustration of the Pythagorean property, which holds for each right triangle.

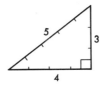

■ *Pythagorean Property*

If a, b, and c are the lengths of the two legs and the hypotenuse, respectively, of a right tri-angle, then $a^2 + b^2 = c^2$.

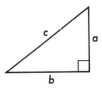

The side opposite the right angle in any right triangle is called the *hypotenuse* and the other two sides are called the *legs*. What is the length of the hypotenuse in a triangle in which each leg is 1″ long?

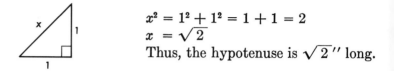

$$x^2 = 1^2 + 1^2 = 1 + 1 = 2$$
$$x = \sqrt{2}$$

Thus, the hypotenuse is $\sqrt{2}$″ long.

We are now ready to demonstrate the existence of a point on the number line which corresponds to the irrational number $\sqrt{2}$.

Consider the part of the number line between the points A and N, the points corresponding to the numbers 0 and 1, respectively.

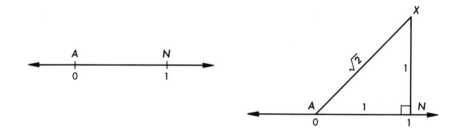

Now, the length of the line segment $\overline{AN}$ is 1. We draw the line segment $\overline{NX}$ perpendicular to $\overline{AN}$, and also of 1 unit length.

From the computations above we know that the length of the hypotenuse $\overline{AX}$ is $\sqrt{2}$. Now, we swing an arc with a radius of $\sqrt{2}$ from X, using point A as a center, down on the number line, like this

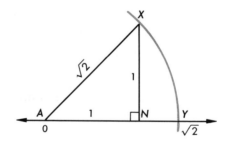

Since $\overline{AX}$ and $\overline{AY}$ are two radii of the same circle, they are of the same length. Thus, the length of $\overline{AY}$ is $\sqrt{2}$ and the number $\sqrt{2}$ corresponds to the point Y.

Since we know that $\sqrt{2}$ is an irrational number, we have demonstrated *the existence on the number line of a point which corresponds to an irrational number*. Of course, there are many more points on the number line which correspond to other irrational numbers.

We can use the same method as above to find the point which corresponds to $\sqrt{3}$ on the number line. Study the picture below and do a similar construction on your paper using a ruler and a compass.

Point T corresponds to the irrational number $\sqrt{3}$.

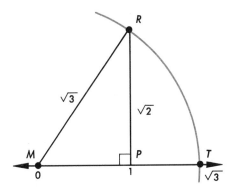

Previously you learned that every rational number has a name in a form of a terminating or a repeating decimal. An irrational number has no such name. For example, if you examine the decimal

$$.172172217222172222\ldots$$

you should discover that it is a non-repeating, non-terminating decimal; that is, no block of digits is repeating on and on. Thus

$$.172172217222172222\ldots$$

is an irrational number.

Let us take another irrational number.

$$.261261126111261111\ldots$$

It is easy to see that there is another irrational number between these two. For example, $.182182218222182222\ldots$ is such a number, because

$$.172172217222172222\ldots < .182182218222182222\ldots$$
$$< .261261126111261111\ldots$$

In fact, it is possible to find an irrational number between any two irrational numbers.

■   If we take the set of rational numbers and the set of irrational numbers and form the union of these two sets, the result is the set of *real* numbers. Thus, the set of all real numbers consists of all rational and all irrational numbers. Since no rational number is irrational, and no irrational number is rational, the two sets are disjoint sets.

Note that we use the phrase "directed numbers" and the phrase "real numbers" to mean the same thing.

If

$$Q = \text{the set of rational numbers}$$
$$S = \text{the set of irrational numbers}$$
$$R = \text{the set of real numbers}$$

then

$$Q \cup S = R$$
$$Q \cap S = \phi$$

EXERCISES

1.   Each pair of numbers below gives the lengths of two legs in a right triangle. Compute the length of the hypotenuse in each case. Then, from the table of square roots, give the three-place approximation to the length h of the hypotenuse.

Example: $2, 9; h^2 = 2^2 + 9^2 = 4 + 81 = 85$
$$h = \sqrt{85} \doteq 9.220$$

[NOTE: We shall use the symbol "$\doteq$" to mean "is approximately equal to".]

   a. 4, 6   **b.** 2, 3   **c.** 7, 4   **d.** 5, 5

2.   The following decimal names for rational numbers are repeating decimals. Change to irrational numbers by inserting number symbols after each repeating block.

Example: .281281281 . . .

The repeating block is 281. We choose to insert 3, 4, 5, 6, 7, . . . after each repeating block.

.2813281428152816 . . .

Thus, .281328142815 . . . is an irrational number.

   a. .14141414 . . .   **c.** .987198719871 . . .
   b. .289289 . . .   **d.** .142857142857142857 . . .

3. Using the method of construction illustrated in this section, locate the points on the number line corresponding to the following numbers.

a. $\sqrt{5}$ **b.** $\sqrt{6}$ **c.** $\sqrt{7}$

HINT: HINT:

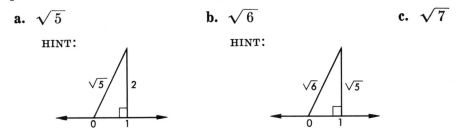

4. Q = the set of rational numbers
S = the set of irrational numbers
R = the set of real numbers

True or false?

a. $Q \subseteq R$ **c.** $S \subseteq R$ **e.** $S \subset R$
b. $Q \cup R = R$ **d.** $S \subseteq Q$ **f.** $R \cap S = \overline{Q}$

Word phrases to mathematical phrases

In solving mathematical problems, we frequently need to write phrases which show relations between various units. For example, to show the number of inches in 7 feet, we write 7×12. To show the worth of x nickels in cents, we write $5x$.

EXERCISES

Write the mathematical phrase for each word phrase.

Examples: *i.* Worth in cents of $4x$ eight-cent stamps
$8 \cdot 4x$ or $32x$

ii. Number of quarts in $3n$ gallons
$4 \cdot 3n$ or $12n$

1. Worth in cents of 12 nickels
2. Worth in cents of m nickels
3. Worth in cents of $3t$ nickels
4. Worth in cents of $(a + b)$ dimes
5. Worth in cents of $4n$ quarters
6. Worth in cents of $(3x + 5)$ dollars
7. Worth in cents of $\dfrac{t}{4}$ dollars
8. Worth in cents of 12 five-cent stamps

9. Worth in cents of y eight-cent stamps
10. Worth in cents of $(3x + 9)$ eight-cent stamps
11. Number of feet in 6 inches
12. Number of feet in x inches
13. Number of feet in $(a + b)$ inches
14. Number of quarts in 5 gallons
15. Number of quarts in s gallons
16. Number of quarts in $10n$ gallons
17. Number of square inches in 1 square foot
18. Number of square inches in 5 square feet
19. Number of square inches in v square feet

VOCABULARY

Use each of the following correctly in a sentence. Numerals in parentheses refer to the pages where these words were used. If you are not sure of the meaning of any word, turn to the indicated page and refresh your memory.

absolute value (61)

dense (71)

directed number (56)

integer (57)

irrational number (73)

is greater than ($>$) (58)

is less than ($<$) (58)

is not equal to ($\neq$) (59)

is not greater than ($\not>$) (59)

is not less than ($\not<$) (59)

negative number (56)

non-terminating decimal (68)

number line (55)

opposite of a number (61)

origin (56)

positive number (56)

Pythagorean Property (75)

rational number (65)

real number (75)

repeating decimal (67)

square root (71)

terminating decimal (67)

REVIEW EXERCISES

1. Add

    a. $^{+}4 + {}^{+}3$

    b. $^{+}27 + {}^{+}32$

    c. $^{-}2 + {}^{+}5$

    d. $^{-}7 + {}^{+}24$

    e. $^{+}3 + {}^{-}4$

    f. $^{+}12 + {}^{-}136$

    g. $^{+}17 + {}^{-}17$

    h. $^{-}219 + {}^{+}219$

    i. $^{-}4 + {}^{-}7$

    j. $^{-}216 + {}^{-}313$

    k. $^{+}\frac{1}{2} + {}^{-}\frac{1}{4}$

    l. $^{+}\frac{1}{3} + {}^{-}\frac{7}{9}$

    m. $^{+}\frac{2}{7} + {}^{-}\frac{1}{14}$

    n. $^{-}\frac{1}{9} + {}^{-}\frac{1}{9}$

    o. $^{-}\frac{2}{3} + {}^{-}\frac{1}{4}$

p. $^+1.02 + ^+3.72$

q. $^+3.6 + ^-2.2$

r. $^-10.2 + ^+3.2$

s. $^-15.6 + ^+20.6$

t. $^-3.9 + ^-4.8$

u. $^-10.12 + ^-10.13$

v. $^-130.76 + ^+130.76$

w. $^+1.6075 + ^-1.6075$

2. True or false?

a. $^-17 < ^-137$

b. $|^-17| < |^-137|$

c. $|^+\frac{1}{2}| > |^-\frac{1}{3}|$

d. $|^-45| \leq ^-45$

e. $|^-\frac{3}{3}| \neq ^+1$

f. $|^-7 + ^-2| \geq |^-7| + |^-2|$

g. $|^-2| + |^-3| = |^-2 + ^-3|$

h. $|^-129 + ^+129| = |^-129| + |^+129|$

i. $|^-4 + ^+16| \nless |^-4| + |^+16|$

j. $|^-2| \leq |^+2|$

k. $^+2 > ^-5000$

l. $0 < ^-3000$

m. $|^-1.5| = |^+1.5|$

n. $\forall_x \ |x| \geq x$

3. Use the set $U = \{^-1, ^-\frac{1}{2}, 0, ^+\frac{1}{2}, ^+1\}$ as the universal set from which to obtain the replacements for x. Give all replacements for x which will produce true statements in each of the following:

a. $x > |^-\frac{1}{2}|$

b. $x < ^-1$

c. $x \leq ^-1$

d. $x > 0$

e. $x \leq 0$

f. $x \neq 0$

g. $x \leq ^+1$

h. $x < ^+1$

i. $x > ^+1$

j. $x \neq ^+1$

4. Using the set U of problem **3**, for each statement tell whether it is true or false.

a. $\{x | x \geq |^-1|\} = \{x | x \geq ^+1\}$

b. $\{x | x \neq |^+\frac{1}{2}|\} = \{x | x \neq |^-\frac{1}{2}|\}$

c. $\{x | x \leq ^-1\} \subseteq \{x | x < ^-1\}$

d. $\{x | x \leq ^+1\} = U$

e. $\{x | x \geq ^-1\} = U$

f. $\{x | x > ^-1\} = U$

g. $\{x | x \neq 0\} \subseteq \{x | x \geq ^-1\}$

5. Let the set of all integers be the universal set. True or false?

a. $\forall_x \forall_y$, if $x \geq 0$, then $x > y$

b. $\forall_x \forall_y$, if $|x| = |y|$, then $x = y$

c. $\forall_x \forall_y$, if $x = y$, then $|x| - |y|$

d. $\forall_x \forall_y$, if $x > 0$ and $y < 0$, then $x > y$

e. $\forall_x \forall_y$, if $x < 0$, then $x + y < 0$

f. $\forall_x \forall_y$, if $x < 0$ and $y > 0$ and $x + y < 0$, then $|x| > |y|$

6. For each rational number, give a decimal name. Tell which of the names are terminating decimals and which are repeating decimals.

a. $\frac{1}{2}$ d. $\frac{1}{3}$ g. $\frac{3}{7}$

b. $\frac{1}{4}$ e. $\frac{2}{3}$ h. $\frac{2}{11}$

c. $\frac{3}{8}$ f. $\frac{1}{9}$ i. $\frac{1}{13}$

7. For each number, determine a name of the form $\frac{a}{b}$, where a and b are natural numbers.

a. .37   d. 1.6   g. $.2\overline{15}$

b. .506   e. 2.3192   h. $1.3\overline{6}$

c. $.\overline{7}$ f. $.\overline{23}$ i. $2.02\overline{506}$

8. Find the rational number midway between

a. $9\frac{1}{2}$ and $11\frac{1}{3}$ c. $^-4$ and $^+3$

b. $\frac{1}{4}$ and $5\frac{1}{2}$ d. $^-2$ and $^+7$

9. Compute each of the following to two decimal places.

a. $\sqrt{12}$ b. $\sqrt{6}$ c. $\sqrt{29}$

10. Using a right triangle, locate by means of a ruler and a compass the point on the number line which corresponds to $\sqrt{7}$.

11. Write the mathematical phrase for each word phrase.

a. Worth in cents of x dimes
b. Worth in cents of $(2a + n)$ quarters
c. Worth in cents of $3m$ eight-cent stamps
d. Worth in cents of $(3c + 9)$ five-cent stamps
e. Number of feet in y inches
f. Number of inches in t feet
g. Number of quarts in u gallons
h. Number of gallons in q quarts

CHAPTER TEST

1. Add

a. $^+9 + {}^+22$ g. $^+\frac{1}{3} + {}^+\frac{1}{4}$ m. $^+1.3 + {}^+2.6$

b. $^+37 + {}^+17$ h. $^+\frac{2}{7} + {}^+\frac{1}{6}$ n. $^+13.9 + {}^+4.2$

c. $^+52 + {}^-4$ i. $^+\frac{2}{3} + {}^-\frac{1}{2}$ o. $^+2.5 + {}^-1.4$

d. $^+12 + {}^-28$ j. $^+\frac{8}{11} + {}^-\frac{21}{22}$ p. $^+7.2 + {}^-13.4$

e. $^-16 + {}^-2$ k. $^-\frac{1}{6} + {}^-\frac{2}{3}$ q. $^-3.6 + {}^-5.5$

f. $^-15 + {}^-49$ l. $^-\frac{1}{4} + {}^-\frac{1}{5}$ r. $^-20.5 + {}^-3.6$

2. True or false?

    a. $^-12 < ^-1$
    b. $0 > ^-1000$
    c. $^+1 < ^-1000$
    d. $|^-10| < |^+3|$
    e. $|^-2 + ^-5| = |^-2| + |^-5|$
    f. $|^-3 + ^+7| = |^-3| + |^+7|$
    g. $|^+10 + ^-2| = |^+10| + |^-2|$
    h. $\forall_x \forall_y \ |x + y| \le |x| + |y|$

3. For each rational number give a decimal name. Tell which of the names are terminating decimals and which are repeating decimals.

    a. $\frac{2}{5}$ **b.** $\frac{3}{8}$ **c.** $\frac{4}{9}$ **d.** $\frac{4}{15}$

4. For each number, determine a name of the form $\frac{a}{b}$, where a and b are natural numbers.

    a. .12   **d.** $.\overline{27}$
    b. .3065   **e.** $.5\overline{3}$
    c. $.\overline{9}$ **f.** $.19\overline{36}$

5. On the number line, locate the point corresponding to $\sqrt{5}$ using a ruler and a compass.

6. Compute $\sqrt{31}$ to two decimal places.

7. Find the rational number midway between

    a. $7\frac{1}{2}$ and $9\frac{1}{3}$ **c.** $^-5$ and $^+13$
    b. $\frac{1}{2}$ and $5\frac{2}{3}$ **d.** $^-2$ and $^+1$

8. Write the mathematical phrase for each word phrase.

    a. Worth in cents of $(5x + 6y)$ nickels
    b. Number of feet in $7t$ yards
    c. Number of yards in $5x$ feet
    d. Number of quarts in $(a + 3t)$ gallons
    e. Number of gallons in $(5x + y)$ quarts
    f. Number of feet in n miles
    g. Number of miles in x feet
    h. Number of inches in $(a + b)$ feet
    i. Number of feet in $12m$ inches

BIBLIOGRAPHY

Adler, Irving. *The New Mathematics*. New York: The John Day Company, 1958. pp. 44-72.

Bakst, A. *Mathematical Puzzles and Pastimes*. New York: Van Nostrand, 1954.

Dubisch, Roy. *The Nature of Number*. New York: Ronald Press, 1952.

Freitag, H. T., and Freitag, A. H. *The Number Story*. Washington, D. C.: National Council of Teachers of Mathematics, 1960.

Nichols, Eugene D.; Kalin, Robert; and Garland, Henry. *Arithmetic of Directed Numbers* (A Programed Unit). New York: Holt Rinehart and Winston, Inc., 1962. Chapters I and II.

Rademacher, H., and Toeplitz, O. *The Enjoyment of Mathematics*. Princeton: Princeton University Press, 1957. pp. 22-26, 111-119, 147-160.

School Mathematics Study Group. *Mathematics for High School: First Course in Algebra, Part 1* (Revised Edition). New Haven: Yale University Press, 1960. pp. 23-34.

Thurston, H. A. *The Number System*. New York: Interscience Pub., 1956.

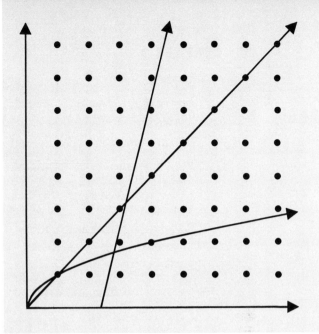

CHAPTER 4

Subtraction, Multiplication, and Division of Real Numbers

SUBTRACTION OF REAL NUMBERS

In arithmetic you learned how to subtract arithmetic numbers. But, even if you knew only how to add, you could change every subtraction problem to a related addition problem and obtain your answer. This is possible because addition and subtraction are inverse operations.

You remember that the problem $7 - 2 = ?$ can be changed into $? + 2 = 7$; and since $5 + 2 = 7$, the answer to the original problem is 5, or $7 - 2 = 5$.

The relation between subtraction and addition of *real* numbers is the same as the relation between subtraction and addition of *arithmetic* numbers.

Study the examples at the top of the next page.

$^+9 - {}^+4 = ?$ is related to $? + {}^+4 = {}^+9$
(To what number is $^+4$ added to give $^+9$?)   Answer: $^+5$
Therefore, $^+9 - {}^+4 = {}^+5$

$^+5 - {}^+8 = ?$ is related to $? + {}^+8 = {}^+5$
(To what number is $^+8$ added to give $^+5$?)   Answer: $^-3$
Therefore, $^+5 - {}^+8 = {}^-3$

$^+3 - {}^-6 = ?$ is related to $? + {}^-6 = {}^+3$
(To what number is $^-6$ added to give $^+3$?)   Answer: $^+9$
Therefore, $^+3 - {}^-6 = {}^+9$

$^+7 - {}^-2 = ?$ is related to $? + {}^-2 = {}^+7$
(To what number is $^-2$ added to give $^+7$?)   Answer: $^+9$
Therefore, $^+7 - {}^-2 = {}^+9$

$^-5 - {}^-2 = ?$ is related to $? + {}^-2 = {}^-5$
(To what number is $^-2$ added to give $^-5$?)   Answer: $^-3$
Therefore, $^-5 - {}^-2 = {}^-3$

$^-6 - {}^-10 = ?$ is related to $? + {}^-10 = {}^-6$
(To what number is $^-10$ added to give $^-6$?)   Answer: $^+4$
Therefore, $^-6 - {}^-10 = {}^+4$

$^-2 - {}^+5 = ?$ is related to $? + {}^+5 = {}^-2$
(To what number is $^+5$ added to give $^-2$?)   Answer: $^-7$
Therefore, $^-2 - {}^+5 = {}^-7$

$^-7 - {}^+3 = ?$ is related to $? + {}^+3 = {}^-7$
(To what number is $^+3$ added to give $^-7$?)   Answer: $^-10$
Therefore, $^-7 - {}^+3 = {}^-10$

EXERCISES

1.   Find the answer to each subtraction problem below by changing it to the related addition problem.

Example: $^-3 - {}^-28 = ?$
                    $? + {}^-28 = {}^-3$
                    (To what number is $^-28$ added to give $^-3$?) Answer: $^+25$
                    Therefore, $^-3 - {}^-28 = {}^+25$

a. $^+3 - {}^+1$ **d.** $^+3 - {}^+13$ **g.** $^+216 - {}^+18$

b. $^+17 - {}^+10$ **e.** $^+27 - {}^+136$ **h.** $^+78 - {}^+92$

c. $^+2 - {}^+7$ **f.** $^+132 - {}^+36$ **i.** $^+320 - {}^+185$

j. $^+6 - {}^-12$

k. $^+3 - {}^-42$

l. $^+7 - {}^-39$

m. $^+100 - {}^-12$

n. $^-17 - {}^+17$

o. $^-85 - {}^+13$

p. $^-199 - {}^+99$

q. $^-85 - {}^-15$

r. $^-17 - {}^-53$

s. $^-55 - {}^-116$

t. $^-168 - {}^-32$

u. $^+\frac{3}{2} - {}^+\frac{1}{2}$

v. $^+1.8 - {}^+1.2$

w. $^+\frac{1}{3} - {}^+\frac{1}{2}$

x. $^+\frac{2}{5} - {}^+\frac{2}{7}$

y. $^-.5 - {}^+.2$

z. $^-\frac{2}{3} - {}^+\frac{1}{3}$

a'. $^-2.14 - {}^+1.14$

b'. $^-115.5 - {}^+105.4$

c'. $^+1.2 - {}^-.8$

d'. $^+3.52 - {}^-7.48$

e'. $^+\frac{2}{9} - {}^-\frac{1}{3}$

f'. $^+\frac{11}{12} - {}^-\frac{3}{4}$

g'. $^-\frac{1}{2} - {}^-\frac{3}{2}$

h'. $^-\frac{3}{4} - {}^-\frac{3}{4}$

i'. $^-1.7 - {}^-3.3$

j'. $^-.333 - {}^-.444$

2. Examine thoughtfully the exercises above. Try to formulate in your mind a theory as to how the subtraction of real numbers works. This theory should suggest a way to work subtraction problems by using the inverse of subtraction. Do not tell your theory to anyone. Let your teacher check your theory by telling you whether or not your answers to the problems below are correct.

a. $^+113 - {}^+14$

b. $^+17 - {}^+56$

c. $^+\frac{1}{2} - {}^+\frac{1}{3}$

d. $^+\frac{7}{8} - {}^+\frac{3}{8}$

e. $^+1.3 - {}^+.7$

f. $^+17.9 - {}^+34.9$

g. $^-16 - {}^-3$

h. $^-35 - {}^-78$

i. $^-\frac{3}{4} - {}^-\frac{1}{4}$

j. $^-\frac{2}{5} - {}^-\frac{3}{5}$

k. $^+100 - {}^-12$

l. $^+200 - {}^-300$

m. $^+\frac{1}{2} - {}^-\frac{1}{3}$

n. $^+\frac{9}{15} - {}^-\frac{13}{15}$

o. $^+\frac{1}{2} - {}^-\frac{1}{5}$

A different look at subtraction

Below are a number of examples of subtraction problems worked out for you. To the right of each subtraction problem is an addition problem. Study all of these examples and see if you can discover how each addition problem is related to the subtraction problem on its left. There is one problem which does not fit into the pattern. Find it!

$^+4 - {}^+11 = {}^-7$

$^+17 - {}^+9 = {}^+8$

$^+7 - {}^-10 = {}^+17$

$^+18 - {}^-12 = {}^+30$

$^-6 - {}^+17 = {}^-23$

$^-\frac{1}{2} - {}^+\frac{1}{2} = {}^-1$

$^-\frac{5}{7} - {}^-\frac{5}{7} = 0$

$^+11.3 - {}^-11.2 = {}^+22.5$

$^-25.1 - {}^-3.4 = {}^-21.7$

$^-\frac{3}{8} - {}^+\frac{5}{8} = {}^-1$

$^+4 + {}^-11 = {}^-7$

$^+17 + {}^-9 = {}^+8$

$^+7 + {}^+10 = {}^+17$

$^+18 + {}^+12 = {}^+30$

$^-6 + {}^-17 = {}^-23$

$^-\frac{1}{2} + {}^-\frac{1}{2} = {}^-1$

$^-\frac{5}{7} + {}^+\frac{5}{7} = 0$

$^+11.3 + {}^+11.2 = {}^+22.5$

$^+25.1 + {}^-3.4 = {}^+21.7$

$^-\frac{3}{8} + {}^-\frac{5}{8} = {}^-1$

You must have observed that the next to the last problem in the pattern given on page 87 was different from the rest. Note that in changing a subtraction problem to an addition problem, we use the opposite of the number which is being subtracted. For example, in the first problem instead of subtracting $^+11$ from $^+4$ we added $^-11$ to $^+4$ and

$$^-11 \text{ is the opposite of } ^+11$$

In the third problem, instead of subtracting $^-10$ from $^+7$, we added $^+10$ to $^+7$ and

$$^+10 \text{ is the opposite of } ^-10$$

Thus we have a pattern which involves addition and subtraction of real numbers.

◾ Subtracting a real number is the same as adding its opposite.

Using letters, we state this property for subtraction as follows:

◾ $\forall_x \forall_y \, x - y = x + $ (the opposite of y) where x and y are to be replaced by numerals for real numbers.

As an example of this property, we replace x by $^+4$ and y by $^+11$, resulting in

$$^+4 - {}^+11 = {}^+4 + \text{(the opposite of } ^+11)$$

We know that every subtraction problem has a related addition problem because every real number has an opposite. Is the opposite of a positive number a negative number? Is the opposite of a negative number a positive number? What is the opposite of 0?

Now look at the following examples.

$$^+5 + {}^-5 = 0$$
$$^+\tfrac{3}{7} + {}^-\tfrac{3}{7} = 0$$
$$^-13.7 + {}^+13.7 = 0$$
$$0 + 0 = 0$$

What property is illustrated by these examples? This property can be stated using letters as follows:

◾ $\forall_x \, x + $ (the opposite of x) $= 0$

Thus, the sum of any real number and its opposite is zero. We call this property the *Property of Opposites*.

EXERCISES

1. Give the opposite of each of the following numbers.

   a. $^-13$

   b. $^-176$

   c. $^+398$

   d. $-\frac{9}{4}$

   e. $^+\frac{17}{3}$

   f. $^-1.078$

   g. the opposite of $^+12$

   h. the opposite of $^-17$

   i. the opposite of the opposite of $^+1$

   j. the opposite of the opposite of $^-3$

2. For each pair of numbers below, tell whether or not one number in each pair is the opposite of the other number.

Examples: *i.* $^+37.5$, $^-73.5$ no

           ii. $^-13\frac{1}{2}$, $^+13\frac{1}{2}$ yes

   a. $^+27$, $^-27$

   b. $^-325$, $^+325$

   c. $^+136$, $^-163$

   d. $^-1221$, $^+2112$

   e. $^+\frac{3}{7}$, $^-\frac{7}{3}$

   f. $^+.4$, $-\frac{2}{5}$

   g. $|^-13\frac{1}{2}|$, $-\frac{27}{2}$

   h. $^+1$, $^+3 + ^-4$

   i. $|^+5 - ^+7|$, $|^-2|$

   j. $|-\frac{1}{2} + -\frac{1}{2}|$, $|^+\frac{1}{4}|$

   k. 0, 0

   l. $^+3 - ^-7$, $^-7 - ^+3$

3. Change each problem to its equivalent involving addition, then give the answer.

Example: $^+3 - ^-7 = ^+3 + ^+7 = ^+10$

   a. $^+4 - ^+1$

   b. $^+21 - ^+17$

   c. $^+39 - ^+121$

   d. $^+16 - ^+215$

   e. $^-13 - ^-4$

   f. $^-12 - ^-8$

   g. $^-25 - ^-72$

   h. $^-98 - ^-113$

   i. $^+12 - ^-4$

   j. $^+25 - ^-23$

   k. $^+29 - ^-37$

   l. $^+41 - ^-68$

   m. $^-16 - ^+4$

   n. $^-58 - ^+13$

   o. $^-62 - ^+85$

   p. $^-75 - ^+109$

   q. $0 - ^+156$

   r. $0 - ^-76$

   s. $-\frac{1}{2} - ^+\frac{3}{4}$

   t. $-\frac{3}{5} - -\frac{17}{5}$

   u. $-\frac{6}{7} - -\frac{13}{7}$

   v. $^+\frac{3}{5} - -\frac{1}{5}$

   w. $^+\frac{6}{11} - ^+\frac{17}{11}$

   x. $^-13.6 - ^-2.3$

   y. $^-19.8 - ^-36.3$

   z. $^-29.2 - ^+13.5$

   a′. $^-40.9 - ^+90.4$

   b′. $^+13.9 - ^-12.8$

   c′. $^+58.45 - ^-67.54$

4. Compute the sum of each pair of numbers given in exercise 2 above.

Examples: i. $^+37.5 + ^-73.5 = ^-36.0$
    ii. $^-13\frac{1}{2} + ^+13\frac{1}{2} = 0$

5. In each case, replace the letter with a numeral to result in a true statement.

a. $^+7 - x = ^+2$

b. $y - ^-6 = ^+9$

c. $^+16 - z = ^-11$

d. $t - ^+9 = ^+14$

e. $^-9 - ^-7 = s$

f. $^+2 - n = ^-5$

g. $m - ^-5 = ^-16$

h. $^+\frac{1}{2} + p = 0$

i. $^-\frac{2}{3} + r = ^-\frac{4}{3}$

j. $^+1.75 - u = ^+1.15$

k. $^-3.5 + ^-1.6 = s$

l. $^-\frac{1}{7} + x = ^-\frac{4}{21}$

m. $^+\frac{2}{9} - ^-\frac{3}{4} = v$

n. $w - ^-\frac{3}{5} = ^+1$

6. Given the universal set $U = \{^-2, ^-\frac{3}{2}, 0, ^+1, ^+2\}$. For each case below, give all replacements for x for which true statements result.

a. $x < 0$

b. $x > 0$

c. $x \geq 0$

d. $x \leq ^-2$

e. $x \neq ^-\frac{3}{2}$

f. $x \nless 0$

g. $x \ngtr 0$

h. $x \nleq 0$

i. $x \ngeq 0$

j. $x > |^-2|$

k. $x \geq |^-2|$

l. $x < |^-2|$

m. $x + ^+1 \geq ^+1$

n. $x - ^+2 \leq 0$

7. True or false? The universal set is the set of all real numbers. Before deciding whether each statement is true or false, try a few specific examples.

a. $\forall_x \forall_{y<x} \ x - y > 0$

b. $\forall_x \forall_{y>x} \ x - y < 0$

c. $\forall_x \forall_{y=x} \ x - y \neq 0$

d. $\forall_{x>0} \forall_{y>0} \ x - y > 0$

e. $\forall_{x>0} \forall_{y<0} \ x - y > 0$

f. $\forall_{x<0} \forall_{y<0} \ x - y < 0$

g. $\forall_{x>0} \forall_{y>0} \ x + y > 0$

h. $\forall_{x<0} \forall_{y<0} \ x + y < 0$

i. $\forall_{x<0} \forall_{y>0} \ x + y > 0$

j. $\forall_{x<0} \forall_{y>0}$, if $|x| < |y|$, then $x + y < 0$

k. $\forall_{x<0} \forall_{y>0}$, if $|x| < |y|$, then $x + y > 0$

l. $\forall_{x<0} \forall_{y>0}$, if $|x| = |y|$, then $x + y = 0$

m. $\forall_x \forall_y \ |x+y| = |x| + |y|$

n. $\forall_x \forall_y \ |x+y| < |x| + |y|$

o. $\forall_x \forall_y \ |x+y| > |x| + |y|$

p. $\forall_x \forall_y \ |x+y| \leq |x| + |y|$

q. $\forall_x \forall_y \ |x+y| \geq |x| + |y|$

r. $\forall_x \forall_y \ |x-y| = |x| - |y|$

s. $\forall_x \forall_y \ |x-y| < |x| - |y|$

t. $\forall_x \forall_y \ |x-y| > |x| - |y|$

u. $\forall_x \forall_y \ |x-y| \leq |x| - |y|$

v. $\forall_x \forall_y \ |x-y| \geq |x| - |y|$

MULTIPLICATION OF REAL NUMBERS

To learn how to multiply real numbers, we shall assume that positive numbers "behave" like the non-zero numbers of arithmetic under multiplication. We can establish a one-to-one correspondence between these numbers of arithmetic and the positive real numbers, as is shown below.

$$
\begin{array}{ccc}
1 & \leftrightarrow & {}^+1 \\
2 & \leftrightarrow & {}^+2 \\
3 & \leftrightarrow & {}^+3 \\
4 & \leftrightarrow & {}^+4 \\
5 & \leftrightarrow & {}^+5 \\
6 & \leftrightarrow & {}^+6 \\
7 & \leftrightarrow & {}^+7 \\
8 & \leftrightarrow & {}^+8 \\
9 & \leftrightarrow & {}^+9 \\
10 & \leftrightarrow & {}^+10 \\
11 & \leftrightarrow & {}^+11 \\
12 & \leftrightarrow & {}^+12 \\
13 & \leftrightarrow & {}^+13 \\
14 & \leftrightarrow & {}^+14 \\
15 & \leftrightarrow & {}^+15 \\
\end{array}
$$

The dots indicate that this array can be continued on and on. Two-headed arrows show how the arithmetic numbers above are associated with positive numbers. Although, in the above array we displayed only natural numbers and positive integers, the same pattern holds for all numbers of arithmetic and for all non-negative real numbers. An array of some of these numbers is displayed on the top of the next page.

$$
\begin{array}{ccc}
0 & \leftrightarrow & 0 \\
\tfrac{1}{3} & \leftrightarrow & {}^+\tfrac{1}{3} \\
\tfrac{1}{2} & \leftrightarrow & {}^+\tfrac{1}{2} \\
1 & \leftrightarrow & {}^+1 \\
\sqrt{2} & \leftrightarrow & {}^+\sqrt{2} \\
1.5 & \leftrightarrow & {}^+1.5 \\
1.97 & \leftrightarrow & {}^+1.97
\end{array}
$$

Why would it be impossible to show all numbers between 0 and $^+\tfrac{1}{3}$?

Let us now see how we use the array on page 91 in learning to multiply positive numbers.

Suppose we have the following problem: $^+2 \cdot {}^+3 = ?$ In the array on page 91 we find the arithmetic number corresponding to $^+2$. It is 2. Then we find the arithmetic number corresponding to $^+3$. It is 3. We know that $2 \cdot 3 = 6$, and we find that to the arithmetic number 6 there corresponds the positive number $^+6$. Since the positive numbers behave like the arithmetic numbers, $^+2 \cdot {}^+3 = {}^+6$. Study the diagram on page 91 and interpret its meaning.

On a sheet of paper, make a display like the one above. Use it, in the same manner as above, to show that $^+3 \cdot {}^+4 = {}^+12$ and $^+5 \cdot {}^+3 = {}^+15$.

It is apparent that

■   A positive number multiplied by a positive number gives a positive number for a product.

Next, we make use of a very important characteristic of mathematics. One mathematician said that "Mathematics is a study of patterns." We can learn a great deal of mathematics by looking for patterns.

Study the following examples and look for a pattern.

$$
\begin{array}{ccc}
^+2 \cdot {}^+4 & = & {}^+8 \\
\downarrow \quad \downarrow & & \downarrow \\
^+2 \cdot {}^+3 & = & {}^+6 \\
\downarrow \quad \downarrow & & \downarrow \\
^+2 \cdot {}^+2 & = & {}^+4
\end{array}
$$

Would you know what to write next? Here it is.

$$
\begin{array}{ccc}
\downarrow \quad \downarrow & & \downarrow \\
^+2 \cdot {}^+1 & = & {}^+2 \\
\downarrow \quad \downarrow & & \downarrow \\
^+2 \cdot \ 0 & = & 0
\end{array}
$$

What comes next? (Answer the question before reading further.)

$$\downarrow \quad \downarrow \quad \downarrow$$
$$^+2 \cdot {}^-1 = {}^-2$$
$$\downarrow \quad \downarrow \quad \downarrow$$
$$^+2 \cdot {}^-2 = {}^-4$$
$$\downarrow \quad \downarrow \quad \downarrow$$
$$^+2 \cdot {}^-3 = {}^-6$$
$$\downarrow \quad \downarrow \quad \downarrow$$
$$^+2 \cdot {}^-4 = {}^-8$$

and so on

Do you know how to continue? Try building a few more such patterns using numbers different from those above. What do you discover about the product of a positive number and a negative number?

Since you know that, for example, $^+2 \cdot {}^-3 = {}^-6$, you also know that $^-3 \cdot {}^+2 = {}^-6$, because we shall retain all of the basic properties for the numbers of arithmetic stated previously. All of these properties also hold for the real numbers. Thus, $^+2 \cdot {}^-3 = {}^-3 \cdot {}^+2$ according to CPM.

Therefore, we can agree that

■ The product of a positive number and a negative number is a negative number.

Let us now build another pattern.

$$^-2 \cdot {}^+4 = {}^-8$$
$$\downarrow \quad \downarrow \quad \downarrow$$
$$^-2 \cdot {}^+3 = {}^-6$$
$$\downarrow \quad \downarrow \quad \downarrow$$
$$^-2 \cdot {}^+2 = {}^-4$$

What would you write next?

Here it is.

$$\downarrow \quad \downarrow \quad \downarrow$$
$$^-2 \cdot {}^+1 = {}^-2$$
$$\downarrow \quad \downarrow \quad \downarrow$$
$$^-2 \cdot \ 0 = \ 0$$

What comes next? Be sure to answer this question for yourself before reading on. Continuing the pattern, we would have the following:

$$^-2 \cdot {}^-1 = {}^+2$$
$$\downarrow \quad \downarrow \quad \downarrow$$
$$^-2 \cdot {}^-2 = {}^+4$$
$$\downarrow \quad \downarrow \quad \downarrow$$
$$^-2 \cdot {}^-3 = {}^+6$$
$$\downarrow \quad \downarrow \quad \downarrow$$
$$^-2 \cdot {}^-4 = {}^+8$$

and so on

Thus, as the pattern on page 93 indicates, we have

■   A negative number multiplied by a negative number is a positive number.

This can be shown to be a consequence of some known facts and the DPMA. Suppose for a moment that we do not know what $^-5 \times {}^-7$ is.
Consider the following:

$$^-5 \times ({}^+7 + {}^-7)$$

According to DPMA

$$^-5 \times ({}^+7 + {}^-7) = ({}^-5 \times {}^+7) + ({}^-5 \times {}^-7)$$

Since we already know that

$$^-5 \times {}^+7 = {}^-35,$$

$$({}^-5 \times {}^+7) + ({}^-5 \times {}^-7) = {}^-35 + ({}^-5 \times {}^-7)$$

We also know that since PZM holds for real numbers

$$^-5 \times ({}^+7 + {}^-7) = {}^-5 \times 0 = 0$$

Therefore $^-35 + ({}^-5 \times {}^-7) = 0$

or $^-35 + ? = 0$

The question is: What number added to $^-35$ gives 0? It is $^+35$.

Thus $^-5 \times {}^-7 = {}^+35$

Later we shall prove that the product of each pair of negative number is a positive number.
Here some products are worked out for you. Check each one to see that it is correct.

$^+6 \cdot {}^+5 = {}^+30$　　　　　　　　　　$^-1 \cdot {}^+12 = {}^-12$

$^+2 \cdot {}^+\frac{1}{3} = {}^+\frac{2}{3}$　　　　　　　　　　$^-5 \cdot {}^+\frac{3}{4} = {}^-\frac{15}{4}$ or $^-3\frac{3}{4}$

$^+\frac{2}{5} \cdot {}^+\frac{3}{7} = {}^+\frac{6}{35}$　　　　　　　　　$^-\frac{7}{8} \cdot {}^+\frac{2}{9} = {}^-\frac{14}{72}$ or $^-\frac{7}{36}$

$^+.2 \times {}^+1.3 = {}^+.26$　　　　　　　$^-10.4 \times {}^+1.5 = {}^-15.6$

$^+2 \cdot {}^-7 = {}^-14$　　　　　　　　　　$^-3 \cdot {}^-12 = {}^+36$

$^+7 \cdot {}^-\frac{2}{3} = {}^-\frac{14}{3}$ or $^-4\frac{2}{3}$　　　　$^-8 \cdot {}^-\frac{5}{6} = {}^+\frac{40}{6}$ or $^+\frac{20}{3}$ or $^+6\frac{2}{3}$

$^+\frac{2}{5} \cdot {}^-\frac{1}{3} = {}^-\frac{2}{15}$　　　　　　　　$^-\frac{4}{3} \cdot {}^-\frac{2}{5} = {}^+\frac{8}{15}$

$^+2.5 \times {}^-.3 = {}^-.75$　　　　　　　　$^-2.5 \times {}^-1.5 = {}^+3.75$

EXERCISES

1. Find the following products.

a. $^+6 \cdot {}^+8$

b. $^+12 \cdot {}^-3$

c. $^-4 \cdot {}^+15$

d. $^-12 \cdot {}^-7$

e. $^+\frac{1}{2} \cdot {}^-2$

f. $^+\frac{2}{3} \cdot {}^+\frac{2}{7}$

g. $^-\frac{4}{5} \cdot {}^+\frac{2}{7}$

h. $^-\frac{11}{12} \cdot {}^-\frac{2}{5}$

i. $^-.5 \times {}^-\frac{2}{5}$

j. $^+1.6 \times {}^-\frac{1}{3}$

k. $^-\frac{4}{5} \times {}^+10.5$

l. $^+.7 \times {}^+\frac{4}{5}$

m. $^-1.3 \times {}^+.5$

n. $^+2.7 \times {}^-1.4$

o. $^-.6 \times {}^+36.5$

p. $^-.5 \times {}^-.12$

q. $^+12 \times {}^-\frac{1}{12}$

r. $^-3 \times {}^-\frac{1}{3}$

s. $^-7 \times {}^+\frac{1}{7}$

t. $^-.1 \times {}^+10$

u. $^+.01 \times {}^-100$

v. $^-\frac{2}{7} \times {}^-\frac{7}{2}$

w. $^+\frac{4}{9} \times {}^-\frac{9}{4}$

x. $^-\frac{11}{5} \times {}^-\frac{5}{11}$

y. $^+\frac{3}{2} \times {}^-\frac{2}{3}$

z. $^-11 \times {}^+111$

a'. $^-.02 \times {}^-.1$

b'. $^-\frac{1}{4} \times {}^-\frac{1}{4}$

c'. $^-.07 \times {}^-.07$

d'. $^-.8 \times {}^+.8$

e'. $0 \times {}^+7$

f'. $^-6 \times 0$

2. Replace the letters with numerals to obtain true statements.

a. $^+2 \cdot x = {}^+16$

b. $n \cdot {}^+4 = {}^-24$

c. $^-3 \cdot y = {}^-6$

d. $^-16 \cdot {}^+\frac{1}{2} = p$

e. $^+5 \cdot s = {}^-25$

f. $^+2 \cdot t = {}^+7$

g. $^-16 \cdot {}^+\frac{5}{2} = n$

h. $^+\frac{2}{3} \cdot r = {}^-\frac{6}{7}$

i. $m \cdot {}^-\frac{5}{8} = {}^+\frac{3}{7}$

j. $^+\frac{5}{9} \cdot {}^-\frac{6}{7} = r$

k. $y \cdot {}^+\frac{4}{3} = {}^-\frac{11}{9}$

l. $z \cdot {}^-\frac{1}{6} = {}^+\frac{1}{2}$

3. Insert one of the symbols $=$, $<$, $>$, between each pair of expressions below to make true statements.

Example: $|^+7 \cdot {}^-5|$? $|^+7| \cdot |^-5|$

$|^-35|$? $^+7 \cdot {}^+5$

$^+35$ $=$ $^+35$

Therefore, $|^+7 \cdot {}^-5| = |^+7| \cdot |^-5|$

a. $|^+2 \cdot {}^+3|$? $|^+2| \cdot |^+3|$

b. $|^+\frac{1}{2} \cdot {}^+\frac{3}{4}|$? $|^+\frac{1}{2}| \cdot |^+\frac{3}{4}|$

c. $|^-5 \cdot {}^-12|$? $|^-5| \cdot |^-12|$

d. $|^-1.2 \cdot {}^-2.5|$? $|^-1.2| \cdot |^-2.5|$

e. $|^+30 \cdot {}^-6|$? $|^+30| \cdot |^-6|$

f. $|^-12 \cdot {}^+12|$? $|^-12| \cdot |^+12|$

g. $|^-\frac{1}{2} \cdot {}^+\frac{1}{2}|$? $|^-\frac{1}{2}| \cdot |^+\frac{1}{2}|$

h. $|0 \cdot {}^+4|$? $|0| \cdot |^+4|$

i. $|^-17 \cdot 0|$? $|^-17| \cdot |0|$

j. $|0 \cdot 0|$? $|0| \cdot |0|$

4. Examine your answers to problem **3**. What generalization is suggested by your answers? State it using letters and "$\forall$".

5. True or false? (Consider the universal set to be the set of real numbers.)

a. $\forall_{x>0} \forall_{y>0}\ xy > 0$ **f.** $\forall_{x\leq 0} \forall_{y\leq 0}\ xy \geq 0$

b. $\forall_{x\geq 0} \forall_{y\geq 0}\ xy > 0$ **g.** $\forall_x\ x \cdot 0 = 0$

c. $\forall_{x<0} \forall_{y>0}\ xy < 0$ **h.** $\forall_x\ x \cdot {}^+1 = {}^+1$

d. $\forall_{x\leq 0} \forall_{y\geq 0}\ xy < 0$ **i.** $\forall_x\ x \cdot {}^-1 = x$

e. $\forall_{x<0} \forall_{y<0}\ xy < 0$ **j.** $\forall_x\ x \cdot {}^-1 = {}^-1 \cdot x$

6. In each exercise below there are two parts to be worked out. If you get the same answer to each part, state the property illustrated by the problem.

a. $({}^-3 + {}^+4) + {}^-2;\ {}^-3 + ({}^+4 + {}^-2)$

b. ${}^-2 \cdot ({}^-6 + {}^+5);\ ({}^-2 \cdot {}^-6) + ({}^-2 \cdot {}^+5)$

c. ${}^-3 \cdot ({}^+2 \cdot {}^-7);\ ({}^-3 \cdot {}^+2) \cdot {}^-7$

d. ${}^-\frac{1}{2} + {}^-\frac{1}{4};\ {}^-\frac{1}{4} + {}^-\frac{1}{2}$

e. ${}^-1.3 \times ({}^+2.9 + {}^-3.2);\ ({}^-1.3 \times {}^+2.9) + ({}^-1.3 \times {}^-3.2)$

f. ${}^-8 + |{}^-4|;\ |{}^-4| + {}^-8$

g. $|{}^-\frac{3}{5}| + |{}^-\frac{3}{4}|;\ |{}^-\frac{3}{4}| + |{}^-\frac{3}{5}|$

h. ${}^-\frac{1}{2} \cdot {}^-\frac{1}{4};\ {}^-\frac{1}{4} \cdot {}^-\frac{1}{2}$

i. $({}^-5 \times {}^-3.4) + ({}^-5 \times {}^+3.6);\ {}^-5 \times ({}^-3.4 + {}^+3.6)$

j. $({}^-6 + {}^+5) \cdot {}^-1;\ {}^+6 + {}^+5$

*7. Using DPMA, prove that ${}^-1 \times {}^-1 = {}^+1$

*8. Using the result of problem ***7**, prove that ${}^-6 \times {}^-4 = {}^+24$

DIVISION OF REAL NUMBERS

You know that multiplication and division of the numbers of arithmetic are related. Any division problem can be changed to a related multiplication problem. For example

$$12 \div 6 = 2 \quad \text{and} \quad 2 \cdot 6 = 12$$
$$2 \div 6 = \tfrac{1}{3} \quad \text{and} \quad \tfrac{1}{3} \cdot 6 = 2$$
$$\tfrac{1}{2} \div \tfrac{2}{3} = \tfrac{3}{4} \quad \text{and} \quad \tfrac{3}{4} \cdot \tfrac{2}{3} = \tfrac{1}{2}$$

The same relation exists between division and multiplication of real numbers. On the basis of this relation, we shall learn how to divide real numbers. Study carefully each example below in order to learn how to divide real numbers.

$+15 \div {}^+3 = ?$ is related to $? \cdot {}^+3 = {}^+15$
(What number multiplied by ${}^+3$ gives ${}^+15$?)   Answer: ${}^+5$
Therefore, $+15 \div {}^+3 = {}^+5$

$+2 \div {}^+6 = ?$ is related to $? \cdot {}^+6 = {}^+2$
(What number multiplied by ${}^+6$ gives ${}^+2$?)   Answer: ${}^+\frac{1}{3}$
Therefore, $+2 \div {}^+6 = {}^+\frac{1}{3}$

$+8 \div {}^-4 = ?$ is related to $? \cdot {}^-4 = {}^+8$
(What number multiplied by ${}^-4$ gives ${}^+8$?)   Answer: ${}^-2$
Therefore, $+8 \div {}^-4 = {}^-2$

$+6 \div {}^-18 = ?$ is related to $? \cdot {}^-18 = {}^+6$
(What number multiplied by ${}^-18$ gives ${}^+6$?)   Answer: ${}^-\frac{1}{3}$
Therefore, $+6 \div {}^-18 = {}^-\frac{1}{3}$

$-14 \div {}^+7 = ?$ is related to $? \cdot {}^+7 = {}^-14$
(What number multiplied by ${}^+7$ gives ${}^-14$?)   Answer: ${}^-2$
Therefore, $-14 \div {}^+7 = {}^-2$

$-5 \div {}^+10 = ?$ is related to $? \cdot {}^+10 = {}^-5$
(What number multiplied by ${}^+10$ gives ${}^-5$?)   Answer: ${}^-\frac{1}{2}$
Therefore, $-5 \div {}^+10 = {}^-\frac{1}{2}$

$-18 \div {}^-3 = ?$ is related to $? \cdot {}^-3 = {}^-18$
(What number multiplied by ${}^-3$ gives ${}^-18$?)   Answer: ${}^+6$
Therefore, $-18 \div {}^-3 = {}^+6$

$-5 \div {}^-25 = ?$ is related to $? \cdot {}^-25 = {}^-5$
(What number multiplied by ${}^-25$ gives ${}^-5$?)   Answer: ${}^+\frac{1}{5}$
Therefore, $-5 \div {}^-25 = {}^+\frac{1}{5}$

This pattern shows how problems in division are related to problems in multiplication. To state this pattern, we say that

■ $\forall_x \; \forall_{y \neq 0} \; \forall_z \;\; (x \div y = z)$ is equivalent to $(z \cdot y = x)$

The statement above is the *Definition of Division.*

Why do we state that $y \neq 0$ in this definition? Perhaps you answered that division by 0 is not allowed. Let us examine more closely this matter of division by 0. We shall distinguish between two cases.

CASE 1:   Division of a non-zero number by zero

$$x \div 0 = ? \quad (x \neq 0)$$

Suppose there is a quotient n, such that $x \div 0 = n$.

Then $n \times 0 = x$ [why?]

But we stated that $x \neq 0$. The last statement means that $n \times 0$ is equal to some number different from 0. What property is contradicted? Thus, there is *no* number which is the quotient of a non-zero number and 0.

CASE 2:   Division of zero by zero

$$0 \div 0 = ?$$

Suppose there is a quotient m, such that $0 \div 0 = m$.

Then $m \times 0 = 0$. We know that this is true for *every* number (according to what property?). Therefore, $0 \div 0$ can be 3 or 7 or 25 or any number you wish. There is a danger in having such a numeral, because someone may rightly claim that

if $\frac{0}{0} = 3$ *and* $\frac{0}{0} = 7$, then $3 = 7$

This would be a dangerous situation indeed!

We, therefore, declare "$\frac{0}{0}$" meaningless.

EXERCISES

1.   Find the answer to each division problem below by changing it to the related multiplication problem.

Example: $^{+}12 \div ^{-}2 = ?$
The related multiplication problem is $? \cdot ^{-}2 = ^{+}12$ or, what number multiplied by $^{-}2$ gives $^{+}12$?
The answer is $^{-}6$, therefore, $^{+}12 \div ^{-}2 = ^{-}6$

a. $^{-}16 \div ^{-}4$	**h.** $^{-}35 \div ^{-}1$	**o.** $^{-}1 \div ^{+}1$
b. $^{+}100 \div ^{-}2$	**i.** $^{+}99 \div ^{-}11$	**p.** $^{+}1 \div ^{+}1$
c. $^{-}100 \div ^{+}50$	**j.** $^{-}99 \div ^{-}11$	**q.** $^{-}\frac{1}{2} \div ^{-}\frac{1}{2}$
d. $^{-}17 \div ^{+}17$	**k.** $^{+}99 \div ^{+}11$	**r.** $^{-}3.673 \div ^{-}3.673$
e. $^{+}35 \div ^{+}1$	**l.** $^{-}99 \div ^{+}11$	**s.** $^{+}4.006 \div ^{-}4.006$
f. $^{+}35 \div ^{-}1$	**m.** $^{-}1 \div ^{-}1$	**t.** $^{-}111.12 \div ^{+}111.12$
g. $^{-}35 \div ^{+}1$	**n.** $^{+}1 \div ^{-}1$	**u.** $0 \div ^{-}25$

2. Examine your answers in exercise **1.** If you have a theory about the division of one real number by another, use it on the problems below. Tell no one your theory. Let your teacher check your answers.

a. $^-17 \div ^+2$

b. $^+52 \div ^-4$

c. $^-21 \div ^-3$

d. $^+10 \div ^-20$

e. $^-255 \div ^+3$

f. $^-1000 \div ^-100$

g. $^-\frac{1}{3} \div ^+4$

h. $^-2 \div ^-\frac{1}{3}$

i. $^-\frac{1}{2} \div ^+\frac{1}{2}$

j. $^+5.6 \div ^-2.8$

k. $^-.1 \div ^-10$

l. $^-2 \div ^+.1$

m. $^+\frac{3}{4} \div ^-\frac{2}{3}$

n. $^-\frac{1}{2} \div ^-\frac{7}{8}$

o. $^-4 \div ^-.002$

p. $0 \div ^-125$

q. $0 \div ^+136$

r. $^-\frac{1}{2} \div ^+5$

s. $^+.7 \div ^-10$

t. $^-.33 \div ^-\frac{1}{16}$

u. $^+17.5 \div ^+\frac{1}{2}$

v. $^+\frac{3}{10} \div ^-\frac{17}{2}$

3. Compute the answer to each pair of exercises below.

a. $^+16 \div ^+4; \ ^+16 \cdot ^+\frac{1}{4}$

b. $^+27 \div ^+3; \ ^+27 \cdot ^+\frac{1}{3}$

c. $^+49 \div ^-7; \ ^+49 \cdot ^-\frac{1}{7}$

d. $^-72 \div ^+8; \ ^-72 \cdot ^+\frac{1}{8}$

e. $^+144 \div ^-12; \ ^+144 \cdot ^-\frac{1}{12}$

f. $^-85 \div ^-5; \ ^-85 \cdot ^-\frac{1}{5}$

g. $^-91 \div ^+7; \ ^-91 \cdot ^+\frac{1}{7}$

h. $^+70 \div ^-5; \ ^+70 \cdot ^-\frac{1}{5}$

i. $^-102 \div ^-6; \ ^-102 \cdot ^-\frac{1}{6}$

j. $^-48 \div ^-\frac{1}{2}; \ ^-48 \cdot ^-2$

4. What is true of each pair of answers in problem **3**?

5. Read the definition of division again. Make a corresponding statement for subtraction.

Division and reciprocals

Let us take a different look at the division of numbers of arithmetic. Here are some examples that point out an interesting relation.

$$18 \div 3 = 6 \text{ and } 18 \cdot \tfrac{1}{3} = 6; \text{ therefore, } 18 \div 3 = 18 \cdot \tfrac{1}{3}$$
$$26 \div 2 = 13 \text{ and } 26 \cdot \tfrac{1}{2} = 13; \text{ therefore, } 26 \div 2 = 26 \cdot \tfrac{1}{2}$$
$$5 \div \tfrac{2}{3} = 7\tfrac{1}{2} \text{ and } 5 \cdot \tfrac{3}{2} = 7\tfrac{1}{2}; \text{ therefore, } 5 \div \tfrac{2}{3} = 5 \cdot \tfrac{3}{2}$$

The examples above show that division can be replaced by multiplication in a way different from the one you already considered.

In the first example we replaced division by 3 by multiplication by $\frac{1}{3}$. In the second example division by 2 was replaced by multiplication by what number? What replacement was made in the third example?

The numbers in each pair

$$3, \tfrac{1}{3} \qquad 2, \tfrac{1}{2} \qquad \tfrac{2}{3}, \tfrac{3}{2}$$

are related in an interesting way. Tell what this relation is from the following:

$$3 \times \tfrac{1}{3} = 1 \qquad 2 \times \tfrac{1}{2} = 1 \qquad \tfrac{2}{3} \times \tfrac{3}{2} = 1$$

We call two numbers whose product is 1 *reciprocals*. Thus, 3 is a reciprocal of $\tfrac{1}{3}$. Is $\tfrac{1}{3}$ a reciprocal of 3? Is 2 a reciprocal of .5? Why?

To extend the definition of reciprocal to real numbers, we shall say that two real numbers whose product is $^+1$ are reciprocals. For example, the following are pairs of reciprocals.

$$^+3, {^+\tfrac{1}{3}} \qquad ^-2, {^-\tfrac{1}{2}} \qquad {^+\tfrac{2}{3}}, {^+\tfrac{3}{2}}$$

Note that

$$^+3 \times {^+\tfrac{1}{3}} = {^+1} \qquad ^-2 \times {^-\tfrac{1}{2}} = {^+1} \qquad {^+\tfrac{2}{3}} \times {^+\tfrac{3}{2}} = {^+1}$$

We thus have the *Property of Reciprocals*

$$\blacksquare \quad \forall_{x \neq 0} \quad x \cdot \frac{1}{x} = {^+1}$$

The pattern shown by the three examples on page 99 can be extended to real numbers.

$$^+18 \div {^+3} = {^+6} \text{ and } {^+18} \cdot {^+\tfrac{1}{3}} = {^+6}; \text{ therefore, } {^+18} \div {^+3} = {^+18} \cdot {^+\tfrac{1}{3}}$$
$$^+18 \div {^-3} = {^-6} \text{ and } {^+18} \cdot {^-\tfrac{1}{3}} = {^-6}; \text{ therefore, } {^+18} \div {^-3} = {^+18} \cdot {^-\tfrac{1}{3}}$$
$$^-12 \div {^-3} = {^+4} \text{ and } {^-12} \cdot {^-\tfrac{1}{3}} = {^+4}; \text{ therefore, } {^-12} \div {^-3} = {^-12} \cdot {^-\tfrac{1}{3}}$$

This pattern for real numbers can be stated as follows:

$$\blacksquare \quad \forall_x \forall_{y \neq 0} \quad x \div y = x \cdot \frac{1}{y}$$

We shall call this pattern the *Property of Division*.

EXERCISES

1. Prove that 0 does not have a reciprocal.

2. There are two real numbers, each of which is its own reciprocal. What are the two numbers?

3. The product of a real number and its reciprocal is $^+1$. Give the reciprocal of each of the following numbers.

a. $^+4$	**d.** $^+8$	**g.** $^+7$
b. $^+3$	**e.** $^-12$	**h.** $^-6$
c. $^-7$	**f.** $^-5$	**i.** $^-\tfrac{1}{2}$

j. $+\frac{1}{4}$ **o.** $^-1.1$ **t.** $^-4.23$

k. $-\frac{2}{3}$ **p.** $-\frac{5}{6}$ **u.** $^-1.01$

l. $+\frac{4}{7}$ **q.** $+\frac{17}{18}$ **v.** $^+2.04$

m. $-\frac{6}{13}$ **r.** $-\frac{3}{4}$ **w.** $^-1.05$

n. $^+1.6$ **s.** $^+3.4$ **x.** $^-2.78$

4. You know that $\forall_{x\neq0} \; \dfrac{1}{x}$ is a reciprocal of x. For each statement tell whether it is true or false.

a. $\forall_{x>0} \; \dfrac{1}{x} > 0$

b. $\forall_{x<0} \; \dfrac{1}{x} < 0$

c. $\forall_{x>1} \; 0 < \dfrac{1}{x} < {}^+1$

d. $\forall_{x\geq1} \; 0 < \dfrac{1}{x} < {}^+1$

e. $\forall_{x<0} \; \dfrac{1}{x} > 0$

f. $\forall_{x>{}^+10} \; 0 < \dfrac{1}{x} < \dfrac{{}^+1}{10}$

g. $\forall_x$, if $|x| \nless {}^+10$, then
$$0 < \dfrac{1}{x} < \dfrac{{}^+1}{10}$$

h. $\forall_{x\neq0}$, the reciprocal of $\dfrac{1}{x}$ is x

i. $\forall_{x\neq0} \; \dfrac{1}{x}$ is the reciprocal of $\dfrac{1}{\frac{1}{x}}$

5. Replace the letters with numerals to obtain true statements.

a. $x \div {}^+2 = {}^+6$ **k.** $+\frac{7}{8} \div -\frac{4}{5} = t$

b. $y \div {}^-4 = {}^+10$ **l.** $^-7 \div w = {}^+\frac{6}{7}$

c. $m \div {}^+10 = {}^-12$ **m.** $z \div {}^+3 = {}^-7$

d. $p \div {}^-15 = {}^-4$ **n.** $^-9 \div x = {}^+\frac{5}{7}$

e. $^+20 \div z = {}^+1$ **o.** $^+5 \div {}^+7 = w$

f. $^-10 \div n = {}^+2$ **p.** $v \div {}^-5 = {}^+9$

g. $^-5 \div p = {}^-2.5$ **q.** $^-13 \div n = {}^+17$

h. $^+10 \div {}^-2.5 = s$ **r.** $^+14 \div {}^+\frac{5}{3} = x$

i. $^-25 \div {}^-75 = n$ **s.** $q \div {}^+\frac{6}{7} = {}^-\frac{5}{9}$

j. $-\frac{1}{2} \div -\frac{1}{4} = r$ **t.** $r \div {}^-3.5 = {}^-1$

Simpler numerals for real numbers

We shall now introduce some simplifications in writing numerals for real numbers.

AGREEMENT: Omit the raised "+" whenever referring to positive numbers. Thus

instead of $^+7$, we write 7

instead of $^+195$, we write 195

With this agreement, we shall keep in mind that whenever we speak of real numbers and use numerals without the raised "⁺" we mean *positive* real numbers.

Now, we introduce one additional simplification in writing. We shall abbreviate "the opposite of" by writing " −". Thus

"the opposite of 7" is abbreviated as " −7"
"the opposite of ⁻5" is abbreviated as " −⁻5"

and we know that − ⁻5 = 5.

Since

the opposite of 7 is the same as negative 7
that is, −7 = ⁻7

we shall write the lowered " −" instead of the raised "⁻".

Thus

instead of writing ⁻7, we write −7
instead of writing ⁻2½, we write −2½
and so on

It follows from the above that

■ $\forall_x$ the opposite of x is $-x$

Note that we do not know whether $-x$ refers to a positive number or a negative number or 0. It depends on what we use as a replacement for x.

For example

5 for x yields -5 for $-x$
-3 for x yields $-(-3)$ for $-x$

We can now simplify the statements of the property of subtraction, the property of opposites and the property of reciprocals by making use of the agreements to omit the raised "⁺" and the replace "the opposite of" by " −".

■   *Property of Subtraction*
$\forall_x \forall_y \ x - y = x + (-y)$

■   *Property of Opposites*
$\forall_x \ x + (-x) = 0$

■   *Property of Reciprocals*
$\forall_{x \neq 0} \ x \cdot \dfrac{1}{x} = 1$

EXERCISES

1. Find the answers.

a. $3 + (-5)$

b. $-7 + 1$

c. $-2\frac{1}{2} + (-3\frac{1}{2})$

d. $-\frac{1}{3} + \frac{1}{2}$

e. $5 + 27\frac{1}{2}$

f. $32\frac{1}{3} + 45\frac{1}{3}$

g. $50 - 60\frac{1}{3}$

h. $32 - (-13)$

i. $75 - 23$

j. $22 - 87$

k. $0 - 5$

l. $0 - (-7)$

m. $-2 \cdot 7$

n. $-3 \cdot (-3\frac{1}{3})$

o. $\frac{1}{2} \cdot \frac{3}{5}$

p. $8 \div (-2)$

q. $-12 \div (-4)$

r. $-36 \div 9$

s. $-\frac{1}{2} \div 5$

t. $-\frac{2}{3} \div (-\frac{2}{5})$

u. $3 \div (-\frac{1}{6})$

v. $-2\frac{1}{3} \div 4$

w. $5\frac{1}{2} \div 3\frac{1}{3}$

x. $-3\frac{1}{3} \div (-4\frac{1}{2})$

y. $-177 \div (-177)$

z. $-177 \div 177$

a'. $0 \div (-250)$

b'. $0 \div 250$

c'. $(-35 \cdot \frac{2}{3}) \cdot \frac{3}{2}$

d'. $17 \times (-6) + 17 \times (-4)$

e'. $9 - 12 + 7 + 6 - 4$

f'. $2 \cdot (-3) \div (-2) \cdot \frac{1}{2} + 12 \div (-6)$

2. In each problem, replace the letters with numerals to obtain true statements.

a. $3 \cdot 7 + (-4) = x$

b. $(-8) \cdot t = 16$

c. $(-27 + 6) + 10 = m + 16$

d. $k \cdot k \cdot k = -1$

e. $-\frac{9}{7} \cdot b = 1$

f. $-12 + 6 = 6 + c$

g. $(-5 \cdot f) \cdot 10 = -5 \cdot (7 \cdot 10)$

h. $p - 6 = -12$

i. $-6 \div m = 1$

j. $-814 \cdot d = 5 \cdot 814$

k. $-5(6 + 11) = -30 + f$

l. $6 + r = -2$

m. $p + (-4) = -6$

n. $-8 + g = 2$

o. $v + v = -28.6$

p. $73 + y = 0$

q. $k - 9 = 9 - k$

r. $12f = -60$

s. $7g = -8 \cdot 7$

t. $16(5k) = 16$

u. $0 - x = 7$

v. $p - (-3) = 4$

w. $-6x = -18$

x. $\dfrac{m}{-2} = -\dfrac{1}{4}$

y. $\dfrac{1 + x}{2} = -2$

z. $5(x - 1) = -10$

a'. $y - 4 = 0$

b'. $n + n + n = -1$

c'. $(x + 1)(x - 1) = 15$

d'. $\dfrac{12}{p} = -\dfrac{1}{2}$

e'. $\dfrac{\frac{3}{4}}{r} = \dfrac{3}{2}$

f'. $\frac{1}{2}t = -100$

THE SET OF REAL NUMBERS AS A FIELD

We shall now state eleven basic properties which the set of real numbers, together with the operations of addition and multiplication, possesses. In the statements below, keep in mind that the set of real numbers is the universal set. To simplify writing, we shall use R for the set of real numbers.

■ Any set of elements which has all eleven properties stated below is called a *field*.

■ *R is closed under addition* [ClPA]
$\forall_a \forall_b \ (a + b) \in R$

■ *R is closed under multiplication* [ClPM]
$\forall_a \forall_b \ (ab) \in R$

■ *Commutative Property of Addition* [CPA]
$\forall_a \forall_b \ a + b = b + a$

■ *Commutative Property of Multiplication* [CPM]
$\forall_a \forall_b \ ab = ba$

■ *Associative Property of Addition* [APA]
$\forall_a \forall_b \forall_c \ (a + b) + c = a + (b + c)$

■ *Associative Property of Multiplication* [APM]
$\forall_a \forall_b \forall_c \ (ab)c = a(bc)$

■ *Distributive Property of Multiplication over Addition* [DPMA]
$\forall_a \forall_b \forall_c \ a(b + c) = (ab) + (ac)$

In addition to the above properties, you know that among real numbers we have the number 1, which has an interesting property. Any number multiplied by 1 gives that number. We, therefore, call the number 1 *the multiplicative identity*. Thus, we have

■ *Property of One for Multiplication* [P1M]
There exists a unique real number 1, such that $\forall_a \ a \cdot 1 = a$

There is also a number among the real numbers which "acts" in addition like the number 1 does in multiplication. That number is 0, because 0 added to any number results in that number. The number 0 is given the name of *additive identity*. Thus,

▪ *Property of Zero for Addition* [PZA]
There exists a unique real number 0, such that $\forall_a\, a + 0 = a$

▪ *Propery of Reciprocals*
$\forall_{a=0}$, there exists a unique real number $\dfrac{1}{a}$ such that $a \cdot \dfrac{1}{a} = 1$

NOTE: Since a reciprocal is also called a *multiplicative inverse*, this property is usually referred to as the *Property of Multiplicative Inverses* [PMI].

▪ *Property of Opposites*
$\forall_a$, there exists a unique real number $(-a)$ such that $a + (-a) = 0$

NOTE: Since an opposite is also called an *additive inverse*, this property is usually referred to as the *Property of Additive Inverses* [PAI].

EXERCISES

1. Consider the set of natural numbers
$$N = \{1,\ 2,\ 3,\ 4,\ 5,\ \ldots\}$$
   a. Check each of the eleven properties of real numbers to see whether or not they also hold for natural numbers. State the properties, if there are any, which do not hold for N.
   b. Is N a number field?

2. Consider the set of integers
$$I = \{\ldots,\ -5,\ -4,\ -3,\ -2,\ -1,\ 0,\ 1,\ 2,\ 3,\ 4,\ 5,\ \ldots\}$$
   a. Check each of the eleven properties of real numbers to see whether or not they also hold for integers. State the properties, if there are any, which do not hold for I.
   b. Is I a number field?

3. Consider the set of rational numbers Q; that is, numbers which have names of the form $\dfrac{a}{b}$ or $-\dfrac{a}{b}$ where a and b are natural numbers (a may also be zero).
   a. Check each of the eleven properties of real numbers to see whether or not they also hold for rational numbers. State the properties, if there are any, which do not hold for Q.
   b. Is Q a number field?

4. Name the property or definition illustrated by each of the following:

a. $-7 \times \frac{3}{4} = \frac{3}{4} \times (-7)$

b. $-5(-1 + 7) = -5 \cdot (-1) + (-5) \cdot 7$

c. $267 + (-267) = 0$

d. $-4 \div (-2) = -4 \times (-\frac{1}{2})$

e. $[-\frac{1}{2} + (-3)] \cdot 1 = -\frac{1}{2} + (-3)$

f. $[-2 \times (-3)] \times (-4) = -2 \times [-3 \times (-4)]$

g. $-\frac{2}{7} \times (-\frac{7}{2}) = 1$

h. $-317 + (-23) = -23 + (-317)$

i. If $-3 \times 4 = -12$, then $-12 = -3 \times 4$.

j. $-8 - 3 = -8 + (-3)$

k. $-7 \times 3 + 0 = -7 \times 3$

l. $(-2 \times 4) + (-2 \times 8) = (-2 \times 8) + (-2 \times 4)$

m. $(-2 \times 4) + (-2 \times 8) = (-2 \times 4) + [8 \times (-2)]$

n. $(-8 + 0) + 1 = -8 + (0 + 1)$

5. Consider a finite number system which contains two elements, say 0 and 1. Here are the addition and multiplication tables for this system.

+	0	1
0	0	1
1	1	0

×	0	1
0	0	0
1	0	1

Check to see whether or not this number system is a field; that is, check to see whether or not each of the eleven properties holds for addition and multiplication in this number system.

6. Suppose we had a "five-hour clock." Three hours after two o'clock the time will be zero o'clock ($2 + 3 = 0$). Three hours after three o'clock will be one o'clock ($3 + 3 = 1$). Finish supplying the numerals in the addition table for the numbers of the "five-hour clock."

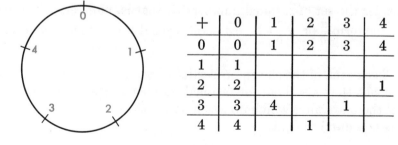

+	0	1	2	3	4
0	0	1	2	3	4
1	1				
2	2				1
3	3	4		1	
4	4		1		

Part of the multiplication table for the numbers of the "five-hour clock" is given below. Supply the missing numerals.

×	0	1	2	3	4
0	0	0	0	0	0
1	0				
2	0	2			
3	0		1	4	2
4	0				1

Check to see whether or not this set of numbers is a field under the operations of addition and multiplication.

7.   Repeat the approach described above for a "four-hour" clock.

Addition:

+	0	1	2	3
0	0	1	2	3
1	1			0
2	2	3		
3	3		1	2

Multiplication:

×	0	1	2	3
0	0	0	0	0
1	0	1		
2	0		0	
3	0		2	1

Complete the tables and determine whether or not this set of numbers is a field under the operations of addition and multiplication.

From word phrases to mathematical phrases

In solving some problems, we need to translate word phrases into mathematical phrases involving various operations. As you learn more about the mathematical operations, you will be able to translate more complicated phrases.

EXERCISES

For each word phrase, write the correct mathematical phrase.

Examples: i. the reciprocal of $x + y$

$$\frac{1}{x + y}$$

ii. Jim is n years old now. How old was he 5 years ago?

$n - 5$

1. the reciprocal of $2m$
2. the reciprocal of $2x + 3y$

5. the reciprocal of $\dfrac{m + n}{2a + 3b}$

3. the reciprocal of $\dfrac{2}{n}$

6. the reciprocal of $\dfrac{3x - 4y}{5x + 4y}$

4. the reciprocal of $\dfrac{3}{a + b}$

7. the reciprocal of $\dfrac{\frac{3}{4}a + b}{a + \frac{1}{2}b}$

8. the sum of the reciprocals of x and y
9. the reciprocal of the sum of x and y
10. the product of the reciprocals of x and y
11. the reciprocal of the product of x and y
12. the difference of the reciprocals of x and y
13. the reciprocal of the difference of x and y
14. the quotient of the reciprocals of x and y
15. the reciprocal of the quotient of x and y
16. If Joe is n years old now, how old will he be m years from now?
17. If Dave is $2n$ years older than Susie and Susie is $(3x + 1)$ years old, how old is Dave?
18. If Dottie is $(2m + 5)$ years old and she is three times as old as Bea, how old is Bea?
19. If Sam is $(x + 2)$ years old, and Dave is n years older than Sam, and Pete is 7 years older than Dave, then how old is Pete?
20. If Ann will be $(x + 3)$ years old 7 years from now, how old is she now?
21. If Bill will be $(2n - 1)$ years old 3 years from now, how old was he 5 years ago?
22. If Paul was $(3x + 2)$ years old 4 years ago, how old will be he 5 years from now?

VOCABULARY

Use each of the following correctly in a sentence. Numerals in the parentheses refer to pages where these words were used. If you are not sure of the meaning of any word, turn to the indicated page and refresh your memory.

additive inverse (105)
field (104)
inverse operations (85)
multiplicative inverse (105)

one-to-one correspondence (91)
opposite (88)
reciprocal (99)

A CHALLENGE TO YOU

Solve each of the following problems. You should give careful thought to each problem because there may be several answers or no answer to some of them.

1. The sum of two positive odd integers is 12. Give two pairs of such integers. How many pairs of such integers are there? List them.

2. Tell why there are no pairs of positive odd integers whose sum is 13.

3. The sum of two integers is 4. Give two pairs of such integers. How many pairs of such integers are there? (NOTE: 2 and 2 are not *two* integers.)

4. The sum of two numbers is the same as the product of these numbers. How many pairs of such numbers can you find?

NOTE: 2 and 2 are *not two* numbers
One such pair is, for example,

$$5 \text{ and } \tfrac{5}{4},$$

because

$$5 + \tfrac{5}{4} = 5\tfrac{5}{4} = 6\tfrac{1}{4}$$

and

$$5 \cdot \tfrac{5}{4} = \tfrac{25}{4} = 6\tfrac{1}{4}$$

5. Your watch is 7 minutes faster than the radio time. The clock in your school is 3 minutes slower than your watch. Is the clock in your school faster or slower than the radio time? By how much?

6. Write names for the numbers 0, 1, 2, 3, and so on using four and only four symbols "4". You are allowed to use any operations you wish.

HINT: $0 = \dfrac{4}{4} - \dfrac{4}{4}$

$$1 = \dfrac{4+4}{4+4}$$

$$2 = \dfrac{4}{4} + \dfrac{4}{4}$$

$$3 = \dfrac{4}{\sqrt{4}} + \dfrac{4}{4}$$

$$4 = \sqrt{4} + \sqrt{4} - 4 + 4$$

Keep going!

PROPERTIES AND DEFINITIONS

■ *Property of Subtraction*
$\forall_x \forall_y \ x - y = x + (-y)$

■ *Property of Additive Inverses (Opposites)* [PAI]
$\forall_x \ x + (-x) = 0$

■ *Definition of Division*
$\forall_x \forall_{y \neq 0} \forall_z \ (x \div y = z)$ is equivalent to $(z \cdot y = x)$

■ *Property of Multiplicative Inverses (Reciprocals)* [PMI]
$\forall_{x \neq 0} \ x \cdot \dfrac{1}{x} = 1$

■ *Property of Division*

$\forall_x \forall_{y \neq 0} \ x \div y = x \cdot \dfrac{1}{y}$

■ *Definition of Subtraction*
$\forall_x \forall_y \forall_z \ x - y = z$ is equivalent to $z + y = x$

REVIEW EXERCISES

1. Find the answers.

a. $4 + 3$

b. $-7 + 24$

c. $89 + (-120)$

d. $-36 + (-112)$

e. $7 - 15$

f. $36 - 17$

g. $-3 - 21$

h. $-7 - (-29)$

i. $3 \cdot 9$

j. $10 \cdot (-23)$

k. $-12 \cdot (-12)$

l. $-150 \cdot 0$

m. $0 \div (-199)$

n. $-17 \div 17$

o. $52 \div (-4)$

p. $-99 \div (-11)$

q. $-\frac{1}{2} \cdot (-4)$

r. $-9 \cdot (-\frac{1}{27})$

s. $\frac{2}{3} \cdot (-\frac{4}{7})$

t. $.6 \times (-1.7)$

u. $-\frac{3}{4} \div 4$

v. $\frac{1}{3} \div \frac{1}{100}$

w. $-\frac{7}{3} \div \frac{3}{8}$

x. $\frac{20}{17} \div (-\frac{1}{2})$

y. $-\frac{1}{2} - \frac{1}{3}$

z. $\frac{2}{7} - (-\frac{3}{5})$

a'. $-8.5 - 9.7$

b'. $-100.1 + (-\frac{4}{5})$

c'. $\frac{3}{4} + (-\frac{4}{6})$

d'. $-\frac{1}{2} + (-7.65)$

e'. $-\frac{7}{11} + (-\frac{3}{2})$

f'. $6.66 + (-3.3)$

2. Simplify each of the following:

Examples: i. $[10 + (-15) - (-3)] \cdot (-2)$
$= [-5 - (-3)] \cdot (-2)$
$= -2 \cdot (-2)$
$= 4$

ii. $\left[\frac{\frac{1}{2}}{-\frac{1}{2}} + (-176 \cdot 0) \right] \cdot \frac{3}{2}$
$= [-1 + 0] \cdot \frac{3}{2}$
$= -1 \cdot \frac{3}{2}$
$= -\frac{3}{2}$
$= -1\frac{1}{2}$

a. $-3 + (-17) - 2 - (-6)$

b. $-4 \cdot (-2) + (-3) + (-1.5)$

c. $3 + (-1.5) - 7 \cdot (-4)$

d. $[3 + (-4)] \cdot (-\frac{1}{2})$

e. $-.75 \times [-3 + (-4)] \cdot (-2 - 3)$

f. $[-\frac{1}{2} + (-\frac{1}{2})] \cdot [-\frac{1}{3} + (-\frac{1}{3}) + (-\frac{1}{3})]$

g. $-\frac{1.6}{1.6} \times (-\frac{3.5}{3.5}) + [176 + (-176)] \cdot (-\frac{1}{176})$

h. $[-6 + (-13)] \cdot [\frac{1}{2} + (-\frac{7}{14})] \div \frac{1}{3}$

i. $\{[\frac{1}{2} \div (-\frac{3}{7})] \div (-\frac{1}{2})]\} \cdot (-\frac{2}{3})$

j. $\frac{\frac{3}{4}}{-\frac{3}{4}} + (13 - 13) \cdot 0 + [176.789 + (-378.97)] \cdot 0$

3. True or false? The universal set is the set of real numbers. In some cases, you will find it necessary to try a few examples before deciding whether the statement is true or false.

a. $\forall_{x>0} \forall_{y<0} \ (x \div y) < 0$

b. $\forall_{x\leq0} \forall_{y<0} \ (x \div y) \leq 0$

c. $\forall_{x=0} \ 0 \div x = 0$

d. $\forall_{x=0} \ x \cdot \frac{1}{x} = 1$

e. $\forall_{x>0} \forall_{y<0} \ (x - y) > 0$

f. $\forall_{x<0} \forall_{y<0} \ (x - y) < 0$

g. $\forall_x \ x + (-x) = 0$

h. $\forall_x \forall_y \ |xy| = |x| \cdot |y|$

i. $\forall_x \forall_{y=0} \ \left|\frac{x}{y}\right| = \left|\frac{x}{y}\right|$

j. $\forall_x \forall_{y=0}$ there exists a unique z such that $x \div y = z$ is equivalent to $yz = x$

4. Given the universal set $U = \{-4, -2, 0, 2, 4\}$. True or false?

 a. $\{x \mid \frac{x}{2} \geq -2\} = U$

 b. $\{x \mid x \geq 0\} = \{x \mid x > -2\}$

 c. $\{x \mid x < 0\} = \{-4\}$

 d. $\{x \mid x \neq 0\} = \{x \mid x > 0\}$

 e. $\{x \mid |x| = 2\} = \{x \mid x = -2 \text{ or } x = 2\}$

 f. $\{x \mid 2x < 0\} = \{-8, -4\}$

 g. $\{x \mid x^2 > 0\} = U$

5. Give the reciprocal (multiplicative inverse) of each of the following numbers.

a. 9	c. -12	e. .7	g. 3.5
b. $\frac{3}{7}$	d. $-\frac{7}{5}$	f. $-.4$	h. -4.2

6. For each word phrase, write the correct mathematical phrase.

 a. the reciprocal of $(2n - 3)$

 b. the reciprocal of $\dfrac{a + b}{c - d}$

 c. the reciprocal of $-(2x + y)$

 d. the sum of the reciprocals of $2x$ and $3y$

 e. the reciprocal of the sum of $2x$ and $3y$

 f. If Carol will be $(2x + 1)$ years old 4 years from now, how old is she now?

 g. If Ted was $(3m - 4)$ years old 5 years ago, how old will he be 10 years from now?

CHAPTER TEST

1. Find the answers.

a. $52 - 19$	k. $-2.3 - 4.7$
b. $4 - 51$	l. $-4.2 - (-3.1)$
c. $22 - (-17)$	m. $-3.6 - (-4.2)$
d. $-12 - (-36)$	n. $-4.2 - (-3.6)$
e. $\frac{1}{2} - \frac{1}{5}$	o. 3×12
f. $\frac{2}{3} - (-\frac{3}{4})$	p. -12×4
g. $\frac{4}{7} - (-\frac{1}{2})$	q. $-4 \times (-13)$
h. $-\frac{1}{3} - (-\frac{3}{4})$	r. $\frac{3}{4} \times \frac{2}{3}$
i. $1.6 - .3$	s. $\frac{2}{5} \times (-\frac{5}{6})$
j. $1.5 - 4.6$	t. $-\frac{3}{7} \times (-\frac{4}{3})$

u. $24 \div 6$

v. $9 \div 63$

w. $-12 \div (-2)$

x. $-4 \div (-36)$

y. $36 \div (-9)$

z. $-42 \div 6$

a'. $-258 \div 1$

b'. $-369 \div (-1)$

c'. $476 \div 1$

d'. $509 \div (-1)$

e'. $\frac{4}{5} \div 5$

f'. $-\frac{3}{7} \div (-4)$

g'. $-\frac{1}{3} \div \frac{3}{4}$

h'. $\frac{2}{7} \div \left(-\frac{2}{5}\right)$

i'. $-1.6 \div (-2)$

j'. $-12.3 \div 3$

k'. $25.6 \div .1$

l'. $-1.3 \div (-.01)$

2. Replace the letters with numerals to obtain true statements.

a. $1 + 13 = x$

b. $4 + (-3) = n$

c. $9 + m = -16$

d. $t + (-10) = -3$

e. $17 - 3 = s$

f. $u - 30 = -20$

g. $-2 - p = 3$

h. $-3 - 2 = r$

i. $-5 - x = -1$

j. $z - (-5) = -5$

k. $10 - (-4) = q$

l. $r - (-25) = 20$

m. $3 \times 25 = w$

n. $-4 \times s = 21$

o. $t \times (-8) = -32$

p. $12 \times (-2) = n$

q. $-18 \div (-3) = v$

r. $-24 \div 8 = z$

s. $5 \div m = -5$

t. $z \div 8 = 30$

u. $0 \div (-3) = t$

v. $u \div (-2) = 0$

w. $-\frac{1}{2} \div (-\frac{1}{4}) = w$

x. $y \div \frac{6}{7} = -\frac{5}{9}$

3. Give the multiplicative inverse (reciprocal) of each of the following numbers.

a. 12

b. $\frac{9}{11}$

c. -5

d. $-\frac{3}{7}$

e. $.2$

f. $-.3$

g. 4.5

h. -7.9

4. The universal set is the set of real numbers. True or false?

a. $\forall_x \forall_y \; x - y = x + (-y)$

b. $\forall_x \forall_y$, if $|x| = |y|$, then $x + y = 2x$

c. $\forall_{x>0} \forall_{y<0}$, if $|x| \geq |y|$, then $x - y \geq 0$

d. $\forall_{x>0} \forall_{y<0}$, if $|x| \geq |y|$, then $x - y \leq 0$

e. $\forall_{x<0} \forall_{y<0}$, if $|x| \geq |y|$, then $x - y \geq 0$

f. $\forall_{x<0} \forall_{y<0}$, if $|x| \geq |y|$, then $x - y \leq 0$

g. $\forall_x \forall_y$, if $|x| = |y|$, then $x - y = 0$

h. $\forall_{x>0} \forall_{y>0} \; xy > 0$

i. $\forall_{x<0} \forall_{y<0} \; xy < 0$

j. $\forall_{x<0} \forall_{y>0} \; \dfrac{x}{y} < 0$

5. Given the set $X = \{-1, 1\}$. True or false?

    a. X is closed under multiplication.

    b. X is closed under division.

    c. X is closed under subtraction.

    d. $\forall_{a \epsilon X} \; a^2 \epsilon X$

    e. $\forall_{a \epsilon X} \; a^2 \geq a$

    f. $\forall_{a \epsilon X} \; \dfrac{a}{a} \geq a$

    g. $\forall_{a \epsilon X} \; [a \cdot (-1)] \epsilon X$

    h. $\forall_{a \epsilon X} \; \left(\dfrac{a}{-1}\right) \epsilon X$

6. For each word phrase, write the correct mathematical phrase.

    a. the reciprocal of $3t$

    b. the reciprocal of $\dfrac{3}{7 - y}$

    c. the reciprocal of $2c - d$

    d. the reciprocal of the sum of $3t$ and $2s$

    e. the sum of the reciprocals of $3t$ and $2s$

    f. If Ed was $(x + 1)$ years old 3 years ago, how old is he now?

    g. If Mary will be $(2y + 4)$ years old 7 years from now, how old was she 10 years ago?

7. For each example, name the property which it illustrates.

    a. $-37 \cdot 1 = -37$

    b. $\sqrt{2} + 0 = \sqrt{2}$

    c. If $-5 + 1 = -4$, then $-4 = -5 + 1$.

    d. $\sqrt{2} + 7 = 7 + \sqrt{2}$

    e. $-73 \cdot (-\tfrac{1}{73}) = 1$

    f. $-\sqrt{10} + \sqrt{10} = 0$

    g. $(5\sqrt{2})\sqrt{3} = 5(\sqrt{2}\sqrt{3})$

    h. $-2(7 + 9) = (-2 \cdot 7) + (-2 \cdot 9)$

    i. $-25 \cdot 1 = -25$

    j. $269 \times 0 = 0$

    k. $-36 \times 25 = 25 \times (-36)$

    l. $1 + [(-2) + 7] = [1 + (-2)] + 7$

CUMULATIVE REVIEW EXERCISES

These exercises are designed for your review of the basic ideas contained in the first four chapters.

1. List the eight different subsets of $\{0, 1, 2\}$.

2. A and B are sets. True or false?

   a. $\forall_A \ A \cup \phi = A$

   b. $\forall_A \ A \cap \phi = A$

   c. $\forall_A \ A \cap A = \phi$

   d. $\forall_A \forall_B \ A \cup B = B \cup A$

   e. $\forall_A \forall_B \ A \cap B \neq \phi$

   f. $\forall_A \forall_B \ \overline{A \cup B} = A \cap B$

3. Let $U = \{1, 3, 5, 7, 9, 11\}$
   $A = \{1, 5, 7\}$ $\qquad$ $B = \{3, 7, 9, 11\}$ $\qquad$ $C = \{1, 7, 9\}$

   Determine the following sets.

   a. $A \cap B$

   b. $B \cap A$

   c. $B \cup A$

   d. $A \cup B$

   e. $(A \cup B) \cup C$

   f. $A \cup (B \cup C)$

   g. $\overline{A} \cap \overline{B}$

   h. $\overline{A \cup B}$

4. $F = \{1, 4, 7, 11, 13\}$ $\qquad$ $G = \{4, 7, 11, 13\}$ $\qquad$ $K = \{4, 6, 7, 13, 11\}$
   True or false?

   a. $F \subseteq G$ $\qquad$ **b.** $G \subseteq K$ $\qquad$ **c.** $G \subset F$ $\qquad$ **d.** $K \subset K$

5. List the elements of the set of all prime numbers less than 20.

6. Suppose the set $X = \{-1, 0, 1\}$. True or false?

   a. X is closed under multiplication
   b. X is closed under division by a non-zero number
   c. X is closed under addition
   d. X is closed under subtraction
   e. $\forall_{x \epsilon X} \ x^2 \epsilon X$
   f. $\forall_{x \epsilon X} \ |x| \epsilon X$

   g. $\forall_{x \epsilon X} \ \left(\dfrac{x}{1}\right) \epsilon X$

   h. $\forall_{x \epsilon X} \ [x \cdot (-1)] \epsilon X$

7. Determine the number midway between each of the following pairs of numbers.

   a. 4, 13 $\qquad$ **c.** $\frac{1}{2}, \frac{4}{7}$ $\qquad$ **e.** $-3.2, 2.1$

   b. 2, -7 $\qquad$ **d.** $\frac{1}{3}, -\frac{4}{9}$ $\qquad$ **f.** $-3.19, 2.11$

8. For each of the following give a name of the form $\frac{a}{b}$ (a and b natural numbers).

 a. 3.29   **b.** .111   **c.** $4\frac{1}{3}$ **d.** $9.\overline{23}$

9. True or false?

 a. $-8 < -117$

 b. $1 > -225$

 c. $0 > -100$

 d. $13 < 0$

 e. $\frac{1}{2} > 1.5$

 f. $-12 \geq -12$

 g. $\frac{3}{4} \leq \frac{3}{4}$

 h. $|-2 \div 2| \neq 1$

 i. $|-8 \div 4| \neq |-8| \div |4|$

 j. $|-3| \times |-4| \neq |-3 \times (-4)|$

 k. $|-3 + 4| < |-3| + |4|$

 l. $|1| + |-4| \leq |1 + (-4)|$

 m. $|-11.78 + \frac{3}{17}| > 0$

 n. $|-17 + (-3)| \times 0 \leq 0$

 o. $|3| - |-3| = 0$

 p. $\frac{3}{7}$ and $-\frac{7}{3}$ are opposites of each other

 q. $\sqrt{2} = 1.414$

10. $R =$ the set of all real numbers
$Q =$ the set of all rational numbers
$S =$ the set of all irrational numbers
$I =$ the set of all integers

True or false?

 a. $I \subseteq R$

 b. $Q \subseteq I$

 c. $I \subseteq Q$

 d. $Q \subseteq R$

 e. $Q \cap S = \phi$

 f. $Q \cap R = S$

 g. $S \cap R = Q$

 h. $Q \cup S = R$

11. Name the property illustrated by each of the following:

 a. $-4 + (-6\frac{1}{3} + 5\frac{1}{9}) = [-4 + (-6\frac{1}{3})] + 5\frac{1}{9}$

 b. $[5 \cdot (-2)] \cdot (-2\frac{1}{4}) = (-2\frac{1}{4}) \cdot [5 \cdot (-2)]$

 c. $(-7) \cdot [(-2\frac{1}{8}) + (-5\frac{1}{9})] = (-7) \cdot (-2\frac{1}{8}) + (-7) \cdot (-5\frac{1}{9})$

 d. $(\frac{7}{3} \cdot \frac{8}{11}) \cdot 1 = (\frac{7}{3} \cdot \frac{8}{11})$

 e. $-3 \div (-\frac{1}{4}) = -3 \times (-4)$

 f. $-\frac{1}{2} - \frac{1}{3} = -\frac{1}{2} + (-\frac{1}{3})$

 g. $\frac{37}{321} \times \frac{321}{37} = 1$

 h. $1376 + (-1376) = 0$

 i. If $3 = 4 + (-1)$, then $4 + (-1) = 3$.

 j. $-1 \times [3 + (-1)] = (-1 \times 3) + [-1 \times (-1)]$

 k. $[2 + (-6)] \times (-3) = -3 \times [2 + (-6)]$

12. Tell which of the following numbers are rational and which are irrational.

    a. $.\overline{135}$ **d.** $\sqrt{3}$

    b. $-.26126112611126\ldots$ **e.** $-.1497813$

    c. $-.\overline{14}$ **f.** $-3\frac{11}{127}$

13. Approximate $\sqrt{13}$ to two decimal places.

14. Write the simplest numeral for each of the following:

    a. $3 \cdot (2 - 5 \cdot 6 + 3\frac{1}{2})$

    b. $[2 \cdot (-3) - 3] \div (-2)$

    c. $\dfrac{4 - 12}{-4} \times \left(-\dfrac{2}{3}\right)$

    d. $-1 \times (-1) \times [3 - (2 \times 4) + 3 \times 7] \times (-1)$

15. In each of the following, replace x to obtain true statements.

    a. $2 \cdot (x + 3) = 2 \cdot (-12) + 2 \cdot (3)$

    b. $\frac{1}{2} - x = \frac{1}{2} + \frac{2}{3}$

    c. $5x = -55$

    d. $(-3 + x) + (-12) = -3 + [-11 + (-12)]$

    e. $17 \div x = -1$

    f. $\frac{4}{7}x = -1$

    g. $x \div (-136) = 1$

    h. $2x = 0$

    i. $x \div (-237) = 0$

    j. $(6 + x) \times (-27) = 0$

    k. $[x - (-4)] \times (-53) = 0$

    l. $|x - 5| = 0$

16. For each word phrase, write the mathematical phrase.

    a. 12 increased by n

    b. $3m$ increased by $-4x$

    c. the product of $(6t + 1)$ and $(5s - 3)$

    d. $(5x - 4)$ divided by $(-x + 7)$

    e. the reciprocal of $\dfrac{3n}{4s}$

    f. the reciprocal of $\dfrac{a - x}{y - b}$

    g. the reciprocal of the product of $2n$ and $3t$

h. the product of the reciprocals of $2n$ and $3t$

i. worth of n nickels in cents

j. worth of $(10x + y)$ quarters in cents

k. worth of 1 cent in dollars

l. worth of c cents in dollars

m. worth of $(a + b)$ dollars in cents

n. If Ed is $6x$ years old now, how old will he be 12 years from now?

o. If Jane will be $2y - 1$ years old 12 years from now, how old was she 6 years ago?

BIBLIOGRAPHY

Committee on the Undergraduate Program, Mathematical Association of America. *Universal Mathematics, Part I, Functions and Limits.* University of Kansas, 1954. pp. 17-41.

Dubisch, Roy. *The Nature of Number.* New York: Ronald Press, 1952.

Lieber, Lillian R., and Lieber, Hugh Gray. *Take a Number.* New York: The Ronald Press Company, 1946.

National Council of Teachers of Mathematics. *Enrichment Mathematics for High School*, Twenty-Eighth Yearbook. Washington, D. C., 1963. pp. 34-45, 46-55, 368-378.

Newman, James R. *The World of Mathematics.* New York: Simon and Schuster, 1956. pp. 528-543.

Nichols, Eugene D.; Kalin, Robert; and Garland, E. Henry. *Arithmetic of Directed Numbers* (A Programed Unit). New York: Holt, Rinehart and Winston, Inc., 1962. Chapters III-V.

Niven, Ivan. *Irrational Numbers.* New York: John Wiley and Sons, 1956.

School Mathematics Study Group. *First Course in Algebra.* New Haven: Yale University Press, 1961. pp. 97-120.

Stein, Sherman K. *Mathematics—The Man-Made Universe.* San Francisco: W. H. Freeman and Company, 1963. Appendix A.

Titchmarsh, E. C. *Mathematics for the General Reader.* New York: Doubleday & Company, Inc., 1959. pp. 75-83.

The University of Chicago, The College Mathematics Staff. *Concepts and Structure of Mathematics.* Chicago: The University of Chicago Press, 1954. pp. 1-29.

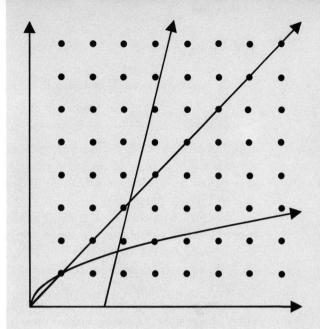

CHAPTER 5

Open Expressions

TERMS AND EXPRESSIONS IN ALGEBRA

By now you are accustomed to the idea of replacing letters by numerals. In algebra such letters are called *variables*. For example, replacing x in $-2x + 1$ by -6 yields $-2(-6) + 1$, which is equal to 13. We say that the *value* of $-2x + 1$, when x is replaced by -6, is 13. Compute the value of $-2x + 1$ for each of the following replacements of x.

$$0, \ 4, \ \tfrac{1}{2}, \ -\tfrac{1}{2} \text{ and } \sqrt{2}$$

Is it true that $\forall_{x<0} \ -2x + 1 > 0$? Defend your answer. Such phrases as $-2x + 1$ are called *expressions*.

We shall now examine certain kinds of expressions more closely. Take a look at each of the following:

$$4 \qquad 3x \qquad -7y \qquad 5ax \qquad -12mv \qquad \tfrac{1}{2}xyc \qquad -1.675mp$$

Each of the above expressions is also called a *term*. Give a few more examples of terms.

119

Now examine each of the following:

$$7 \qquad 5x + 7x \qquad \tfrac{1}{2}abc - 7.63x + 16u$$
$$5cy \qquad -13y + 16ax \qquad 4.6xy - \tfrac{7}{3}a + 1.2mn - 3cd$$

Each of the above is called an *expression*. Notice that each term is also an expression. Whenever an expression contains one or more variables, it is called an *open expression*. Which one of the six expressions above is not an *open* expression?

A term is also called a *monomial*. Thus, 4, $3x$, and $-1.675mp$ are monomials. Expressions like $3x + 10y$, $-13y + 16ax$, and $-\tfrac{1}{2}y - 3ab$ are called *binomials*. Expressions like $\tfrac{1}{2}abc - 7.63x + 16u$, $x + y - z$, $-\tfrac{1}{2}a + 3b - 4c$ are called *trinomials*. Each of these belongs to the set of *polynomials*.

One of the important algebraic skills is the ability to tell when two open expressions have the same value as the result of replacing the corresponding variables by the same numerals. For example, does $5x + 7x$ and $12x$ have the same value for every replacement of x? In other words, is

$$\forall_x\ 5x + 7x = 12x$$

true?

Let us try some replacements.

i. -2 for x
   $5x + 7x$: $5 \cdot (-2) + 7 \cdot (-2) = -10 - 14 = -24$
   $12x$: $12 \cdot (-2) = -24$

ii. $\tfrac{1}{2}$ for x
   $5x + 7x$: $5 \cdot \tfrac{1}{2} + 7 \cdot \tfrac{1}{2} = \tfrac{12}{2} = 6$
   $12x$: $12 \cdot \tfrac{1}{2} = 6$

Try a few more replacements for x to convince yourself that the expressions $5x + 7x$ and $12x$ have the same value for the same replacements of x.

If we agree that the replacement set for x is the set of all real numbers, then we would never be able to display *all* replacements for x. Explain why. Thus, we could not *verify* by means of replacements whether $5x + 7x$ and $12x$ have the same values for *all* replacements of x. To establish this, we resort to *proof*, which we shall deal with in the next section. We give the name of *equivalent expressions* to those expressions which have the same value for every replacement of the variable or variables by the same numerals.

The several replacements we made in $5x + 7x$ and in $12x$ strengthened our faith in the fact that $5x + 7x$ and $12x$ may be equivalent expressions, but we cannot be sure until we *prove* it.

We make one more observation about $5x + 7x$ and $12x$: of the two, $12x$ is "simpler looking" than $5x + 7x$. When working with expressions, we ordinarily use the simpler of given equivalent expressions. The process of arriving at an equivalent expression which is simpler looking than a given expression is called *simplification*.

EXERCISES

1. Find the value of each expression below for the designated replacements of variables.

Example:　　　　$6x - 2m$
　　　　i. -2 for x; $\frac{1}{2}$ for m
　　　　　$6 \cdot (-2) - 2 \cdot \frac{1}{2} = -12 - 1 = -13$
　　　　ii. 0 for x; 7 for m
　　　　　$6 \cdot 0 - 2 \cdot 7 = 0 - 14 = -14$

a. $4p - 3$
　　i. -7 for p
　　ii. $\frac{1}{3}$ for p

b. $11x - 25y$
　　i. $-\frac{1}{2}$ for x; 2 for y
　　ii. 0 for x; 0 for y

c. $3mv + \frac{1}{2}m$
　　i. 1 for m; -2 for v
　　ii. 0 for m; 100 for v

d. $x^2 + x^2$
　　i. -1 for x
　　ii. 1 for x
　　iii. 0 for x
　　iv. -5 for x
　　v. 5 for x

e. $\dfrac{x^3}{x^2}$
　　i. -1 for x
　　ii. 1 for x
　　iii. -2 for x
　　iv. 2 for x

f. $x + y$
　　i. -1 for x; -2 for y
　　ii. 3 for x; -1 for y
　　iii. 0 for x; 0 for y

g. $\dfrac{a + b}{a - b}$
　　i. 2 for a; -15 for b
　　ii. $\frac{1}{2}$ for a; $-\frac{1}{2}$ for b
　　iii. $\frac{2}{3}$ for a; $-\frac{1}{3}$ for b

h. $r^2 - s^2$
　　i. -1 for r; -1 for s
　　ii. 3 for r; 2 for s
　　iii. $\frac{1}{2}$ for r; $-\frac{3}{4}$ for s

i. $\dfrac{m^2 - n^2}{m - n}$
　　i. 1 for m; 2 for n
　　ii. 3 for m; 2 for n

j. $m + n$
　　i. 1 for m; 2 for n
　　ii. 3 for m; 2 for n

k. $x(y - z)$
　　i. 1 for x; 2 for y; 3 for z
　　ii. -1 for x; -5 for y; 4 for z

l. $xy - xz$
　　i. 1 for x; 2 for y; 3 for z
　　ii. -1 for x; -5 for y; 4 for z

2. In each exercise below, there are two given expressions. In each case, make the indicated replacements of the variables to see whether it is reasonable to suspect that the two given expressions may be equivalent expressions.

Example: i. $x^2 - y^2$; $(x - y)(x + y)$

     i. -2 for x; 5 for y

$x^2 - y^2$	$(x - y)(x + y)$
$(-2)^2 - 5^2$	$(-2 - 5)(-2 + 5)$
$4 - 25$	$-7 \cdot 3$
-21 =	-21

     ii. 0 for x; $-\frac{1}{2}$ for y

$x^2 - y^2$	$(x - y)(x + y)$
$0^2 - (-\frac{1}{2})^2$	$[0 - (-\frac{1}{2})][0 + (-\frac{1}{2})]$
$0 - \frac{1}{4}$	$\frac{1}{2} \cdot (-\frac{1}{2})$
$-\frac{1}{4}$ =	$-\frac{1}{4}$

     iii. -4 for x; $.7$ for y

$x^2 - y^2$	$(x - y)(x + y)$
$(-4)^2 - .7^2$	$(-4 - .7)(-4 + .7)$
$16 - .49$	$-4.7 \cdot (-3.3)$
15.51 =	15.51

There is reason to believe that $x^2 - y^2$ and $(x - y)(x + y)$ are equivalent expressions.

Example: ii. $x \cdot x$; $2x$

     i. 0 for x

$x \cdot x$	$2x$
$0 \cdot 0$	$2 \cdot 0$
0 =	0

     ii. 2 for x

$x \cdot x$	$2x$
$2 \cdot 2$	$2 \cdot 2$
4 =	4

     iii. -5 for x

$x \cdot x$	$2x$
$-5 \cdot (-5)$	$2 \cdot (-5)$
25 $\neq$	-10

The last replacement is sufficient to dispel any suspicion that $x \cdot x$ and $2x$ are equivalent expressions. Explain why.

a. $x^2 + x$; $x(x + 1)$
   i. 2 for x
   ii. -3 for x
   iii. $\frac{1}{3}$ for x

b. $3x + 3y$; $3(x + y)$
   i. 5 for x, 1 for y
   ii. -2 for x, 0 for y
   iii. 1 for y, 7 for x

c. $-x - y$; $(x + y)(-1)$
   i. 5 for x, 2 for y
   ii. -1 for x, 2 for y
   iii. $\frac{1}{2}$ for x, $\frac{1}{3}$ for y

d. $x + x$; x^2
   i. 0 for x
   ii. 10 for x
   iii. -7 for x

e. $x + x$; $2x$
   i. 4 for x
   ii. -12 for x
   iii. 3.6 for x

f. $x \cdot x \cdot x$; $3x$
   i. 0 for x
   ii. 1 for x
   iii. -2 for x

g. $x \cdot x \cdot x$; x^3
   i. 1 for x
   ii. -2 for x
   iii. $-\frac{1}{3}$ for x

h. $x^2 \cdot x^2$; x^4
   i. 0 for x
   ii. -2 for x
   iii. 3 for x

i. $(-n)(-n)$; $-n^2$
   i. 0 for n
   ii. 1 for n
   iii. -2 for n

j. $(-n)(-n)$; $(-n)^2$
   i. 0 for n
   ii. 1 for n
   iii. -2 for n

k. $(-n)(-n)(-n)$; $-n^3$
   i. 0 for n
   ii. 1 for n
   iii. -2 for n

l. $(-n)(-n)(-n)$; $(-n)^3$
   i. 0 for n
   ii. 1 for n
   iii. -2 for n

m. $\dfrac{m}{m}$ $(m \neq 0)$; 1
   i. 3 for m
   ii. -10 for m
   iii. $\frac{1}{3}$ for m

n. $\left|\dfrac{c}{c}\right|$ $(c \neq 0)$; $\left|\dfrac{c}{c}\right|$ $(c \neq 0)$
   i. 5 for c
   ii. -3 for c
   iii. $\frac{1}{4}$ for c

o. $(a + b)^2$; $a^2 + b^2$
   i. 0 for a, 0 for b
   ii. 1 for a, 1 for b
   iii. 1 for a, 2 for b

p. $(a + b)^2$; $a^2 + 2ab + b^2$
   i. 1 for a, 2 for b
   ii. -3 for a, 4 for b
   iii. 5 for a, -1 for b

q. $\dfrac{d^3}{d^2} \ (d \neq 0); d$

   i. 3 for d

   ii. -2 for d

   iii. $\frac{1}{2}$ for d

u. $(a + b)^3; \ a^3 + b^3$

   i. 0 for a, 0 for b

   ii. 1 for a, 1 for b

   iii. -1 for a, 2 for b

r. $\dfrac{p^4}{p^2} \ (p \neq 0); p^2$

   i. 3 for p

   ii. -2 for p

   iii. $\frac{1}{2}$ for p

v. $(a + b)^3; \ a^3 + 3a^2b + 3ab^2 + b^3$

   i. 0 for a, 0 for b

   ii. 1 for a, 1 for b

   iii. -1 for a, 2 for b

s. $(a - b)^2; \ a^2 - b^2$

   i. 0 for a, 0 for b

   ii. 1 for a, 1 for b

   iii. 4 for a, 1 for b

w. $(a - b)^3; \ a^3 - b^3$

   i. 0 for a, 0 for b

   ii. 1 for a, 1 for b

   iii. -1 for a, 2 for b

t. $(a - b)^2; \ a^2 - 2ab + b^2$

   i. 0 for a, 0 for b

   ii. 1 for a, 1 for b

   iii. 4 for a, 1 for b

x. $(a - b)^3; \ a^3 - 3a^2b + 3ab^2 - b^3$

   i. 0 for a, 0 for b

   ii. 1 for a, 1 for b

   iii. -1 for a, 2 for b

PROVING EXPRESSIONS EQUIVALENT

Now that you know some properties of numbers and operations, you can prove that other true statements follow from these properties by logical reasoning. The process of reasoning from some accepted statements to other true statements is called *proof*. The properties we have accepted serve as foundations for the proofs. These properties are sometimes referred to as assumptions, axioms, or postulates.

Is the following statement true?

$$\forall_m \ 2m + 3m = 5m$$

In other words, are $2m + 3m$ and $5m$ equivalent expressions?

We already observed that, since the set of real numbers which we use as the replacement set is an infinite set, we cannot verify the truth of this statement. We will show that it is true by reasoning from assumed properties; that is, we start with $2m + 3m$ and hope to arrive at $5m$, each step being justified by the property listed on the right.

Proof

$$
\begin{aligned}
2m + 3m &= m \cdot 2 + m \cdot 3 && \text{CPM, used twice} \\
&= m(2 + 3) && \text{DPMA and Sym. Prop. Eq.} \\
&= m \cdot 5 && \text{Arith. fact} \\
&= 5m && \text{CPM}
\end{aligned}
$$

Thus, we proved that $\forall_m \ 2m + 3m = 5m$ or that $2m + 3m$ and $5m$ are equivalent expressions. Which of the two is the simpler expression?

Any statement which is proved to be true is called a *theorem*. Once a theorem is proved, it may be used in subsequent proofs to justify other statements.

EXERCISES

Prove each of the following. Use the form of writing as shown above and be sure to list the reason for each statement.

1. $\forall_x \ 3x + 15x = 18x$
2. $\forall_y \ -2y + 7y = 5y$
3. $\forall_z \ -3z + (-12z) = -15z$
4. $\forall_n \ n + 3n = 4n$ [HINT: $n = n \cdot 1$]
5. $\forall_m \ m(-1) + 5m = 4m$
6. $\forall_t \ t(-4) + t(-2) = -6t$

Distributivity and rearrangement

In Chapter 2 we stated the distributive property of multiplication over addition [DPMA].

$$\forall_x \forall_y \forall_z \ x(y + z) = (xy) + (xz)$$

This property is also called the *Left* Distributive Property of Multiplication over Addition, abbreviated LDPMA. Using LDPMA as a basis, we shall prove the following:

Theorem 1 $\forall_x \forall_y \forall_z \ (x + y)z = xz + yz$

Proof $(x + y)z = z(x + y)$ Why?
$= zx + zy$ Why?
$= xz + yz$ Why?

Thus, $\forall_x \forall_y \forall_z \ (x + y)z = (xz) + (yz)$

This is called the *Right* Distributive Property of Multiplication over Addition, abbreviated RDPMA.

The left and right distributive properties which we considered so far involved three numbers. Let us now investigate examples involving more than three numbers.

i. $2(5 + 3 + 4)$ $(2 \cdot 5) + (2 \cdot 3) + (2 \cdot 4)$
$2(12)$ $10 + 6 + 8$
24 24

Therefore, $2(5 + 3 + 4) = (2 \cdot 5) + (2 \cdot 3) + (2 \cdot 4)$

ii. $(-3)[-4 + 6 + (-7)]$ $(-3)(-4) + (-3)(6) + (-3)(-7)$
$-3(-5)$ $12 - 18 + 21$
15 15

Therefore, $(-3)[-4 + 6 + (-7)] = (-3)(-4) + (-3)(6) + (-3)(-7)$

iii. $(-\frac{1}{2})[4 + 7 + (-9)]$ $(-\frac{1}{2})(4) + (-\frac{1}{2})(7) + (-\frac{1}{2})(-9)$
$(-\frac{1}{2})(2)$ $-2 - 3\frac{1}{2} + 4\frac{1}{2}$
-1 -1

Therefore, $(-\frac{1}{2})[4 + 7 + (-9)] = (-\frac{1}{2})(4) + (-\frac{1}{2})(7) + (-\frac{1}{2})(-9)$

It appears that the following is true.

Theorem 2 $\forall_w \forall_x \forall_y \forall_z \; w(x + y + z) = wx + wy + wz$

Proof $w(x + y + z) = w[(x + y) + z]$ [See agreement on p. 35.]
       $= w(x + y) + wz$ LDPMA
       $= wx + wy + wz$ Why?

Thus, we have an extension of LDPMA to four numbers. It would be helpful also if we could deal with more than three numbers where the commutative and associative properties apply. For example, in computing the answer to $97 + 65 + 3 + 35$, we would save a lot of work if we would know that

$$97 + 65 + 3 + 35 = (97 + 3) + (65 + 35)$$

Explain why the last is easy to compute.
  We *can* prove that

$$97 + 65 + 3 + 35 = (97 + 3) + (65 + 35)$$

Proof $97 + 65 + 3 + 35 = [(97 + 65) + 3] + 35$
            [See agreement on p. 35.]
       $= [97 + (65 + 3)] + 35$ Why?
       $= [97 + (3 + 65)] + 35$ Why?
       $= [(97 + 3) + 65] + 35$ Why?
       $= (97 + 3) + (65 + 35)$ APA

This is a tedious way to get a result which is easily foreseen, since you can by now see a result which is a consequence of repeated applications of commutative and associative properties. For example, you should see that we could prove that

$$\forall_u \forall_w \forall_x \forall_y \forall_z \; u + w + x + y + z = z + w + x + u + y$$

In a similar fashion, we can handle expressions which involve both addition and multiplication. Examine each example below to see that the results can be justified by the commutative and associative properties of addition and of multiplication.

$$2(-3) + (-75) + 2(-7) + (-25) = 2(-3) + 2(-7) + (-75) + (-25)$$

$$9(-6) + 13(-2) + (-6)12 + (-2)(-13)$$
$$= 9(-6) + 12(-6) + 13(-2) + (-13)(-2)$$

$$\forall_x \forall_y \quad x + (-y) + (-x) + y = x + (-x) + y + (-y)$$

When we make this kind of rearrangement based on repeated applications of the commutative and associative properties, we will refer to it simply as "rearrangement".

EXERCISES

1. Prove: $\forall_u \forall_w \forall_x \forall_y \forall_z \quad u(w + x + y + z)$
$$= (uw) + (ux) + (uy) + (uz)$$

2. Prove: $\forall_w \forall_x \forall_y \forall_z \quad (w + x + y)z = (wz) + (xz) + (yz)$

3. Apply CPA and APA to obtain $2(-3) + 2(-7) + (-75) + (-25)$ from $2(-3) + (-75) + 2(-7) + (-25)$

4. Apply the necessary properties to obtain
$9(-6) + 12(-6) + 13(-2) + (-13)(-2)$
from $9(-6) + 13(-2) + (-6)12 + (-2)(-13)$

Then use the appropriate distributive property to simplify and compute the answer to $9(-6) + 12(-6) + 13(-2) + (-13)(-2)$.

5. Apply CPA repeatedly to obtain $x + (-x) + y + (-y)$ from $x + (-y) + (-x) + y$. Then use PAI to simplify $x + (-x) + y + (-y)$

6. True or false?

   a. $13 + 19 + 27 + 31 = (13 + 27) + (19 + 31)$

   b. $8 + 24 + 16 + 12 = (8 + 12) + (24 + 16)$

   c. $17 + 25 + (-7) + (-5) = [17 + (-7)] + [25 + (-5)]$

   d. $(-9) + 14 + (-24) + (-11) = [(-9) + (-11)] + [14 + (-24)]$

   e. $8 + 15 + 42 + 35 = 8 + 42 + 15 + 35$

   f. $2(4) + 3(7) + 4(5) + 7(6) = 3(7) + 4(5) + 7(6) + 2(4)$

   g. $9 + (-18) + (-19) + (-2) = (-18) + (-2) + 9 + (-19)$

   h. $8 + (-13) + (-8) + (13) = 13 + (-13) + 8 + (-8)$

   i. $(-4) + 7 + (-7) + 4 = 4 + (-4) + 7 + 7$

   j. $2(5) + 5(-2) + 3(4) + 4(-3) = 4(-3) + 3(4) + 5(-2) + 2(5)$

7. Tell whether or not the following are true for all replacements of the variables.

    a. $x + y + z + t = x + t + z + y$
    b. $t + y + (-t) + (-y) = y + (-y) + t + (-t)$
    c. $y + t + r + 2(-y) = y + 2(-y) + r + t$
    d. $2x + (-3)r + (-3)x + (-4)r = 2x + (-3)x + (-3)r + (-4)r$
    e. $9y + 3x + (-2)y + (-5)x = 3x + (-5)x + 9y + (-2)y$
    f. $7a + (-3)b = 3b + (-7)a$
    g. $(3 - 10)x = (10 - 3)x$

*8. Prove: $\forall_{x_0} \forall_{x_1} \forall_{x_2} \ldots \forall_{x_n} \; x_0(x_1 + x_2 + \ldots + x_n) =$
$$(x_0 x_1) + (x_0 x_2) + \ldots + (x_0 x_n)$$
[Read: "x_0" as "x sub-zero," "x_1" as "x sub-one," "x_n" as "x sub-n".]

Multiplication and division by -1

We are now ready to explore various patterns when operating with real numbers and to prove a number of theorems. These theorems will serve as a foundation for dealing with various algebraic expressions.

Observe the following:

$5(-1) = -5$
$-3(-1) = -(-3) = 3$
$\frac{1}{2}(-1) = -\frac{1}{2}$
$-\frac{4}{5}(-1) = -(-\frac{4}{5}) = \frac{4}{5}$

The pattern displayed by these examples is: $x(-1) = -x$. Replace x in $x(-1) = -x$ by 5, -3, $\frac{1}{2}$, and $-\frac{4}{5}$. Do you get the examples above?

Theorem 3 (Multiplication by -1) $\forall_x \; x(-1) = -x$
    We know from the property of opposites (additive inverses) that $\forall_x \; x + (-x) = 0$. If we can show that $\forall_x \; x + x(-1) = 0$, we would know that $x(-1)$ is the opposite of x and, therefore, equal to $-x$. We are assuming that each real number has only one opposite, which we shall prove later.

Proof
    $\begin{aligned} x + x(-1) &= x \cdot 1 + x(-1) && \text{P1M} \\ &= x[1 + (-1)] && \text{Why?} \\ &= x \cdot 0 && \text{PAI} \\ &= 0 && \text{Why?} \end{aligned}$

    Since $x + x(-1) = 0$, $x(-1)$ is the opposite of x, and, therefore, $x(-1) = -x$.

Now observe another pattern in these examples.

$$\frac{6}{-1} = -6 \qquad\qquad \frac{\frac{2}{3}}{-1} = -\frac{2}{3}$$

$$\frac{-4}{-1} = -(-4) = 4 \qquad\qquad \frac{-\frac{1}{4}}{-1} = -(-\frac{1}{4}) = \frac{1}{4}$$

This pattern is: $\dfrac{x}{-1} = -x$

Theorem 4 (Division by -1) $\forall_x \ \dfrac{x}{-1} = -x$

Proof $\qquad \dfrac{x}{-1} = x \cdot \left(\dfrac{1}{-1}\right)$ $\qquad\qquad$ Prop. div.

$\qquad\qquad\quad = x \cdot (-1)$ $\qquad\qquad\qquad \dfrac{1}{-1} = -1$

$\qquad\qquad\quad = -x$ $\qquad\qquad\qquad\quad$ Why?

EXERCISES

True or false?

1. $(-7)(-1) = -(-7)$

2. $\dfrac{-1.7}{-1} = -1.7$

3. $(-1)[-(-2)] = -2$

4. $\dfrac{-(-4)}{-1} = 4$

5. $-1[-3 + (-4)] = 3 + 4$

6. The opposite of -1 is $-(-1)$.

7. $\dfrac{5}{-1} + \dfrac{-5}{-1} = 0$

8. $\dfrac{7}{-1} + (-7)(-1) = 0$

9. $\dfrac{-7 + (-3)}{-1} = -10$

10. $\dfrac{-\frac{1}{2} + (-\frac{1}{2})}{-1} = -1$

Opposites of binomials

We now explore some other useful patterns. Observe the pattern in the following examples.

$$2 - 3 = -1 \qquad\qquad 3 - 2 = 1$$
$$5 - 2 = 3 \qquad\qquad 2 - 5 = -3$$
$$6 - 3 = 3 \qquad\qquad 3 - 6 = -3$$
$$2 - (-1) = 3 \qquad\qquad -1 - 2 = -3$$
$$-5 - 1 = -6 \qquad\qquad 1 - (-5) = 6$$
$$-4 - (-7) = 3 \qquad\qquad -7 - (-4) = -3$$

It appears that replacements in $x - y$ and $y - x$ yield opposites.

Theorem 5 (Opposite of $x - y$) $\forall_x \forall_y$ $y - x$ is the opposite of $x - y$.
If we prove that $(x - y) + (y - x) = 0$, then it means that
$y - x$ is the opposite of $x - y$.

Proof $(x - y) + (y - x) = [x + (-y)] + [y + (-x)]$ Prop. Subt.

$$= [x + (-x)] + [y + (-y)] \quad \text{Rearrange.}$$

$$= 0 \qquad\qquad\qquad \text{Why?}$$

Thus, $\forall_x \forall_y$ $y - x$ is the opposite of $x - y$. We may conclude that $-(x - y) = y - x$ *or* $(x - y) = -(y - x)$ for
every x and for every y.

Here are some examples that suggest another pattern.

$5 + 7 = 12$	$-5 + (-7) = -12$	$-(5 + 7) = -12$
$3 + (-6) = -3$	$-3 + 6 = 3$	$-[3 + (-6)] = 3$
$-4 + 9 = 5$	$4 + (-9) = -5$	$-(-4 + 9) = -5$
$-7 + (-6) = -13$	$7 + 6 = 13$	$-[-7 + (-6)] = 13$

It appears that $x + y$ and $(-x) + (-y)$ yield opposites for replacements
of x and y, and $(-x) + (-y) = -(x + y)$.

Theorem 6 (Opposite of $x + y$) $\forall_x \forall_y$ $(-x) + (-y)$ is the opposite of
$x + y$, or $(-x) + (-y) = -(x + y)$

If we prove that $(x + y) + [(-x) + (-y)] = 0$, then we
have proved that $(-x) + (-y)$ is the opposite of $(x + y)$,
which is $-(x + y)$.

Proof $(x + y) + [(-x) + (-y)]$

$$= [x + (-x)] + [y + (-y)] \qquad \text{Rearrangement}$$

$$= 0 \qquad\qquad\qquad\qquad\qquad \text{Why?}$$

Thus, $\forall_x \forall_y$ $(-x) + (-y) = -(x + y)$

EXERCISES

True or false?

1. The opposite of $7 - 4$ is $4 - 7$.
2. The opposite of $-216.3 + 17.65$ is $-17.65 + 216.3$.
3. The opposite of $\frac{3}{11} + \frac{4}{7}$ is $-\frac{4}{7} - \frac{3}{11}$.
4. $\forall_m \forall_n$ $-(-m + n) = -(n + m)$
5. $\forall_x \forall_y$ $-(y - x) = -[-(x - y)]$

6. $\forall_s \forall_t -(-s - t) = -s - t$
7. The opposite of $-14 + (-17.6)$ is $14 + 17.6$.
8. The opposite of $-(-\frac{1}{2}) - (-\frac{3}{7})$ is $-\frac{1}{2} + \frac{3}{7}$.
9. The opposite of $12.75 + 27.1$ is $-12.75 + (-27.1)$.
10. The opposite of -5 is $|-5|$.
11. The opposite of -5 is $|5|$.
12. The opposite of $|6|$ is $|-6|$.

Distributivity—multiplication and subtraction

Recall the following true statements from work with directed numbers.

$(-2)(3) = -6$ $\qquad\qquad$ $-[(2)(3)] = -6$
$(-4)(5) = -20$ $\qquad\qquad$ $-[(4)(5)] = -20$
$(-\frac{1}{3})(\frac{2}{5}) = -\frac{2}{15}$ $\qquad\qquad$ $-[(\frac{1}{3})(\frac{2}{5})] = -\frac{2}{15}$
$(-5)(\frac{3}{5}) = -3$ $\qquad\qquad$ $-[(5)(\frac{3}{5})] = -3$
$(3)(-4) = -12$ $\qquad\qquad$ $-[(-3)(-4)] = 12$
$(-2)(-3) = 6$ $\qquad\qquad$ $-[(2)(-3)] = 6$

This leads us to feel that $(-x)y$ and $-(xy)$ are equivalent expressions. We state another theorem and prove it.

Theorem 7 $\forall_x \forall_y (-x)y = -(xy)$

Proof $\quad (-x)y = [x \cdot (-1)]y$ $\qquad$ Why?
$\qquad\qquad = x \cdot [(-1) \cdot y]$ $\qquad$ Why?
$\qquad\qquad = x \cdot [y \cdot (-1)]$ $\qquad$ Why?
$\qquad\qquad = (xy)(-1)$ $\qquad$ Why?
$\qquad\qquad = -(xy)$ $\qquad$ Theorem 3

We shall now investigate distributivity in relation to multiplication and subtraction. Read carefully each detail in the examples below.

Examples: $\quad$ *i.* $4(5 - 2)$ $\qquad\qquad$ $(4 \cdot 5) - (4 \cdot 2)$
$\qquad\qquad\quad 4 \cdot 3$ $\qquad\qquad\qquad\quad 20 - 8$
$\qquad\qquad\quad 12$ $\qquad\qquad\qquad\qquad 12$

Therefore, $4(5 - 2) = (4 \cdot 5) - (4 \cdot 2)$.

$\quad\quad$ *ii.* $-5(-3 - 5)$ $\qquad\qquad$ $(-5)(-3) - (-5)(5)$
$\qquad\qquad -5(-8)$ $\qquad\qquad\qquad 15 - (-25)$
$\qquad\qquad 40$ $\qquad\qquad\qquad\qquad 40$

Therefore, $-5(-3 - 5) = (-5)(-3) - (-5)(5)$.

Example: *iii.* $\frac{1}{2}[-2 - (-10)]$ $(\frac{1}{2})(-2) - (\frac{1}{2})(-10)$
                $\frac{1}{2}(8)$ $-1 - (-5)$
                4 4

        Therefore, $-5(-3 - 5) = (-5)(-3) - (-5)(5)$.

It appears that the following is true.

$$\forall_x \, \forall_y \, \forall_z \quad x(y - z) = (xy) - (xz)$$

Theorem 8 (Left Distributivity of Multiplication over Subtraction)

$$\forall_x \, \forall_y \, \forall_z \quad x(y - z) = (xy) - (xz) \quad \text{[LDMS]}$$

Proof $x(y - z) = x[y + (-z)]$ Why?
                    $= (xy) + x(-z)$ Why?
                    $= (xy) + (-z)x$ Why?
                    $= (xy) + [-(zx)]$ Theorem 7
                    $= (xy) - (zx)$ Prop. Subt.
                    $= (xy) - (xz)$ Why?

EXERCISES

1. Prove: $\forall_x \, \forall_y \quad x(-y) = -(xy)$

2. Prove the Right Distributivity of Multiplication over Subtraction, that is, prove that $\forall_x \, \forall_y \, \forall_z \, (x - y)z = (xz) - (yz)$.

3. You are now familiar with four cases of distributivity: two cases involving multiplication and addition, and two involving multiplication and subtraction. Using the universal quantifier $\forall$ and the variables x, y, and z, state these four cases.

4. True or false?

  a. $\forall_p \quad 7p - 2p = 5p$
  b. $\forall_c \quad 3c - 7c = 4c$
  c. $\forall_u \quad \frac{1}{2}u - \frac{3}{4}u = -\frac{1}{4}u$
  d. $(-2)(-5) = -[2(-5)]$ is an example which fits Theorem 7.
  e. $\forall_x \, \forall_y \, (-x)(-y) = -[(-x)y]$
  f. $\forall_x \quad x \cdot 5 - x \cdot 7 = -2x$
  g. $\forall_y \quad y \cdot \frac{1}{2} - y \cdot \frac{1}{4} = -\frac{1}{4}y$

5. Prove: $\forall_x \quad x - x = 0$ [HINT: Use P1M, LDMS, and PZM.]

6. Prove: $\forall_w \, \forall_x \, \forall_y \, \forall_z \quad w(x - y - z) = (wx) - (wy) - (wz)$

*7. Prove: $\forall_{x_0} \, \forall_{x_1} \, \forall_{x_2} \ldots \forall_{x_n} \quad x_0(x_1 - x_2 - \ldots - x_n) =$
                                          $(x_0x_1) - (x_0x_2) - \ldots - (x_0x_n)$

SIMPLIFICATION OF EXPRESSIONS

When putting algebra to use, frequent occasions call for finding simple expressions which are equivalent to the given more involved expressions. The theorems we proved so far will prove helpful for this purpose. We will prove several more theorems and illustrate their use in simplifying expressions.

From our work with directed numbers we know the following is true.

$$-(-6) = 6 \qquad -(-\tfrac{1}{2}) = \tfrac{1}{2} \qquad -(-1.9) = 1.9$$

It appears that the following is true: $\forall_x - (-x) = x$

Theorem 9 $\forall_x - (-x) = x$

To prove this theorem, we need to prove that $-(-x)$ and $-x$ are opposites (additive inverses), that is, to prove that $-(-x) + (-x) = 0.$

Proof

$$\begin{aligned}
-(-x) + (-x) &= -[x \cdot (-1)] + x \cdot (-1) && \text{Theorem 3} \\
&= (-x) \cdot (-1) + x(-1) && \text{Theorem 7} \\
&= (-x + x)(-1) && \text{Why?} \\
&= 0 \cdot (-1) && \text{Why?} \\
&= 0 && \text{Why?}
\end{aligned}$$

Thus, $-(-x) + (-x)$ are opposites and, therefore, $\forall_x - (-x) = x.$

Our work with directed numbers would tell us that the following statements are true.

$(2)(3) = 6$	$-[(-2)(3)] = 6$
$(3)(4) = 12$	$-[(-3)(4)] = 12$
$(6)(5) = 30$	$-[(-6)(5)] = 30$
$(-2)(3) = -6$	$-[(2)(3)] = -6$
$(3)(-4) = -12$	$-[(-3)(-4)] = -12$
$(-4)(-6) = 24$	$-[(4)(-6)] = 24$

Thus, we are led to believe that xy and $-(-x)y$ are equivalent expressions.

Theorem 10 $\forall_x \forall_y -(-x)y = xy$

Proof   According to Theorem 9, $\forall_x - (-x) = x$

Therefore, $-(-x)y = xy$

We know from our work with directed numbers that the following statements are true.

$(4)(3) = 12$ $(-4)(-3) = 12$
$(2)(3) = 6$ $(-2)(-3) = 6$
$(5)(7) = 35$ $(-5)(-7) = 35$
$(-2)(3) = -6$ $(2)(-3) = -6$
$(4)(-3) = -12$ $(-4)(3) = -12$
$(-5)(-6) = 30$ $(5)(6) = 30$

Thus, we are led to believe that xy and $(-x)(-y)$ are equivalent.

Theorem 11 $\forall_x \forall_y$ $(-x)(-y) = xy$

Proof
$$
\begin{aligned}
(-x)(-y) &= [x \cdot (-1)][y \cdot (-1)] & &\text{Theorem 3}\\
&= (xy)[(-1)(-1)] & &\text{Rearrangement}\\
&= (xy) \cdot 1 & &(-1)(-1) = 1\\
&= xy & &\text{Why?}
\end{aligned}
$$

We shall now illustrate how the theorems we proved can be used in simplifying expressions.

Example: i.   Simplify $9x + 6y - 3x - 4y$
$\forall_x \forall_y$ $9x + 6y - 3x - 4y$
$$
\begin{aligned}
&= 9x + 6y + [-(3x)] + [-(4y)] & &\text{Prop. Subt.}\\
&= 9x + [-(3x)] + 6y + [-(4y)] & &\text{Rearrangement}\\
&= 9x + [(-3)x] + 6y + [(-4)y] & &\text{Theorem 7}\\
&= [9 + (-3)]x + [6 + (-4)]y & &\text{Why?}\\
&= 6x + 2y & &\text{Why?}
\end{aligned}
$$
Thus, $\forall_x \forall_y$ $9x + 6y - 3x - 4y = 6x + 2y$

As you become proficient in dealing with expressions of this kind, you will write down the minimum number of steps. Would you be able to do this problem by writing down only the following steps?

$$9x + 6y - 3x - 4y = (9x - 3x) + (6y - 4y)$$
$$= 6x + 2y$$

It is important that, whenever asked, you would be able to fill in all the steps and justify each step.

Example: ii. Simplify $6.7a + 4.6b - 4.3a - 2.4b$
We shall take shortcuts in finding a simpler equivalent expression. If necessary, fill in the detailed steps.
$\forall_a \forall_b$ $6.7a + 4.6b - 4.3a - 2.4b$
$$
\begin{aligned}
&= (6.7a - 4.3a) + (4.6b - 2.4b)\\
&= 2.4a + 2.2b
\end{aligned}
$$

Examples: *iii.* Simplify $-3(2x + y) - 4(x - y)$

$\forall_x \forall_y \; -3(2x + y) - 4(x - y)$
$= (-3)(2x) + (-3)y - (4x - 4y)$
$= -6x - 3y - 4x + 4y$
$= (-6x - 4x) + (-3y + 4y)$
$= -10x + y$

iv. Give a reason for each step in the following proof.

$\forall_s \forall_x \forall_y \; s - (x - y)$
$= s + [-(x - y)]$
$= s + (y - x)$
$= (s + y) - x$

v. Give a reason for each step in the following proof.

$\forall_x \forall_y \; x + y - (-x + y)$
$= x + y + [-(-x + y)]$
$= x + y + \{-[y + (-x)]\}$
$= x + y + [-(y - x)]$
$= x + y + (x - y)$
$= (x + x) + (y - y)$
$= 2x + 0$
$= 2x$

EXERCISES

1. Prove each of the following:

  a. $\forall_x \; 10x - 4x = 6x$
  b. $\forall_y \; 3y - 7y = -4y$
  c. $\forall_m \; \frac{1}{2}m - \frac{3}{4}m = -\frac{1}{4}m$
  d. $\forall_m \forall_n \; 10m + 6n - 4m - 2n = 6m + 4n$
  e. $\forall_r \forall_s \; 6rs - 2rs = 4rs$
  f. $\forall_y \forall_r \forall_s \; 4 + 3y - 2rs - 4 + 7rs - 4y = 5rs - y$

2. Find simpler equivalent expressions for the following:

  a. $5x - 3x$
  b. $7y - 10y$
  c. $\frac{1}{2}a - \frac{1}{4}a$
  d. $\frac{1}{3}b - \frac{5}{6}b$
  e. $1.5m - .6m$
  f. $3.7n - 4.8n$
  g. $9xy - 4xy$
  h. $2mn - 16mn$
  i. $5x - 3y + 6x$

  j. $6n - 2t + 3n - t$
  k. $x - 2y - x + y$
  l. $c - 3d - c + 4$
  m. $3r + 5s - 6 - 7r + 4s + 4$
  n. $-u + 3t + 2w - 5 - 3t$
  o. $-x - 3x - 5x + 7x - 2x$
  p. $3x - 4y - 5x + 7y$
  q. $1.7r + 3.2v - 4.5 + 2.5r$
  r. $\frac{4}{3}x - 7 + \frac{2}{5}y - \frac{3}{4}x + 5$

    s. $-4.9r - 6.7r + .2s - 5.8r$ **w.** $10xy - 5rs - 3xy + 9rs - xy$

    t. $4st + 5xy - 7st - 3xy + 4$ **x.** $6 - 3x + 5y - 9 + 6x - 7y$

    u. $3am - 11am + 3c - 17c$ **y.** $4 + 3y - 2rs + (-4) + 7rs - 4y$

    v. $4xy - 2xy + 6xy$ **z.** $5uv + 7uv - 9uv$

3.   Give simpler equivalent expressions for each of the following:

    a. $(-3)(8x)$ **f.** $(-x)(-3y)(-4)$

    b. $(-6)(-1)(r)$ **g.** $(1.4y)(-3x)$

    c. $5(s)(-3)$ **h.** $(-6.3x)(-y_p)(5)$

    d. $-6.2(-3x)$ **i.** $-1.5(-3r)$

    e. $-(-5x)(3y)$ **j.** $(-2)(-s)(-5)$

4.   Tell whether or not the following are true for all replacements of the variables.

    a. $a - b = -(b - a)$

    b. $-(x + y) = -x + y$

    c. $-2 + x = x - 2$

    d. $(-1)(a - 3) = 3 - a$

    e. $(-x + y - 1)(-1) = -x + y + 1$

    f. $(-2)(x - 6) = 12 - 2x$

    g. $(x - y)(r - s) = -(y - x)(r - s)$

    h. $-y = -(-y)$

    i. $-[(-x) + y] = x - y$

    j. $(r - s)(x - y) = (s - r)(y - x)$

    k. $-(x - y) = -x - y$

    l. $-y - x = -x - y$

    m. $x - y = -y + x$

    n. $-[(-x) + (-y)] = x + y$

    o. $x + (-y) = -[y + (-x)]$

    p. $-[-(-x)] = -x$

    q. $-[-(x)] + (-x) = 0$

    r. $-[(-x) + x] = x$

    s. $(-x)yz = -[(-x)yz]$

    t. $xy(-z) = -xyz$

    u. $(r - s)(x - y)(w - v) = -(s - r)(x - y)(w - v)$

    v. $r + s - (x + y) = -x + r + s - y$

5.   Tell whether or not the following are true for all replacements of the variables.

    a. $x - y - (x + y) = 0$

    b. $2r + 3s - (2r - 4s) = 7s$

    c. $7x - (3x + y) - (2x - 2y) = 2x$

d. $12x - 2(3x + 4) = 6x + 8$

e. $4.3r - 6(1.8r - .3) = 6.5r + 1.8$

f. $3s - (4s + t) - 2(3s - t) = -7s + t$

g. $3x - [13x - (4x + 5)] = -6x + 5$

h. $3y - 2[3x + 5 - (2x + 4y - 5)] = -2x + 11y - 20$

i. $5x - 3[2x - 2y - (3x + 4y)] = 8x - 18y$

j. $5(3x - 2y) - 2(2x + y) = 11x - 12y$

6. Find simpler equivalent expressions for the following:

a. $2(a + b) + 4(a - b)$

b. $-3(x - y) + (x + y)$

c. $4(t - u) + (-2)(t - u)$

d. $\frac{1}{2}(2m - 4n) + \frac{1}{3}(9m + 12n)$

e. $-(2x - 3y) + (-4)(y - x)$

f. $\frac{1}{4}(8y + 12z) - (z + y)$

g. $(2c - d)(-4) + 9c$

h. $(x - y)(-2) + (2x + 3y)(-1)$

i. $(2p - 3s) - (3s - 2p)$

j. $2(x + 2y) - (-2)(x + 2y)$

k. $4(2k - m) - (8k - 4m)$

l. $0.1(10t + 20n) - 0.2(10t + 20n)$

m. $0.5(2h - 4k) + 0.6(10h + 20k)$

n. $3(x + 2y + 3z) - 2(3x + 2y + z)$

o. $-4(2a + b - 3c) + 3(a + b)$

p. $5(9 + 6x + y) - 3(x - y)$

From word phrases to mathematical phrases

As you gain ability to deal with more complicated algebraic expressions, you will be able to translate more complicated word phrases into mathematical phrases. Below are some practice exercises. Learning to translate them freely will help you solve problems.

EXERCISES

For each word phrase, write the correct mathematical phrase.

Examples: *i.* the number of square units in a square with a side of x units: x^2

ii. the sum of x and twice y: $x + 2y$

iii. the sum of n and 3, divided by -2: $\dfrac{n + 3}{-2}$

iv. the sum of x and y, multiplied by the difference of x and y: $(x + y)(x - y)$

1. the number of units in the perimeter of a square with a side of m units

2. the number of units in the perimeter of a rectangle with the length of x units and the width of y units

3. the number of units in the circumference of a circle with a radius of r units (Give the answer in terms of π.)

4. the number of square units in the area of a circle with a radius of s units (Give the answer in terms of π.)

5. the number of units in the perimeter of a regular pentagon with a side of k units

6. the sum of twice n and three times k

7. the difference of three times t and 4 times u

8. one-third of x added to one-fourth of p

9. the opposite of the sum of x and y

10. the opposite of the difference of twice u and three times r

11. the sum of the absolute value of c and of the absolute value of d

12. the absolute value of the sum of x and y

13. the sum of t squared and v squared

14. the sum of t and v, squared

15. the sum of $x - 2$ and $3y + z$

16. three less than x squared

17. .3 less than $6r$

18. the sum of x and y, divided by the difference of x and y

19. the quotient of x and the opposite of y

20. the reciprocal of $3a - 5$

21. the sum of the reciprocal of a and b

22. the reciprocal of the sum of m and n

23. If Sally is $(5x + 1)$ years older than Bonnie is and if Bonnie is $(y - 2)$ years old, how old is Sally?

24. If Ken was $(2y + 3)$ years old five years ago, how old will he be nine years from now?

25. worth in cents of $(4y - 1)$ nickels

26. number of inches in $7t$ feet

27. number of feet in $2y$ inches

28. number of quarts in $3x$ gallons

29. number of feet in $(x - 1)$ miles

30. number of miles in $(5x + 7y)$ feet

PROPERTIES AND THEOREMS

■ *Left Distributive Property of Multiplication over Addition* [LDPMA]
$$\forall_x \forall_y \forall_z \; x(y + z) = (xy) + (xz)$$

Theorem 1 (Right Distributive Property of Multiplication over Addition [RDPMA])
$$\forall_x \forall_y \forall_z \; (x + y)z = (xz) + (yz)$$

Theorem 2 $\forall_w \forall_x \forall_y \forall_z \; w(x + y + z) = wx + wy + wz$

Theorem 3 (Multiplication by -1) $\forall_x \; x(-1) = -x$

Theorem 4 (Division by -1) $\forall_x \; \dfrac{x}{-1} = -x$

Theorem 5 (Opposite of $x - y$) $\forall_x \forall_y \; -(x - y) = y - x$

Theorem 6 (Opposite of $x + y$) $\forall_x \forall_y \; -(x + y) = (-x) + (-y)$

Theorem 7 $\forall_x \forall_y \; (-x)y = -(xy)$

Theorem 8 Left Distributivity of Multiplication over Subtraction [LDMS]
$$\forall_x \forall_y \forall_z \; x(y - z) = (xy) - (xz)$$
Right Distributivity of Multiplication over Subtraction [RDMS]
$$\forall_x \forall_y \forall_z \; (x - y)z = (xz) - (yz)$$

Theorem 9 $\forall_x \; -(-x) = x$

Theorem 10 $\forall_x \forall_y \; -(-x)y = xy$

Theorem 11 $\forall_x \forall_y \; (-x)(-y) = xy$

VOCABULARY

Use each of the following correctly in a sentence. Numerals in the parentheses refer to pages where these words were used. If you are not sure of the meaning of any word, turn to the indicated page and refresh your memory.

binomial (120)
equivalent expressions (120)
expression (119)
Left Distributive Property of Multiplication over Addition [LDPMA] (125)
Left Distributivity Property of Multiplication over Subtraction [LDMS] (132)
monomial (120)
open expression (120)
polynomial (120)

proof (124)
Right Distributive Property of Multiplication over Addition [RDPMA] (125)
Right Distributive Property of Multiplication over Subtraction [RDMS] (132)
simplification (121)
term (119)
theorem (125)
trinomial (120)
variable (119)

REVIEW EXERCISES

1.   Classify each of the following as either a monomial, a binomial, or a trinomial (all letters are variables).

a. $5x$
b. $-\frac{1}{3}abc$
c. $x + y$
d. $5 - x$
e. 9
f. -10
g. -3.6
h. $a + b + c$

i. $-3.1mpn$
j. $xy - xz$
k. $\frac{1}{2}x + \frac{1}{3}m + \frac{1}{4}p$
l. $\frac{4}{7}$
m. $3y - 15$
n. $3mn - \frac{1}{2}rs + xyz$
o. $9 - x - n$
p. $26mprx$

2.   Find the value of each expression for the following values of x and y.

i. -1 for x, 3 for y *ii.* 0 for x, 1 for y *iii.* $\frac{1}{2}$ for x, $\frac{1}{3}$ for y

a. $x - y$
b. $x^2 - y^2$
c. $x(x + y)$
d. $x^3 - y^3$

e. $\dfrac{x + y}{x - y}$

f. $\dfrac{1}{x^2 + y^2}$

3. For each statement in the left column give the letter of the property or definition from the right column which is illustrated by the statement.

(1) $1.5 + (-3.7) = -3.7 + 1.5$

a. commutative property of multiplication [CPM]

(2) $[(-2)4](-6) = (-2)[4(-6)]$

b. closure property of the set of natural numbers [ClPN]

(3) $-5 \cdot (-\frac{1}{5}) = 1$

c. left distributive property of multiplication over addition [LDPMA]

(4) $-497 \cdot 1 = -497$
(5) $-29.38 + 29.38 = 0$
(6) $999.87 \times 0 = 0$
(7) $(\frac{1}{2} + \frac{1}{3})\frac{1}{4} = (\frac{1}{2} \cdot \frac{1}{4}) + (\frac{1}{3} \cdot \frac{1}{4})$

d. symmetric property of equality
e. definition of division
f. property of division
g. commutative property of addition [CPA]

(8) $9 + [(-1) + 4]$
$= [9 + (-1)] + 4$
(9) $-299 + 0 = -299$

h. property of one for division [P1D]
i. associative property of multiplication [APM]

(10) $2[(-3) + 5] = 2(-3) + 2 \cdot 5$
(11) $(1 - 5)3 = 1 \times 3 - 5 \times 3$

j. definition of subtraction
k. property of zero for addition [PZA]

(12) $4 + 9$ is a natural number.
(13) $34.67 \div 1 = 34.67$

l. property of subtraction
m. property of zero for multiplication [PZM]

(14) If $4 = 5 + (-1)$,
then $5 + (-1) = 4$
(15) $(-2)(-7) = (-7)(-2)$

n. property of one for multiplication [P1M]
o. associative property of addition [APA]

(16) $(-2)(5 - 7)$
$= -2 \times 5 - (-2)(7)$

p. right distributive property of multiplication over addition [RDPMA]

(17) $3 - (-1) = 4$ is equivalent to $4 + (-1) = 3$

q. left distributive property of multiplication over subtraction [LDMS]

(18) $9 \div (-5) = 9 \cdot (-\frac{1}{5})$

r. right distributive property of multiplication over subtraction [RDMS]

(19) $12 \div 3 = 4$ is equivalent to $4 \times 3 = 12$

s. property of multiplicative inverses (reciprocals) [PMI]

(20) $3 - (-4) = 3 + 4$

t. property of additive inverses (opposites) [PAI]

4. Prove each of the following, stating the reason for each step in the proof.

   a. $\forall_x \ 2x + 4x = 6x$
   b. $\forall_y \ \frac{1}{2}y - \frac{1}{3}y = \frac{1}{6}y$
   c. $\forall_n \ 2n - 7n = -5n$
   d. $\forall_m \forall_n \ 3m + 2n - 7m + 3n = -4m + 5n$
   e. $\forall_s \forall_t \ st - 4st = -3st$

5. True or false?

   a. $-2(-3 - 6) = 6 - 6$
   b. $\forall_x \ -(-x)$ is the opposite of $-x$
   c. $\dfrac{-8}{-1} = -8$
   d. The opposite of $8 - 5$ is $5 - 8$
   e. The opposite of $-7 - 3$ is $-3 - (-7)$
   f. $\forall_x \forall_y \ x - y$ is the opposite of $y - x$
   g. $\forall_n \ n - 4m = 3m$
   h. $\forall_x \forall_y \ x + y$ is the opposite of $|-(x + y)|$
   i. $\forall_x \forall_y \ (-x)(-y) = xy$
   j. $\forall_x \ 2x - x = x$
   k. $-1(3 - 5) = -1 \times 3 - 1 \times (-5)$
   l. $\forall_s \ 1 - 2s = -(2s - 1)$
   m. $\forall_t \forall_u \ -(t + u) = (t + u)(-1)$
   n. $\forall_x \forall_y \ (-1)(x + y) = (-x) + (-y)$
   o. $-(2 - 3) = -1$
   p. $-(\frac{1}{3} - \frac{1}{2}) = \frac{1}{6}$

6. Find simpler equivalent expressions for the following:

   a. $9y - 5y$
   b. $12x - 4x$
   c. $24a - a$
   d. $2m - 5m$
   e. $\frac{1}{2}n - \frac{3}{4}n$
   f. $\frac{1}{4}p - \frac{1}{8}p$
   g. $3.7h - 1.3h$
   h. $1.2s - 3.9s$
   i. $3t - 5t + 7t$
   j. $3xy + 12xy$
   k. $2x - 5y + 3x$

   l. $a - 3k + 4a + 5k$
   m. $7c - 4d + 2c + d$
   n. $4ay - 2bx - 6ay + 3bx$
   o. $3mv - 2nt - 3mv - 2nt$
   p. $4 - 2ax + 4ay + 6ax - 3ay$
   q. $(-4)(-2x) + \frac{1}{2}(-8x)$
   r. $3(-t)(-5)(t) + t$
   s. $-(a - b) + (a + b)$
   t. $-(3x + 4y) + 2(2y - x)$
   u. $2(u+v+w) - 3(-2u-3v-4w)$

7.   Tell whether or not each of the following is true for all replacements of the variables.

    a. $x - y = -(y - x)$
    b. $-(a + b) = (-a) + (-b)$
    c. $3 + t = -(t - 3)$
    d. $(-2)(4 - u) = 2u + 8$
    e. $-(x + y + z) = (-x) + y + z$
    f. $(a + b)(c + d) = -(a + b)[-(c + d)]$
    g. $-n = -(-n)$
    h. $x(-y) = (-x)y$
    i. $-x + [-(-x)] = 0$
    j. $-1(-r - s) = r - s$
    k. $(a - b)(c - d) = (b - a)(d - c)$

8.   For each word phrase, write the correct mathematical phrase.

    a. the number of units in the perimeter of an equilateral triangle with the side of n units long

    b. the number of units in the perimeter of a rectangle with the width of a units and the length of b units

    c. the sum of twice x and three times y

    d. the quotient of a squared and b cubed

    e. If Tim is n years old now, how old was he three years ago?

    f. If Mary is $(2x - 1)$ years old now, how old will she be $(x + 3)$ years from now?

    g. worth in cents of $3x$ dimes

    h. number of inches in $2y$ feet

    i. number of feet in $(x - y)$ miles

CHAPTER TEST

1.   Find the value of each expression for the following values of a and b.

    i. -2 for a; 2 for b *ii.* -1 for a; 5 for b *iii.* $-\frac{1}{2}$ for a; $\frac{1}{4}$ for b

    a. $a + b$ **d.** $-2(a - b)$

    b. $(a - b)(a + b)$ **e.** $\frac{1}{2}(2a + 3b)$

    c. $\dfrac{a + b}{a - b}$ **f.** $\dfrac{1}{a^2 + b^2}$

2. Classify each of the following as either a monomial, a binomial, or a trinomial (all letters are variables).

a. $x + y$

b. $4m$

c. $-\frac{1}{2}nry$

d. $2x - y - z$

e. 26

f. $4.5a - 1.2b + 3.6c$

g. $\frac{1}{3}n - \frac{1}{4}m + \frac{1}{5}s$

h. $3xyz - 2ab$

3. Name the property illustrated by each example.

a. $3 \times (4 - 6) = (3 \times 4) - (3 \times 6)$

b. $-3 + 7 = 7 + (-3)$

c. $-\frac{4}{15} \times 1 = -\frac{4}{15}$

d. $37.65 + 0 = 37.65$

e. $[(-4)(-3)](-9) = (-4)[(-3)(-9)]$

f. $-\frac{7}{12} \times 0 = 0$

4. Prove each of the following, stating the reason for each step in the proof.

a. $\forall_n\ 5n + 7n = 12n$

b. $\forall_x \forall_y\ 3x + 4y - 5x - 5y = -2x - y$

c. $\forall_m \forall_n\ 2(m + n) - 3(2m - n) = -4m + 5n$

5. True or false?

a. $\forall_x\ -2(5 - x) = -10 - 2x$

b. $-(3 - 8) = 5$

c. The opposite of $-9 + 4$ is $-4 - 9$.

d. $\forall_x\ 5x - 12x = 7x$

e. $\forall_r \forall_s\ (r - s)(-r) = r(s - r)$

f. $\forall_u\ 3u - 4u + 5u = 4u$

g. $-(\frac{1}{2} - \frac{1}{3}) = \frac{1}{3} - \frac{1}{2}$

h. $-2(5 - 13) = 2(13 - 5)$

6. For each word phrase, write the correct mathematical phrase.

a. the number of units in the perimeter of a regular octagon with the measure of each side equal to $3x$ units

b. the sum of twice n and three times m

c. number of pennies in $5x$ quarters

d. number of yards in $4n$ miles

e. the quotient of the sum of x and y and the difference of x and y

7. Find simpler equivalent expressions for the following:

    a. $12n - 9n$

    b. $m + 7m$

    c. $4x - 5x - 6x$

    d. $3(-6)t$

    e. $\frac{1}{2}ax - \frac{1}{4}ax$

    f. $5(x - y) - 2(x + y)$

    g. $-(4a - b) - (2b - 3a)$

    h. $2(h + 2k - 4) - 3(5 - k + h)$

    i. $-4(a + 2b + 3c) + 3(c + a + b)$

BIBLIOGRAPHY

Hogben, L. *Mathematics for the Million.* New York: W. W. Norton and Company, Inc., 1951.

Johnson, Donovan A., and Glenn, William H. *Sets, Sentences, and Operations.* St. Louis: Webster Publishing Company, 1960.

Kane, Robert B. "Linear Programming, An Aid to Decision Making." *The Mathematics Teacher.* March, 1960. pp. 177-179.

Lichtenberg, Donovan, and Zweng, Marilyn. "Linear Programming Problems for First-Year Algebra." *The Mathematics Teacher.* March, 1960. pp. 171-176.

Nichols, Eugene D.; Kalin, Robert; and Garland, Henry. *Equations and Inequalities* (A Programed Unit). New York: Holt, Rinehart and Winston, Inc., 1963.

School Mathematics Study Group. *First Course in Algebra.* New Haven: Yale University Press, 1961. pp. 77-96.

Titchmarsh, E. C. *Mathematics for the General Reader.* New York: Doubleday & Company, Inc., 1959. pp. 34-47.

Whitehead, Alfred North. *An Introduction to Mathematics.* New York: Oxford University Press, 1958. pp. 7-13, 39-60.

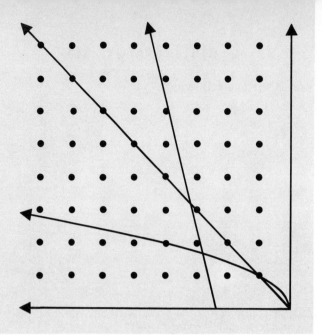

CHAPTER 6

Open Rational Expressions

THREE PATTERNS IN MULTIPLICATION OF RATIONAL NUMBERS

In arithmetic you learned various rules for operations with natural numbers. All of these rules have their foundations in the basic properties of numbers and their operations. We are going to combine our new knowledge of variables with basic properties of numbers and operations to justify some of these rules for operations with rational numbers.

We know that the following statements are true.

$$\frac{2 \cdot 3}{7} = \frac{6}{7} \qquad\qquad \left(\frac{2}{7}\right) \cdot 3 = \frac{6}{7}$$

$$\frac{7 \cdot 3}{11} = \frac{21}{11} \qquad\qquad \left(\frac{7}{11}\right) \cdot 3 = \frac{21}{11}$$

$$\frac{3 \cdot (-4)}{2} = -6 \qquad\qquad \frac{3}{2} \cdot (-4) = -6$$

$$\frac{-5 \cdot (-4)}{2} = 10 \qquad\qquad \frac{-5}{2} \cdot (-4) = 10$$

146

This leads us to surmise that

$$\frac{xz}{y} \text{ and } \left(\frac{x}{y}\right) \cdot z \quad (y \neq 0)$$

are equivalent expressions. We prove this as a theorem.

Theorem 1 $\forall_x \forall_{y \neq 0} \forall_z \quad \dfrac{xz}{y} = \left(\dfrac{x}{y}\right)(z)$

Proof $\dfrac{xz}{y} = (xz)\left(\dfrac{1}{y}\right)$ Prop. Div.

$\quad\quad\quad = \left(x \cdot \dfrac{1}{y}\right)(z)$ Rearrangement

$\quad\quad\quad = \left(\dfrac{x}{y}\right)(z)$ Prop. Div.

Now you prove

Theorem 2 $\forall_x \forall_{y \neq 0} \forall_z \quad \dfrac{xz}{y} = (x)\left(\dfrac{z}{y}\right)$

Now observe the pattern in the following examples.

$$\frac{2 \cdot 3}{7} = \frac{6}{7} \qquad\qquad \frac{1}{7} \cdot (2 \cdot 3) = \frac{6}{7}$$

$$\frac{7 \cdot 3}{11} = \frac{21}{11} \qquad\qquad \frac{1}{11} \cdot (7 \cdot 3) = \frac{21}{11}$$

$$\frac{2 \cdot (-6)}{4} = -3 \qquad\qquad \frac{1}{4} \cdot [2 \cdot (-6)] = -3$$

$$\frac{-6 \cdot (-3)}{2} = 9 \qquad\qquad \frac{1}{2} \cdot [-6 \cdot (-3)] = 9$$

The pattern displayed by these examples is

$$\frac{xz}{y} = \frac{1}{y}(xz) \quad (y \neq 0)$$

Supply the reason for each step in the proof.

Theorem 3 $\forall_x \forall_{y \neq 0} \forall_z \quad \dfrac{xz}{y} = \left(\dfrac{1}{y}\right)(xz)$

Proof $\dfrac{xz}{y} = (xz)\dfrac{1}{y}$ Why?

$\quad\quad\quad = \dfrac{1}{y}(xz)$ Why?

We can summarize these three theorems as follows:

$$\forall_x \forall_{y \neq 0} \forall_z \quad \frac{xz}{y} = \left(\frac{x}{y}\right)(z) = (x)\left(\frac{z}{y}\right) = \left(\frac{1}{y}\right)(xz)$$

EXERCISES

1. True or false?

a. $\dfrac{9 \cdot 3}{4} = \dfrac{9}{4} \cdot 3$

b. $\dfrac{-2 \cdot 5}{11} = \dfrac{1}{11}(-10)$

c. $\dfrac{5 \cdot 6}{7} = \dfrac{5}{7} \cdot \dfrac{6}{7}$

d. $\frac{1}{3}(5 \cdot 7) = \dfrac{35}{3}$

e. $\dfrac{(-5)(-11)}{12}$
$= \dfrac{1}{12} \cdot \left(-\dfrac{11}{12}\right) \cdot \left(-\dfrac{5}{12}\right)$

f. $\dfrac{3}{7}(-4) = \dfrac{-4 \cdot 3}{7}$

g. $\dfrac{4 \cdot 9}{-1} = (-4)(-9)$

h. $\frac{1}{-2} \cdot [(-3)(-5)] = (-3)(\frac{-5}{-2})$

i. $\dfrac{-3}{-11}(-6) = \dfrac{-6}{-11} \cdot \dfrac{-3}{-11}$

j. $\frac{1}{-9}[(-2)(-9)] = -2$

k. $3(-8) \cdot \frac{1}{-3} = -8$

l. $\dfrac{4 \cdot 9}{-4} = -9$

m. $(-12)(\frac{5}{12}) = 5$

n. $\dfrac{25 \cdot (-6)}{50} = -12$

o. $\dfrac{(-10)(-20)}{-200} = 1$

p. $\forall_a \forall_{b=0} \dfrac{ab}{b} = a$

q. $\forall_a \forall_{b=0} \frac{1}{b}[(-a)(-b)] = -a$

2. Apply CPM to the right side of each of the following to obtain another equivalent pattern.

a. $\dfrac{xz}{y} = \dfrac{x}{y}(z)$ **b.** $\dfrac{xz}{y} = (x)\left(\dfrac{z}{y}\right)$ **c.** $\dfrac{xz}{y} = \left(\dfrac{1}{y}\right)(xz)$

3. Give three different expressions equivalent to the following:

Example: $\dfrac{3(6)}{5}$

$(\frac{3}{5})(6)$; $\frac{1}{5}[3(6)]$; $3(\frac{6}{5})$

a. $\dfrac{(5)(6)}{7}$ **d.** $\frac{1}{3}(4 \times 5)$ **g.** $\dfrac{(4)(9)}{7}$

b. $\dfrac{(3)(7)}{5}$ **e.** $\frac{4}{7} \cdot (6)$ **h.** $\frac{1}{4}(3 \cdot 9)$

c. $8 \cdot (\frac{7}{6})$ **f.** $9(\frac{7}{8})$ **i.** $5(\frac{7}{6})$

Two more patterns in multiplication of rational numbers

You know from working with rational numbers that the following statements are true.

$\frac{1}{2} \cdot \frac{1}{3} = \frac{1}{6}$ $\qquad\qquad$ $\frac{1}{-2} \cdot \frac{1}{4} = \frac{1}{-8}$

$\frac{1}{5} \cdot \frac{1}{4} = \frac{1}{20}$ $\qquad\qquad$ $\frac{1}{-3} \cdot \frac{1}{-5} = \frac{1}{15}$

$\frac{1}{6} \cdot \frac{1}{3} = \frac{1}{18}$ $\qquad\qquad$ $\frac{1}{6} \cdot \frac{1}{-3} = \frac{1}{-18}$

We are led to guess that $\left(\frac{1}{x}\right)\left(\frac{1}{y}\right)$ and $\frac{1}{xy}$ might be equivalent expressions.

We know that

$$\forall_{x=0} \, \forall_{y=0} \left(\frac{1}{xy}\right)(xy) = 1$$

is true by the Property of Reciprocals. If we could show that

$$\forall_{x=0} \, \forall_{y=0} \left[\left(\frac{1}{x}\right)\left(\frac{1}{y}\right)\right] \cdot xy = 1$$

is true, we would know that $\left(\frac{1}{x}\right)\left(\frac{1}{y}\right)$ and $\frac{1}{xy}$ are equivalent expressions. We will assume for now (but prove later) that every real number except zero has a unique reciprocal.

Proof

$$\left[\left(\frac{1}{x}\right)\left(\frac{1}{y}\right)\right]xy$$

$$= \left[x\left(\frac{1}{x}\right)\right]\left[y\left(\frac{1}{y}\right)\right] \qquad \text{Rearrangement}$$

$$= (1) \cdot (1) \qquad \text{Why?}$$

$$= 1 \qquad \text{Why?}$$

This proof results in the following theorem.

Theorem 4 $\forall_{x=0} \, \forall_{y=0} \left(\frac{1}{x}\right)\left(\frac{1}{y}\right) = \frac{1}{xy}$

Is $\left(\frac{x}{y}\right) \cdot \left(\frac{r}{s}\right) = \frac{xr}{ys}$, where $y \neq 0$, $s \neq 0$, true for all values of x, y, r and s?

Proof

$$\left(\frac{x}{y}\right)\left(\frac{r}{s}\right) = \left[x\left(\frac{1}{y}\right)\right]\left[r\left(\frac{1}{s}\right)\right] \qquad \text{Prop. div.}$$

$$= x\left[\left(\frac{1}{y}\right)r\right]\left(\frac{1}{s}\right) \qquad \text{Why?}$$

$$= x\left[r\left(\frac{1}{y}\right)\right]\left(\frac{1}{s}\right) \qquad \text{Why?}$$

$$= (xr)\left(\frac{1}{y} \cdot \frac{1}{s}\right) \qquad \text{Why?}$$

$$= (xr)\left(\frac{1}{ys}\right) \qquad \text{Why?}$$

$$= \frac{xr}{ys} \qquad \text{Why?}$$

Hence we have proved the theorem stated on the top of the next page.

Theorem 5 $\forall_x \forall_{y=0} \forall_r \forall_{s=0} \left(\dfrac{x}{y}\right)\left(\dfrac{r}{s}\right) = \dfrac{xr}{ys}$

You, no doubt, observed that the theorems we have proved do not tell you anything new about work with rational numbers. You have really been using these theorems with rational numbers all along. The point is, however, that now you are able to *derive* these theorems from other known facts. Proving theorems is perhaps the most typical work that a mathematician does.

EXERCISES

1. Many times, the order of proving theorems is arbitrary. Theorem 5 in this chapter could have been proved independently of Theorem 4 and then Theorem 4 could follow easily. Give the replacements for x, y, r, and s to be used in Theorem 5 to result in Theorem 4.

2. A student was given a problem of finding the replacement for x in $\frac{3}{4}x = \frac{5}{7}$ to result in a true statement. He showed the following work.

$$\tfrac{3}{4} \cdot (\tfrac{4}{3} \cdot \tfrac{5}{7}) = \tfrac{5}{7}$$

therefore, $\frac{4}{3} \cdot \frac{5}{7}$ or $\frac{20}{21}$ in place of x gives a true statement.

   a. Verify that $\frac{20}{21}$ in place of x does result in a true statement.
   b. Justify the student's reasoning.

3. Use the student's method of problem **2** to find the replacements for x to result in true statements.

   a. $\frac{3}{5}x = \frac{5}{9}$ **f.** $\frac{9}{2}x = -\frac{1}{3}$

   b. $\frac{4}{7}x = \frac{9}{11}$ **g.** $\frac{4}{3}x = -\frac{5}{11}$

   c. $\frac{2}{3}x = \frac{5}{12}$ **h.** $-\frac{5}{6}x = -\frac{11}{7}$

   d. $-\frac{5}{6}x = \frac{1}{2}$ **i.** $-\frac{11}{12}x = -\frac{13}{2}$

   e. $-\frac{4}{9}x = \frac{5}{4}$

4. True or false?

   a. $\frac{1}{9} \cdot \frac{1}{7} = \frac{1}{63}$ **f.** $\frac{-4}{3} \cdot \frac{5}{-9} = \frac{-20}{-27}$

   b. $\frac{1}{-3} \cdot \frac{1}{4} = \frac{1}{-12}$ **g.** $\frac{-5}{6} \cdot \frac{7}{-3} = \frac{35}{-18}$

   c. $\frac{1}{-6} \cdot \frac{1}{-5} = \frac{1}{30}$ **h.** $\frac{-3}{-2} \cdot \frac{-5}{-4} = \frac{15}{8}$

   d. $\frac{2}{7} \cdot \frac{1}{5} = \frac{2}{12}$ **i.** $\frac{1}{3} \cdot \frac{-4}{-5} = \frac{-4}{-2}$

   e. $\frac{3}{5} \cdot \frac{2}{-5} = \frac{6}{-25}$

MULTIPLICATIVE IDENTITY THEOREM

We know from working with rational numbers that the following statements are true.

$$\frac{1 \cdot 2}{2 \cdot 2} = \frac{2}{4} = \frac{1}{2} \qquad\qquad \frac{3 \cdot (-4)}{5 \cdot (-4)} = \frac{-12}{-20} = \frac{3}{5}$$

$$\frac{1 \cdot 3}{3 \cdot 3} = \frac{3}{9} = \frac{1}{3} \qquad\qquad \frac{-2 \cdot 3}{-7 \cdot 3} = \frac{-6}{-21} = \frac{-2}{-7}$$

$$\frac{1 \cdot 5}{5 \cdot 5} = \frac{5}{25} = \frac{1}{5} \qquad\qquad \frac{-5 \cdot (-2)}{-7 \cdot (-2)} = \frac{10}{14} = \frac{-5}{-7}$$

$$\frac{1 \cdot 4}{2 \cdot 4} = \frac{4}{8} = \frac{1}{2} \qquad\qquad \frac{-1 \cdot (-5)}{-2 \cdot (-5)} = \frac{5}{10} = \frac{-1}{-2}$$

We are led to think that $\frac{xr}{yr}$ and $\frac{x}{y}$, where $y \neq 0$, $r \neq 0$, may be equivalent expressions. Let us see whether or not this is the case.

Proof

$$\frac{xr}{yr} = \left(\frac{x}{y}\right)\left(\frac{r}{r}\right) \qquad\qquad \text{Theorem 5}$$

$$= \frac{x}{y} \cdot \left[r\left(\frac{1}{r}\right)\right] \qquad\qquad \text{Prop. div.}$$

$$= \frac{x}{y} \cdot (1) \qquad\qquad \text{Why?}$$

$$= \frac{x}{y} \qquad\qquad \text{Why?}$$

Thus we have proved the following theorem.

Theorem 6 (Multiplicative Identity Theorem)

$$\forall_x \ \forall_{y=0} \ \forall_{r=0} \ \frac{xr}{yr} = \frac{x}{y}$$

The Multiplicative Identity Theorem serves as a basis for simplifying such expressions as $\frac{6}{39}$. We find the greatest common factor of 6 and 39, which is 3, and proceed as follows:

$$\frac{6}{39} = \frac{2 \cdot 3}{13 \cdot 3} = \frac{2}{13}$$

Since 2 and 13 have no common factor greater than 1 (that is, 2 and 13 are relatively prime), we say that $\frac{2}{13}$ is in the *simplest form*.

EXERCISES

1.   Simplify each of the following:

   a. $\frac{12}{18}$ **c.** $\frac{51}{85}$ **e.** $\frac{121}{-1001}$ **g.** $\frac{117}{26}$

   b. $\frac{26}{32}$ **d.** $\frac{-81}{33}$ **f.** $\frac{625}{750}$ **h.** $\frac{153}{183}$

2.   True or false?

   a. $\dfrac{2 \times (-7)}{-7 \times 5} = \dfrac{2}{5}$

   b. $\dfrac{3 \times (-5)}{5 \times (-4)} = \dfrac{3}{-4}$

   c. $\dfrac{7 \times (-6)}{6 \times (-3)} = \dfrac{7}{3}$

   d. $\forall_{x=-3} \dfrac{5 + x}{3 + x} = \dfrac{5}{3}$

   e. $\forall_{n=4} \dfrac{3 - n}{4 - n} = \dfrac{3}{4}$

   f. $\forall_{y=0} \dfrac{4y}{5y} = \dfrac{4}{5}$

   g. $\forall_{m=-7} \dfrac{3m}{7 + m} = \dfrac{3}{7}$

   h. $\forall_{t=0} \dfrac{2 + t}{3t} = \dfrac{2}{3}$

ADDITION AND SUBTRACTION THEOREMS

   We recall from working with rational numbers that the following statements are true.

$$\frac{1}{4} + \frac{2}{5} = \frac{1 \times 5}{4 \times 5} + \frac{2 \times 4}{5 \times 4} = \frac{5}{20} + \frac{8}{20} = \frac{5 + 8}{20} = \frac{13}{20}$$

$$\frac{2}{3} + \frac{5}{7} = \frac{2 \times 7}{3 \times 7} + \frac{5 \times 3}{7 \times 3} = \frac{14}{21} + \frac{15}{21} = \frac{14 + 15}{21} = \frac{29}{21}$$

$$\frac{1}{3} + \frac{1}{2} = \frac{1 \times 2}{3 \times 2} + \frac{1 \times 3}{2 \times 3} = \frac{2}{6} + \frac{3}{6} = \frac{2 + 3}{6} = \frac{5}{6}$$

$$\frac{1}{4} + \frac{1}{5} = \frac{1 \times 5}{4 \times 5} + \frac{1 \times 4}{5 \times 4} = \frac{5}{20} + \frac{4}{20} = \frac{5 + 4}{20} = \frac{9}{20}$$

   We are led to believe that $\dfrac{x}{y} + \dfrac{r}{s}$ and $\dfrac{xs}{ys} + \dfrac{ry}{sy}$ and $\dfrac{xs + ry}{ys}$ where $y \neq 0$, $s \neq 0$, are equivalent expressions.

Proof

$$\frac{x}{y} + \frac{r}{s} = \frac{xs}{ys} + \frac{ry}{sy} \qquad \text{Theorem 6}$$

$$= \frac{xs}{ys} + \frac{ry}{ys} \qquad \text{Why?}$$

$$= (xs)\left(\frac{1}{ys}\right) + (ry)\left(\frac{1}{ys}\right) \qquad \text{Why?}$$

$$= (xs + ry)\left(\frac{1}{ys}\right) \qquad \text{Why?}$$

$$= \frac{xs + ry}{ys} \qquad \text{Theorem 1}$$

Thus we have the following theorem.

Theorem 7 (Addition Theorem)

$$\forall_x \, \forall_{y=0} \, \forall_r \, \forall_{s=0} \; \frac{x}{y} + \frac{r}{s} = \frac{xs}{ys} + \frac{ry}{ys} = \frac{xs + ry}{ys}$$

When using this theorem, do you always obtain the sum in the form of the simplest fractional numeral? To answer this question, apply the theorem to this problem: $\frac{1}{3} + \frac{5}{6}$.

EXERCISES

1. Use the Addition Theorem to find the sum in each of the following problems. For each case tell whether the theorem yields the sum in the simplest form or not. Simplify the answer wherever possible.

a. $\frac{1}{2} + \frac{1}{3}$

b. $\frac{4}{5} + \frac{2}{3}$

c. $\frac{3}{5} + \frac{7}{10}$

d. $\frac{1}{3} + \frac{1}{6}$

e. $\frac{2}{3} + \frac{-3}{4}$

f. $\frac{1}{4} + \frac{-3}{8}$

g. $\frac{1}{2} + \frac{7}{11}$

h. $\frac{3}{4} + \frac{5}{12}$

i. $\frac{4}{3} + \frac{-5}{12}$

j. $\frac{-3}{4} + \frac{-5}{6}$

k. $\frac{9}{4} + \frac{5}{16}$

l. $\frac{5}{3} + \frac{-7}{5}$

2. Examine your answers in problem 1. Make a statement which reveals in what cases the answers are not in the simplest form and in what cases they are in the simplest form.

3. Supply a reason for each step of the following proof of the Subtraction Theorem.

Proof

$$\frac{x}{y} - \frac{r}{s} = \frac{xs}{ys} - \frac{ry}{sy}$$

$$= \frac{xs}{ys} + \left(-\frac{ry}{sy}\right)$$

$$= \frac{xs}{ys} + \frac{-(ry)}{sy}$$

$$= \frac{xs}{ys} + \frac{-(ry)}{ys}$$

$$= \frac{xs + [-(ry)]}{ys}$$

$$= \frac{xs - ry}{ys}$$

Thus we have proved the following theorem.

Theorem 8 (Subtraction Theorem)

$$\forall_x \, \forall_{y=0} \, \forall_r \, \forall_{s=0} \; \frac{x}{y} - \frac{r}{s} = \frac{xs - ry}{ys}$$

DIVISION OF RATIONAL NUMBERS, OPPOSITES

In dividing rational numbers we use the procedure illustrated in the two examples below.

$$\tfrac{1}{2} \div \tfrac{3}{5} = \frac{\tfrac{1}{2}}{\tfrac{3}{5}} = \frac{\tfrac{1}{2} \cdot \tfrac{5}{3}}{\tfrac{3}{5} \cdot \tfrac{5}{3}} = \frac{\tfrac{5}{6}}{1} = \tfrac{5}{6} \quad \text{and} \quad \tfrac{1}{2} \cdot \tfrac{5}{3} = \tfrac{5}{6}$$

Therefore, $\dfrac{\tfrac{1}{2}}{\tfrac{3}{5}} = \tfrac{1}{2} \cdot \tfrac{5}{3}$

$$\tfrac{6}{7} \div \tfrac{4}{5} = \frac{\tfrac{6}{7}}{\tfrac{4}{5}} = \frac{\tfrac{6}{7} \times \tfrac{5}{4}}{\tfrac{4}{5} \times \tfrac{5}{4}} = \frac{\tfrac{30}{28}}{1} = \tfrac{30}{28} = 1\tfrac{1}{14} \quad \text{and} \quad \tfrac{6}{7} \cdot \tfrac{5}{4} = \tfrac{30}{28} = 1\tfrac{1}{14}$$

Therefore, $\dfrac{\tfrac{6}{7}}{\tfrac{4}{5}} = \tfrac{6}{7} \cdot \tfrac{5}{4}$

We are led to expect that, for all x, y, r, and s, where $y \neq 0$, $r \neq 0$, $s \neq 0$,

$$\frac{\tfrac{x}{y}}{\tfrac{r}{s}} = \frac{x}{y} \cdot \frac{s}{r}$$

Proof

$$\frac{\tfrac{x}{y}}{\tfrac{r}{s}} = \frac{\tfrac{x}{y} \cdot \left(\tfrac{s}{r}\right)}{\tfrac{r}{s} \cdot \left(\tfrac{s}{r}\right)} \qquad \text{Theorem 6}$$

$$= \frac{\tfrac{x}{y} \cdot \left(\tfrac{s}{r}\right)}{1} \qquad \text{PMI}$$

$$= \frac{x}{y} \cdot \frac{s}{r} \qquad \text{P1D}$$

This proof results in the following theorem.

Theorem 9 (Division Theorem) $\forall_x \; \forall_{y \neq 0} \; \forall_{r \neq 0} \; \forall_{s \neq 0} \quad \dfrac{\tfrac{x}{y}}{\tfrac{r}{s}} = \dfrac{x}{y} \cdot \dfrac{s}{r}$

We shall now state three theorems which deal with opposites of numbers in the context of rational numbers.

Observe the pattern in these examples.

$$\frac{-2}{5} = -\frac{2}{5} \qquad\qquad \frac{-1}{12} = -\frac{1}{12} \qquad\qquad \frac{2}{3} = -\frac{-2}{3}$$

$$\frac{-4}{7} = -\frac{4}{7} \qquad\qquad \frac{-3}{4} = -\frac{3}{4} \qquad\qquad \frac{-4}{-5} = \frac{4}{-5}$$

Theorem 10 $\forall_x \forall_{y \neq 0} \dfrac{-x}{y} = -\dfrac{x}{y}$

Proof $\dfrac{-x}{y} = \dfrac{x(-1)}{y}$ Theorem 1, Chap. 5

$= (-1) \cdot \dfrac{x}{y}$ CPM and Theorem 2

$= -\dfrac{x}{y}$ CPM and Theroem 1, Chap. 5

Now observe the pattern in these examples.

$$\frac{3}{-7} = -\frac{3}{7} \qquad\qquad \frac{1}{-2} = -\frac{1}{2} \qquad\qquad \frac{3}{4} = -\frac{3}{-4}$$

$$\frac{2}{-11} = -\frac{2}{11} \qquad\qquad \frac{5}{-3} = -\frac{5}{3} \qquad\qquad \frac{-5}{-6} = -\frac{-5}{6}$$

Theorem 11 $\forall_x \forall_{y \neq 0} \dfrac{x}{-y} = -\dfrac{x}{y}$

Proof $\dfrac{x}{-y} = \dfrac{x \cdot 1}{y \cdot (-1)}$ P1M and Theorem 3, Chap. 5

$= \dfrac{x}{y} \cdot \dfrac{1}{-1}$ Theorem 5

$= \dfrac{x}{y} \cdot (-1)$ Theorem 4, Chap. 5

$= -\dfrac{x}{y}$ Theorem 3, Chap. 5

And the third pattern involving opposites and rational numbers is illustrated by these examples.

$$\frac{-2}{-3} = \frac{2}{3} \qquad\qquad \frac{-5}{-9} = \frac{5}{9} \qquad\qquad \frac{-(-2)}{-3} = \frac{-2}{3}$$

$$\frac{-4}{-7} = \frac{4}{7} \qquad\qquad \frac{-1}{-7} = \frac{1}{7} \qquad\qquad \frac{-(-3)}{-(-4)} = \frac{-3}{-4}$$

Theorem 12 $\forall_x \forall_{y \neq 0} \dfrac{-x}{-y} = \dfrac{x}{y}$

Proof $\dfrac{-x}{-y} = \dfrac{x \cdot (-1)}{y \cdot (-1)}$ Why?

$= \dfrac{x}{y}$ Why?

We have shown that the rules for operations with rational numbers can be proved starting with basic properties. You should be able to prove more of these rules on your own.

EXERCISES

1. Apply the Division Theorem to simplify each of the following:

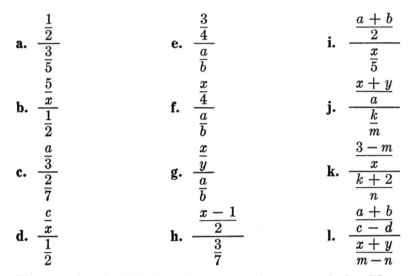

a. $\dfrac{\frac{1}{2}}{\frac{3}{5}}$ e. $\dfrac{\frac{3}{4}}{\frac{a}{b}}$ i. $\dfrac{\frac{a+b}{2}}{\frac{x}{5}}$

b. $\dfrac{\frac{5}{x}}{\frac{1}{2}}$ f. $\dfrac{\frac{x}{4}}{\frac{a}{b}}$ j. $\dfrac{\frac{x+y}{a}}{\frac{k}{m}}$

c. $\dfrac{\frac{a}{3}}{\frac{2}{7}}$ g. $\dfrac{\frac{x}{y}}{\frac{a}{b}}$ k. $\dfrac{\frac{3-m}{x}}{\frac{k+2}{n}}$

d. $\dfrac{\frac{c}{x}}{\frac{1}{2}}$ h. $\dfrac{\frac{x-1}{2}}{\frac{3}{7}}$ l. $\dfrac{\frac{a+b}{c-d}}{\frac{x+y}{m-n}}$

2. First apply the Division Theorem, then one of the Theorems 10 through 12 to simplify each of the following (you may use other properties and theorems also). In each case the denominator is not zero.

Examples:

i. $\dfrac{\frac{3}{4}}{\frac{5}{-7}} = \frac{3}{4}\cdot\frac{-7}{5} = \frac{-21}{20} = -\frac{21}{20}$

ii. $\dfrac{\frac{a}{-b}}{\frac{c}{d}} = \frac{a}{-b}\cdot\frac{d}{c} = \frac{ad}{-b\cdot c} = \frac{ad}{-(bc)} = -\frac{ad}{bc}$

iii. $\dfrac{\frac{x+y}{-(a+b)}}{\frac{x+1}{y-2}} = \frac{x+y}{-(a+b)}\cdot\frac{y-2}{x+1} = \frac{(x+y)(y-2)}{-(a+b)(x+1)}$
$= -\frac{(x+y)(y-2)}{(a+b)(x+1)}$

a. $\dfrac{\frac{1}{2}}{\frac{-3}{5}}$ c. $\dfrac{\frac{-3}{5}}{\frac{5}{4}}$ e. $\dfrac{\frac{-1}{2}}{\frac{-3}{-10}}$

b. $\dfrac{\frac{2}{-5}}{\frac{3}{7}}$ d. $\dfrac{\frac{-4}{3}}{\frac{-5}{7}}$ f. $\dfrac{\frac{a}{b}}{\frac{-x}{y}}$

g. $\dfrac{\dfrac{-x}{k}}{\dfrac{-m}{n}}$ j. $\dfrac{\dfrac{-(a+x)}{3}}{\dfrac{-(b+y)}{4}}$ m. $\dfrac{\dfrac{-(k-2)}{m+1}}{\dfrac{x+1}{-(y-2)}}$

h. $\dfrac{\dfrac{x+1}{2}}{\dfrac{-4}{3}}$ k. $\dfrac{\dfrac{k+1}{x+1}}{\dfrac{m}{n}}$

i. $\dfrac{\dfrac{k+2}{m-3}}{\dfrac{x}{y}}$ l. $\dfrac{\dfrac{a+b}{-(x+y)}}{\dfrac{s}{t}}$ n. $\dfrac{\dfrac{a+b+c}{x}}{\dfrac{m+n+p}{-y}}$

3. Supply the reasons for each step in the following proof.

Proof
$$-\left(\frac{x}{-y}\right) = (-1)\left(\frac{x}{-y}\right)$$
$$= \frac{(-1) \cdot x}{(-y)}$$
$$= \frac{(-1) \cdot x}{(-1) \cdot y}$$
$$= \frac{x}{y}$$

Thus we have proved the following theorem.

Theorem 13 $\forall_x \forall_{y \neq 0}\ -\left(\dfrac{x}{-y}\right) = \dfrac{x}{y}$

4. Prove.

Theorem 14 $\forall_x \forall_{y \neq 0}\ -\left(\dfrac{-x}{y}\right) = \dfrac{x}{y}$

5. Supply a reason or reasons for each step in the following proof.

Theorem 15 $\forall_x \forall_y \forall_{r \neq 0} \forall_{s \neq 0}\ \dfrac{x(-y)}{r(-s)} = \dfrac{xy}{rs}$

Proof
$$\frac{x(-y)}{r(-s)} = \frac{-(xy)}{-(rs)}$$
$$= \frac{xy}{rs}$$

6. Prove each of the following:

a. $\forall_a \forall_b\ \dfrac{a-b}{b-a} = -1,\quad (a \neq b)$

b. $\forall_x \forall_y \forall_{r \neq 0} \forall_{s \neq 0}\ -\dfrac{x(-y)}{rs} = \dfrac{xy}{rs}$

c. $\forall_x \forall_y \forall_r \forall_s \quad -\dfrac{(x-y)}{r-s} = \dfrac{y-x}{r-s}, \quad (r \neq s)$

d. $\forall_x \forall_y \forall_{r \neq 0} \forall_{s \neq 0} \quad \dfrac{(-x)(-y)}{rs} = \dfrac{xy}{rs}$

e. $\forall_x \forall_y \forall_{r \neq 0} \forall_{s \neq 0} \quad \dfrac{(-x)(-y)}{(-r)(-s)} = \dfrac{xy}{rs}$

7. True or false?

a. $-\dfrac{1}{5-3} = \dfrac{1}{3-5}$

b. $-\dfrac{1}{3-7} = \dfrac{1}{7-3}$

c. $-\dfrac{1}{5-1} = \dfrac{1}{5-1}$

d. $-\dfrac{1}{2+3} = \dfrac{1}{-2-3}$

e. $-\dfrac{1}{4+1} = \dfrac{1}{4+1}$

f. $-\dfrac{1}{2+(-3)} = \dfrac{1}{-2-(-3)}$

g. $-\dfrac{1}{-1+(-1)} = \dfrac{1}{1-(-1)}$

h. $-\dfrac{-(2-1)}{3-2} = \dfrac{2-1}{3-2}$

i. $-\dfrac{-(2-6)}{5-9} = \dfrac{6-2}{5-9}$

j. $-\dfrac{-(5-1)}{3-7} = \dfrac{5-1}{7-3}$

k. $-\dfrac{1}{-(5-3)} = \dfrac{-1}{5-3}$

l. $-\dfrac{1}{-(1-7)} = \dfrac{-1}{7-1}$

8. Tell whether or not the following are true for all replacements of the variables.

a. $(2a)(3b) = 6ab$

b. $(-5x)(7y) = 2xy$

c. $(\frac{1}{2}xy)(4a) = 2axy$

d. $5xy - 3ab + xy + 7ab$
$\quad = 4ab + 5xy$

e. $3mn + 2k - mn - 6k$
$\quad = -4k + 3$

f. $\dfrac{10a}{5b} = \dfrac{2a}{b}, \quad (b \neq 0)$

g. $\dfrac{10r}{2rs} = \dfrac{5}{s}, \quad (r \neq 0, \ s \neq 0)$

h. $\dfrac{-3x}{2y} = -\dfrac{3x}{2y}, \quad (y \neq 0)$

i. $-\dfrac{-5x}{-3x} = \dfrac{5x}{3x}, \quad (x \neq 0)$

j. $-\dfrac{-w}{r} = \dfrac{-w}{-r}, \quad (r \neq 0)$

k. $-\dfrac{s}{-t} = \dfrac{s}{t}, \quad (t \neq 0)$

l. $-\dfrac{(-x)(3)}{(y)(-7)} = \dfrac{(x)(3)}{(y)(7)}, \quad (y \neq 0)$

m. $\dfrac{t}{-y} = \dfrac{-t}{y}, \quad (y \neq 0)$

n. $-\dfrac{-s}{x} = -\dfrac{s}{x}, \quad (x \neq 0)$

o. $-\dfrac{1}{r-s} = \dfrac{1}{s-r}, \quad (r \neq s)$

p. $-\dfrac{1}{(x+y)} = \dfrac{1}{-x-y}$, $(x+y \neq 0)$

q. $-\dfrac{-(r-s)}{(x-y)} = \dfrac{r-s}{x-y}$, $(x \neq y)$

r. $-\dfrac{1}{-(y-x)} = \dfrac{-1}{y-x}$, $(x \neq y)$

s. $-\dfrac{(x-y)}{(r-s)} = \dfrac{xy}{s-r}$, $(s \neq r)$

t. $-\dfrac{-(x-y)}{(r-s)} = \dfrac{y-x}{r-s}$, $(r \neq s)$

u. $-\dfrac{-(x-y)}{-(r-s)} = \dfrac{x-y}{r-s}$, $(r \neq s)$

v. $-\dfrac{-(x-y)(r-s)}{(s-t)(x+y)} = \dfrac{(x-y)(r-s)}{(s-t)(x+y)}$, $(s \neq t, \, x+y \neq 0)$

w. $-\dfrac{(x-y)(r-s)}{-(s-t)(x+y)} = \dfrac{(x-y)(r-s)}{(t-s)(x+y)}$, $(t \neq s, \, x+y \neq 0)$

9. For each expression, write a single fractional expression equivalent to it.

Example: $\dfrac{y}{3} + \dfrac{x}{4} = \dfrac{4y+3x}{12}$

a. $\dfrac{3}{r} + \dfrac{7}{s}$, $(r \neq 0, \; s \neq 0)$

b. $\dfrac{x}{3} - \dfrac{x}{4}$

c. $\dfrac{x}{4} \times \dfrac{y}{7}$

d. $\dfrac{2}{x} + \dfrac{3}{y}$, $(x \neq 0, \; y \neq 0)$

e. $\dfrac{r}{3} \times \dfrac{2}{s}$, $(s \neq 0)$

f. $\dfrac{y}{s} + \dfrac{x}{r}$, $(r \neq 0, \; s \neq 0)$

g. $\dfrac{3}{x} - \dfrac{1}{s}$, $(x \neq 0, \; s \neq 0)$

h. $\dfrac{6}{r} \div \dfrac{7}{s}$, $(r \neq 0, \; s \neq 0)$

i. $\dfrac{x}{r} - \dfrac{y}{s}$, $(r \neq 0, \; s \neq 0)$

j. $\dfrac{5}{x} \times \dfrac{(-3)}{y}$, $(x \neq 0, \; y \neq 0)$

k. $\dfrac{4}{-x} \div \dfrac{r}{s}$, $(x \neq 0, \, r \neq 0, \, s \neq 0)$

l. $\dfrac{x}{3} + \dfrac{x}{2} + \dfrac{x}{5}$

m. $\dfrac{1}{rs} + \dfrac{3}{xy}$, $(r \neq 0, \, s \neq 0, \\ x \neq 0, \, y \neq 0)$

n. $\dfrac{y}{x} \div \dfrac{5}{6}$, $(x \neq 0)$

o. $\dfrac{s}{y} \times \dfrac{x}{5}$, $(y \neq 0)$

p. $\dfrac{r}{t} - \dfrac{x}{y}$, $(t \neq 0, \, y \neq 0)$

q. $\dfrac{(1-x)}{t} + \dfrac{y}{r}$, $(t \neq 0, \, r \neq 0)$

r. $\dfrac{(-2)}{y} \times \dfrac{x}{(-3)}$, $(y \neq 0)$

s. $\dfrac{3}{y} \div \dfrac{r}{s}$, $(y \neq 0, \, s \neq 0, \, r \neq 0)$

t. $\dfrac{3}{x} - \dfrac{5}{r} + \dfrac{2}{s}$, $(x \neq 0, \, r \neq 0, \, s \neq 0)$

10. For each expression, give a simpler expression equivalent to it.

Example: $\qquad -25 \cdot \frac{1}{5}(\frac{1}{2}x)$

$$= -5(\tfrac{1}{2}x)$$

$$= -\tfrac{5}{2}x$$

a. $12(\frac{1}{3}x)$

b. $(-18r)(-\frac{1}{9})$

c. $-(\frac{1}{2})(-28x)$

d. $(-\frac{1}{3})(\frac{5}{7}x)(-\frac{6}{11}t)$

e. $(-\frac{3}{7}x)(\frac{4}{9}y)$

f. $\dfrac{16xr}{2r}$

g. $25r \div \frac{1}{5}$

h. $\dfrac{(-27)x}{9}$

i. $\dfrac{4xy}{8y}$

j. $-26y \div [\frac{1}{2}(-x)]$

k. $\dfrac{-15xrs}{-3xs}$

l. $\dfrac{5x}{-15rt}$

m. $(\frac{1}{5}x)[\frac{1}{3}(-y)]$

n. $-39xy \div (\frac{1}{3}y)$

o. $\dfrac{(-7)xrt}{49r}$

p. $-\dfrac{-16xyt}{4yt}$

q. $-\dfrac{-32xt}{-4t}$

11. Tell whether or not each of the following is true for all replacements of the variables.

a. $(6r - 12s) \div 6 = r - 22$

b. $\frac{1}{3}(4x - 5y) = \frac{4}{3}x - \frac{5}{3}y$

c. $(35x - 28y)\frac{1}{7} = 5x - 4y$

d. $\dfrac{18x - 21t}{(-3)} = -6x - 7t$

e. $\dfrac{-(2r + 5s)}{2} = -r + \frac{5}{2}s$

f. $(x + 5) \div (-5) = -\frac{x}{5} - 1$

g. $\dfrac{r - 2y}{3} = \frac{r}{3} - \frac{2}{3}y$

h. $\frac{5}{6}(24x - 3y) = 20x - \frac{5}{2}y$

i. $(3x - 7y) \div \frac{1}{3} = x - \frac{7}{3}y$

j. $\frac{2}{3}r \div \frac{4}{5}s = \dfrac{5r}{6s}, \quad (s \neq 0)$

k. $\dfrac{\frac{3}{5}x}{\frac{2}{8}t} = \dfrac{12x}{5t}, \quad (t \neq 0)$

l. $\dfrac{3(x - y)}{2(y - x)} = \dfrac{3}{2}, \quad (x \neq y)$

m. $\frac{6}{5}r \div \frac{5}{3}s = 2\frac{r}{s}, \quad (s \neq 0)$

n. $\dfrac{3xy - 8xr}{2x} = \frac{3}{2}y - 4r, \quad (x \neq 0)$

o. $\frac{1}{3}(6x - 4y) + \frac{1}{4}(8x + 3y) = 4x - \frac{7}{12}y$

p. $\frac{1}{5}(x - y) - \frac{1}{3}(y - x) = \frac{8}{15}x + \frac{2}{15}y$

q. $\dfrac{4r - 3s}{5} - \dfrac{2r + 5s}{7} = \dfrac{18}{35}r - \dfrac{8}{7}s$

r. $\frac{2}{7}(4x - 7) + \frac{1}{7}(3x + 8) = \frac{11}{7}x + \frac{6}{7}$

s. $\dfrac{-5x - 11y}{5} - \dfrac{4x + 3y}{7} = -\dfrac{11}{7}x - \dfrac{92}{35}y$

12. For each expression, give a simpler equivalent expression.

a. $\frac{1}{2}(3r - 7s) - \frac{4}{3}(r + 5s)$

b. $\frac{3}{8}(5x - 4y) - \frac{5}{3}x$

c. $\frac{2}{3}(2x + 4y - 5r) - \frac{5}{6}r$

d. $\frac{2}{3}(\frac{5}{8}r - \frac{15}{7}s) + \frac{2}{9}(r + 2s)$

e. $(5x - \frac{3}{7}y) \div \frac{4}{3}$

f. $\dfrac{\frac{5}{8}x}{\frac{3}{4}y}$

g. $\dfrac{\frac{7}{9}r}{\frac{3}{11}}$

h. $\frac{4}{5}(3x - 2y) \div 5$

i. $\dfrac{\frac{7}{3}(y - r) + \frac{1}{3}y}{5}$

COMPLEX RATIONAL EXPRESSIONS

Below are several examples of *complex rational expressions.*

$$\dfrac{\dfrac{2}{3}}{\dfrac{1}{2}} \qquad \dfrac{\dfrac{a}{b}}{\dfrac{c}{d}} \qquad \dfrac{\dfrac{2x+3}{2}}{\dfrac{x+y}{z}}$$

$$\dfrac{\dfrac{x}{8}}{7} \qquad \dfrac{x + \dfrac{y}{2}}{3x - \dfrac{7}{3}} \qquad \dfrac{\dfrac{x+y}{x-y}}{\dfrac{a}{b}}$$

$$\dfrac{\dfrac{x}{y}}{3} \qquad \dfrac{\dfrac{a}{b+2}}{\dfrac{c}{4}} \qquad \dfrac{\dfrac{a}{b} + \dfrac{c}{d}}{\dfrac{x}{y} + \dfrac{r}{s}}$$

We would like to find an expression equivalent to each of those above and which is not as complicated. You already had some experience in doing this by the use of the Division Theorem. For example, according to this theorem

$$\dfrac{\frac{2}{3}}{\frac{1}{2}} = \frac{2}{3} \cdot \frac{2}{1} = \frac{4}{3} \quad \text{also} \quad \dfrac{\frac{x}{8}}{7} = \frac{x}{8} \cdot \frac{1}{7} = \frac{x}{56} \quad \text{and so on}$$

There is another method for simplifying complex expressions. It is based on two properties.

$$\forall_{x \neq 0} \frac{x}{x} = 1 \quad \text{and} \quad \forall_x x \cdot 1 = x$$

We illustrate on the next two pages the use of this method in simplifying some of the expressions given above.

Simplify $\dfrac{\frac{2}{3}}{\frac{1}{2}}$; since $\frac{6}{6} = 1$, we have $\dfrac{\frac{2}{3}}{\frac{1}{2}} = \dfrac{\frac{2}{3}}{\frac{1}{2}} \cdot \dfrac{6}{6} = \dfrac{\frac{2}{3} \cdot 6}{\frac{1}{2} \cdot 6} = \dfrac{4}{3}$. Why do you think we chose $\frac{6}{6}$ as the name for 1 in this particular problem?

Simplify $\dfrac{\frac{x}{8}}{7}$; we choose $\frac{8}{8}$ as the name for 1 in this case; why is this the most convenient name to choose in this problem?

$$\dfrac{\frac{x}{8}}{7} = \dfrac{\frac{x}{8}}{7} \cdot \dfrac{8}{8} = \dfrac{\frac{x}{8} \cdot 8}{7 \cdot 8} = \dfrac{x}{56}$$

Study each of the examples below, paying particular attention to the way we choose the various names for 1 in each case.

Examples: i. $\dfrac{\frac{x}{y}}{3} = \dfrac{\frac{x}{y}}{3} \cdot \dfrac{y}{y} = \dfrac{\frac{x}{y} \cdot y}{3 \cdot y} = \dfrac{x}{3y}$, $(y \neq 0)$

ii. $\dfrac{\frac{a}{b}}{\frac{c}{d}} = \dfrac{\frac{a}{b}}{\frac{c}{d}} \cdot \dfrac{bd}{bd} = \dfrac{\frac{a}{b} \cdot bd}{\frac{c}{d} \cdot bd} = \dfrac{ad}{bc}$, $(b \neq 0, c \neq 0, d \neq 0)$

Do you see that $\forall_{b \neq 0} \ \forall_{d \neq 0} \ \dfrac{bd}{bd} = 1$?

iii. $\dfrac{6}{\frac{7}{11}} = \dfrac{6}{\frac{7}{11}} \cdot \dfrac{11}{11} = \dfrac{6 \cdot 11}{\frac{7}{11} \cdot 11} = \dfrac{66}{7}$

iv. $\dfrac{x + \frac{y}{2}}{3x - \frac{7}{3}} = \dfrac{x + \frac{y}{2}}{3x - \frac{7}{3}} \cdot \dfrac{6}{6}$

$$= \dfrac{\left(x + \frac{y}{2}\right) \cdot 6}{\left(3x - \frac{7}{3}\right) \cdot 6}$$

$$= \dfrac{6x + 3y}{18x - 14}, \quad (18x - 14 \neq 0)$$

v. $\dfrac{\frac{a}{b+2}}{\frac{c}{4}} = \dfrac{\frac{a}{b+2}}{\frac{c}{4}} \cdot \dfrac{4(b+2)}{4(b+2)} = \dfrac{\frac{a}{b+2} \cdot 4(b+2)}{\frac{c}{4} \cdot 4(b+2)}$

$$= \dfrac{4a}{c(b+2)}, \quad (c \neq 0, \ b+2 \neq 0)$$

How was 1 renamed to be used in example *v.*?

Example: vi.
$$\frac{\dfrac{2x+3}{2}}{\dfrac{x+y}{z}} = \frac{\dfrac{2x+3}{2}}{\dfrac{x+y}{z}} \cdot \frac{2z}{2z} = \frac{\dfrac{2x+3}{2} \cdot 2z}{\dfrac{x+y}{z} \cdot 2z}$$

$$= \frac{(2x+3)z}{(x+y)2}$$

$$= \frac{z(2x+3)}{2(x+y)}, \quad (x+y \neq 0,\ z \neq 0)$$

Now examine all of the preceding examples to see whether you can save yourself a few steps. Do you see the following pattern?

$$\forall_a \ \forall_{b \neq 0} \ \forall_{c \neq 0} \ \forall_{d \neq 0} \quad \frac{\dfrac{a}{b}}{\dfrac{c}{d}} = \frac{ad}{bc}$$

Why is zero a permissible replacement for a? Why cannot b be replaced by 0?

$$\frac{\dfrac{x+y}{x-y}}{\dfrac{a}{b}} = \frac{b(x+y)}{(ax-y)}$$ State the limitations on the replacements of the variables.

$$\frac{\dfrac{a}{b}+\dfrac{c}{d}}{\dfrac{x}{y}+\dfrac{r}{s}} = \frac{\dfrac{ad+bc}{bd}}{\dfrac{xs+ry}{sy}} = \frac{sy(ad+bc)}{bd(xs+ry)}$$

What are the restrictions on replacements of the variables?

EXERCISES

1. Using the method you prefer, simplify each of the following:

a. $\dfrac{\frac{1}{2}}{\frac{2}{3}}$ e. $\dfrac{\frac{1}{7}}{10}$ i. $\dfrac{\frac{5}{9}}{3}$ m. $\dfrac{-2}{\frac{3}{2}}$

b. $\dfrac{\frac{3}{7}}{\frac{4}{5}}$ f. $\dfrac{\frac{3}{2}}{15}$ j. $\dfrac{5}{\frac{1}{3}}$ n. $\dfrac{-4}{-\frac{5}{3}}$

c. $\dfrac{\frac{1}{3}}{\frac{5}{7}}$ g. $\dfrac{\frac{1}{3}}{12}$ k. $\dfrac{6}{\frac{2}{7}}$ o. $\dfrac{-\frac{1}{2}}{6}$

d. $\dfrac{\frac{3}{2}}{5}$ h. $\dfrac{\frac{4}{7}}{2}$ l. $\dfrac{7}{\frac{1}{4}}$ p. $\dfrac{-\frac{5}{6}}{-7}$

2.   Using the method you prefer, find a simpler equivalent expression for each of the following (in each case specify the restriction on the replacements of variables):

a. $\dfrac{\dfrac{a}{2}}{\dfrac{3}{5}}$

b. $\dfrac{\dfrac{x}{3}}{\dfrac{1}{3}}$

c. $\dfrac{\dfrac{2}{m}}{\dfrac{2}{5}}$

d. $\dfrac{\dfrac{4}{5}}{\dfrac{a}{3}}$

e. $\dfrac{\dfrac{1}{7}}{\dfrac{3}{c}}$

f. $\dfrac{\dfrac{a}{b}}{\dfrac{2}{3}}$

g. $\dfrac{\dfrac{1}{2}}{\dfrac{m}{n}}$

h. $\dfrac{\dfrac{a}{b}}{\dfrac{c}{d}}$

i. $\dfrac{13}{\dfrac{x}{3}}$

j. $\dfrac{12}{\dfrac{2}{n}}$

k. $\dfrac{9}{\dfrac{x}{y}}$

l. $\dfrac{m}{\dfrac{a}{b}}$

m. $\dfrac{\dfrac{3}{2}}{x}$

n. $\dfrac{\dfrac{a}{3}}{k}$

o. $\dfrac{\dfrac{a}{b}}{c}$

p. $\dfrac{\dfrac{a+b}{2}}{6}$

q. $\dfrac{5}{\dfrac{x-y}{k}}$

r. $\dfrac{a}{\dfrac{b+c}{x}}$

s. $\dfrac{x+y}{\dfrac{a}{b}}$

t. $\dfrac{\dfrac{m}{n}}{x-y}$

u. $\dfrac{\dfrac{a-b}{3}}{\dfrac{x}{y}}$

v. $\dfrac{6-\dfrac{7}{r}}{3+\dfrac{2}{r}}$

w. $\dfrac{6x-y}{\dfrac{3}{y}}$

x. $\dfrac{\dfrac{3}{x}-4}{x+2}$

y. $\dfrac{1}{\dfrac{x}{y}}$

z. $\dfrac{2-\dfrac{7}{s}}{s-\dfrac{3}{2}}$

a'. $\dfrac{x-\dfrac{3-y}{x}}{2x-3}$

b'. $\dfrac{\dfrac{-x}{y}}{\dfrac{r}{t}}$

c'. $\dfrac{r+\dfrac{s}{t}}{r-\dfrac{s}{t}}$

d'. $\dfrac{2x-y}{\dfrac{3}{2}-\dfrac{x}{3}}$

e'. $\dfrac{3+\dfrac{r}{5}}{r-\dfrac{6}{7}}$

f'. $\dfrac{3+\dfrac{5}{x+y}}{7+\dfrac{3}{x+y}}$

g'. $\dfrac{7-\dfrac{1}{2x}}{6+\dfrac{1}{x^2}}$

h'. $\dfrac{r-\dfrac{7}{9}}{\dfrac{2}{r}-3}$

i'. $\dfrac{\dfrac{a-b}{a+b}}{\dfrac{a+b}{a-b}}$

j'. $\dfrac{\dfrac{x^2-y^2}{x+y}}{\dfrac{x-y}{x+y}}$

k'. $\dfrac{\dfrac{a+b+c}{2}}{\dfrac{a+b+c}{3}}$

l'. $\dfrac{\dfrac{(x+y)^3}{n}}{\dfrac{(x+y)^3}{m}}$

From word phrases to mathematical phrases

You are now able to work with rational expressions. Many word phrases, when translated into mathematical phrases, result in rational expressions. Some of the problems below will involve rational expressions.

EXERCISES

1. Use the letter x in place of a given number and write the mathematical phrase for each word phrase.

   a. five more than a given number
   b. sixteen less than a certain number
   c. five times a given number
   d. one-half of a certain number
   e. three more than four times a given number
   f. Subtract a given number from seventeen.
   g. four times the sum of eight and a certain number
   h. the product of four and the sum of some number and three
   i. the product of two and six less than a given number
   j. Subtract a given number from eleven and then multiply the result by six.
   k. Multiply three by some number and add the result to the product of six and eight.

2. Change the following to mathematical phrases. Choose your own letters and state in each case what the letter stands for.

Examples: *i.* The phrase "six more wieners than I bought Friday" can be written as the mathematical phrase "$x + 6$," where x stands for the number of wieners I bought Friday.

        ii. The phrase "seven less than twice as many rockets as we made last year" can be written as the mathematical phrase "$2r - 7$," where r stands for the number of rockets we made last year.

        iii. The phrase "three more dollars than I made last week multiplied by two" can be written as the mathematical phrase "$(t + 3) \cdot 2$," where t stands for the number of dollars I made last week.

   a. five less pounds than I weighed in 1964
   b. ten more fish than I caught last year
   c. twice as many doughnuts as we bought last week

    d. six points more than I made in the game yesterday

    e. one-fourth of the number of tickets to the Rose Bowl game

    f. two-thirds of the number of club members

    g. four more than three times the number of cookies in the jar

    h. eight hundred dollars less than half of last year's salary

    i. five times as many customers as last year

    j. two dollars less than I earned in a week multiplied by two

    k. two thousand more than twice as many people who visited the state park

    l. three times as many stamps as Susan collected

    m. six dollars less than Sam saved

    n. fourteen apples more than ordered Saturday

    o. four more than the number of golf balls you found last year multiplied by two

3. Write the mathematical phrase for each word phrase. Simplify whenever possible.

    a. number of feet in a inches

    b. number of feet in $4x$ inches

    c. number of feet in $15y$ inches

    d. number of yards in n feet

    e. number of yards in $(x - y)$ feet

    f. number of dollars in d dimes

    g. number of dollars in n nickels

    h. number of dollars in $(p + r)$ cents

    i. the reciprocal of $\dfrac{x}{y}$

    j. the reciprocal of $\dfrac{m + n}{x}$

    k. the reciprocal of $\dfrac{\frac{a}{b}}{c}$

    l. the reciprocal of $\dfrac{\frac{x}{y}}{\frac{a}{b}}$

    m. the reciprocal of $\dfrac{\frac{x + y}{a}}{\frac{m + n}{b}}$

n. number of square yards in 1 square foot

o. number of square yards in s square feet

p. number of square yards in $(a + b)$ square feet

q. number of square yards in $\dfrac{x}{y}$ square feet

r. number of pounds in 16 ounces

s. number of pounds in 1 ounce

t. number of pounds in a ounces

u. number of pounds in $(x - 1)$ ounces

v. number of pounds in $\dfrac{a}{b}$ ounces

w. number of pounds in $\dfrac{x + a}{y + b}$ ounces

x. number of inches in the perimeter of a square with x inches for the length of a side

y. number of inches in the perimeter of a square with x feet for the length of a side

z. number of inches in the perimeter of a square with $(a + b)$ feet for the length of a side

a'. number of inches in the perimeter of a rectangle with the width of x inches and the length of y inches

b'. number of inches in the perimeter of a rectangle with the width of a feet and the length of b feet

c'. number of inches in the perimeter of an isosceles triangle with the measure of the base b inches and of one arm a inches

d'. number of inches in the perimeter of an isosceles triangle with the measure of the base, x feet, and of one arm, y feet

VOCABULARY

Use each of the following correctly in a sentence. Numerals in the parentheses refer to pages where these words were used. If you are not sure of the meaning of any word, turn to the indicated page and refresh your memory.

Addition Theorem (153)

complex rational expression (161)

Division Theorem (154)

Multiplicative Identity Theorem (151)

open rational expression (146)

simplest form (151)

Subtraction Theorem (153)

THEOREMS

Theorem 1 $\forall_x \forall_{y\neq 0} \forall_z \; \dfrac{xz}{y} = \left(\dfrac{x}{y}\right)(z)$

Theorem 2 $\forall_x \forall_{y\neq 0} \forall_z \; \dfrac{xz}{y} = (x)\left(\dfrac{z}{y}\right)$

Theorem 3 $\forall_x \forall_{y\neq 0} \forall_z \; \dfrac{xz}{y} = \left(\dfrac{1}{y}\right)(xz)$

Theorem 4 $\forall_{x\neq 0} \forall_{y\neq 0} \; \left(\dfrac{1}{x}\right)\left(\dfrac{1}{y}\right) = \dfrac{1}{xy}$

Theorem 5 $\forall_x \forall_{y\neq 0} \forall_r \forall_{s\neq 0} \; \left(\dfrac{x}{y}\right)\left(\dfrac{r}{s}\right) = \dfrac{xr}{ys}$

Theorem 6   (Multiplicative Identity Theorem) $\forall_x \forall_{y\neq 0} \forall_{r\neq 0} \; \dfrac{xr}{yr} = \dfrac{x}{y}$

Theorem 7   (Addition Theorem) $\forall_x \forall_{y\neq 0} \forall_r \forall_{s\neq 0} \; \dfrac{x}{y} + \dfrac{r}{s} = \dfrac{xs + ry}{ys}$

Theorem 8   (Subtraction Theorem) $\forall_x \forall_{y\neq 0} \forall_r \forall_{s\neq 0} \; \dfrac{x}{y} - \dfrac{r}{s} = \dfrac{xs - ry}{ys}$

Theorem 9   (Division Theorem) $\forall_x \forall_{y\neq 0} \forall_{r\neq 0} \forall_{s\neq 0} \; \dfrac{\frac{x}{y}}{\frac{r}{s}} = \dfrac{x}{y} \cdot \dfrac{s}{r}$

Theorem 10 $\forall_x \forall_{y\neq 0} \; \dfrac{-x}{y} = -\dfrac{x}{y}$

Theorem 11 $\forall_x \forall_{y\neq 0} \; \dfrac{x}{-y} = -\dfrac{x}{y}$

Theorem 12 $\forall_x \forall_{y\neq 0} \; \dfrac{-x}{-y} = \dfrac{x}{y}$

Theorem 13 $\forall_x \forall_{y\neq 0} \; -\left(\dfrac{x}{-y}\right) = \dfrac{x}{y}$

Theorem 14 $\forall_x \forall_{y\neq 0} \; -\left(\dfrac{-x}{y}\right) = \dfrac{x}{y}$

Theorem 15 $\forall_x \forall_y \forall_{r\neq 0} \forall_{s\neq 0} \; \dfrac{x(-y)}{r(-s)} = \dfrac{xy}{rs}$

REVIEW EXERCISES

1. Prove each of the following:

a. $\forall_{x\neq0} \ \forall_{y\neq0} \ \forall_n \ \left(\dfrac{1}{x}\right)\left(\dfrac{n}{y}\right) = \dfrac{n}{xy}$

b. $\forall_{x\neq0} \ \forall_y \ \dfrac{y-2}{x} = -\dfrac{2-y}{x}$

c. $\forall_{x\neq0} \ \forall_y \ \dfrac{3y}{12x} = \dfrac{y}{4x}$

d. $\forall_{x\neq0} \ \forall_{y\neq0} \ \dfrac{1}{x}+\dfrac{1}{y} = \dfrac{x+y}{xy}$

e. $\forall_{x\neq0} \ \forall_{y\neq0} \ \dfrac{1}{x}-\dfrac{1}{y} = \dfrac{y-x}{xy}$

f. $\forall_{x\neq0} \ \forall_{y\neq0} \ \dfrac{\frac{1}{x}}{\frac{1}{y}} = \dfrac{y}{x}$

g. $\forall_x \ \forall_y \ \forall_{z\neq0} \ \dfrac{-x-y}{z} = -\dfrac{x+y}{z}$

h. $\forall_x \ \forall_y \ \dfrac{-x-y}{x+y} = -1, \quad (x+y \neq 0)$

i. $\forall_x \ \forall_y \ \forall_{r\neq0} \ \forall_{s\neq0} \ \dfrac{(-x)\,(-y)}{(-r)\,s} = -\dfrac{xy}{rs}$

j. $\forall_x \ \forall_{y\neq0} \ \dfrac{-(-x)}{y} = \dfrac{x}{y}$

2. For each of the following expressions, write a single fractional expression equivalent to it.

a. $\dfrac{2}{r}+\dfrac{3}{t}, \quad (r \neq 0, t \neq 0)$

b. $\dfrac{6}{r} \div \dfrac{11}{t}, \quad (r \neq 0, t \neq 0)$

c. $\dfrac{5}{t} \times \dfrac{r}{-6}, \quad (t \neq 0)$

d. $\dfrac{3}{y} - \dfrac{4}{t}, \quad (y \neq 0, t \neq 0)$

3. For each of the following find a simpler equivalent expression.

a. $\dfrac{\frac{3}{4}}{\frac{7}{8}}$

b. $\dfrac{\frac{2}{7}}{\frac{7}{2}}$

c. $\dfrac{\frac{5}{3}}{\frac{3}{7}}$

d. $\dfrac{\frac{4}{5}}{6}$

e. $\dfrac{\frac{a}{3}}{\frac{x}{4}}$

f. $\dfrac{\frac{m}{n}}{\frac{4}{x}}$

g. $\dfrac{\frac{a+b}{3}}{\frac{c}{d}}$

h. $\dfrac{\frac{2a-b}{3}}{\frac{a+b}{2}}$

i. $\dfrac{\frac{x-y}{a}}{\frac{x+y}{b}}$

j. $\dfrac{\frac{a+b}{c+d}}{\frac{x+y}{z+w}}$

k. $\dfrac{x-\frac{1}{2}}{x+\frac{3}{4}}$

l. $\dfrac{1-\frac{a}{b}}{1-\frac{c}{d}}$

m. $\dfrac{3-\frac{1}{x}}{4-\frac{1}{y}}$

n. $\dfrac{5a-\frac{1}{2}}{3a+\frac{1}{2}}$

o. $\dfrac{\frac{a}{b}+\frac{c}{d}}{\frac{x}{y}}$

p. $\dfrac{\frac{a}{b}+\frac{c}{d}}{\frac{m}{n}+\frac{p}{r}}$

q. $\dfrac{\frac{3(a+b)}{2}}{\frac{6(a-b)}{8}}$

r. $\dfrac{\frac{4(x-y)}{3u}}{\frac{10(a+b)}{6}}$

4.   True or false?

a. $\dfrac{3\cdot 7}{5}=\dfrac{3}{5}\cdot\dfrac{7}{5}$

b. $\dfrac{1}{2}+\dfrac{1}{3}=\dfrac{1+1}{2+3}$

c. $\forall_{x=0}\forall_{y=0}\ \dfrac{1}{x}+\dfrac{1}{y}=\dfrac{1}{x+y}$

d. $\forall_{x=0}\forall_{y=0}\ \dfrac{1}{x}\cdot\dfrac{1}{y}=\dfrac{1}{xy}$

e. $\forall_{x=0}\forall_{y=0}\ \dfrac{1}{x}-\dfrac{1}{y}=\dfrac{x-y}{xy}$

f. $\forall_{x=0}\forall_{y=0}\ \dfrac{1}{-x}\cdot\dfrac{1}{-y}=\dfrac{1}{xy}$

g. $\tfrac{1}{2}(3\cdot 4)=6$

h. $3(\tfrac{3}{4})=\tfrac{9}{12}$

i. $\forall_{x=3}\ \dfrac{1}{x-3}=-\dfrac{1}{3-x}$

j. $\dfrac{3(-4)}{-4\cdot 12}=\dfrac{1}{4}$

k. $\dfrac{\frac{3}{4}}{\frac{1}{2}}=\dfrac{3}{2}$

l. $\forall_{x=0}\forall_{y=0}\ \dfrac{\frac{1}{x}}{y}=\dfrac{y}{x}$

m. $\forall_{x=0}\forall_{y=0}\ \dfrac{\frac{1}{x}}{\frac{x}{y}}=\dfrac{y}{x}$

n. $\forall_{x=0}\ \dfrac{1}{x}+\dfrac{2}{x}=\dfrac{3}{x}$

o. $\forall_{x=0}\ \dfrac{5}{x}-\dfrac{2}{x}=\dfrac{3}{x}$

p. $\forall_{x}\forall_{y=0}\ \dfrac{-(-x)}{-y}=-\dfrac{x}{y}$

q. $\forall_{x=0}\ \dfrac{1}{-\frac{1}{x}}=-x$

r. $\forall_x \forall_y \ -\dfrac{x - y}{x + y} = \dfrac{y - x}{x + y}, \quad (x + y \neq 0)$

s. $\forall_x \forall_y \forall_r \forall_s \ \dfrac{x - y}{r - s} = \dfrac{y - x}{s - r}, \quad (r \neq s)$

5. Write the mathematical phrase for each word phrase.

a. the reciprocal of $\dfrac{a}{b}$

b. the reciprocal of $\dfrac{x + y}{z}$

c. the reciprocal of $\dfrac{a + b}{c + d}$

d. number of feet in $(a + x)$ inches

e. number of yards in $(m + n)$ feet

f. number of miles in $(p + s)$ feet

g. number of pounds in $(x + y)$ ounces

h. number of dollars in $(r + s)$ cents

i. number of square feet in t square inches

j. number of cubic yards in m cubic feet

CHAPTER TEST

1. Write a single fractional expression equivalent to each of the following.

a. $\dfrac{x}{3} + \dfrac{y}{3}$

b. $\dfrac{a}{2} + \dfrac{b}{6}$

c. $\dfrac{a}{x} + \dfrac{m}{3x}$

d. $\dfrac{x}{t} - \dfrac{r}{s}$

e. $\dfrac{x}{3} \cdot \dfrac{y}{5}$

f. $\dfrac{a}{x} \cdot \dfrac{b}{y}$

g. $\dfrac{a + b}{x} \cdot \dfrac{m + n}{y}$

h. $\dfrac{y}{t} \div \dfrac{3}{2}$

i. $\dfrac{a}{m} \div \dfrac{x}{y}$

2. True or false?

a. $\dfrac{3 \cdot (-4)}{7} = \dfrac{3}{7} \cdot \left(-\dfrac{4}{7}\right)$

b. $\dfrac{(-2)(-5)}{9} = (-5)\left(-\dfrac{2}{9}\right)$

c. $(-\tfrac{1}{2})(-\tfrac{1}{3})(-\tfrac{1}{4}) = -\dfrac{1}{24}$

d. $\forall_a \forall_b \forall_x \ \dfrac{x(a + b)}{a + b} = x,$
$(a + b \neq 0)$

e. $\forall_x \forall_{y \neq 0} \left(\dfrac{1}{y}\right)[(-x)(y)] = -x$

f. $\forall_a \forall_b \ \dfrac{a - b}{-1} = b - a$

g. $\forall_a \forall_b \ (-1)(a - b) = -a - b$

h. $\forall_{x \neq 0} \forall_{y \neq 0} \ \dfrac{1}{x} + \dfrac{1}{y} = \dfrac{1}{xy}$

i. $\forall_{m \neq 0} \forall_{n \neq 0} \ \dfrac{m}{n} - \dfrac{n}{m} = 0$

j. $\forall_{r\neq0}\ r - \dfrac{1}{r} = 0$

k. $\forall_{n\neq-2}\ \dfrac{1+n}{2+n} = \dfrac{1}{2}$

l. $\forall_{m\neq1}\ \dfrac{2-m}{1-m} = 2$

m. $\forall_a\ \forall_{b\neq0}\ \forall_{c\neq0}\ \forall_{d\neq0}\ \dfrac{\dfrac{a}{b}}{\dfrac{c}{d}} = \dfrac{ac}{bd}$

r. $\forall_m\ \forall_n\ \forall_{x\neq0}\ \forall_{y\neq0}\ \dfrac{\dfrac{m+n}{x}}{y} = \dfrac{m+n}{yx}$

s. $\forall_m\ \forall_n\ \forall_{x\neq0}\ \forall_{y\neq0}\ \dfrac{m+n}{\dfrac{x}{y}} = \dfrac{(m+n)x}{y}$

t. $\forall_x\ \forall_y\ \forall_z\ (-2z)(\tfrac{1}{2}yx) = -xyz$

u. $\forall_a\ \forall_b\ \forall_x\ \dfrac{(a+b)x}{-a-b} = -x,\quad (a+b \neq 0)$

n. $\forall_x\ \forall_{y\neq x}\ -\dfrac{x+y}{x-y} = \dfrac{x+y}{y-x}$

o. $\dfrac{\frac{1}{3}}{-\frac{2}{5}} = -\dfrac{5}{6}$

p. $\dfrac{-\frac{4}{3}}{-\frac{5}{7}} = \dfrac{15}{28}$

q. $\dfrac{\frac{2}{5}}{\frac{1}{8}} = \dfrac{1}{20}$

3. Prove each of the following:

a. $\forall_x\ \forall_y\ \forall_{s\neq0}\ \forall_{s\neq0}\ \dfrac{(-x)(-y)}{(-r)(-s)} = \dfrac{xy}{rs}$

b. $\forall_x\ \forall_y\ \forall_{z\neq0}\ \dfrac{-(x-y)}{z} = \dfrac{y-x}{z}$

c. $\forall_m\ \forall_{n\neq0}\ \dfrac{m}{n} + \dfrac{m}{2n} = \dfrac{3m}{2n}$

d. $\forall_t\ \forall_{u\neq0}\ \dfrac{15t}{5u} = \dfrac{3t}{u}$

4. For each of the following find a simpler equivalent expression. No denominator is zero.

a. $\dfrac{\frac{9}{4}}{\frac{7}{10}}$

b. $\dfrac{\frac{6}{x}}{\frac{y}{5}}$

c. $\dfrac{\frac{x+y}{4}}{\frac{x-y}{5}}$

d. $\dfrac{\frac{a+b}{x+y}}{\frac{x+y}{a+b}}$

e. $\dfrac{\frac{3(m+n)}{4}}{\frac{9(m-n)}{12}}$

f. $\dfrac{\frac{-4(a+b)}{x+y}}{\frac{8(a+b)}{3(x+y)}}$

g. $\dfrac{x + \frac{1}{3}}{y + \frac{1}{4}}$

i. $\dfrac{\frac{x}{y} + \frac{n}{m}}{\frac{1}{2}}$

h. $\dfrac{3 - \dfrac{1}{m}}{4 - \dfrac{1}{n}}$

j. $\dfrac{\frac{a}{b} + \frac{c}{d}}{\frac{e}{f}}$

5. Write the mathematical phrase for each word phrase.

   a. number of nickels in $(x + y)$ cents
   b. number of dollars in $(a - b)$ cents

   c. number of feet in $\dfrac{m}{n}$ inches

   d. number of square feet in $\dfrac{a}{b}$ square inches

   e. number of square inches in $\dfrac{a + b}{3}$ square feet

   f. number of feet in the perimeter of a square with the length of a side $\dfrac{a}{3}$ inches

   g. number of pounds in $\dfrac{t}{y}$ ounces

BIBLIOGRAPHY

Nichols, E. D.; Heimer, R. T.; and Garland, E. H.; *Modern Intermediate Algebra.* New York: Holt, Rinehart and Winston, Inc., 1965. Chapter 4.

Sawyer, W. W. *Mathematician's Delight.* Baltimore: Penguin Books, 1956. Chapter 7.

Sawyer, W. W. *Prelude to Mathematics.* Baltimore: Penguin Books, 1959. Chapter 7.

School Mathematics Study Group. *First Course in Algebra.* New Haven: Yale University Press, 1961. pp. 313-375.

Smith, David Eugene. *A Source Book in Mathematics.* Volumes I and II. The Field of Number and the Field of Algebra. New York: Dover Publications, Inc., 1959.

Titchmarsh, E. C. *Mathematics for the General Reader.* New York: Doubleday & Company, Inc., 1959. pp. 48-58.

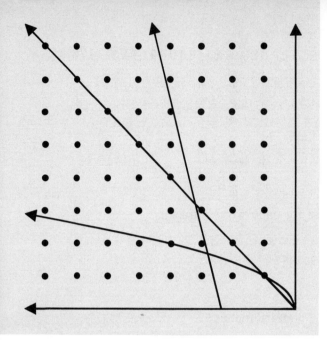

CHAPTER 7

Solution Sets of Equations and Inequalities

WHAT IS AN EQUATION?

From your previous study, you have gained some familiarity with equations. Below are a few examples of equations.

$$\tfrac{1}{2} = \tfrac{4}{8} \qquad\qquad 1.7 = 20 \qquad\qquad 1\% = 56$$

$$.5 = 50\% \qquad\qquad \frac{1}{y} = 2 + \frac{2}{y} \qquad\qquad |c| = -2$$

$$.07 = \tfrac{14}{200} \qquad\qquad\qquad\qquad\qquad 16d + 4 = 20$$

$$4x = -27 \qquad\qquad a = a + 1 \qquad\qquad 3 + x = x + 3$$

Equations are mathematical sentences. The equations above can be classified into three kinds of sentences.

    i. True sentences; for example, $\tfrac{1}{2} = \tfrac{4}{8}$. Find all true sentences among the above sentences.

    ii. False sentences; for example, $1.7 = 20$. Find all false sentences among the above sentences.

174

iii. Sentences which are neither true nor false, that is open sentences; for example, $4x = -27$. Those sentences which are neither true nor false can be further classified into three types.

 a. Sentences in which at least one replacement for the variable, perhaps several, but not all will yield a true sentence; for example, $4x = -27$. What number name in place of x will yield a true sentence? Find all other sentences of this type among the examples above.

 b. Sentences in which no replacement for the variable will yield a true sentence; for example, $a = a + 1$. Find all other sentences of this type among the examples above.

 c. Sentences in which every replacement of the variable will produce a true sentence. One sentence above is such a sentence. Find it.

In this chapter you will concentrate on sentences which are neither true nor false, that is, open sentences. You will develop a method of discovering replacements for the variables which will result in true sentences. In each case you will need to know the replacement set for the variables.

AGREEMENT: Whenever the replacement set is not specified, it is the set of real numbers.

EXERCISES

Classify each of the sentences below into one of the following categories.

T: true sentence

F: false sentence

R: sentence which is neither true nor false, that is, an open sentence, but in which at least one replacement for the variable, but not all, will result in a true sentence; find the replacement or several replacements

N: sentence which is neither true nor false and in which there is no replacement for the variable which will result in a true sentence

E: sentence which is neither true nor false, and in which every replacement for the variable will result in a true sentence

Examples: i. $\dfrac{x}{x} = 2$

N; $\dfrac{x}{x} = 2$ is neither true nor false, that is, it is an open sentence. There is no replacement for x which yields a true sentence, for we know that any non-zero number divided by itself is 1, and $1 \neq 2$. [Remember, $\frac{0}{0}$ is meaningless.]

ii. $\frac{2}{3} = .66$

F; $\frac{2}{3} = .66$ is a false sentence. $\frac{2}{3}$ and .66 are names for two different numbers, although $\frac{2}{3}$ is only a very little larger than .66.

iii. $175\% = 1.75$

T; $175\% = 1.75$ is a true sentence.

iv. $5x + 2 = -3$

R; $5x + 2 = -3$ is neither true nor false, that is, it is an open sentence. Replacing x by -1 results in a true sentence.

$$5 \cdot (-1) + 2 = -3$$

v. $21u - 6u = 15u$

E; $21u - 6u = 15u$ is neither true nor false. Every replacement of u by a numeral for a real number produces a true sentence. We give proof for this.

$$21u - 6u = (21 - 6)u = 15u \qquad \text{Why?}$$

Therefore, $\forall_u \ 21u - 6u = 15u$

1. $\sqrt{6.25} = 2.5$
2. $\left| -\frac{6}{2} \right| = 3$
3. $.01 = .1\%$
4. $10^4 = 10,000$
5. $(-1)^5 = -1$
   [HINT: $(-1)^2 = (-1)(-1)$;
   $(-1)^3 = (-1)(-1)(-1)$]
6. $10x = \frac{1}{2}$
7. $|y - y| = 0$
8. $a^2 = a^3$
9. $12m + 3 = 0$
10. $p(p - 1) = 0$
11. $75\% = \frac{3}{4}$
12. $z^3 = -1$

13. $11n + 12n = 23$
14. $|2d| = 5$
15. $s^2 = 9$
16. $(-4)^3 = 64$
17. $\dfrac{2g}{g} = -2$
18. $17 = \dfrac{b}{2}$
19. $\dfrac{3}{v} = 5$
20. $w^2 = -16$
21. $x \cdot x = x^2$
22. $|3a - a| = |a - 3a|$

SOLVING EQUATIONS

Consider the following equation.

$$2x + 3 = 1$$

It is easy to see that -1 in place of x will result in a true sentence.

$$2 \cdot (-1) + 3 = -2 + 3 = 1$$

The number -1 is called *the root* of the equation $2x + 3 = 1$. The *solution set* of this equation is $\{-1\}$, that is, a set consisting of one element, namely, the number -1. A root is said *to satisfy an equation;* thus the number -1 *satisfies* the equation $2x + 3 = 1$. To solve an equation means to find all numbers that satisfy the equation.

What is the root of each of the following equations?

$m = -7$	$c - 3 = 8$
$t + 3 = 5$	$n - \frac{1}{2} = -\frac{1}{2}$
$s + 7 = 1$	$5d = 10$
$x + 3 = 3$	$3u = 1$
$y - 4 = 2$	$-2f = 10$

You probably had no difficulty telling the roots of the equations above because they are very simple. For example, in the second equation above, you may ask yourself the question

What number added to 3 gives 5? $[t + 3 = 5]$

The answer, of course, is 2. Therefore, the number 2 is the root of this equation, and $\{2\}$ is the solution set.

In the equation $n - \frac{1}{2} = -\frac{1}{2}$, the question to ask yourself is
$\frac{1}{2}$ subtracted from what number gives $-\frac{1}{2}$?

The answer, of course, is 0, because $0 - \frac{1}{2} = -\frac{1}{2}$. Thus, 0 is the root of the equation $n - \frac{1}{2} = -\frac{1}{2}$. Its solution set is $\{0\}$.

EXERCISES

Determine the solution set of each of the following equations.

1. $m + 3 = 7$	**5.** $s - 10 = 15$	**9.** $15 - c = 20$
2. $n + 8 = 1$	**6.** $t - 13 = 0$	**10.** $6 - h = -5$
3. $x + 2 = 0$	**7.** $2 - b = 0$	**11.** $3y = 12$
4. $a - 5 = 2$	**8.** $22 - v = 7$	**12.** $5z = -60$

13. $4d = \frac{1}{2}$

14. $\frac{1}{3}w = 10$

15. $\frac{1}{5}p = -5$

16. $\frac{s}{6} = 10$

17. $\frac{2}{j} = 2$

18. $\frac{5}{k} = -2.5$

19. $\frac{-10}{z} = -100$

20. $-13x = 0$

21. $\frac{m}{-4} = 0$

22. $\frac{4}{n} = 20$

23. $\frac{3}{s} = -36$

24. $\frac{\frac{1}{3}}{u} = \frac{1}{12}$

25. $\frac{\frac{1}{2}}{x} = -\frac{1}{6}$

26. $\frac{\frac{2}{3}}{s} = -\frac{2}{9}$

27. $\frac{-\frac{3}{4}}{y} = \frac{3}{20}$

28. $\frac{t}{\frac{1}{3}} = 6$

29. $\frac{u}{\frac{1}{2}} = -10$

30. $\frac{z}{-\frac{2}{3}} = 6$

Solving more difficult equations

By asking the right questions we can solve even more difficult equations.

Example: *i.* Solve $3x - 11 = 7$

We cover up $3x$ like this

$$\boxed{3x} \;\; - 11 = 7$$

and ask

What number minus 11 is equal to 7?
Answer: 18; therefore $3x = 18$

Now: 3 multiplied by what number is equal to 18?

Answer: 6

CHECK: $3x - 11 = 3 \cdot 6 - 11 = 18 - 11 = 7$

Thus, $\{6\}$ is the solution set of $3x - 11 = 7$.

Example: *ii.* Solve $3(x + 4) = 9$

We cover up $x + 4$ like this

$$3 \;\; \boxed{(x + 4)} \;\; = 9$$

and ask

3 times what number is equal to 9?
Answer: 3; therefore $x + 4 = 3$

Now: What number plus 4 is equal to 3?

Answer: -1

CHECK: $3(x + 4) = 3(-1 + 4) = 3 \cdot 3 = 9$

Thus, $\{-1\}$ is the solution set of $3(x + 4) = 9$.

Example: *iii.* Solve $\dfrac{y+3}{6} = 2$

$$\dfrac{y+3}{6} = 2$$

Question: What number divided by 6 is equal to 2?

Answer: 12; therefore $y + 3 = 12$

The solution of $y + 3 = 12$ is 9.

CHECK: $\dfrac{y+3}{6} = \dfrac{9+3}{6} = \dfrac{12}{6} = 2$

Therefore, the solution set of $\dfrac{y+3}{6} = 2$ is $\{9\}$.

Example: *iv.* Solve $5 - (2z + 3) = 4$

$$5 - \boxed{(2z + 3)} = 4$$

Question: 5 minus what number is equal to 4?

Answer: 1; therefore $\boxed{2z} + 3 = 1$.

Question: What number plus 3 is equal to 1?

Answer: -2; therefore $2z = -2$. The root of the last equation is -1.

CHECK: $5 - (2z + 3) = 5 - [2 \cdot (-1) + 3]$
$$= 5 - (-2 + 3) = 5 - 1 = 4$$

Therefore, the solution set of $5 - (2z + 3) = 4$ is $\{-1\}$.

EXERCISES

Determine the solution set of each of the following:

1. $2x - 3 = 5$
2. $5y + 3 = 8$
3. $2m - 1 = -3$
4. $4z + 9 = 1$
5. $3t - 10 = 0$
6. $4u - 3 = -3$
7. $\frac{1}{2}t + 4 = 3$
8. $\frac{s}{5} - 5 = -4$
9. $3 + x = 4$
10. $-2 + y = 0$
11. $-5 + 5z = 0$

12. $3 + 2t = -1$
13. $4 - 6u = 1$
14. $5 + 7n = 5$
15. $2(x + 1) = 6$
16. $3(v - 2) = -3$
17. $4(2m - 3) = 12$
18. $5(4m - 1) = -5$
19. $-2(3n + 3) = 6$
20. $-5(-x - 4) = -5$
21. $3(-4m + 3) = 12$
22. $5(1 + p) = 0$
23. $2(2 + 3s) = -2$

24. $3(3 - 2t) = 27$

25. $4(1 - 6u) = 0$

26. $2(x + 1) + 3(2x + 1) = 13$

27. $3(2y - 1) - 2(y + 3) = -17$

28. $4(1 + 2t) - 5(1 - t) = -14$

29. $\dfrac{x + 1}{2} = 3$

30. $\dfrac{2x - 3}{3} = 3$

31. $\dfrac{1 + 2m}{-5} = -7$

32. $\dfrac{5 - n}{-4} = -1$

33. $\dfrac{3t + 5}{7} = -1$

34. $\dfrac{4s + 1}{3} = -3$

35. $\dfrac{x + 1}{2} + \dfrac{x + 3}{2} = 7$

[HINT: First determine a single rational expression equivalent to $\dfrac{x + 1}{2} + \dfrac{x + 3}{2}$.]

36. $3 + (4x + 1) = -8$

37. $9 - (3y + 4) = 11$

38. $4 - (3 - z) = 0$

39. $5 + (4 - 2t) = 8$

40. $\frac{1}{2} - (9u + 2) = -6$

Simple uses of equations

In Chapter 8 we shall see equations as a powerful tool in solving various kinds of problems. Let us now see some examples of simple problems to which we find solutions by means of equations.

Example: *i.* I thought of a number, multiplied it by 2, added 5 to the product, and obtained 3 as a result. What is the number I thought of?

Since we don't know what this number is, we shall use a letter, say x, in place of a name of this number. Now we shall write expressions corresponding to the things said about this number in the problem.

> multiplied the number by 2: $x \cdot 2$ or $2x$
> added 5 to the product: $2x + 5$
> the result is 3: $2x + 5 = 3$

Now we have the equation

$$2x + 5 = 3$$

Solving this equation, we find that the root is -1. Thus, I thought of the number -1.

Let us check.

> multiply the number by 2: $-1 \times 2 = -2$
> add 5 to the product: $-2 + 5 = 3$

The result is 3, and therefore -1 *is* the correct answer to the problem.

Example: ii. How long is a rectangular plot if its length is 10 ft. longer than its width, and its perimeter is 52 ft.?

Let m be the number of feet in the width of the rectangle. Then the number of feet in the length is $m + 10$. Let us draw a picture to help us analyze and solve the problem.

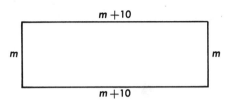

The number of feet in the perimeter is

$m + (m + 10) + m + (m + 10)$, or $4m + 20$

We are now ready to write an equation which fits the problem.

$$4m + 20 = 52$$

Solving the equation, $4m + 20 = 52$

$$4m = 32$$
$$m = 8$$

CHECK: The length is 10 ft. longer than the width, because $18 - 8 = 10$. The perimeter is $8 + 18 + 8 + 18 = 52$.

Thus, the rectangle is 8 ft. wide and 18 ft. long.

EXERCISES

Solve each of the following problems.

1. A number is multiplied by 3; 1 is added to the product, yielding -2. What is the number?

2. If 2 is added to a number and the sum is multiplied by 3, the result is zero. What is the number?

3. If 5 is subtracted from a number and the difference is multiplied by 4, the result is -12. What is the number?

4. The sum of a number and -1 is doubled, yielding 50. What is the number?

5. The sum of a number and 1 is doubled and the result is added to three times the difference of the number and 2. The result is 61. What is the number?

6. How long is a rectangular plot if its length is 9 ft. longer than its width, and its perimeter is 94 ft.?

7. The length of a rectangle is equal to five times its width. What is the width and the length of this rectangle if its perimeter is equal to 44 ft.?

8. The width of a rectangle is equal to one-third of its length. What is the width and the length of this rectangle if its perimeter is equal to 32 ft.?

9. The difference between the length and the width of a rectangle is 11 inches. What is the length and the width of the rectangle if its perimeter is equal to 26 inches?

10. Give all possible pairs of natural numbers which can be used for the length and the width of a rectangle in which the perimeter is 18 inches.

SIMPLE INEQUALITIES

You will recall that an open sentence like $x > 5$ is called an *inequality*. It is read "x is greater than 5." The sentence "$5 < x$" means the same as the previous sentence. It is read "5 is less than x."

The sentence "$x \not< 5$" is read "x is not less than 5," which, of course, means that x is greater than or equal to 5. What is the meaning of $x \not> 5$?

Inequalities, like equations, have *solution sets*. Solution sets of inequalities are sets of those numbers which satisfy the inequalities. For example, in the system of real numbers, the solution set of the inequality $x > 5$ is the set of all numbers greater than 5. If we call this set A, we will write

$$A = \{x \mid x > 5\}$$

which is read "A is the set of all x such that x is greater than 5."

At the beginning of this course, you learned to establish a one-to-one correspondence between numbers and points on a number line. Using the number line, we can locate points which correspond to the numbers which make up the solution set $A = \{x \mid x > 5\}$. On the graph at the top of the next page, this set is pictured by the part of the number line marked with a heavy trace.

$$A = \{x \mid x > 5\}$$

You should notice how we have shown that the point corresponding to the number 5 does not belong to the set. To include 5 in the set, we would write $\{x \mid x \geq 5\}$, which is read "the set of all x such that x is greater than *or* equal to 5." This set can be viewed as the union of the two sets

$$\{x \mid x > 5\} \cup \{x \mid x = 5\}$$

Its graph is as follows:

Notice that to show that 5 belongs to the set we did not circle the point corresponding to 5.

Here is another inequality and its graph.

$$-5 \leq m < 3$$

It is read "negative five is less than or equal to m and m is less than three." It can be written as $B = \{m \mid -5 \leq m < 3\}$ and viewed as the intersection of two sets.

$$\{m \mid m \geq -5\} \cap \{m \mid m < 3\}$$

$$B = \{m \mid -5 \leq m < 3\} = \{m \mid m \geq -5\} \cap \{m \mid m < 3\}$$

The graph of this set is a set of points making up a line segment with one endpoint missing. Notice that one endpoint belongs to the line segment (which?) and the other does not (which?). Explain why one endpoint is a part of the graph of the solution set and the other endpoint is not.

EXERCISES

1. *i.* Write out in words the description of each set listed on the next page.

    ii. Graph the solution set.

    iii. Describe the graph in words.
    (Assume in each case that the universal set is the set of real numbers.)

Example: $A = \{n|0 \le n \le 1\}$

   i. A is a set of real numbers n, where zero is less than or equal to n and n is less than or equal to one.

$A= \{n|0 \le n \le 1\}$

ii.

$$-3\ -2\ -1\quad 0\quad 1\quad 2\quad 3$$

   iii. The graph is a line segment.

a. $B = \{p|p > -3\}$ **g.** $T = \{u|1 \le u \le 2.3\}$

b. $R = \{a|a < 0\}$ **h.** $V = \{w|w \ne 0\}$

c. $M = \{s|s \ge 3\}$ **i.** $G = \{c|c \ne -2\}$

d. $X = \{b|b \le -1\}$ **j.** $W = \{m|m < 5 \text{ or } m > 7\}$

e. $Y = \{t|-2 < t < 3\}$ **k.** $J = \{x|-1 \le x \le 1\}$

f. $C = \{r|-\frac{1}{2} \le r < \frac{1}{2}\}$ **l.** $S = \{d|-1 \le d < 1\}$

2.   Graph the following sentences. Describe their graphs and solution sets. The universal set is the set of real numbers.

Example: *i.* $B = \{a|a < -1 \text{ and } a > \frac{1}{2}\}$

Graphing

$$-3\quad -2\quad -1\quad 0\quad 1\quad 2\quad 3$$

We observe that the graphs of $\{a|a < -1\}$ and $\{a|a > \frac{1}{2}\}$ have no points in common; therefore, the solution set is the empty set. Thus

$$B = \{a|a < -1 \text{ and } a > \tfrac{1}{2}\} = \phi$$

This can also be written as

$$B = \{a|a < -1\} \cap \{a|a > \tfrac{1}{2}\} = \phi$$

Example: *ii.* $R = \{s|s \ge 3 \text{ and } s < 4\frac{1}{2}\}$

Graphing

$$-2\quad -1\quad 0\quad 1\quad 2\quad 3\quad 4\quad 5\quad 6$$

We see that there are points common to both parts of the graph. Therefore the solution set is not the empty set. Thus

$$R = \{s|s \ge 3 \text{ and } s < 4\tfrac{1}{2}\} \ne \phi$$

This can also be written as

$$R = \{s|s \ge 3\} \cap \{s|s < 4\tfrac{1}{2}\} \ne \phi$$

a. $A = \{x | x > 5 \text{ and } x < -1\}$

b. $M = \{a | a \le -1\} \cap \{a | a \ge -1\}$

c. $P = \{n | n > -5 \text{ or } n < -5\}$

d. $E = \{c | c \le 6 \text{ or } c \ge 6\}$

e. $X = \{s | \frac{1}{2} < s < 0\}$

f. $C = \{g | -1 < g < -2\}$

g. $D = \{r | r < 2 \text{ or } r < -3\}$

3. Frequently we do not choose the set of real numbers R as the universal set. The universal set may be the set of natural numbers, N, the set of integers, I, or the set of rational numbers, Q.

Example: i. $T = \{x | x \in I \text{ and } -2 < x < 3\}$
is read

"the set of elements x such that x is an element of the set of integers, and -2 is less than x and x is less than 3."

If we graph on the "number line" the points which we associate with these numbers, we have this graph

Note that for integers, the "number line" consists of points which are not connected.

Example: ii. However, if the set $Y = \{w | w \in R \text{ and } -2 < x < 3\}$ is graphed on the number line, we have this graph.

$$\begin{array}{c} \xleftarrow{\quad} + \;\; + \;\; \oplus \;\; + \;\; + \;\; + \;\; + \;\; \oplus \;\; + \xrightarrow{\quad} \\ -4 \;\; -3 \;\; -2 \;\; -1 \;\;\;\; 0 \;\;\;\; 1 \;\;\;\; 2 \;\; 3 \;\;\;\; 4 \end{array}$$

   i. Write out in words the description of each set listed below.

   ii. Graph the solution set.

   iii. Describe the graph in words.

a. $T = \{s | s \in I \text{ and } s > 9 \text{ or } s < 13\}$

b. $G = \{x | x \in N \text{ and } 6 < x < 9\}$

c. $H = \{r | r \in R \text{ and } r < 3.5 \text{ and } r > 2.5\}$

d. $J = \{t | t \in I \text{ and } -3 \le t \le 5\}$

e. $C = \{y | y \in R \text{ and } -2.5 < y < 1 \text{ or } y > 5\}$

f. $K = \{z | z \in N \text{ and } z \not> 8\}$

g. $L = \{x | x \in R \text{ and } x > 2\frac{1}{2} \text{ and } x \ne 4\}$

h. $M = \{p | p \in I \text{ and } -7 < p < -5\}$

USING COVER-UP TECHNIQUE IN SOLVING EQUATIONS INVOLVING ABSOLUTE VALUE

From your study of the absolute value, you will recall that the equation

$$|a| = 3$$

has two roots, -3 and 3, because $|-3| = 3$ and $|3| = 3$. Thus, the equation $|a| = 3$ is equivalent to

$$a = 3 \quad or \quad a = -3$$

This observation will help us in solving more complicated equations.

Example: *i.* Solve $|z - 5| = 8$

$$|\quad z - 5 \quad| = 8$$

Question: The absolute value of what numbers is equal to 8?
Answer: 8 and -8; $z - 5 = 8$ or $z - 5 = -8$.

The root of $z - 5 = 8$ is 13.
The root of $z - 5 = -8$ is -3.

CHECK: $|z - 5| = |13 - 5| = |8| = 8$
$|z - 5| = |-3 - 5| = |-8| = 8$

Thus, the solution set of $|z - 5| = 8$ is $\{13, -3\}$.

Example: *ii.* Solve $|2m + 7| = 5$

$$|\quad 2m + 7 \quad| = 5$$

Question: The absolute value of what numbers is equal to 5?
Answer: 5 and -5; therefore $2m + 7 = 5$
         or $2m + 7 = -5$.

The root of $2m + 7 = 5$ is -1.
The root of $2m + 7 = -5$ is -6.

CHECK: $|2m + 7| = |2(-1) + 7| = |-2 + 7| = |5| = 5$
$|2m + 7| = |2(-6) + 7| = |-12 + 7| = |-5| = 5$

Thus, the solution set of $|2m + 7| = 5$ is $\{-1, -6\}$.

Example: *iii.* Solve $3 - |2t + 1| = 3$

$$3 - \boxed{|2t + 1|} = 3$$

Question: 3 minus what number is equal to 3?
Answer: 0; therefore, $|2t + 1| = 0$.

Question: The absolute value of what number is equal to 0?
Answer: 0; therefore, $2t + 1 = 0$.
The root of $2t + 1 = 0$ is $-\frac{1}{2}$.

CHECK: $3 - |2t + 1| = 3 - |2 \cdot (-\frac{1}{2}) + 1|$
$$= 3 - |-1 + 1| = 3 - |0| = 3 - 0 = 3$$

Thus, the solution set of $3 - |2t + 1| = 3$ is $\{-\frac{1}{2}\}$.

Example: *iv.* Solve $|s + 1| - 5 = -3$

$$\boxed{|s + 1|} - 5 = -3$$

Question: What number minus 5 is equal to -3?
Answer: 2; therefore, $|s + 1| = 2$.

$$| \boxed{s + 1} | = 2$$

Question: The absolute value of what numbers is equal to 2?
Answer: 2 and -2; thus, $s + 1 = 2$ or $s + 1 = -2$.

The root of $s + 1 = 2$ is 1.
The root of $s + 1 = -2$ is -3.

CHECK: $|s + 1| - 5 = |1 + 1| - 5 = |2| - 5 = 2 - 5 = -3$
$|s + 1| - 5 = |-3 + 1| - 5 = |-2| - 5 = 2 - 5 = -3$

Thus, the solution set of $|s + 1| - 5 = -3$ is $\{1, -3\}$.

Example: *v.* Solve $|5 - 7v| = -1$

Note that in this equation it is stated that the absolute value of some number is equal to -1. But we know that the absolute value of any real number is a positive number or 0. Therefore, there is no real number for which the absolute value is -1. Thus, the solution set of $|5 - 7v| = -1$ is ϕ.

Some equations are more complicated than the examples on pages 186 and 187, and it may be more difficult to solve them. In such cases it helps to have some kind of a "method," or "system," by which to "compute" the roots. In the next section, you will be taught a method which will enable you to solve more complicated equations.

EXERCISES

Solve each of the following equations and check.

1. $\lvert n \rvert = 10$	**12.** $\lvert \frac{1}{3}z + 6 \rvert = 15$	**23.** $3 - \lvert v \rvert = 2$
2. $\lvert 3d \rvert = 12$	**13.** $\lvert 14t - 6 \rvert = -12$	**24.** $\lvert 2n \rvert + 1 = 7$
3. $\lvert 4s \rvert = -5$	**14.** $\lvert 3p - 5 \rvert = 4$	**25.** $\lvert x + 1 \rvert - 2 = 9$
4. $\lvert 6t \rvert = 3$	**15.** $\lvert 2r \rvert = \lvert -3 \rvert$	**26.** $\lvert 2y - 3 \rvert + 1 = 0$
5. $\lvert 10u \rvert = 1$	**16.** $\lvert y \rvert = 0$	**27.** $\lvert \frac{1}{2}x + 4 \rvert - 2 = 5$
6. $\lvert \frac{1}{2}x \rvert = 5$	**17.** $\lvert 36z \rvert = 0$	
7. $\lvert 5 + y \rvert = 3$	**18.** $\lvert s + 2 \rvert = 0$	**28.** $\left\lvert \dfrac{y - 1}{4} \right\rvert = 8$
8. $\lvert t - 3 \rvert = 5$	**19.** $\lvert 3t + 3 \rvert = 0$	
9. $\lvert a + 2 \rvert = 1$	**20.** $\lvert 1 - 2u \rvert = 0$	**29.** $\left\lvert \dfrac{2 + z}{3} \right\rvert = 2$
10. $\lvert 2b - 1 \rvert = 9$	**21.** $\lvert 2b + 5 \rvert = 0$	
11. $\lvert 3n - 2 \rvert = 10$	**22.** $\lvert s + 1 \rvert = \frac{1}{2}$	**30.** $\left\lvert \dfrac{2 - v}{3} \right\rvert = 2$

EQUATION PROPERTIES

You learned to use the cover-up technique to solve some equations. We now would like to introduce a method which would enable us to solve any equation. This we shall do by introducing four *equation properties*, two for addition and two for multiplication.

The equation properties for addition

◼ *Right-hand Addition Property*
$\forall_x \forall_y \forall_z$, if $x = y$, then $x + z = y + z$

Using commutativity we obtain

◼ *Left-hand Addition Property*
$\forall_x \forall_y \forall_z$, if $x = y$, then $z + x = z + y$

In essence, these properties tell us that if we add the same number to each member of an equation, then the equation we obtain is equivalent to the original equation.

For example, if $x - 7 = 12$, then
$$x - 7 + 7 = 12 + 7$$
$$x = 19$$

and, thus, the solution set of $x - 7 = 12$ is $\{19\}$, which is easily verified.

We have seen that subtraction is the inverse of addition. Therefore, the equation property for addition can be extended to an equation property for subtraction (right-hand only).

■ $\forall_x \forall_y \forall_z$, if $x = y$, then $x + (-z) = y + (-z)$ or $x - z = y - z$

For example, if $x + 3 = 12$, then
$$x + 3 - 3 = 12 - 3$$
$$x = 9$$

Thus, the solution set of $x + 3 = 12$ is $\{9\}$.

The two equations above are very simple and could have been solved without the use of the equation property for addition. We used them to illustrate the use of this property which will prove a "life-saver" when we are confronted by more complicated equations.

EXERCISES

Use the appropriate equation properties to find the solution set of each equation.

Example: i. $x - 2 = -13$
$$x - 2 + 2 = -13 + 2$$
$$x = -11$$

CHECK: $x - 2 = -11 - 2 = -13$

The solution set of $x - 2 = -13$ is $\{-11\}$.

Example: ii. $3 - y = 17$
$$3 - y + y = 17 + y$$
$$3 = 17 + y$$
$$17 + y = 3$$
$$y + 17 = 3$$
$$y + 17 - 17 = 3 - 17$$
$$y = -14$$

CHECK: $3 - y = 3 - (-14) = 3 + 14 = 17$

The solution set of $3 - y = 17$ is $\{-14\}$.

Example: *iii.*

$$m + 4 = 3$$
$$m + 4 - 4 = 3 - 4$$
$$m = -1$$

CHECK: $m + 4 = -1 + 4 = 3$

The solution set of $m + 4 = 3$ is $\{-1\}$.

Example: *iv.*

$$12 + n = 14.5$$
$$n + 12 = 14.5$$
$$n + 12 - 12 = 14.5 - 12$$
$$n = 2.5$$

CHECK: $12 + n = 12 + 2.5 = 14.5$

The solution set of $12 + n = 14.5$ is $\{2.5\}$.

Example: *v.*

$$1.5 = 3.2 + s$$
$$3.2 + s = 1.5$$
$$s + 3.2 = 1.5$$
$$s + 3.2 - 3.2 = 1.5 - 3.2$$
$$s = -1.7$$

CHECK: $3.2 + s = 3.2 + (-1.7) = 1.5$

The solution set of $1.5 = 3.2 + s$ is $\{-1.7\}$.

1. $y + 6 = 21$
2. $a + 5 = 17$
3. $c + \frac{1}{3} = \frac{1}{2}$
4. $.7 + x = 0$
5. $d - 3 = 9$
6. $z - 7 = 1$
7. $b - 1 = -3$
8. $m - 15 = -8$
9. $r - \frac{1}{3} = \frac{1}{2}$
10. $s - 16 = 0$
11. $f - \frac{2}{3} = -\frac{1}{3}$
12. $t + \frac{3}{11} = \frac{1}{11}$
13. $u + \frac{4}{7} = -\frac{3}{7}$
14. $w - \frac{3}{2} = -\frac{5}{7}$
15. $-7 + r = -8$
16. $-11 = x + 7$
17. $s - 3.1 = 4.7$
18. $x - (-11) = 14$

19. $(-3.5) - y = 7.5$
20. $14.1 = z - 7.9$
21. $x - \frac{4}{3} = -\frac{5}{3}$
22. $t - 2.2 = -5.3$
23. $-4\frac{1}{4} = s - \frac{3}{4}$
24. $1.4 - x = 7.2$
25. $w + \frac{4}{9} = \frac{1}{9}$
26. $-1.9 + v = -41.7$
27. $-4.3 = 7.2 + k$
28. $y - \frac{5}{3} = -\frac{4}{9}$
29. $-1.6 - x = 14.1$
30. $-7.9 = 1.3 - y$
31. $4\frac{7}{8} + x = -17\frac{1}{8}$
32. $-\frac{7}{5} + z = \frac{4}{3}$
33. $v - \frac{5}{3} = -\frac{9}{4}$
34. $-5.9 = x - 3.4$
35. $m - 3\frac{1}{2} = 6\frac{3}{4}$
36. $-x + 7 = 19$

37. $-4 - y = 13$

38. $-5.9 = y - 7.1$

39. $\frac{4}{3} + r = 1$

40. $t + \frac{7}{8} = \frac{1}{4}$

41. $-y + \frac{4}{3} = -\frac{7}{5}$

42. $-\frac{7}{5} = \frac{7}{10} - z$

43. $\frac{5}{11} - x = \frac{1}{11}$

44. $6.23 + y = -7.96$

45. $6\frac{3}{8} = z - 3\frac{1}{4}$

46. $-21.8 = x + 7.3$

47. $-3.9 - y = -5.9$

48. $-1.1 = -1.1 - t$

The equation properties for multiplication

We now state a third equation property, which we call the Right-hand Multiplication Property.

■ *Right-hand Multiplication Property*
$\forall_x \forall_y \forall_{z \neq 0}$, if $x = y$, then $xz = yz$

We obtain the Left-hand Multiplication Property by using commutativity.

■ *Left-hand Multiplication Property*
$\forall_x \forall_y \forall_{z \neq 0}$, if $x = y$, then $zx = zy$

These properties tell us that if we multiply each member of an equation by the same non-zero number, then the equation we obtain is equivalent to the original equation.

For example, if $\frac{1}{3}x = \frac{1}{2}$, then
$$(\tfrac{1}{3}x)3 = \tfrac{1}{2} \cdot 3$$
$$x = \tfrac{3}{2}$$

and, thus, the solution set of $\frac{1}{3}x = \frac{1}{2}$ is $\{\frac{3}{2}\}$, since $(\frac{1}{3})(\frac{3}{2}) = \frac{1}{2}$. That is, $\frac{3}{2}$ in place of x in $\frac{1}{3}x = \frac{1}{2}$ gives a true statement.

Since division is the inverse of multiplication, the equation property for multiplication (right-hand only) also applies to division.

■ $\forall_x \forall_y \forall_{z \neq 0}$, if $x = y$, then $xz = yz$ or $x \cdot \dfrac{1}{z} = y \cdot \dfrac{1}{z}$ or $\dfrac{x}{z} = \dfrac{y}{z}$

For example, if $5x = -3$, then
$$\frac{5x}{5} = \frac{-3}{5}$$
$$x = -\frac{3}{5}$$

and the solution set of $5x = -3$ is $\{-\frac{3}{5}\}$. Verify this.

EXERCISES

Use the appropriate equation properties to find the solution set of each equation.

Examples: i. $\frac{1}{3}y = -2$
$$(\tfrac{1}{3}y)3 = -2 \cdot 3$$
$$y = -6$$

Verify that $\{-6\}$ is the solution set of $\frac{1}{3}y = -2$.

ii. $5t = -70$
$$\frac{5t}{5} = \frac{-70}{5}$$
$$t = -14$$

Verify that $\{-14\}$ is the solution set of $5t = -70$.

iii. $\frac{2}{3}u = \frac{1}{2}$
$$(\tfrac{2}{3}u)\tfrac{3}{2} = \tfrac{1}{2} \cdot \tfrac{3}{2}$$
$$u = \tfrac{3}{4}$$

Verify that $\{\frac{3}{4}\}$ is the solution set of $\frac{2}{3}u = \frac{1}{2}$.

We can also solve this equation using division.

$$\frac{2}{3}u = \frac{1}{2}$$
$$\frac{\frac{2}{3}u}{\frac{2}{3}} = \frac{\frac{1}{2}}{\frac{2}{3}}$$
$$u = \tfrac{3}{4}$$

and again we obtain $\{\frac{3}{4}\}$ for the solution set.

1. $\frac{1}{2}x = 2$
2. $\frac{1}{3}y = -1$
3. $\frac{1}{4}t = -\frac{1}{2}$
4. $-\frac{1}{2}u = 3$
5. $-\frac{1}{5}s = -1$
6. $4s = 36$
7. $3a = -27$
8. $16x = -48$
9. $-96y = -16$
10. $100z = 1$
11. $10p = -2$
12. $-\frac{2}{3}t = \frac{2}{3}$
13. $\frac{1}{4}u = -\frac{3}{2}$
14. $67r = -67$
15. $\frac{9}{2}c = \frac{1}{9}$
16. $-\frac{1}{3}r = \frac{1}{3}$

17. $-\frac{10}{3}h = -\frac{1}{3}$
18. $-70 = 3.5r$
19. $\frac{5}{7}x = -\frac{4}{7}$
20. $-4.7y = 9.4$
21. $.7y = 8.4$
22. $-\frac{1}{5} = \frac{1}{7}y$
23. $-\frac{2}{3}x = -\frac{2}{3}$
24. $\frac{3}{4}r = \frac{7}{4}$
25. $-\frac{5}{2} = 10y$
26. $\frac{2}{3} = \frac{w}{7}$
27. $-4.2x = 2.1$
28. $2\frac{1}{3}y = -\frac{7}{8}$
29. $-3.9 = \frac{1.3}{x}$

30. $-2.1 = .7r$
31. $-\frac{4}{9} = -\frac{1}{3}x$
32. $-\frac{7}{12}y = -\frac{5}{6}$
33. $\frac{y}{2.5} = 1.2$
34. $.36 = 3.6x$
35. $-10 = -\frac{r}{1.9}$
36. $\frac{6}{7}t = -1.2$
37. $1.2 = -3.6w$
38. $-\frac{5}{7}v = -\frac{3}{14}$
39. $-\frac{9}{8} = -\frac{1}{4}x$
40. $-\frac{3}{19}x = \frac{3}{38}$
41. $\frac{8}{13}y = -\frac{1}{26}$
42. $-1.3t = -3.9$

Using the equation properties

We shall now illustrate the use of the equation properties in solving equations. We shall also use properties and theorems which were established earlier.

Example: i. $2x + 1 = x - 3$
$$2x + 1 - 1 = x - 3 - 1$$
$$2x = x - 4$$
$$2x - x = x - 4 - x$$
$$x = -4$$

CHECK:

$2x + 1$	$=$	$x - 3$
$2(-4) + 1$		$-4 - 3$
$-8 + 1$		-7
-7		

Thus, $\{-4\}$ is the solution set of $2x + 1 = x - 3$.

Example: ii. $3(y + 2) = 2(2y - 1)$
$$3y + 6 = 4y - 2$$
$$3y + 6 + 2 = 4y - 2 + 2$$
$$3y + 8 = 4y$$
$$3y + 8 - 3y = 4y - 3y$$
$$8 = y$$
$$y = 8$$

CHECK:

$3(y + 2)$	$=$	$2(2y - 1)$
$3(8 + 2)$		$2(2 \cdot 8 - 1)$
$3 \cdot 10$		$2(16 - 1)$
30		$2 \cdot 15$
		30

Thus, $\{8\}$ is the solution set of $3(y + 2) = 2(2y - 1)$.

Example: iii. $5a + 1 - 3a = 4a - 2$
$$5a - 3a + 1 = 4a - 2$$
$$2a + 1 = 4a - 2$$
$$2a + 1 - 2a = 4a - 2 - 2a$$
$$2a - 2a + 1 = 4a - 2a - 2$$
$$1 = 2a - 2$$
$$1 + 2 = 2a - 2 + 2$$
$$3 = 2a$$
$$a = \tfrac{3}{2}$$

CHECK:

$$5a + 1 - 3a \quad = \quad 4a - 2$$

$5a + 1 - 3a$	$4a - 2$
$5 \cdot \frac{3}{2} + 1 - 3 \cdot \frac{3}{2}$	$4 \cdot \frac{3}{2} - 2$
$\frac{15}{2} + 1 - \frac{9}{2}$	$\frac{12}{2} - 2$
$\frac{6}{2} + 1$	$6 - 2$
$3 + 1$	4
4	

Thus, $\{\frac{3}{2}\}$ is the solution set of the given equation.

Example: iv.
$$2(2m - 1) + 3 = 4(m + 4) - 2$$
$$4m - 2 + 3 = 4m + 16 - 2$$
$$4m + 1 = 4m + 14$$
$$4m + 1 - 4m = 4m + 14 - 4m$$
$$1 = 14$$

The last statement is false, no matter what the replacement for m is.

Thus, the solution set of $2(2m - 1) + 3 = 4(m + 4) - 2$ is ϕ.

Some equations are of the form $\frac{a}{b} = \frac{c}{d}$, where $b \neq 0$ and $d \neq 0$. Using bd to multiply by and applying the right-hand multiplication property, we obtain

$$\left(\frac{a}{b}\right)(bd) = \left(\frac{c}{d}\right)(bd)$$

$$\frac{abd}{b} = \frac{bcd}{d}$$

$$ad = bc \text{ and so we have proved}$$

Theorem 1 $\forall_a \, \forall_{b \neq 0} \, \forall_c \, \forall_{d \neq 0}$, if $\frac{a}{b} = \frac{c}{d}$, then $ad = bc$

We now illustrate the use of this theorem in solving an equation.

$$\frac{2t + 1}{3} = \frac{3t + 8}{-2}$$
$$(2t + 1)(-2) = 3(3t + 8)$$
$$-4t - 2 = 9t + 24$$
$$-4t - 2 + 4t = 9t + 24 + 4t$$
$$-2 = 13t + 24$$
$$13t + 24 = -2$$
$$13t + 24 - 24 = -2 - 24$$
$$13t = -26$$
$$t = -2$$

Check to see whether $\{-2\}$ is the solution set of the original equation.

Example: i.

$$2 - \frac{4}{r} = \frac{7}{5r}, \quad (r \neq 0)$$

$$5r\left(2 - \frac{4}{r}\right) = 5r\left(\frac{7}{5r}\right)$$

$$5r \cdot 2 - 5r \cdot \frac{4}{r} = 7$$

$$10r - 20 = 7$$

$$10r = 27$$

$$r = \tfrac{27}{10}$$

$$r = 2.7$$

Check to see whether $\{2.7\}$ is the solution set of

$$2 - \frac{4}{r} = \frac{7}{5r}.$$

Example: ii.

$$\frac{7}{t} = \frac{5}{t} + \frac{3}{t-5}, \quad (t \neq 0, \, t \neq 5)$$

$$t(t-5) \cdot \frac{7}{t} = t(t-5)\left(\frac{5}{t} + \frac{3}{t-5}\right)$$

Note that $t(t-5)$ is a good choice of replacement for z in the left-hand multiplication property.

$$(t-5) \cdot 7 = (t-5) \cdot 5 + t \cdot 3$$

$$7t - 35 = 5t - 25 + 3t$$

$$7t - 35 = 8t - 25$$

$$-35 + 25 = 8t - 7t$$

$$-10 = t$$

Check to see whether $\{-10\}$ is the solution set of

$$\frac{7}{t} = \frac{5}{t} + \frac{3}{t-5}.$$

EXERCISES

Find the solution set of each equation.

1. $6c - 3c = 9$
2. $5t - 7t = -12$
3. $x - 2x = -\frac{1}{2}$
4. $\frac{1}{3}r + \frac{1}{2}r = 5$
5. $1.7d - .3d = -4.2$
6. $4s - \frac{1}{2}s = 2s + 3$
7. $3 + 4z = z - 4$
8. $\frac{1}{4}m - \frac{3}{4}m + \frac{1}{2} = 2m - \frac{1}{2}$
9. $3x - 2 + x = x - 4x$

10. $3.6b - 1.7b = 2b - .5$
11. $\frac{1}{2} - z = 2z + \frac{3}{4}$
12. $8a - .73 = .36 + 7a$
13. $-19 = \frac{3}{2}x - 13$
14. $.7r - 1.2 = 4.7r$
15. $\frac{x}{-5} + 7 = -11$
16. $\frac{-3}{y} - 1.4 = 7.6$

17. $\frac{4}{3}x - 7 = 6 + \frac{7}{3}x$

18. $\dfrac{6}{7 - x} = -4$

19. $7x + 13 = 13x - 16$

20. $7 - 12x = 7x + 17$

21. $\dfrac{7}{t} - 6 = \dfrac{-9}{t}$

22. $-5 + \dfrac{4}{y} = \dfrac{7}{y} - 6$

23. $3(x + 4) = -7$

24. $\frac{7}{3}(7 - y) = -21$

25. $\dfrac{y - 6}{y} = -3$

26. $7 = \dfrac{3 + s}{s}$

27. $\dfrac{y}{y - 6} = \dfrac{7}{3}$

28. $\dfrac{6 - x}{7} = 4x$

29. $\dfrac{x + 13}{-5} = -7x$

30. $\frac{4}{3}x + 5 = \frac{7}{9}x + 7$

31. $7 = -\dfrac{x + 3}{x}$

32. $3(5 + v) = 4v + 7$

33. $-7s + \dfrac{4}{9} = \dfrac{7s - 11}{9}$

34. $\frac{8}{9} + 3w = w + \frac{2}{9}$

35. $-\dfrac{7}{2} + 2r = \dfrac{5(6 + 7r)}{2}$

36. $\frac{7}{5}s = \frac{3}{5} + 2s$

37. $-5 = \dfrac{-7}{x + 9}$

38. $\frac{5}{3}x + 13 - \frac{7}{3}x = 15$

39. $\dfrac{4u - 1}{2} = \dfrac{2u + 22}{4}$

40. $\dfrac{1 + 3n}{4} = \dfrac{-7 - n}{-3}$

41. $\dfrac{1 + y}{2} = \dfrac{-(2 - y)}{5}$

42. $\dfrac{3 + 5n}{4} + \dfrac{n - 15}{3} = 10$

43. $\dfrac{-(m + 1)}{3} + \dfrac{4 - m}{2} = 10$

44. $\dfrac{-(2x + 3)}{4} = \dfrac{-(10 + 6x)}{8}$

45. $\dfrac{\frac{1}{2} - m}{3} = \dfrac{2m - 9}{2}$

Writing equivalent expressions

You have already had some experience in writing an expression equivalent to a given expression. For example, $3x - 5x + 1.5 + 4x$ and $2x + 1.5$ are two equivalent expressions, because on replacing x throughout by the name of any one number, each expression will name the same number. That this is so can be easily proved.

$$3x - 5x + 1.5 + 4x = [3x + (-5)x + 4x] + 1.5$$
$$= [3 + (-5) + 4]x + 1.5$$
$$= 2x + 1.5$$

Of course, there are many other ways of proving these two expressions equivalent.

You no doubt observe that, for many purposes, the second expression above is "simpler" than the first expression.

In solving equations, you frequently found it convenient to write, in place of expressions containing parentheses, equivalent expressions which do not contain parentheses. Let us consider, for example, $2(x + 3)$. An expression which is equivalent to this, and which does not contain parentheses, is $2x + 6$. $2x + 6$ is obtained from $2(x + 3)$ by applying LDPMA.

Examples: *i.* Write an expression equivalent to $-3(y + 7)$.
$$-3(y + 7) = -3y + (-3) \cdot 7$$
$$= -3y - 3 \cdot 7$$
$$= -3y - 21$$

Thus, $-3(y + 7)$ and $-3y - 21$ are equivalent expressions. One contains parentheses, the other does not.

ii. Write an expression equivalent to $4(a - b)$.

$$4(a - b) = 4a - 4b$$

Thus, $4(a - b)$ and $4a - 4b$ are equivalent expressions.

iii. Write an expression equivalent to $-2(m - n - 5)$.

$$-2(m - n - 5) = -2[m + (-n) + (-5)]$$
$$= -2m + (-2) \cdot (-n) + (-2) \cdot (-5)$$
$$= -2m + 2n + 10$$

Thus, $-2(m - n - 5)$ and $-2m + 2n + 10$ are equivalent expressions.

iv. Write an expression equivalent to $(5c - 3d)(-\frac{1}{2})$.

$$(5c - 3d)(-\tfrac{1}{2}) = (5c)(-\tfrac{1}{2}) - (3d)(-\tfrac{1}{2})$$
$$= -\tfrac{5}{2}c + \tfrac{3}{2}d$$

Thus, $(5c - 3d) \cdot (-\frac{1}{2})$ and $-\frac{5}{2}c + \frac{3}{2}d$ are equivalent expressions.

You should by now be able to skip the intermediate steps when writing equivalent expressions. In the examples below some steps are omitted. Can you see how each step is obtained? If not, fill in the missing steps using the appropriate properties and theorems.

Examples: *i.* $\frac{1}{3}(a - 3b + 6c) = \frac{1}{3}a - b + 2c$

ii. $(x - y + 2z)(-3) = -3x + 3y - 6z$

iii. $m \cdot \left(\dfrac{4 - a}{x}\right) = m \cdot \left(\dfrac{4}{x} - \dfrac{a}{x}\right)$
$$= \dfrac{4m}{x} - \dfrac{am}{x}$$

Examples: iv. $\left(-\frac{1}{2}\right) \cdot \left(\frac{2}{x-y}\right) = \frac{-1}{x-y}$

$$= \frac{1}{y-x}$$

v. $\left(\frac{4a-3b}{3}\right) \cdot \left(-\frac{4}{5}\right) = \frac{(4a-3b)(-4)}{3 \cdot 5}$

$$= \frac{-16a+12b}{15}$$

$$= -\frac{16a}{15} + \frac{12b}{15}$$

$$= -\frac{16a}{15} + \frac{4b}{5}$$

EXERCISES

For each expression below, write an expression which is equivalent to it and which does not contain parentheses.

1. $3(m+2)$
2. $-1(2x+5)$
3. $-\frac{3}{4}(6+3d)$
4. $(x+y) \cdot (-5)$
5. $12(a-4)$
6. $-3(b-7)$
7. $9(M-N)$
8. $-\frac{2}{5}(3k-5s)$
9. $(1.5u-3.7) \cdot 5$
10. $4(a+b-c)$
11. $-3(s-t+11)$
12. $(-2x-3y-4z) \cdot (-2)$
13. $(u+v+w) \cdot a$
14. $-b \cdot (2a+3c-4d)$
15. $-\frac{3}{4}k \cdot (-m-p-r)$
16. $\frac{7}{8}(16x+\frac{8}{7}y)$
17. $\left(-\frac{3}{4}\right) \cdot (r-2s+3t)$
18. $(-3) \cdot \left(\frac{x-y}{2}\right)$
19. $6 \cdot \left(\frac{x}{y}+13\right)$
20. $(3.5+v) \cdot (-6)$
21. $(-3) \cdot (w+3t)$

22. $\left(\frac{1}{4}\right) \cdot \left(\frac{2}{3}y - \frac{3}{4}x\right)$
23. $(.07-1.3r) \cdot (-.2)$
24. $4 \cdot \left(\frac{3x-y}{x}\right)$
25. $-5 \cdot (x-2y+3z)$
26. $(w+7v-9t) \cdot (-3)$
27. $\left(\frac{3}{4}\right) \cdot \left(\frac{1}{2x+y}\right)$
28. $\left(\frac{3}{7x-3y}\right) \cdot \left(-\frac{5}{6}\right)$
29. $\left(\frac{3}{4}\right) \cdot \left(3x - \frac{4}{5}y - 6z\right)$
30. $\left(\frac{2x-3y}{5}\right) \cdot \left(-\frac{7}{3}\right)$
31. $\left(\frac{3}{5}\right) \cdot \left(\frac{4}{x+2y}\right)$
32. $\left(-\frac{7}{8}\right) \cdot (13-x)$
33. $\left(7 - \frac{x}{3}\right) \cdot \left(-\frac{1}{7}\right)$
34. $\left(-\frac{4}{9}\right)(3x-2w)$
35. $(-7) \cdot (3x-4y-7z)$
36. $(4w-7r+6t) \cdot \left(-\frac{3}{7}\right)$

POLYNOMIALS

In Chapter 5 you have seen that algebraic expressions are classified according to the number of terms they contain.

Each of the following is a term or a monomial.

5 $3x$ $-\frac{1}{2}y$ $.7ab$ $3xyz$ $-1.6amxr$

Each of the following is a binomial.

$a + x$ $3 + acxy$ $.6 + 3x$

$-ay + bx$ $-\frac{1}{2}ab + (-\frac{1}{3}xyz)$ $4xmu - 2ya$

Each of the following is a trinomial.

$2 + x + y$ $\frac{1}{5} - 4m + ab$

$3x - 2y + 7xyz$ $-anr + 2bc - 1.7an$

$-\frac{1}{2}a + .7b + (-3abc)$

Expressions consisting of one term, two terms, three terms, and more than three terms are called *polynomials*. Look up the meaning of the prefix "poly" in your dictionary.

You have already learned how to find expressions equivalent to a given expression by the use of basic properties and theorems. You found, for example, that the distributive properties are extremely useful in finding equivalent expressions.

To find an expression equivalent to a given expression, you perform some operations. Each operation must be based on some property or theorem. Study the examples below and see whether you understand each step.

Examples: Multiplication of two monomials

$i.$ $(3a) \cdot (-2c) = 3[a \cdot (-2)]c$
$= 3[-2 \cdot a]c$
$= [3 \cdot (-2)]ac$
$= -6ac$

Thus, $\forall_a \forall_c (3a) \cdot (-2c) = -6ac$

$ii.$ $(-\frac{1}{2}xy) \cdot (-18ab) = -\frac{1}{2}x(-18yab)$
$= -\frac{1}{2}(-18xyab)$
$= 9xyab$

Thus, $\forall_x \forall_y \forall_a \forall_b (-\frac{1}{2}xy) \cdot (-18ab) = 9xyab$

Examples: Multiplication of a binomial and a monomial

i. $4m[-2x + (-3y)] = 4m \cdot (-2x) + 4m \cdot (-3y)$
$$= [4 \cdot (-2)]mx + [4 \cdot (-3)]my$$
$$= -8mx + (-12)my$$
$$= -8mx - 12my$$

Thus, $\forall_m \forall_x \forall_y \; 4m[-2x + (-3y)] = -8mx - 12my$

ii. $(4am - xy)(-2ay) = (4am)(-2ay) - (xy)(-2ay)$
$$= -8a^2my + 2axy^2$$

Thus, $\forall_a \forall_m \forall_y \forall_x \; (4am - xy)(-2ay) = -8a^2my + 2axy^2$

Examples: Multiplication of two binomials

i. $(a + b)(x + y) = (a + b)x + (a + b)y$
$$= ax + bx + ay + by$$

Thus, $\forall_a \forall_b \forall_x \forall_y \; (a + b)(x + y) = ax + bx + ay + by$

ii. $(a + b)(x - y) = (a + b)x - (a + b)y$
$$= ax + bx - ay - by$$

Thus, $\forall_a \forall_b \forall_x \forall_y \; (a + b)(x - y) = ax + bx - ay - by$

iii. $(a - b)(x - y) = (a - b)x - (a - b)y$
$$= ax - bx - ay + by$$

Thus, $\forall_a \forall_b \forall_x \forall_y \; (a - b)(x - y) = ax - bx - ay + by$

There are certain binomials which recur quite frequently in algebra. It is to your advantage to be thoroughly familiar with the results of multiplying these binomials. The first of these is the result of multiplying a binomial by itself.

$$(x + y)(x + y) = (x + y)x + (x + y)y$$
$$= xx + yx + xy + yy$$
$$= x^2 + xy + xy + y^2$$
$$= x^2 + 2xy + y^2$$

Thus, $\forall_x \forall_y \; (x + y)(x + y) = x^2 + 2xy + y^2$

Another important result is that of multiplying a sum of two terms by their difference.

$$(x + y)(x - y) = (x + y)x - (x + y)y$$
$$= xx + yx - xy - yy$$
$$= x^2 + xy - xy - y^2$$
$$= x^2 - y^2$$

Thus, $\forall_x \forall_y \; (x + y)(x - y) = x^2 - y^2$

EXERCISES

1.   Classify each of the following as a monomial, binomial, or trinomial (all letters are variables).

a. $2x + 3y$

b. $m + p + s$

c. $-2s + 3t - 4xy$

d. $3x$

e. $-2xyz$

f. $105a + 2b - c$

g. -3

h. $5u - 7v$

i. $25dx$

j. $-xy + xz$

k. $4abc$

l. $u + m$

2.   Multiply and simplify wherever possible.

a. $3x \cdot 4y$

b. $4(m + n)$

c. $-3(x + y)$

d. $(2a + 5)(5)$

e. $(3c + 4d)(-8)$

f. $(\frac{1}{2}r + \frac{1}{3}s)(-6)$

g. $13(.3t - .4u)$

h. $15[-5d + (-7f)]$

i. $100(-2r + s)$

j. $(a + b)(x + t)$

k. $(2f - g)(f + 2g)$

l. $(m + s)(m - s)$

m. $(3a + 4b)(3a - 4b)$

n. $(2c + d)(2c + d)$

o. $(q + u)(3u - q)$

p. $5(x + z)(x + z)$

q. $13(5m + 3)(3n - 7)$

r. $\frac{1}{3}(6n + 15)(6n - 15)$

s. $(m + n)(m + n)(m + n)$

t. $(a + b + c)(a + b + c)$

u. $(x+y+z+w)(x+y+z+w)$

v. $[(x + y) - z][(x + y) + z]$

w. $(x - w + v)(x + w - v)$

x. $(3r + 4s)(7r + 5s)$

y. $(3y + 4x)(7x + 13y)$

z. $(11r + 6s)(7r - 5s)$

More equations

Frequently, in solving equations, you first find expressions which are simpler looking and which are equivalent to the expressions involved in the equations. For example, in solving the equation $4m - 1.5m = 2m + 5$, you would proceed as follows:

$$4m - 1.5m = 2m + 5$$
$$2.5m = 2m + 5$$
$$2.5m - 2m = 2m + 5 - 2m$$
$$.5m = 5$$
$$m = 10$$

CHECK:

$4m - 1.5m$	$= 2m + 5$
$4 \times 10 - 1.5 \times 10$	$2 \times 10 + 5$
$40 - 15$	$20 + 5$
25	25

The solution set is $\{10\}$. This is sometimes written as
$$\{m \mid 4m - 1.5m = 2m + 5\} = \{10\}$$
and is read "the set of all real numbers m such that $4m - 1.5m = 2m + 5$ is the set consisting of the number 10."

Now let us solve other equations.

Example: i. $-\frac{1}{2}(3t - 5) = 4t - 3(t + \frac{1}{4})$

$$-\frac{3}{2}t + \frac{5}{2} = 4t - 3t - \frac{3}{4}$$

$$-\frac{3}{2}t + \frac{5}{2} = t - \frac{3}{4}$$

$$-\frac{3}{2}t + \frac{5}{2} - t = t - \frac{3}{4} - t$$

$$-\frac{5}{2}t + \frac{5}{2} = -\frac{3}{4}$$

$$-\frac{5}{2}t + \frac{5}{2} - \frac{5}{2} = -\frac{3}{4} - \frac{5}{2}$$

$$-\frac{5}{2}t = -\frac{13}{4}$$

$$(-\frac{2}{5})(-\frac{5}{2}t) = (-\frac{2}{5})(-\frac{13}{4})$$

$$t = \frac{26}{20}$$

$$t = \frac{13}{10}, \text{ or } t = 1.3$$

CHECK:

$-\frac{1}{2}(3t - 5)$	$=$	$4t - 3(t + \frac{1}{4})$
$-\frac{1}{2}(3 \cdot 1.3 - 5)$		$4 \cdot 1.3 - 3(1.3 + \frac{1}{4})$
$-\frac{1}{2}(3.9 - 5)$		$5.2 - 3 \cdot 1.55$
$-\frac{1}{2} \cdot (-1.1)$		$5.2 - 4.65$
$.55$		$.55$

The solution set is $\{1.3\}$

As before, this can be stated

$$\{t \mid \tfrac{1}{2}(3t - 5) = 4t - 3(t + \tfrac{1}{4})\} = \{1.3\}$$

Example: ii. Consider the equation

$$5(y + \tfrac{2}{5}) - 3y = -5 - (-2y - 7)$$

Simplifying, we get

$$5y + 2 - 3y = -5 + 2y + 7$$
$$2y + 2 = 2y + 2$$
$$2 = 2$$

$2 = 2$ is a true statement no matter what replacement is made for y. Hence the equation
$$5(y + \tfrac{2}{5}) - 3y = -5 - (-2y - 7)$$
has as its roots *all* real numbers. Its solution set is the set of all real numbers. This can be written as

$$\{y \mid 5(y + \tfrac{2}{5}) - 3y = -5 - (-2y - 7)\}$$
$$= \text{the set of all real numbers}$$

This set is equivalent to the set $\{y \mid 2 = 2\}$, meaning the set of all y for which $2 = 2$. The last sentence is true no matter what replacement is made for y.

Example: *iii.* Consider one more equation

$$5(x - 2) + 2(x + 6) = 3x + 6 + 4(x + 1)$$

Simplifying

$$5x - 10 + 2x + 12 = 3x + 6 + 4x + 4$$
$$7x + 2 = 7x + 10$$
$$2 = 10$$

There is no replacement for x such that $2 = 10$, hence we say that the equation

$$5(x - 2) + 2(x + 6) = 3x + 6 + 4(x + 1)$$

has no roots, or that its solution set is the empty set. We are thinking of a set of values of x for which $5(x - 2) + 2(x + 6) = 3x + 6 + 4(x + 1)$ is true. This is written

$$\{x \mid 5(x - 2) + 2(x + 6) = 3x + 6 + 4(x + 1)\} = \phi$$

and is read "the set of all x (assumed to be real numbers) such that $5(x - 2) + 2(x + 6)$ equals $3x + 6 + 4(x + 1)$ is the empty set." This can also be written, as has been shown

$$\{x \mid 2 = 10\} = \phi$$

EXERCISES

Determine the solution sets if the universal set is the set of real numbers. No denominator is zero.

1. $\{m \mid 5(m + 2) = 10\}$
2. $\{x \mid 3(x - 6) = -9\}$
3. $\{t \mid -2(2t - 3) = -6\}$
4. $\{y \mid -6(7y + 5) = 12\}$
5. $\{a \mid 3(2a + 5) - 7(a - 6) = 2(19 - 10a)\}$
6. $\{r \mid -1 + 3r = 3(r - 1)\}$
7. $\left\{y \mid \dfrac{y - 7}{6} = 2y + 8\right\}$
8. $\{x \mid 3x + 2 + x = -(x + 2) + 3\}$
9. $\{v \mid 4(3v + 2) = 5(v + \tfrac{8}{5}) + 7v\}$
10. $\{x \mid 3(x - 5) = 3(4 - x)\}$

11. $\left\{v \left| \dfrac{1}{v} + \dfrac{3}{v-1} = \dfrac{7}{v} \right.\right\}$

12. $\{x \mid 7 + 6x + 5 = -3(2 - 2x) + 18\}$

13. $\{y \mid y + 13 = -(y + 3)\}$

14. $\left\{x \left| \dfrac{x+3}{2} = 7 \right.\right\}$

15. $\{v \mid 5(3 - 2v) = 4(2 - v) - 6v\}$

16. $\{x \mid 3(x - 3) = 4(3 - x)\}$

17. $\left\{y \left| \dfrac{y}{\frac{1}{3}} = -6 \right.\right\}$

18. $\left\{r \left| \dfrac{3}{r-3} + \dfrac{5}{r} = \dfrac{25}{2r} \right.\right\}$

19. $\{x \mid 3x - 7 = -(7 - 3x)\}$

20. $\left\{x \left| \dfrac{4x+7}{3} = \dfrac{4}{3}x + 7 \right.\right\}$

21. $\left\{t \left| \dfrac{t+6}{4} = 2(t + 2.5) \right.\right\}$

22. $\{y \mid y - 1 = -y - (y + 1) + 2y\}$

23. $\left\{v \left| \dfrac{v-3}{v} = \dfrac{1}{4} \right.\right\}$

24. $\left\{x \left| \dfrac{4(x-1)}{2} = 2x - 3 \right.\right\}$

25. $\left\{s \left| \dfrac{4}{3}(s - 3) = s + 2 - \left(6 - \dfrac{s}{3}\right) \right.\right\}$

26. $\left\{x \left| \dfrac{4}{x} + \dfrac{3}{x} + \dfrac{7}{8} = \dfrac{6}{x} \right.\right\}$

27. $\left\{t \left| 4t = \dfrac{1}{3}t - \dfrac{11}{3} \right.\right\}$

28. $\left\{y \left| \dfrac{7}{y+2} = \dfrac{11}{y} \right.\right\}$

29. $\left\{v \left| \dfrac{3}{2-v} = \dfrac{3}{v-2} \right.\right\}$

30. $\left\{s \left| \dfrac{3}{4-s} = \dfrac{-5}{2s-5} \right.\right\}$

31. $\left\{r \left| \dfrac{5}{r-3} = \dfrac{9}{3r-1} \right.\right\}$

32. $\left\{c \left| \dfrac{c+1}{c} = \dfrac{1}{2} \right.\right\}$

33. $\{s \mid -4s + 3(2s - 5) = 3(s - 6) + \frac{1}{2}(4 - 2s)\}$

34. $\{n \mid 3(n - 5) + 4(3n - 7) = -43\}$

35. $\{z \mid 17(z + 7) = 15(z + 7)\}$

36. $\{d \mid 5(2d - 6) = 5(6 - 2d)\}$

37. $\{u \mid 6 \cdot |u + 5| = 6\}$

38. $\{w \mid |4w - 1| = 15\}$

39. $\{f \mid 1.5(12 - f) = 3 + 1.5f\}$

40. $\{x \mid \frac{1}{2}(3x - 5) = -\frac{1}{2}(3x - 5)\}$

41. $\{x \mid 2 \cdot |3 - x| = 2\}$

42. $\left\{ r \mid 5 - 8r = \dfrac{3(7 + 13r)}{2} \right\}$

43. $\left\{ x \mid \dfrac{7}{x} - \dfrac{3}{x} - \dfrac{5}{x} = \dfrac{1}{2} \right\}$

44. $\left\{ x \mid \dfrac{1 - 3x}{-7x} = \dfrac{1}{5} \right\}$

45. $\left\{ y \mid y + 3 = \dfrac{3y + 14}{4} \right\}$

46. $\left\{ x \mid \dfrac{2x - 1}{7} = \dfrac{1 - x}{3} \right\}$

47. $\left\{ y \mid 7 + \dfrac{4}{y} = \dfrac{1}{y} - \dfrac{3}{y} \right\}$

48. $\{r \mid |7r - 3| = 17\}$

49. $\{x \mid |x| - 7(x + 3) + 7(3 + x) = -15\}$

50. $\left\{ t \mid \dfrac{5 - t}{2} = \dfrac{t + 4}{7} \right\}$

51. $\{s \mid (s - 7) \cdot 3 + 5(6 - s) = 8 \cdot (s + 9)\}$

52. $\{x \mid 8 \cdot (4x - 7) = (6 + 7x) \cdot (-4)\}$

53. $\{y \mid 6y + 9 = y\}$

54. $\left\{ s \mid \dfrac{4}{s} - 3 = \dfrac{5}{s} - 7 \right\}$

55. $\left\{ t \mid \dfrac{1}{t} + 5 = \dfrac{2}{t} + 5\frac{1}{2} \right\}$

56. $\{u \mid |u| = -2\}$

57. $\left\{ x \mid \dfrac{5x - 3}{7} = x + 4 \right\}$

58. $\{r \mid .3r + 1.5 = 1.5r + .5\}$

59. $\{x \mid 5(x - 3) - 6x = 13\}$

60. $\left\{x \mid \dfrac{2x + 11}{4} = \dfrac{3x - 7}{5}\right\}$

61. $\left\{x \mid \dfrac{x - 4}{5} = \dfrac{3(x - 5)}{10}\right\}$

62. $\{x \mid -5(x + 11) = 5x + 5\}$

63. $\left\{r \mid \dfrac{3r - 1}{-7} = r + 9\right\}$

64. $\left\{x \mid \dfrac{4x - 7}{x + 3} = \dfrac{1}{2}\right\}$

65. $\left\{x \mid \dfrac{\frac{1}{2}}{x - 1} = \dfrac{\frac{1}{3}}{2x + 6}\right\}$

VOCABULARY

Use each of the following correctly in a sentence. Numerals in the parentheses refer to pages where these words were used. If you are not sure of the meaning of any word, turn to the indicated page and refresh your memory.

absolute value (186)

binomial (199)

cover-up technique (178)

equation (174)

equivalent expressions (196)

inequality (182)

Left-hand Addition Property (188)

Left-hand Multiplication Property (191)

monomial (199)

perimeter (181)

polynomial (199)

Right-hand Addition Property (188)

Right-hand Multiplication Property (191)

root (177)

satisfy an equation (177)

solution set (177)

trinomial (199)

PROPERTIES AND THEOREMS

■ *Right-hand Addition Property*
$\forall_x \forall_y \forall_z$, if $x = y$, then $x + z = y + z$

■ *Left-hand Addition Property*
$\forall_x \forall_y \forall_z$, if $x = y$, then $z + x = z + y$

■ *Right-hand Multiplication Property*
$\forall_x \forall_y \forall_{z=0}$, if $x = y$, then $xz = yz$

■ *Left-hand Multiplication Property*
$\forall_x \forall_y \forall_z$, if $x = y$, then $zx = zy$

Theorem $\forall_a \forall_{b=0} \forall_c \forall_{d=0}$, if $\dfrac{a}{b} = \dfrac{c}{d}$, then $ad = bc$

REVIEW EXERCISES

1. Classify each sentence into one of the following categories.

T: true sentence

F: false sentence

R: sentence which is neither true nor false, that is, an open sentence, but in which there is at least one replacement, but not all, for the variable which will result in a true sentence; find the replacement or several replacements

N: sentence which is neither true nor false and in which there is no replacement for the variable which will result in a true sentence

E: sentence which is neither true nor false, and in which every replacement for the variable will result in a true sentence

a. $x + 1 = 2x$

b. $\sqrt{2} = 1.4$

c. $\sqrt{9} = 3$

d. $|x| = -2$

e. $|y + 1| = 0$

f. $1\% = .1$

g. $a = 2a$

h. $c + 1 = c$

i. $7r - r = 6r$

j. $\pi = 3.14$

k. $\pi \doteq 3.14$

l. $d^2 = -4$

m. $\frac{1}{8} = .125$

n. $\frac{1}{3} = 33\frac{1}{3}\%$

o. $5s - s = 5$

p. $\dfrac{3u}{u} = 3$

q. $-\dfrac{2}{k} = -1$

r. $-(x - y) = y - x$

s. $\dfrac{m - n}{m + n} = \dfrac{n - m}{-(m + n)}$

t. $-1(x - 4) = 4 - x$

u. $-2t + t = t$

v. $x - y = y - x$

w. $\dfrac{3 - m}{-1} = m - 3$

x. $-2(x - y) = (y - x) \cdot 2$

2. Solve each problem.

a. The sum of a number and 1 is equal to the product of 3 and the number. What is the number?

b. A number divided by the sum of the number and 1 is equal to 3. What is the number?

c. If 5 is multiplied by the sum of a number and 1, and 12 is subtracted from the product, the result is 38. What was the original number?

d. One-half of the sum of 2 and a number is equal to the number. What is the number?

e. The length of a rectangle is equal to twice the width plus 1. If the perimeter of the rectangle is equal to 20 in., determine the length and the width of the rectangle.

f. The perimeter of a rectangle is equal to 72 ft. If the length is eight times the width, determine the length and the width of the rectangle.

3. On the number line, graph the solution set of each inequality. The universal set is the set of all real numbers.

a. $A = \{b \mid b > 2\}$

b. $C = \{d \mid d < 0\}$

c. $E = \{f \mid f \geq -\frac{1}{2}\}$

d. $G = \{h \mid h \leq 4\}$

e. $I = \{k \mid -2 \leq k < 3\}$

f. $L = \{m \mid m \neq 1\}$

g. $N = \{p \mid p < 3 \text{ or } p \leq -2\}$

h. $R = \{s \mid s \leq -2 \text{ or } s \geq 0\}$

4. For each expression, write an expression equivalent to it and containing no parentheses.

a. $5(x + 3)$

b. $4(7y - 1)$

c. $(3 - 2x)(-4)$

d. $(-\frac{1}{2})(4a - 6c)$

e. $(-3)(2a - 5m + 4n)$

f. $(-10)\left(\dfrac{x - n}{2}\right)$

g. $(3n)\left(\dfrac{1}{3n} + \dfrac{5}{12n}\right)$

h. $(-\frac{3}{2})(\frac{2}{3}a + 2k)$

i. $(8m - 12n + 16xy)(-\frac{1}{4})$

j. $(a + 4n)(a - n)$

k. $(x + y)(x - y)$

l. $(a + b)(a + b)$

m. $(3 - t)(3 + t)$

n. $(4 + 5s)(5s - 4)$

o. $(x + y - 3)(x + y + 3)$

p. $(a - b - c)(a + b + c)$

5. Solve each equation.

a. $x + 4 = 19$

b. $y + 12 = 3$

c. $3 - m = 1$

d. $2n + 3 = 17$

e. $1 - 4s = -7$

f. $5k + 4 = 49$

g. $3 - 6p = 12$

h. $\dfrac{5}{t} = -2.5$

i. $\dfrac{s + 1}{-2} = 3$

j. $\dfrac{2u - 4}{3} = -4$

k. $12y + 7 = 7$

l. $|x| = 8$

m. $|z - 3| = 4$

n. $|3t + 1| = 7$

o. $|4 - 2t| = 1$

p. $6 - 2|k| = 2$

q. $\left|\dfrac{1 + v}{3}\right| = 3$

r. $|2r + 6| = -7$

s. $4(s - 3) = 16$

t. $-3(1 - 2h) = 21$

u. $-5(3d - 1) = 0$

v. $3(2w - 1) + 2(3 - 4w) = 9$

w. $\dfrac{2}{3s - 4} = 3$

x. $\dfrac{3c - 1}{2} = \dfrac{2 - 5c}{3}$

y. $\dfrac{3}{x} - 2 = 6 - \dfrac{1}{x}$

z. $\dfrac{1 - v}{2} = \dfrac{2v + 1}{3}$

a'. $\dfrac{-(4 - x)}{2} = \dfrac{3x - 1}{3}$

b'. $\dfrac{-(1 + y)}{4} + 1 = \dfrac{2y - 1}{3} + 4$

CHAPTER TEST

1. Classify each of the following sentences into one of the following categories.

T: true sentence

F: false sentence

R: sentence which is neither true nor false, that is, an open sentence, but in which there is at least one replacement, but not all, for the variable which will result in a true sentence; find the replacement or several replacements

N: sentence which is neither true nor false and in which there is no replacement for the variable which will result in a true sentence

E: sentence which is neither true nor false, and in which every replacement for the variable will result in a true sentence

a. $16\% = \frac{4}{25}$

b. $|-4| = -4$

c. $x + 3 = -1$

d. $a^4 = 0$

e. $y(y + 1) = 0$

f. $x^3 - 1 = 0$

g. $2m - m = 5$

h. $|u| = u$

i. $\frac{4}{x} = 0$

j. $y + 1 = y + 2$

k. $\dfrac{u + 3}{u} = 1, \quad (u \neq 0)$

l. $\dfrac{c}{c} = 1, \quad (c \neq 0)$

m. $\left|\dfrac{n}{n}\right| = 1, \quad (n \neq 0)$

n. $3x - 2x = x$

o. $-2(m - 3) = 6 - 2m$

p. $3(n + 1) = 3n + 1$

q. $|x + 6| = 0$

r. $|y - 1| = -3$

s. $|m + 6| = 1$

2. Solve each of the following equations.

a. $2x = 4$

b. $3y = 17$

c. $15z = 8$

d. $-4a = 9$

e. $-\frac{2}{3}c = -\frac{4}{5}$

f. $-1.6d = 6.4$

g. $3u + 5 = 1$

h. $x - 6 = 7$

i. $2w + 3 = 5$

j. $7 - 5m = .5$

k. $\frac{1}{2} + \frac{1}{3}v = 1$

l. $6 + 3h = -2$

m. $3n + 47 = -13$

n. $\dfrac{p + 1}{2} = 2$

o. $2(x + 1) = 1$

p. $3y + 2(y + 2) = 4$

q. $7(z + 1) - 2(2z - 3) = 0$

r. $3(2t - 1) - 10(t + 13) = 12$

s. $-4(s - 5) + 2(3s + 6) = 10$

3. Solve each problem.

   a. A number added to three times that number is 8. What is the number?

   b. The product of a number and 3 divided by the sum of twice the number and 1 is equal to 3. What is the number?

   c. The perimeter of a rectangle is 24 inches. What is the length and the width if the length exceeds the width by 6 inches?

4. Which of the following pairs of expressions are equivalent?

   a. $(3r + 7) + (-9s)$, $(7 - 9s) + 3r$

   b. $\frac{4}{3}(r + 6) - 9t$, $\frac{4}{3}r + 8 - 12t$

   c. $x(y + \frac{2}{3})$, $y(x + \frac{2}{3})$

   d. $1.3x + .8 + 4.2y$, $2(2.1y + .4 + 1.3x)$

   e. $-(x - y - z)$, $y + z - x$

   f. $|y - x|$, $|x - y|$

5. For each of the following expressions, write an expression which is equivalent to it and which does not contain parentheses.

   a. $-3(x - \frac{4}{3})$

   b. $(r - 2t + 5) \cdot (-4)$

   c. $(4 - x)(x + 4)$

   d. $\frac{1}{3}(3x - 12y + 15z)$

   e. $(2a + 3)(2a + 3)$

   f. $-(x - 1)(1 - x)$

6. On the number line, graph the solution set of each inequality. The universal set is the set of real numbers.

   a. $K = \{x \mid x > -4\}$

   b. $T = \{n \mid n < 0\}$

   c. $A = \{y \mid y \geq -2\}$

   d. $Y = \{k \mid -3 \leq k < -2\}$

   e. $B = \{z \mid -2 \leq z \leq \frac{1}{2}\}$

   f. $C = \{a \mid a < 3 \text{ or } a \geq 5\}$

   g. $M = \{p \mid p \leq -1 \text{ or } p \geq 1\}$

   h. $Q = \{s \mid s < 1 \text{ or } s > -1\}$

BIBLIOGRAPHY

Heimer, R. T.; Kocher, F.; and Lottes, J. J. *A Program in Contemporary Algebra*. Book 2, Equations and Inequalities in One Variable. New York: Holt, Rinehart and Winston, Inc., 1963.

Kasner, E. and Newman, J. *Mathematics and the Imagination*. New York: Simon and Schuster, 1940. pp. 95-99.

Nichols, Eugene D.; Kalin, Robert; and Garland, E. Henry. *Equations and Inequalities* (A Programed Unit). New York: Holt, Rinehart and Winston, Inc., 1963.

School Mathematics Study Group. *First Course in Algebra*. New Haven: Yale University Press, 1961. pp. 377-404.

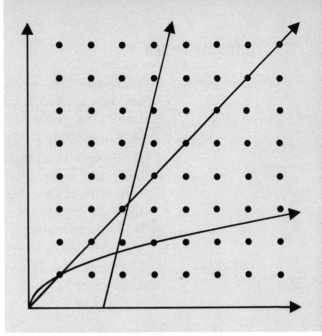

CHAPTER 8

Applications of Equations and Inequalities

WRITING PROBLEMS TO FIT EQUATIONS

In Chapter 7, you learned to write equations which fit given problems. You solved the equations to find the answers. It should be interesting to start with an equation and make up a story which will fit the given equation. It should be possible to make up several stories for one equation. This equation may be viewed as a generalization; and the stories which fit this equation may be viewed as specific instances of that generalization. Answers to the specific instances may be found by solving the equation.

Example: Let us make up stories for the equation $2x + 3 = 11$.

    i. I thought of a number, multiplied it by 2, and added 3 to the product. The result is 11. What is the number? Do you see that the root of the equation $2x + 3 = 11$ is the solution of this problem?

Examples: *ii.* Mary has 11¢. She buys two apples at a certain price and has 3¢ left. What is the cost of one apple? Do you think the equation $2x + 3 = 11$ fits this situation? How is x used in this situation?

iii. If the area in square feet of a certain rectangle is doubled, and 3 square feet added, an area of 11 square feet is obtained. What is the area of the rectangle? Does the equation $2x + 3 = 11$ fit this situation? What is the meaning of x in this case?

iv. Johnny lives a certain number of miles from school. If this number is doubled and 3 miles added, then the distance of 11 miles is obtained. How many miles from school does Johnny live?

It is possible to make up a story for a given equation such that, after solving the equation, you will discover that the answer is not realistic; that is, the answer does not make sense.

Example: $3y + 6 = 3$

Suppose you made up the following story.
If I multiply the number of years in Susie's age by 3 and add 6 to the product, I obtain 3.
Now let us solve the equation.
$$3y + 6 = 3$$
$$3y = -3$$
$$y = -1$$

Thus, the root of the equation is -1. Therefore, Susie is -1 years old. This answer is not realistic in terms of the story. The number -1 is not in the replacement set of the variable. When we speak of the age of a person, the replacement set of the variable is the set of positive numbers.

EXERCISES

For each equation below, make up three stories which fit the equation. After you have made up each story, solve the equation. If the root of the equation is not realistic in terms of any of the stories, tell why it is not.

1. $4m + 1 = 9$

2. $\dfrac{5t - 3}{3} = 9$

3. $2 - \tfrac{1}{2}y = 0$

4. $4x + 1 = 2x + 11$

FORMULAS AS EQUATIONS

Formulas are used in mathematics, in business, in science and in other areas. They are quite useful in obtaining answers to significant problems. Since formulas are equations, we can draw on our knowledge of equations in dealing with formulas. In the problems below you will practice in the use of formulas concerned with geometry.

EXERCISES

1.   In each problem, you are given a formula. Do the required computations. In exercises that involve π, use $\pi \doteq 3.14$. (Remember, "$\doteq$" means "is approximately equal to.")

Example: Volume of a rectangular solid: $V = lwh$. Compute the volume when $l = 12$ in., $w = 9$ in., and $h = 3$ in.
$V = 12 \cdot 9 \cdot 3$ cu. in.
$\quad = 324$ cu. in.
The volume is 324 cu. in.

a. Perimeter of a square: $p = 4s$
  i. The perimeter when $s = 7$ in.
  ii. The length of the side of the square when $p = 37$ in.

b. Perimeter of a rectangle: $p = 2l + 2w$
  i. The perimeter when $l = 2$ ft., $w = 13$ in.

  ii. The length of the rectangle if the perimeter is 100 in. and the width is 15 in.

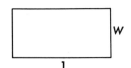

c. Volume of a cube: $V = e^3$
  i. The volume of the cube if $e = 7$ in.
  ii. The length of one edge if $V = 1000$ cu. in.

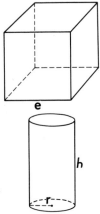

d. Volume of a right circular cylinder: $V = \pi r^2 h$
  i. The volume when $r = 3.5$ in., $h = 17$ in.
  ii. The height when $V = 255$ cu. in., $r = 2$ in.

e. Volume of a sphere: $V = \frac{4}{3}\pi r^3$
   i. The volume when $r = 5$ in.
   ii. The length of a radius of a sphere
      if $V = 1200$ cu. in.

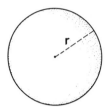

f. Surface area of a sphere: $A = 4\pi r^2$.
   Compute the area when $r = 1.5$ ft.

2. Solve each formula for the indicated letter.

Example: $V = lwh$

   i. for l *ii.* for w *iii.* for h

$$l = \frac{V}{wh} \qquad\qquad w = \frac{V}{lh} \qquad\qquad h = \frac{V}{lw}$$

a. $p = 4s$; for s **d.** $V = \pi r^2 h$; *i.* for h
b. $p = 2l + 2w$; *i.* for l *ii.* for r
        ii. for w **e.** $V = \frac{4}{3}\pi r^3$; for r
c. $V = e^3$; for e

Practice in using equations to solve problems

You have seen that in order to solve a problem by using an equation you need to write an equation that fits the problem, find the root of the equation, then convince yourself that the root of the equation "works" in the problem.

It is very important that you first read the problem thoughtfully until you fully understand it. Then you should write the conditions of the problem in the form of mathematical sentences.

Below are three examples of problems and their solutions. You should always attempt to develop your own ways of solving problems. There are often many different ways of solving the same problem. Use your ingenuity and be clever about it!

Problem: Alice has a bank which contains $2.65 in dimes and nickels. If Alice has eleven more nickels than dimes, how many of each type of coin does she have?

One Way to Solve: Since there are only two kinds of coins, we know that the product of .05 (value of a nickel) and the number of nickels, added to the product of .10 (value of a dime) and the number of dimes will yield 2.65 ($2.65 in the bank).

      We don't actually know how many dimes or nickels she has, but we do know that there are eleven more nickels than dimes.

If we let x stand for the number of dimes, then $x + 11$ would stand for the number of nickels. Why? Then the following equation fits the story of the problem.

$$.05(x + 11) + .10x = 2.65$$

Solving the equation

$$100[.05(x + 11) + .10x] = 100 \times 2.65$$

Why is it good to use 100 here as a multiplier?

$$5(x + 11) + 10x = 265$$
$$5x + 55 + 10x = 265$$
$$15x = 210$$
$$x = 14$$

Thus, there are 14 dimes and $14 + 11$ or 25 nickels.

CHECK:
dimes $14 \times .10 = 1.40$ or $1.40
nickels $25 \times .05 = 1.25$ or $1.25
           total $2.65

Use another method to solve this problem.

Problem:

A family vacation budget allowed three times as much for food as for camping expenses and four times as much for travel as for camping expenses. If the total allowed for food, camping expenses, and travel was $168, how much was allotted to travel?

One Way to Solve:

We note the relationship between food and camping expenses, and also between camping expenses and travel.

If we let x stand for the number of dollars spent on food, then $\frac{1}{3}x$ would stand for the number of dollars spent for camping expenses. It would then follow that $\frac{4}{3}x$ would stand for the number of dollars allowed for travel. The sum of x, $\frac{1}{3}x$, and $\frac{4}{3}x$ should be 168.

Perhaps a less complicated approach would be to let y stand for the amount spent for camping; then $3y$ would stand for food expense and $4y$ would stand for the travel expense in dollars.

Thus, our equation is

$$y + 3y + 4y = 168$$
$$8y = 168$$
$$y = 21$$

The camping expense was $21. The travel expense allotment was 4×21 which is 84, or $84. The food allotment was 3×21 which is 63, or $63.

CHECK:

food	$63
camping	$21
travel	$84
total	$168

Solve the problem using the first suggested approach.

Problem: The sum of two numbers is 97. One number is 19 greater than the other number. What are the two numbers?

One Way to Solve: One number is 19 greater than the other. If we let y stand for the smaller number, the larger number may be represented by $y + 19$.

Our equation is $y + (y + 19) = 97$

Solve:
$$2y + 19 = 97$$
$$2y = 78$$
$$y = 39$$

Thus, the smaller number is 39 and the larger of the two is $39 + 19 = 58$.

CHECK:

smaller number	39
larger number	58
sum	97

The difference is $58 - 39 = 19$.

Use a different method to solve this problem.

EXERCISES

Solve each problem and check.

1. Miss Thrifty has $9.00 in nickels and dimes. She has twice as many dimes as she has nickels. How many coins of each kind does Miss Thrifty have?

2. Mr. Tight has a jar full of nickels. If he removes 50 nickels and replaces them with 70 dimes, he will have $1\frac{1}{2}$ times the original amount. How much money does Mr. Tight have in the jar?

3. A jar full of pennies and nickels contains three times as many nickels as pennies. The total amount of money in the jar is $5.60. How many coins of each kind are there in the jar?

4. Mr. Games has dice, marbles, and coins, 136 of these objects in all. If the number of marbles is twice the number of dice, and the number of coins is five times the number of dice, how many of each kind does he have?

5. Mrs. Homemaker buys three cans of different vegetables. Can A weighs $2\frac{1}{2}$ ounces more than can B, and can C weighs $10\frac{1}{3}$ ounces more than can B. The total weight of the three cans is $48\frac{5}{6}$ ounces. How many ounces does can A weigh?

6. Multiplying a number by 3 gives the same result as adding 4 to the number. What is the number?

7. Taking one-half of a number gives the same result as adding 5 to the number. What is the number?

8. Dividing a number by 5 gives the same result as adding 16 to the number. What is the number?

9. Multiplying a number by 3 and adding 5 to the product gives the same result as multiplying the number by -2. What is the number?

10. What two numbers have 59 as their sum and 11 as their difference?

Formulas in science

Mathematics has been instrumental in the development of our present age of science. We will concern ourselves in this section with some of the formulas which arise in various sciences. We will have neither space nor time to attempt explanation of all physical phenomena involved when using these formulas. Rather, we will be mainly concerned with the principles and manipulations which the scientist encounters when seeking answers to his problems.

We know that water freezes at a temperature of 32° on the Fahrenheit scale, and that it boils at 212° on the same scale. There is another important temperature scale in science called the Celsius (Centigrade) scale, on which the freezing point of water is 0° and the boiling point is 100°. It is necessary to be able to interchange temperature measurements from either of these scales to the other.

We let F stand for the Fahrenheit reading and C for the reading on the Celsius scale. A formula which defines the relationship between these two scales is

$$F = 1.8C + 32$$

To verify this formula for the freezing point of water, we replace C in the formula by 0 to mean 0°.

$$F = 1.8 \times 0 + 32$$
$$F = 0 + 32$$
$$F = 32$$

Thus, the temperature of 0 degrees Celsius is the same as 32 degrees Fahrenheit.

For the boiling point of water, we replace C by 100 to mean 100°.

$$F = 1.8 \times 100 + 32$$
$$F = 180 + 32$$
$$F = 212$$

Thus, the temperature of 100° Celsius is the same as 212° Fahrenheit.

What Fahrenheit reading corresponds to the 25 degree Celsius reading? To answer this, we replace C by 25 in the formula.

$$F = 1.8(25) + 32$$
$$F = 45 + 32$$
$$F = 77; \text{ or } 25° C \text{ corresponds to } 77° F$$

If we replace F by 68, can we determine the value of C?

$$68 = 1.8\,C + 32$$
$$36 = 1.8\,C$$

$$C = \frac{36}{1.8}$$

$$C = 20; \text{ or } 68° F \text{ is equivalent to } 20° C$$

Could we express C in terms of F?

$$F = 1.8\,C + 32$$
$$F - 32 = 1.8\,C$$

$$\frac{F - 32}{1.8} = C$$
$$\text{or } C = \frac{F - 32}{1.8}$$

We say that the formula $F = 1.8\,C + 32$ was *solved* for C.

EXERCISES

1. The formula for the specific heat (S) of a substance in terms of heat in calories (H), mass in grams (m), final temperature (t_2), and initial temperature (t_1) is

$$S = \frac{H}{m(t_2 - t_1)}$$

    a. Determine S to one decimal place for the following given replacements.

        27 for H 16 for m 23 for t_2 19 for t_1

    b. Solve the formula for H in terms of other variables.

    c. Solve the formula for m.

    d. Solve the formula for t_2.

    e. Solve the formula for t_1.

2. The formula for distance traveled by a freely falling object is $d = \frac{1}{2}gt^2$, where g is the acceleration due to gravity and t is time.

    a. Determine d for the following given replacements.

            32 for g 6 for t

    b. Express g in terms of d and t.

    c. Express t in terms of d and g.

3. The formula for electric current (I) in a circuit of two cells connected in series in terms of the electromotive force (E) of the cell, external resistance (R), and internal resistance (r) is

$$I = \frac{2E}{R + 2r}$$

    a. Determine I to one decimal place for the following given replacements.

            2.2 for E 14 for R 7 for r

    b. Solve the formula for E.

    c. Solve the formula for R.

    d. Solve the formula for r.

4. The formula involving the effect of temperature and pressure on the volume of a confined gas is $\frac{P_1 V_1}{T_1} = \frac{P_2 V_2}{T_2}$, where P_1, V_1, and T_1 are the original pressure, volume, and temperature, respectively. P_2, V_2, and T_2 are the final pressure, volume, and temperature, respectively.

    a. Solve the formula for P_1.

    b. Solve the formula for V_2.

    c. Solve the formula for T_2.

5. The formula relating the density (D) of an object to its weight (W) and volume (V) is $D = \frac{W}{V}$.

    a. If W is replaced by 13 and V by 6.5, determine D.

    b. Express W in terms of D and V.

    c. Express V in terms of D and W.

6. The formula for the total resistance (R) of two conductors in a parallel hook-up is $\frac{r_1 r_2}{r_1 + r_2}$, where r_1 and r_2 are the resistances of the two conductors, respectively.

    a. If r_1 is replaced by 48 and r_2 by 62, determine R to one decimal place.

    b. Express r_1 in terms of r_2 and R.

7. The formula relating the rate (I) of flow of an electric current to the electromotive force or voltage (E) and resistance (R) of the wire through which the current flows is $I = \dfrac{E}{R}$.

    a. If E is replaced by 110 and R by 20, determine I.
    b. Solve the formula for E.
    c. Solve the formula for R.

8. The formula for the kinetic energy (E) of a moving object in terms of weight (W), velocity (v), and the acceleration due to gravity (g) is $E = \dfrac{Wv^2}{2g}$.

    a. Solve the formula for W.
    b. Solve the formula for v.

9. The formula for greatest height (h) attained by a body projected vertically upward is $h = \dfrac{v^2}{2g}$, where v is velocity and g is the acceleration due to gravity.

    a. Solve the formula for v.
    b. Solve the formula for g.
    c. If v is doubled and g remains the same, how will h change?

10. The formula for the heat (H) in calories developed from a current flowing through a wire is $H = \dfrac{Eit}{4.18}$, where E is the difference in potential or voltage, i is the rate of flow in amperes, and t is time in seconds.

    a. Solve the formula for E.
    b. Solve the formula for t.
    c. If each of E, i, and t is doubled, how will H change?
    d. If E is doubled, i is tripled, and t is quadrupled, how will H change?

11. The formula for the velocity (v) of a liquid flowing through an opening is $v = \sqrt{2gh}$, where g is the acceleration due to gravity and h is the height of the liquid above the opening.

    a. If g is replaced by 32 and h by 2, determine v.
    b. Solve the formula for h.
    c. If h is quadrupled, how is v changed?

Further uses of equations in solving problems

We shall illustrate the use of equations in solving problems involving situations different from those we considered previously. You will note, however, that there is essentially nothing new in solving these problems. Still, the important thing is to write an equation which fits the problem and to solve the equation.

Problem: Joe is now fifteen years younger than Jane. In six years Jane will be twice as old as Joe will be then. What are their ages now?

One Way to Solve: We know that the difference in their ages is fifteen years.

If we let x stand for Jane's present age in years, then we can express Joe's age in terms of x. It is $x - 15$. We may represent Jane's age six years from now by $x + 6$, and Joe's age six years from now by $(x - 15) + 6$, or $x - 9$. Are these expressions, $x + 6$ and $x - 9$ equivalent? Rereading the problem reveals that Jane's age six years from now is twice as great as Joe's age. That is, Joe's age must be doubled (multiplied by 2) to make it equal to Jane's age. Thus, we have

$$2(x - 9) = x + 6$$

Solve:
$$2(x - 9) = x + 6$$
$$2x - 18 = x + 6$$
$$x = 24$$

Thus, Jane is 24 years old, and Joe is $24 - 15$ or 9 years old.

CHECK:

Ages now		Ages six years from now	
Jane	24 years	Jane	30 years
Joe	9 years	Joe	15 years

Difference: 15 years

Jane will be twice as old as Joe six years from now.

Problem: The number of tickets sold for a church supper was 215. Adult tickets were $.75 each and children's tickets were $.35 each. The sale of both kinds of tickets amounted to $135.25. How many adult tickets were sold?

One Way to Solve: The product of .75 and the number of adults, added to the product of .35 and the number of children will yield 135.25. (We are dropping the dollar signs temporarily to simplify writing.) If we sold 100 adult tickets, we would have 215 − 100 or 115 children. If we had 150 adults, we would have 215 − 150 or 65 children. Thus, if we let r stand for the number of adult tickets, then 215 − r will stand for the number of children's tickets.

Thus, our equation is

$$.75r + .35(215 - r) = 135.25$$

Solve:
$$100[.75r + .35(215 - r)] = 100 \times 135.25$$
$$75r + 35(215 - r) = 13{,}525$$
$$75r + 7525 - 35r = 13{,}525$$
$$40r + 7525 = 13{,}525$$
$$40r = 6000$$
$$r = 150$$

Thus, 150 adult tickets and 215 − 150 or 65 children's tickets were sold.

CHECK:
$$150 \times .75 = 112.50 \quad \text{or} \quad \$112.50$$
$$65 \times .35 = 22.75 \quad \text{or} \quad \$22.75$$
$$\text{total} \quad \$135.25$$

Use a different approach in solving this problem.

EXERCISES

Solve each problem and check.

1. Joe Old is presently five years older than Suzie Young. When Joe's age doubles, Suzie's age will triple. How old is each of them?

2. John is six years older than Jerry. In nine years Jerry will be $\frac{2}{3}$ as old as John. What is John's age now?

3. Ann has $4.75 made up of half dollars and quarters. If there is a total of thirteen coins, how many coins of each kind does she have?

4. A piggy bank contained 4 fewer dimes than quarters, 10 more nickels than dimes, three times as many half dollars as quarters. The total value of the coins was $11.30. How many dimes were there?

5. College Y has 1431 students, and it has $3\frac{1}{2}$ times as many boys as girls. What is the enrollment of girls?

6. The number of women at a mixed gathering was 4 less than $\frac{1}{3}$ of the entire group present. This number of women was also equal to one-fourth of the entire number of people present. How many women were present?

7. There are 36 pupils in a mathematics class. The girls outnumber the boys 2 to 1. How many boys are there in the class?

8. The number of students in room A is $\frac{3}{4}$ of the number in room B. If room B has eight more students than room A, determine the number of students in each room.

FORMULAS IN BUSINESS

Many problems encountered in business require an understanding of per cent. You recall that 2% is just another way of saying .02 or $\frac{2}{100}$ or $\frac{1}{50}$. Similarly, $\frac{6}{100}$ may be used interchangeably with 6%.

Suppose 6% of Mr. Jones's annual salary is deducted for a retirement fund. If the amount deducted is $348, can we determine Mr. Jones's annual salary?

We might reason that 6% of some number which is his salary is equal to 348. If we let y stand for his salary, then

$$6\% \, y = 348$$
$$.06 \, y = 348$$
$$\tfrac{6}{100} y = 348$$
$$6 \, y = 34,800$$
$$y = 5800$$

Thus, we could conclude that Mr. Jones's annual salary is $5800. If we replace y with 5800 in $6\% \cdot y = 348$, a true statement is obtained.

$$6\% \cdot (5800) = \tfrac{6}{100} \cdot (5800) \text{ or } 348$$

Let us consider another business situation. Suppose the total cost of a lot and a new house is $16,000. If the cost of the lot is $3200, what per cent of the total cost is the cost of the lot?

If we let x be the per cent of the total cost of the lot, we have

$$x \cdot 16000 = 3200$$
$$x = \tfrac{3200}{16000}$$
$$x = .20 \text{ or } 20\%$$

Thus, the cost of the lot is 20% of the total cost.

When one borrows money from a bank, he pays a sum of money called *interest* for the privilege of using the bank's money. The amount paid for this privilege depends upon the amount borrowed, the length of time the money was needed, and the rate of interest. The amount borrowed is called the *principal*. The time is usually measured in years or fractions of a year. The rate of interest is expressed as a per cent. An annual interest of 6% would mean that one would pay $6 interest for using $100 of the bank's money for one year. The formula for this relationship is

$$i = prt$$

where i is interest, p is principal, r is the rate of interest, and t is the time in years.

When interest is determined on the basis of the original principal only, it is called simple interest.

Example: *i.* Suppose Mr. Downs borrows $800. If the rate of interest is 5% and he repays the loan in two years, how much interest must he pay?

$$
\begin{aligned}
i &= prt \\
&= (800) \times .05 \times 2 \\
&= 80
\end{aligned}
$$

Thus, Mr. Downs will pay $80 interest for using $800 for two years at a 5% interest rate.

Example: *ii.* Mr. Jones borrowed $560 for nine months. If the interest paid was $25.20, what was the rate of interest?

$$i = prt$$

If we solve for r in terms of i, p, and t, we have

$$r = \frac{i}{pt}$$

Replacing the variables with their values gives us

$$r = \frac{25.20}{(560) \cdot \left(\frac{3}{4}\right)} = .06 \qquad (\text{9 months is } \tfrac{3}{4} \text{ of a year})$$

Thus, the rate of interest paid was 6%.

EXERCISES

Solve each problem.

1. A real estate salesman received a 5% commission for selling a house for $16,800. How much commission did he receive, and how much money did the house owner get?

2. An appliance salesman sells a record player for $145, making a profit of 15% on the cost. How much did the record player cost the salesman originally?

3. If a house has an assessed valuation of $14,000 and the tax rate is $21 per $1000 of assessed valuation, how much tax will be paid on the property?

4. Mr. Smith invested money in two different businesses. One paid him 5% and the other paid him 7% on his investment. He invested $2000 more in the business paying the higher rate than he did in the other business. If he received a total of $250 at the end of the year, how much did he have invested in each business?

5. The tax rate of a suburban area was 12 mills for every dollar assessed valuation. (A mill is $\frac{1}{10}$ of one cent.) If Mr. Jenson's assessed evaluation was $13,500, compute his tax.

6. A business man borrowed $1500, which he agreed to pay back with interest at 5%. If we know that he paid $25 interest, determine how long he kept the money.

7. Mr. Enterprise borrowed $3300 for a period of 20 months at 5% interest. How much interest must he pay for the use of the money?

8. A rancher borrowed a sum of money for a period of 15 months. If he paid back $1800, which included the amount he borrowed in addition to his interest at 6%, how much money did he borrow?

9. A company developing a new shopping center borrowed $2,000,000 for a period of five years. If the interest paid was $550,000, determine the rate of interest.

10. How long will it take for a given amount of principal to double when invested at 4% simple interest?

11. Mr. Smith bought a new television set. He was allowed a discount of $25 more than one-fourth the price of the new set. He actually paid $155 in cash to make up the balance of the cost of the new set. What was the price of the television set?

12. Mr. Jenson paid $2678 for his new car; the price included a 3% sales tax. What was the actual purchase price of the car before tax?

13. Mr. Jenson's property tax is $339. This is a 13% increase over last year's tax. What was the tax last year?

14. Three boys worked on a job. Harry received $4 less than twice as much as John. George received $7 more than Harry. How much did each receive if their total wages were $199?

PROBLEMS ABOUT NUMBERS AND DISTANCES

Now we give some examples of problems which deal with numbers and some which deal with motion and distance.

One problem deals with consecutive integers. Two integers are said to be consecutive if their difference is 1.

Problem: The sum of three consecutive integers is 51. What are the integers?

One Way to Solve: If the smallest of the three integers is x, then the next two are $x + 1$ and $x + 2$. The equation which fits the problem is

$$x + (x + 1) + (x + 2) = 51$$

Solve:
$$3x + 3 = 51$$
$$3x = 48$$
$$x = 16$$

Thus, the three integers are 16, 17, and 18.

CHECK: $16 + 17 + 18 = 51$

Problem: Jim and Joe ride their motorbikes in opposite directions from Joe's house on the highway. They start at the same time. We find them 19 miles apart 15 minutes later. The average speed of Joe's bike is 8 miles per hour less than the average speed of Jim's bike. Can we determine the average speed of Joe's bike?

One Way to Solve: We know that if one travels at an average speed of 15 miles per hour for two hours he has covered a distance of 30 miles; or if one covered a distance of 40 miles in a time of two hours, his average speed would be 20 miles per hour. You are probably familiar with the formula

$$d = rt$$

where d is distance, r is speed (or rate), and t is time.

We know that the two bikes end up 19 miles apart after 15 minutes. We observe that both bikes have been traveling for the same period of time, but they have covered different distances because of traveling at unequal rates. However, the sum of their distances will be equal to the distance they are apart. If we let z stand for the speed of Jim's bike in miles per hour, then we may represent the speed of Joe's bike in miles per hour by $z - 8$.

To find the distance traveled by Joe, we find the product of Joe's speed $(z - 8)$ m.p.h., and the number of hours he traveled, $\frac{15}{60}$ or $\frac{1}{4}$ hour. Thus, $\frac{1}{4}(z - 8)$ represents the miles traveled by Joe.

Similarly, we determine that $\frac{1}{4}z$ represents the distance traveled by Jim in the same length of time. We may now write the following equation.

$$\tfrac{1}{4}(z - 8) + \tfrac{1}{4}z = 19$$

Solve:
$$4[\tfrac{1}{4}(z - 8) + \tfrac{1}{4}z] = 4 \times 19$$
$$(z - 8) + z = 76$$
$$2z - 8 = 76$$
$$2z = 84$$
$$z = 42$$

Thus, Jim's average speed was 42 m.p.h., and Joe's average speed was $42 - 8$ or 34 m.p.h.

CHECK: Joe $(\tfrac{1}{4}$ hr.$) \times (34$ m.p.h.$) = \tfrac{34}{4}$ miles

Jim $(\tfrac{1}{4}$ hr.$) \times (42$ m.p.h.$) = \tfrac{42}{4}$ miles

total $\tfrac{34}{4} + \tfrac{42}{4} = \tfrac{76}{4}$ or 19 miles

Can you obtain the same answer using a different approach?

EXERCISES

Solve each problem.

1. The sum of three consecutive integers is 45. What are the integers?

2. The sum of four consecutive *even* integers is 276. What are the integers? [Example of four consecutive even integers: 4, 6, 8, 10.]

3. The sum of three consecutive *odd* integers is 273. What are the integers? [Example of three consecutive odd integers: 7, 9, 11.]

4. The sum of four consecutive odd integers is 104. What are the integers?

5. We have a number represented by two digits. The sum of the numbers represented by the tens digit and units digit is 11. If the number represented by the tens digit is 3 greater than the number represented by the units digit, what is the original number?

6. Given the fraction $\tfrac{4}{11}$, what number may be added to the numerator and subtracted from the denominator to produce the fraction $\tfrac{7}{8}$?

7. The difference between the squares of two consecutive odd numbers is 32. What are the numbers?

8. If three is added to the quotient of sixteen divided by a given number, the result is the reciprocal of the given number. Determine the given number.

9. A number is divided by a number 33 greater than itself. The quotient is added to one-third. The result is three-fourths. Determine the original number.

10. On a trip to the city, Mr. Go traveled at an average speed of 45 m.p.h. His average speed on the return trip was 55 m.p.h. If the time of coming and returning over the same route amounted to 6 hours, how far was the city from Mr. Go's house?

11. Mr. Fleet can run three times as fast as Mr. Sluggish. They started from the same spot at the same time and ran in opposite directions. The distance between them after 5 minutes was $1\frac{1}{4}$ miles. What distance did Mr. Fleet run?

12. A new car leaves Detroit traveling at an average speed of 45 m.p.h. One and one-half hours later another car leaves Detroit on the same route. If the second car catches up with the first car in $4\frac{1}{2}$ hours, find the speed of the second car.

13. A plane makes a trip of 900 miles. If the average speed had been increased by 75 m.p.h., the plane could have covered 1350 miles in the same time. Determine the average speed of the plane.

14. John vacationed at a river resort featuring float trips. His motorboat ordinarily travels at an average speed of 12 m.p.h. He found that he could travel 18 miles upstream in the same time that he could travel 24 miles downstream. Compute the speed of the current.

Using equations in solving geometry problems

In studying the sizes of geometric figures, like rectangles, we are concerned with the number of linear units in their sides and the number of square units in their areas. For the study of areas, the area of a square each of whose sides is one unit in length serves as our unit of area, or a standard for comparison. The area of such a square is 1 square unit.

Since upper elementary school days, you have accepted the following principle.

> The area of a rectangle is equal to the product of its length and width, or, written as a formula
> $$A = l \times w$$

The formula contains the variables A, l, and w. If l and w stand for the length and width of the rectangle, $l \times w$ stands for the area. In order to maintain a consistent unit of area, we require that the measures of both l and w be in terms of the same unit of length. Actually, a more precise expression of the above principle would be

▪   The number of square units in the area of a rectangle is equal to the product of the number of linear units in its length and its width.

Suppose we were asked to determine the area of a rectangle whose length is 12 inches and whose width is 7 inches. If we replace l by 12 and w by 7, in the formula, we get

$$A = 12 \times 7$$

Thus, the number 84 is the area. In this case, we would say that the area is 84 square inches.

Example: Suppose we have a rectangle whose area is 78 square feet and whose length is 60 feet. Could we determine its width?

In the formula, $A = lw$, if we replace A by 78 and l by 60, we obtain $78 = 60 \cdot w$

Solve: $w = \frac{78}{60}$
        or $w = 1.3$

Thus, the width of this rectangle is 1.3 ft.

The formulas used in finding the areas of some of the other geometric figures are related to the formula for the area of the rectangle.

With a little experimenting, you will discover that cutting any rectangle into two parts by a diagonal divides the rectangle into two triangles which are exactly alike. Thus, the triangles $A D C$ and $A B C$ on the right have the same measure for their areas. Or, the area of each triangle is one-half the area of the rectangle. Thus

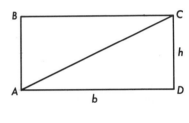

Fig. 1

Area of $\triangle ADC = \frac{1}{2}bh$ and Area of $\triangle ABC = \frac{1}{2}bh$

Notice that each triangle is a right triangle.

In triangle ABC (figure 2), we may form right triangles by constructing a perpendicular line from C to $\overline{AB}$, as in figure 3.

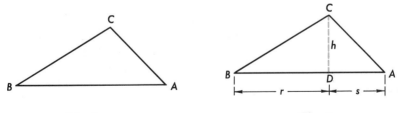

Fig. 2   Fig. 3

This perpendicular from one of the corners (called vertices) of the triangle to the opposite side of the triangle (or its extension) is called an altitude. We have two right triangles, BCD and CDA. If we designate the measure of $\overline{CD}$ as h, the measure of $\overline{BD}$ as r, and the measure of $\overline{AD}$ as s, the areas of the triangles are given by

$$A_{\triangle BCD} = \frac{1}{2} \cdot r \cdot h; \; A_{\triangle CDA} = \frac{1}{2} \cdot s \cdot h$$

The total area of triangle ABC is the sum of these areas

$$A_{\triangle ABC} = \tfrac{1}{2}rh + \tfrac{1}{2}sh$$

Applying the LDPMA, we get

$$A_{\triangle ABC} = \tfrac{1}{2}h(r + s)$$

where $(r + s)$ stands for the measure of the side $\overline{AB}$ to which the perpendicular (the altitude) was drawn from C. If we agree that the measure of the base $\overline{AB}$ will be designated by b, we will have

$$A_{\triangle ABC} = \tfrac{1}{2} \cdot b \cdot h$$

Note that we use "$\overline{AB}$" to designate "segment from A to B."

Example: i.   Suppose we are asked to determine the area of the following triangle.

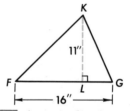

The measure of $\overline{KL}$ (perpendicular to $\overline{FG}$ from K) is 11 inches. The measure of $\overline{FG}$ is 16 inches.

Using the formula for the area of a triangle, we have

$$\begin{aligned} A &= \tfrac{1}{2} \cdot b \cdot h \\ &= \tfrac{1}{2} \cdot 16 \cdot 11 \\ &= 88 \end{aligned}$$

The area is 88 square inches.

Example: ii.   Suppose the area in the first example was 72 square inches, and the measure of the base 16 inches; could we determine the measure of the altitude $\overline{KL}$?
Substituting in $A = \tfrac{1}{2} \cdot b \cdot h$, we get

$$72 = \tfrac{1}{2} \cdot 16 \cdot h$$

Solving this equation, we obtain $h = 9$. Thus, the measure of the altitude $\overline{KL}$ would be 9 inches.

Example: iii.   If the altitude of a given triangle is tripled and the base is cut to one-fourth of the original measure, how will the area of the new triangle compare with the original?

If we express the area of the original triangle as

$$A_1 = \tfrac{1}{2} \cdot b \cdot h = \frac{bh}{2}$$

we may express the area of the new triangle as

$$A_2 = \tfrac{1}{2} \cdot (\tfrac{1}{4}b) \cdot (3h) \text{ or } A_2 = \frac{3bh}{8}$$

Thus, no matter what measure b stands for in the original triangle, $\tfrac{1}{4}b$ will represent $\tfrac{1}{4}$ of this measure. Similarly, no matter what measure h represents, $3h$ will always represent three times this measure.

Now

$$\frac{A_1}{A_2} = \frac{\dfrac{bh}{2}}{\dfrac{3bh}{8}} = \frac{8bh}{6bh} = \frac{8}{6} = \frac{4}{3}$$

Thus, the area of the first triangle is $\tfrac{4}{3}$ the area of the second, or the area of the second triangle is $\tfrac{3}{4}$ the area of the first.

The perimeter of any polygon may be determined by adding the measures of the sides. Thus, the perimeter of a rectangle is given by the formula

$$P = l + w + l + w \text{ or } P = 2(l + w)$$

where l and w are the length and width of the rectangle, respectively.

The perimeter of a square is

$$P = s + s + s + s \text{ or } P = 4s$$

where s is the measure of one of the sides.

The perimeter of any triangle ABC, in which the measures of the three sides are a, b, c, is

$$P = a + b + c$$

It is easy to see that the area of a square is found by using the formula for the area of a rectangle. For the square, the length and width are the same, thus

$$A_{\text{square}} = s^2$$

where s stands for the measure of one of its sides.

EXERCISES

Solve each problem.

1. One rectangle has a width of 5″ and length of 7″. Another rectangle has a width of 5″ and a length of 14″. Determine the difference between the areas of the two rectangles.

2. How does the area of a rectangle change if its length is doubled while the width is left the same? Its width is doubled while the length is left the same? Work out your answers using the general formula.

3. How does the area of a rectangle change if its length is tripled while the width is left the same? Its width is tripled while the length is left the same?

4. How does the area of a rectangle change if its length and the width are both doubled? both tripled?

5. If the measure of one side of a rectangle is multiplied by n, what change takes place in the area?

6. If the measure of both the width and length of a rectangle is multiplied by n, what change takes place in the area of the rectangle?

7. How does the area of a square change if we double each of its sides? How does the area change if we triple each of its sides?

8. Determine the area of triangle ACD at the right.

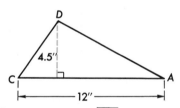

9. $ABCD$ and $FGHK$ are rectangles. If the measure of $\overline{HG}$ is 4″ and the measure of $\overline{FG}$ is 7″, determine the area of the shaded region.

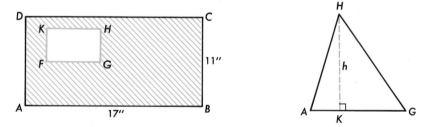

10. If the area of triangle AGH is 72 sq. in. and the measure of $\overline{AG}$ is 12″, what is the measure of the altitude?

11. Determine the area of a square whose perimeter is 44″.

12. If the perimeter of triangle GHK is 144″, find the measure of $\overline{HK}$.

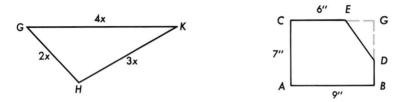

13. $ABGC$ is a rectangle. If a triangular piece of the corner (EGD) is removed, what is the area of the remaining pentagon $ABDEC$ if the measure of $\overline{DB}$ is 3″?

14. $ARST$ is a rectangle. Determine the area of triangle TSR.

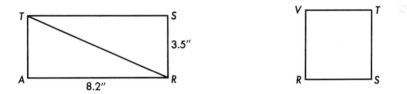

15. If the area of the square $VTSR$ is 84.6 sq. in., determine the measure of $\overline{RS}$.

16. The length of a rectangle is three times its width. If the perimeter of the rectangle is 114″, determine the length and the width.

17. If a rectangle is 13 inches long and 8 inches wide, what is the measure of the sides of a square of equal area?

18. If the areas of the square and the rectangle above are equal, determine the measure of l.

19. The measures of the altitude and of side $\overline{AB}$ of triangle ABC are equal and the area of triangle ABC is 24.5 sq. in. Determine the measure of $\overline{AB}$.

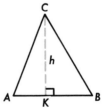

20. The sum of the perimeters of two squares is 100″. If the perimeter of one square is three times the perimeter of the other, find the measure of the side of each square.

21. The length of a rectangle is four times its width. The perimeter is 300 inches. Determine the measure of each side of the rectangle.

22. The sum of the perimeters of two equilateral triangles is 30 inches. Determine the length of the sides of each triangle if a side of the larger triangle is nine times as long as a side of the smaller triangle.

23. The perimeter of an isosceles triangle is 29 inches. If one leg is 4 inches longer than the base, determine the length of each side of the triangle. [An isosceles triangle has two sides of the same length. Each of these sides is called a leg. The third side is called the base.]

24. A square and a rectangle have the same perimeter. The rectangle's dimensions are: length, 27 ft.; width, 12 ft. How long is each side of the square?

25. In a $\triangle ABC$, the measure of $\angle A$ is twice the measure of $\angle B$ and three times that of $\angle C$. Determine the measure of each angle in $\triangle ABC$. (The sum of the measures of three angles in a triangle is 180°.)

26. Supplementary angles are angles the sum of whose measures is 180°. What are the measures of two supplementary angles if the measure of one is five times that of the other? If the measure of one is 37° more than that of the other?

27. Complementary angles are angles the sum of whose measures is 90°. What are the measures of two complementary angles if the measure of one angle is five times that of the other angle? If one is 37° more than the other?

28. Complete the following table. The first line is completed for you.

Measure of angle	(1) Complement of angle	(2) Supplement of angle	Difference (2) − (1)
5°	85°	175°	175 − 85 = 90
38°			
	89°		
		126°	
	30°25′		
		179°59′	

Examine your answers in the column headed "Difference" above. What can you conclude on the basis of the answers in this column?

Further uses of equations in solving problems

We now illustrate some more uses of equations in solving problems.

Problem: A seed dealer mixed grass seed selling at $1.20 a pound with clover seed selling at $1.60 a pound. If he wanted a mixture of 90 lbs. to sell at $1.24 a pound, how many pounds of each did he use in the mixture?

One Way to Solve: We know that the cost of the mixture is obtained by multiplying the cost per pound ($1.24) by the number of pounds (90 lbs.). The cost of this mixture is $111.60.

We don't know how many pounds of the grass seed or clover we have, but we know their total weight is 90 pounds. Thus, if we let x stand for the number of pounds of grass used, then $90 - x$ is the number of pounds of clover used. The cost of grass in dollars is $1.20x$. The cost of clover in dollars is $1.60(90 - x)$. Thus, our equation is

$$1.20x + 1.60(90 - x) = 111.60$$

Solve:
$$100[1.20x + 1.60(90 - x)] = 100 \times 111.60$$
$$120x + 160(90 - x) = 11{,}160$$
$$120x + 14{,}400 - 160x = 11{,}160$$
$$-40x = -3240$$
$$x = 81$$

Thus, we used 81 lbs. of grass seed and $90 - 81$ or 9 lbs. of clover seed.

CHECK:

grass	81 lbs. at $1.20 per pound	$97.20
clover	9 lbs. at $1.60 per pound	$14.40
	total cost	$111.60

Problem: A 20% antifreeze solution is a solution which consists of 20% antifreeze and 80% water. That is, the solution contains one volume pure antifreeze to every four volumes of water, or one volume of pure antifreeze in every five volumes of solution. Suppose we had 10 quarts of such a solution.

i. How much pure antifreeze does it contain?

ii. How much water should be added to yield a solution containing 15% antifreeze?

One Way to Solve: *i.* Since 20% of the solution is pure antifreeze, the solution contains $.20 \times 10$ or 2 quarts of pure antifreeze.

ii. Before we answer the question, let's see what procedure we can use to find the per cent of antifreeze in our solution after adding various volumes of water.

If we add one quart of water to our original ten quarts of solution, our total volume of solution would then be eleven quarts. However, the volume of pure antifreeze remains the same; that is, we still have two quarts of antifreeze in the solution. Therefore, there is

$$\frac{2 \text{ quarts of antifreeze}}{(10 + 1) \text{ quarts of solution}} = \frac{2}{11}$$

or about 18% antifreeze in this mixture.

If we had added six quarts of water, our total volume would be sixteen quarts. Again, the volume of pure antifreeze is the same both before and after diluting with water, that is, 2 quarts of antifreeze. We now have

$$\frac{2}{10 + 6} = \frac{1}{8}$$

or 12.5% antifreeze solution.

If we had added ten quarts of water, the resulting mixture would be 10% antifreeze. In all cases, the volume of pure antifreeze remains the same before and after diluting with water, that is, 2 quarts of antifreeze.

Let's reverse this procedure to find the volume of water that has to be added to produce a solution with a given new per cent of antifreeze. How much water must be added to ten quarts of the 20% solution to produce a 12.5% solution? We see that the original solution contains two quarts of pure antifreeze. Thus, 12.5%, or $\frac{1}{8}$, of the sum of the volume of original solution and the volume of water added should be equal to two, i.e., $\frac{1}{8}(10 + \text{volume of water added}) = 2$. Do you see why?

Now let's answer the original question: What volume of water should be added to our original ten quarts of 20% antifreeze solution to produce a 15% solution? Fifteen per cent, or $\frac{15}{100}$, of the sum of the original volume (10 quarts) and the volume of water added should be equal to 2. If we let x represent the number of quarts of water added, we formulate the following equation.

$$2 = \tfrac{15}{100}(10 + x)$$

Solve:
$$200 = 15(10 + x)$$
$$200 = 150 + 15x$$
$$50 = 15x$$
$$x = 3\tfrac{1}{3}$$

Thus if $3\tfrac{1}{3}$ quarts of water are added to our original 10 quarts of 20% antifreeze, a 15% solution is produced.

CHECK: We check the first answer, 2 quarts of antifreeze, by seeing if it is the correct volume in 10 quarts of solution which is already a 20% solution.

$$\frac{2 \text{ quarts of antifreeze}}{10 \text{ quarts of solution}} = 20\% \text{ solution}$$

We check the second answer, $3\tfrac{1}{3}$ quarts of water, by seeing if it is the correct volume to *add* to the original 10 quarts of solution to make a 15% solution. We see that we obtain $13\tfrac{1}{3}$ quarts of weaker solution.

$$\frac{2 \text{ quarts of antifreeze}}{10 \text{ quarts of solution} + 3\tfrac{1}{3} \text{ quarts of water}}$$
$$= \frac{2 \text{ quarts of antifreeze}}{13\tfrac{1}{3} \text{ quarts of weaker solution}}$$
$$= \frac{2}{\frac{40}{3}} = \frac{6}{40} = .15 \text{ and } .15 = 15\%$$

Thus, the new solution contains 15% of antifreeze.

EXERCISES

Solve each problem.

1. If it takes a woman nine days to clean house, by working at the same rate, how much of the job will she complete in six days? In three days? In one day? In y days?

2. If Mary completes one-third of a task in one day, how long would it take her to complete the whole task? Ann completes one-sixth of the same task in one day. Compare their rates of work. How long would it take Mary and Ann to complete the task working together? (We will assume their respective rates of work to remain the same as they were before.)

3. If Jim completes one-fourth of a job in one day and Joe completes three-eighths of the job in one day, who is the faster worker? Compare their rates (use a ratio). How long would it take Jim to complete the job by himself? How long would it take Joe by himself? Working at these rates how long would it take them working together?

4. If two boys working together complete a job in five hours, what part of the job will they complete in one hour? If the combination of the boys requires x hours to complete the task, what part of the task will they complete in one hour? If the boys' rates of work are the same, what part of the job will each of them complete in x hours? Each will complete a fraction of the job in x hours. What will these two fractions total?

5. If it takes Ed five hours to complete a job, and Bob completes the same job in three hours, how much of the job would each boy complete in one hour? How long would it take both working together to complete the job?

6. It would take Bill four hours to wash the windows by himself. Joe could complete the job in six hours. Working together at their own rates, how long will it take them to do the job?

7. It takes Roy one-half hour to cut the back lawn, while his brother, Bob, completes the task in 45 minutes. Working together at these rates, how long will it take them to complete the job?

8. Jim agrees to help John paint his house. It would take Jim 44 hours to do it by himself, while John could do it alone in 40 hours. They want to complete the job in a two-day weekend. Working together at their usual rates, how many hours must they work to complete the job in the weekend?

9. John usually took 50 minutes to mow the front lawn. After mowing for five minutes, he persuaded Greg to bring over his power mower and help him. Together, they finished the task in 15 minutes. How long would it have taken Greg to do the mowing by himself?

10. Suppose your science teacher has 5 quarts of 25% sulphuric acid solution. He would like to obtain a sulphuric acid solution of 35% acid by adding a solution of 75% acid to his original solution. How much of the more concentrated acid must be added to achieve the desired concentration?

11. A chemist has 18 quarts of 90% solution of sulphuric acid. How much additional water must be used to have a 22% acid solution?

12. An alloy of lead and tin weighs 78 pounds and contains 67% tin. How much lead must be melted in to make an alloy containing 60% lead?

13. A candy store proprietor wishes to mix caramels selling at $.95 a pound with 32 lbs. of creams selling at $1.10 a pound. If he wishes to sell the resulting mixture for $1.00 a pound, how many pounds of caramels should he use in the mixture?

INEQUALITIES

In this chapter, so far, we explored the uses of equations in solving various problems. In the previous chapter, we learned to find solution sets of simple inequalities. We now explore the inequalities and their applications to a greater extent. First, we show how a number of theorems concerning inequalities can be proved starting with three definitions and four properties. These definitions, properties, and many of the theorems are familiar to you, but we show them here so that we can view the development of inequalities as a deductive system; that is, we prove theorems starting with definitions and properties. We assume the universal set to be the set of real numbers.

■ *Definitions Concerning Inequalities*

$a > b$ means *a is greater than b.*

$a > b$ means the same as $b < a$, which means *b is less than a.*

$a > 0$ means *a is positive;* $a < 0$ means *a is negative.*

■ *Properties of Inequalities*

$\forall_a \forall_b$ only one of the following is true: $a < b$ $a = b$ $a > b$

This property is called the *Trichotomy Property.*

$\forall_a \forall_b \forall_c$, if $a < b$ and $b < c$, then $a < c$

$\forall_a \forall_b \forall_c$, if $a < b$, then $a + c < b + c$

$\forall_a \forall_b \forall_{c>0}$, if $a < b$, then $ac < bc$

What property of $=$ does the second one listed remind you of? Would it be logical to call it the *Transitive Property of Inequalities?*

What property of $=$ does the third one listed remind you of? Would it be logical to call it the *Inequality Property for Addition?*

What property of $=$ does the last property listed remind you of? What restriction is made in it which is not made in the property of equations? Would it be logical to call this one the *Inequality Property for Multiplication?*

You already know that any positive number is greater than any negative number. Let us see whether we can prove this.

Theorem 1 $\forall_{p>0} \forall_{n<0} \; p > n$

Proof

$p > 0$ and $n < 0$	Given
$p > 0$ and $0 > n$	Def. $b < a$
$p > n$	Trans. Prop. of Ineq.

Now let us examine a few pairs of examples which suggest another theorem.

$$5 < 6 \quad \text{and} \quad -5 > -6$$
$$1 < 7 \quad \text{and} \quad -1 > -7$$
$$-1 < 0 \quad \text{and} \quad 1 > 0$$
$$-4 < -1 \quad \text{and} \quad 4 > 1$$
$$-2 < 3 \quad \text{and} \quad 2 > -3$$

Theorem 2 $\forall_a \forall_b$, if $a < b$, then $-a > -b$

Proof

$a < b$	Given
$a + (-a - b) < b + (-a - b)$	Ineq. Prop. for Add.
$-b < -a$	Rearrangement
$-a > -b$	Def. $a > b$

Let us now examine the following examples and observe a pattern in them.

$$2 + 3 < 6 \qquad\qquad 2 < 6 - 3 \quad (2 < 3)$$
$$-5 + 8 < 7 \qquad\qquad -5 < 7 - 8 \quad (-5 < -1)$$
$$-4 + 1 < -2 \qquad\qquad -4 < -2 - 1 \quad (-4 < -3)$$
$$9 + (-2) < 8 \qquad\qquad 9 < 8 - (-2) \quad (9 < 10)$$
$$1 + (-5) < -3 \qquad\qquad 1 < -3 - (-5) \quad (1 < 2)$$
$$-2 + (-5) < -5 \qquad\qquad -2 < -5 - (-5) \quad (-2 < 0)$$

These examples suggest the following theorem.

Theorem 3 $\forall_a \forall_b \forall_c$, if $a + b < c$, then $a < c - b$

Proof

$a + b < c$	Given
$a + b + (-b) < c + (-b)$	Ineq. Prop. of Add.
$a < c - b$	Why?

EXERCISES

1. Supply a reason for each statement in the proofs of the following two theorems.

Theorem 4 $\forall_a \forall_b \forall_c$, if $a < b$, then $c - a > c - b$

Proof

$$a < b$$
$$-a > -b$$
$$-a + c > -b + c$$
$$c + (-a) > c + (-b)$$
$$c - a > c - b$$

Theorem 5 $\forall_a \forall_b \forall_{c<0}$, if $a < b$, then $ac > bc$

Proof $\qquad a < b$ and $c < 0$

$\qquad\qquad 0 + a < b$

$\qquad\qquad\quad 0 < b - a$

$\qquad\qquad b - a$ is positive

$\qquad\qquad (b - a)c$ is negative

$\qquad\qquad (b - a)c < 0$

$\qquad\qquad bc - ac < 0$

$\qquad\qquad\quad bc < ac$

$\qquad\qquad\quad ac > bc$

2.   Prove each of the following inequality theorems.

Theorem 6 $\forall_a \forall_b \forall_c \forall_d$, if $a < b$ and $c < d$, then $a + c < b + d$

Theorem 7 $\forall_{a<0}$ $-a > 0$

Theorem 8 $\forall_{a>0} \forall_{b>0}$ $a + b > 0$

Theorem 9 $\forall_{a>0} \forall_{b>0}$ $ab > 0$

Theorem 10 $\forall_{a>0} \forall_{b<0}$ $ab < 0$

Theorem 11 $\forall_{a<0} \forall_{b<0}$ $ab > 0$

Theorem 12 $\forall_{a<0} \forall_{b<0}$ $a + b < 0$

SOLUTION SETS OF INEQUALITIES

You will find the inequality theorems we just proved helpful in finding solution sets of inequalities.

Example: *i.* What is the solution set of the inequality

$$3x + 5 > 10?$$

$$3x + 5 > 10 \qquad \text{(Justify each step.)}$$

$$3x + 5 + (-5) > 10 + (-5)$$

$$3x > 5$$

$$3x \cdot \tfrac{1}{3} > 5 \cdot \tfrac{1}{3}$$

$$x > \tfrac{5}{3}$$

The solution set of the inequality $3x + 5 > 10$ is the set of all numbers greater than $\tfrac{5}{3}$. Using set notation, we can describe this set by

$$S = \{x \mid x > \tfrac{5}{3}\}$$

Choose several numbers each greater than $\tfrac{5}{3}$ and check to see whether they satisfy $3x + 5 > 10$.

The graph of this solution set on the number line would be

$S = \{x \mid x > \frac{5}{3}\}$

Example: *ii.* What is the solution set of the inequality
$$-5m - 6 > 17?$$

$$-5m - 6 > 17 \qquad \text{(Justify each step.)}$$
$$-5m - 6 + 6 > 17 + 6$$
$$-5m > 23$$
$$-5m \cdot (-\tfrac{1}{5}) < 23 \cdot (-\tfrac{1}{5})$$
$$m < -\tfrac{23}{5}$$

The solution set of the inequality $-5m - 6 > 17$ is $T = \{m \mid m < -\tfrac{23}{5}\}$, that is, the set consisting of all numbers less than $-\tfrac{23}{5}$.

Make a graph of this solution set.

The sentence $x \leq 5$ means "x is less than *or* equal to 5." The solution set of this sentence, in the universe of real numbers, is the set of numbers consisting of 5 and all numbers less than 5. Thus, the solution set is the union of the solution sets of two sentences: $x < 5$ and $x = 5$.

Example: *iii.* What is the solution set of the inequality
$$2 + 2x \leq 5x - 3?$$

The solution set is the union of the solution sets of $2 + 2x < 5x - 3$ and $2 + 2x = 5x - 3$. We determine first the solution set of $2 + 2x < 5x - 3$.

$$2 + 2x < 5x - 3$$
$$2 + 2x - 2x < 5x - 3 - 2x$$
$$2 < 3x - 3$$
$$2 + 3 < 3x - 3 + 3$$
$$5 < 3x$$
$$\frac{5}{3} < \frac{3x}{3}$$
$$\frac{5}{3} < x$$
$$\text{or} \quad x > \frac{5}{3}$$

Thus, $\{x \mid 2 + 2x < 5x - 3\} = \{x \mid x > \frac{5}{3}\}$

Do you see that $\{x \mid x = \frac{5}{3}\}$ is the solution set of the sentence $2 + 2x = 5x - 3$?

Thus, we have $\{x \mid 2 + 2x \leq 5x - 3\} = \{x \mid x \geq \frac{5}{3}\}$

Example: *iv.* Determine the solution set of

$$|x+1| < 3$$

$|x+1| < 3$ is equivalent to

$$x+1 < 3 \text{ and } x+1 > -3$$

We solve $x+1 < 3$ and $x+1 > -3$ separately and take the intersection of the two solution sets.

$$A = \{x|x+1 < 3\} = \{x|x < 2\}$$
$$B = \{x|x+1 > -3\} = \{x|x > -4\}$$

Now, $\{x| |x+1| < 3\} = A \cap B$
$$= \{x|x < 2\} \cap \{x|x > -4\}$$
$$= \{x| -4 < x < 2\}$$

$$\left\{ x \| x+1|<3 \right\}$$

Example: *v.* Determine the solution set of

$$|s-3| > 2$$

$|s-3| > 2$ is equivalent to

$$s-3 > 2 \text{ or } s-3 < -2$$

We solve $s-3 > 2$ and $s-3 < -2$ separately and take the union of the two sets.

$$M = \{s|s-3 > 2\} = \{s|s > 5\}$$
$$N = \{s|s-3 < -2\} = \{s|s < 1\}$$

Now, $\{s| |s-3| > 2\} = M \cup N$
$$= \{s|s > 5\} \cup \{s|s < 1\}$$
$$= \{s|s > 5 \text{ or } s < 1\}$$

$$\left\{ s \| s-3|>2 \right\}$$

Example: *vi.* Determine the solution set of

$$|3y-7| < -\tfrac{1}{2}$$

Since there is no real number whose absolute value is a negative number, there is no solution of $|3y-7| < -\tfrac{1}{2}$. Thus, $\{y| |3y-7| < -\tfrac{1}{2}\} = \phi$

EXERCISES

1. Using the inequality definitions, properties, and theorems, determine the solution sets of the following inequalities. The universe is the set of real numbers.

a. $3x > -6$

b. $2x + 2 < -4$

c. $\frac{1}{2}y + 1 < y - 2$

d. $\frac{m}{3} + \frac{1}{2} > m - 1$

e. $\frac{n+1}{2} < n - 1$

f. $\frac{3}{4}t > t - 7$

g. $2x \leq 10$

h. $3y - 1 \geq 17$

i. $2z - 5 \geq z + 3$

j. $\frac{5u - 3}{2} \geq 3u + 1$

k. $\frac{3w - 1}{3} \leq \frac{2w + 3}{2}$

l. $\frac{n}{2} + \frac{n}{3} \leq 1$

m. $3(m + 1) \geq 5(3 - m)$

n. $-2(x - 1) \leq 3(2 - x)$

o. $|p| < 1$

p. $|r + 1| > 15$

q. $|s + 2| > 1$

r. $|5h| < 0$

s. $|x| \geq 0$

t. $|y - 1| \geq 3$

2. Copy each statement and replace ○ by one of the symbols $<$, $>$, $\leq$, or $\geq$, to obtain a true statement.

a. If $x < y$, then $3x \bigcirc 3y$.

b. If $-3a \geq -3b$, then $a \bigcirc b$.

c. If $c \leq d$, then $c + (-a) \bigcirc d + (-a)$.

d. If $-8x > 16$, then $x \bigcirc -2$.

e. If $r \leq s$, then $-2r \bigcirc -2s$.

f. If $-x > -y$, then $-4 - x \bigcirc -4 - y$.

g. If $-5 + m < -5 + n$, then $m \bigcirc n$.

h. If $6(x + y) \geq 6(u - w)$, then $x + y \bigcirc u - w$.

3. True or false?

a. If $x < y$ and $y < 0$, then $xy > 0$.

b. If $x < y$ and $y < 0$, then $x + y > 0$.

c. If $x < y$ and $y < 0$, then $y - x < 0$.

d. If $x < y$ and $x > 0$, then $xy > 0$.

e. If $x < y$ and $x > 0$, then $y - x > 0$.

f. If $x < y$ and $x > 0$, then $x - y < 0$.

English sentences and inequalities

You already learned to make up stories to fit a given equation. Let us now do the same with inequalities.

Examples: *i.*   Given the inequality $2n - 1 \geq 5$, make up a story which fits the inequality.

Ed had a certain number of pebbles. If this number is doubled and one pebble is thrown away, he has at least five pebbles left. How many pebbles did Ed have to start with?

Note first that the universe here is the set of natural numbers. Why?

Could Ed have had one pebble? The answer is "no". because $2 \cdot 1 - 1 \geq 5$ is a false statement.

Do you see that he had at least three pebbles? Here is a proof for this answer.

$2n - 1 \geq 5$ means $2n \geq 6$, which means $n \geq 3$. The solution set is $\{3, 4, 5, 6, 7, \ldots\}$

  ii.   The following story will fit the inequality $t + 7 \geq 18$.

On a canoe trip we paddle for one day. If we paddle seven miles the next day, we cover at least 18 miles during the two days. How many miles did we paddle during the first day?

The solution set here is $\{t \mid t \geq 11\}$. Thus, we paddled at least 11 miles during the second day.

  iii.   For the inequality $y + 7 \leq 18$, the following story can be given.

If Joe puts 7 dollars in the bank, he will have at most 18 dollars. At most, how many dollars did he have to start with? (What is the restriction on the replacement set here?) The answer is: Joe had at most $11.

EXERCISES

1. Make up one story for each of the following sentences.

  a. $2x + 1 \geq 11$ **c.** $3n - 2 > n$

  b. $\dfrac{m}{2} - 1 \leq 100$ **d.** $s + 2 < 2s - 1$

2. Write open sentences which fit the following stories. Determine the solution set of each sentence. State the universal set in each case.

Example: Five added to a number results in a number that is greater than twice the original number. From what set could the original number have been chosen?

Open sentence:
$$n + 5 > 2n$$
$$n + 5 - n > 2n - n$$
$$5 > n$$
$$n < 5$$

Letting the universal set be the set of real numbers, the solution set consists of all real numbers less than 5; that is, $\{n \mid n + 5 > 2n\} = \{n \mid n < 5\}$.

a. Five less than three times a certain number is less than the number increased by two. What numbers satisfy this condition?

b. Joe is 7 years younger than Bill. The sum of their ages is less than 49. At most how old is Joe?

c. I am thinking of a number which when added to 7, results in a number less than 11. What numbers satisfy this condition?

d. Section A of algebra has 10 more students than section B. Half of the number of students in section A added to half the number of students in section B gives at least 30 students. How many students are there in each section?

e. The sum of twice a certain number and twenty-four is greater than five times the number. What natural numbers satisfy this condition?

f. Mary has a number of sea shells. If she finds 9 more than twice this number, she will have at most 45 sea shells. How many did she have at first?

g. Jim has a stamp collection. If he triples the number of the collection and adds 5 more stamps to it, he will have at least 47 stamps. At least how many stamps did he have in the original collection?

VOCABULARY

Use each of the following correctly in a sentence. Numerals in the parentheses refer to pages where these words were used. If you are not sure of the meaning of any word, turn to the indicated page and refresh your memory.

Celsius scale (217)

even integer (227)

Fahrenheit scale (217)

formula (213)

odd integer (227)

perimeter (213)

rectangular solid (213)

right circular cylinder (213)

sphere (214)

DEFINITIONS, PROPERTIES, AND THEOREMS

◼ *Definition of "a is greater than b"* $a > b$ means a is greater than b.

◼ *Definition of "a is less than b"* $a < b$ (a is less than b) means the same as $b > a$ (b is greater than a).

◼ *Definition of a positive; a negative* $a > 0$ means a is positive; $a < 0$ means a is negative.

◼ *Trichotomy Property of Order* $\forall_a \forall_b$ only one of the following is true
$$a < b \qquad a = b \qquad a > b$$

◼ *Transitive Property of "Is Less Than"*
$\forall_a \forall_b \forall_c$, if $a < b$ and $b < c$, then $a < c$

◼ *Inequality Property for Addition*
$\forall_a \forall_b \forall_c$, if $a < b$, then $a + c < b + c$

◼ *Inequality Property for Multiplication*
$\forall_a \forall_b \forall_{c>0}$, if $a < b$, then $ac < bc$

Theorem 1 $\quad \forall_{p>0} \forall_{n<0} \ p > n$

Theorem 2 $\quad \forall_a \forall_b$, if $a < b$, then $-a > -b$

Theorem 3 $\quad \forall_a \forall_b \forall_c$, if $a + b < c$, then $a < c - b$

Theorem 4 $\quad \forall_a \forall_b \forall_c$, if $a < b$, then $c - a > c - b$

Theorem 5 $\quad \forall_a \forall_b \forall_{c<0}$, if $a < b$, then $ac > bc$

Theorem 6 $\quad \forall_a \forall_b \forall_c \forall_d$, if $a < b$ and $c < d$, then $a + c < b + d$

Theorem 7 $\quad \forall_{a<0} \ -a > 0$

Theorem 8 $\quad \forall_{a>0} \forall_{b>0} \ a + b > 0$

Theorem 9 $\quad \forall_{a>0} \forall_{b>0} \ ab > 0$

Theorem 10 $\quad \forall_{a>0} \forall_{b<0} \ ab < 0$

Theorem 11 $\quad \forall_{a<0} \forall_{b<0} \ ab > 0$

Theorem 12 $\quad \forall_{a<0} \forall_{b<0} \ a + b < 0$

REVIEW EXERCISES

1. For each mathematical sentence, make up a story which fits it.

Example: $(2t + 5) + t = 200$

How to Solve: Mr. Jones and his son, Bob, weigh a total of 200 lbs. Mr. Jones weighs 5 lbs. more than twice Bob's weight.

a. $x + 2 = 7$

b. $3 + 4y = 83$

c. $\dfrac{n}{2} - 7 = 8$

d. $\dfrac{m - 1}{3} = m - 15$

2. In each problem, you are given a formula. Do the required computations.

    a. Surface area of a cube: $A = 6e^2$, where e is the measure of an edge.
      i. Solve for e.
      ii. Compute e when A is 24 sq. in.
    b. Perimeter of an isosceles triangle: $p = b + 2a$, where b is the measure of the base and a is the measure of each arm.
      i. Solve for a.
      ii. Compute a when p is 40 in. and b is 9 in.
    c. Surface area of a regular tetrahedron: $S = a^2\sqrt{3}$, where a is the measure of each edge.
      i. Solve for a.
      ii. Compute a, when s is $9\sqrt{3}$ sq. ft.
    d. Interest rate, which is equivalent to a discount rate d, is

$$i = \frac{d}{1 - nd},$$ where n is the number of years.

      i. Solve for d.
      ii. Compute d in per cent when i is 6% and n is 25 years.
    e. Einstein's equation relating mass and energy: $e = mc^2$, where e is energy in ergs, m is mass in grams, and c is the speed of light in centimeters per second.
      i. Solve for m.
      ii. Solve for c.
      iii. If the light travels at 30 billion centimeters per second, compute the number of ergs produced by the conversion of 1 gram of mass to energy.

3. The average of three consecutive odd numbers is 17. What are the three numbers? Do you see a quick way of telling the numbers? Can the average of three consecutive odd numbers be an even number? Why?

4. The average of three consecutive even numbers is 12. What are the three numbers? If the average is 102, what are the three numbers? Do you see a quick way of telling the numbers? Can the average of three consecutive even numbers be an odd number?

5. An article usually selling at $1.75 is put on sale at the reduction of 15% of the regular price. What is the reduced cost of the article?

6. An article sells at a certain price. After the reduction of 25% of the selling price, the article sold for $1.65. What was its original selling price?

7. The perimeter of a square is the same as the length of a rectangle. The width of the rectangle is one-fourth of the length of the side of the square. If the width of the rectangle is 2″, what is the area of the square? Of the rectangle?

8. There are 49 marbles in a box. If the number of red marbles is twice the number of white marbles, and the number of green marbles is twice the number of red marbles, how many marbles of each color are there in the box?

9. One-half of a number plus one-fourth of the number is 9. What is the number?

10. How many miles will Johnny travel on his bicycle in 4 hours and 10 minutes if his average speed is 10 m.p.h.?

11. The selling price of an article is $1.54. This price includes 10% markup computed on the basis of the cost. What is the cost of the article?

12. Joe is at present twice as old as his sister. In eight years he will be $1\frac{1}{2}$ times as old as she will be. Determine their present ages.

13. The sum of one-fifth of a number and two-thirds of the number is 36. What is the number?

14. If $a \neq 0$ means $a > 0$ or $a < 0$, prove each of the following:

   a. $\forall_{a \neq 0}\ a^2 > 0$
   b. $1 > 0$
   c. $\forall_a \forall_b,\ ab > 0$ if and only if $(a > 0$ and $b > 0)$ or $(a < 0$ and $b < 0)$
   d. $\forall_a \forall_b,\ ab < 0$ if and only if $(a > 0$ and $b < 0)$ or $(a < 0$ and $b > 0)$

15. Determine the solution set of each of the following inequalities, then graph each solution set on a number line.

   a. $r + 5 > 12$

   b. $2y - 3 < 14$

   c. $\dfrac{m + 4}{3} \leq 1$

   d. $3(x - 6) \leq 0$

e. $\dfrac{n-1}{2} \geq \dfrac{n+2}{3}$

g. $|s-1| \geq 2$

f. $|t| < 2$

h. $|3n - \frac{7}{8}| \leq -3$

16. True or false?

a. $-11 \not< 1$

d. $6 \leq 6$

b. $|-6| > 2$

e. $4 \leq |-5|$

c. $7 \neq -6$

f. $-6 \not> -5$

17. Write open sentences which fit the following stories. Determine the solution set of each sentence. State the universal set in each case.

a. Jim is allowed to save at most $180 over a three-month period in the following way: the second month he can save $\frac{1}{2}$ of the amount he saved the first month, and the third month $\frac{1}{3}$ of the amount saved the first month. At most how much money can he save the first month?

b. I am thinking of a number, which, when subtracted from 5, results in a number greater than 12. What numbers satisfy this condition?

c. Judy walks at least 9 miles each day. She and Carol together walk at most 22 miles in any one day. At most how many miles does Carol walk in any one day?

CHAPTER TEST

1. For each mathematical sentence, make up a story that fits it.

a. $x + 1 = 7$

b. $2y - 1 = 5$

c. $\dfrac{m+3}{2} = 1$

2. Solve each formula for the indicated letters.

a. $z^2 = az + b^2$; for a; for b

b. $x + \dfrac{x}{7} = 19$; for x

c. $ax^2 + bx + c = 0$; for a; for b; for c

d. $y = \dfrac{px + q}{rx + s}$; for x; for q

e. $y = \dfrac{x(x^2 + 3D)}{3x^2 + D}$; for D

f. $\dfrac{2E}{n} + \dfrac{2E}{r} - E = 2$; for E; for n

3. Miss Coins has $4.50 in nickels and dimes. She has three times as many nickels as dimes. How many nickels and how many dimes does Miss Coins have?

4. Multiplying a number by 3 and adding 3 to the product gives the same result as multiplying this number by 2 and adding 10 to the result. What is the number?

5. Mary is now 5 years younger than her brother Ken. Ken was twice as old as Mary was 8 years ago. How old is Mary now?

6. The enrollment in a college is 6000 students with the ratio of boys to girls 3 to 1. How many girls are there in this college?

7. Mr. Needy obtains a loan of $1200 at $4\frac{1}{2}\%$ annual interest rate. If he pays the total sum of $162 in interest, for how many years did he have this loan?

8. Mr. Neighborly visits his friends in another city. On the trip to the city he averages 40 m.p.h. and on the return trip 60 m.p.h. If the entire trip took him 3 hrs. and 20 min., what was the distance between the two cities?

9. The width of a rectangle is one-sixth of its length. Determine the length and width of the rectangle, if the perimeter is equal to 28 inches.

10. Each leg of an isosceles triangle is one-half as long as the base of the triangle. If the perimeter of the triangle is equal to 18 inches, what is the measure of each side of the triangle?

11. A chemist adds a certain number of quarts of water to 26 quarts of 15% sulphuric acid solution. How many quarts of water did he add if the result was a 12% solution?

12. Pipe A fills a swimming pool in 4 hours and Pipe B does it in 6 hours. How long will it take, if both pipes are filling the pool simultaneously?

13. Which of the following is an example of the transitive property of "is less than"?

    a. If $2 < 4$, then $2 + 3 < 4 + 3$.
    b. If $1 < 3$, and $3 < 7$, then $1 < 7$.
    c. If $5 < 9$, then $5 \times 6 < 9 \times 6$.

14. True or false?

    a. $\forall_x \forall_y \forall_a$, if $x < y$ and $a < 0$, then $xa < ya$.
    b. $\forall_x \forall_y \forall_a$, if $x < y$ and $a > 0$, then $xa > ya$.

c. $\forall_x \forall_y$, if $x < 0$ and $y > 0$, then $x + y > 0$.
d. $\forall_x \forall_y$, if $x < 0$ and $y < 0$, then $x + y < 0$.
e. $\forall_x \forall_y$, if $x > 0$ and $y < 0$ and $|y| > x$, then $x + y < 0$.
f. $\forall_x \forall_y$, if $x < 0$ and $y < 0$, then $\dfrac{x}{y} > 0$.

g. $\forall_x \forall_y$, if $x < 0$ and $y > 0$, then $\dfrac{x}{y} > 0$.

h. $\forall_x \forall_y$, if $|x| > |y|$, then $x > y$.
i. $\forall_x \forall_y$, if $x > y$, then $|x| > |y|$.

j. $\forall_x \forall_y$, if $\dfrac{x}{y} > 1$, then $|x| > |y|$.

15. Determine the solution set of each inequality.   The universe is the set of real numbers.

a. $5y < -10$
b. $3m + 1 < 9$
c. $4n - 2 > n + 6$
d. $\dfrac{3x - 1}{2} \le \dfrac{2 - x}{3}$

e. $4(s - 2) \ge 3(1 + 2s)$
f. $|t| > 3$
g. $|u| \le 9$
h. $|z - 4| \ge 10$

CUMULATIVE REVIEW EXERCISES

These exercises are designed for your review of the basic ideas in Chapters 5 through 8.

In exercises **1-12** choose the correct answer.

1. Which of the following pairs of equations is a pair of equivalent equations?

a. $\dfrac{x + 3}{x + 2} = 5, \quad 4x + 10 = 3$
b. $5 - x = 7, \quad 2(x - 8) + 3(7 - x) = 7$
c. $-3 = \dfrac{-5}{x - 5}, \quad x - 5 = \dfrac{5}{3}$
d. all of these
e. none of these

2. An equation whose solution set is $\{-\frac{8}{7}\}$ is

a. $\frac{7}{8}y + 4 = 5$
b. $\frac{8}{7}y + 5 = 4$
c. $-\frac{7}{8}y + 4 = -5$

d. $-\frac{7}{8}y - 4 = 5$
e. none of these

3. Which of the following sets is equivalent to $\{x|\frac{4}{3}x + \frac{5}{6}x = 2\}$?

   a. $\{x|4x + 5x = 36\}$ **d.** $\{x|8x + 5x = 6\}$

   b. $\{x|x = 4\}$ **e.** none of these

   c. $\{x|4x + 5x = 18\}$

4. The solution set of the equation $|3r + 5| = 8$ is

   a. $\{\frac{13}{3}, 1\}$ **d.** ϕ

   b. $\{\frac{3}{13}, -1\}$ **e.** none of these

   c. $\{1, -\frac{13}{3}\}$

5. The cost in dollars of 111 tickets, if n of them are 75¢ tickets and the remainder are 90¢ tickets is

   a. $.90n + .75(n - 111)$ **d.** $.75(111 - n) + .90n$

   b. $.75n + .90(n - 111)$ **e.** none of these

   c. $.90(111 - n) + .75n$

6. The age of a boy now, if 7 years ago he was two-thirds as old as his mother and his mother is now t years of age, is given by the expression

   a. $\frac{2}{3}(t + 7) + 7$ **d.** $\frac{2}{3}(t - 7) + 7$

   b. $\frac{3}{2}(t - 7) + 7$ **e.** none of these

   c. $\frac{3}{2}(7 + t) + 7$

7. The selling price of a house which sells at a profit of 16% of its cost c is given by the expression

   a. $c + 16c$ **d.** $.16(c + .16)$

   b. $.16c + c$ **e.** none of these

   c. $c - .16c$

8. If Jerry were three years younger, he would be two-thirds as old as Jim. Jim is 12 years older than Jerry. If we let x stand for Jerry's age, which of the following open sentences would lead to a correct solution of the problem?

   a. $\frac{2}{3}(x - 3) = x + 9$ **d.** $x + 3 = \frac{2}{3}(x - 12)$

   b. $\frac{2}{3}(x + 3) = x + 9$ **e.** none of these

   c. $x - 3 = \frac{2}{3}(x + 12)$

9. If x is an even integer, then the next two even integers are

   a. $x + 1$ and $x + 2$ **d.** $x + 2$ and $x + 4$

   b. $x - 1$ and $x + 1$ **e.** none of these

   c. $x - 1$ and $x - 2$

10. If $2n$ and $2n + 2$ represent two consecutive even integers, their product is represented by

  a. $4n + 4$ **d.** $2n + 4n^2$
  b. $4n + 2$ **e.** none of these
  c. $4n^2 + 4n$

11. If x represents the tens digit and y the units digit of a two-digit numeral then the value of every two-digit numeral may be represented as

  a. $y + x$ **d.** $10x + y$
  b. xy **e.** none of these
  c. yx

12. If $x = y$, then $rx = ry$ is always true only if

  a. x and y are integers   **d.** x and y are rational numbers
  b. $r \neq 0$ **e.** none of these
  c. $x \neq 0$ and $y \neq 0$

13. For each step, state the property which justifies it.

  a. $[r6 \cdot (-7)]t \overset{(1)}{=} [6r \cdot (-7)] \cdot t$
  $\overset{(2)}{=} [6(-7) \cdot r] \cdot t$
  $\overset{(3)}{=} (-42 \cdot r) \cdot t$
  $\overset{(4)}{=} -42(rt)$

  b. $(r + t)(x + y) \overset{(1)}{=} (r + t) \cdot x + (r + t) \ y$
  $\overset{(2)}{=} x \cdot (r + t) + y \cdot (r + t)$
  $\overset{(3)}{=} xr + xt + yr + yt$

14. Using the word descriptions of the following sets, rewrite them using shorthand set notation.

Example: S is a set of real numbers x, such that -3 is less than x and x is less than 4.
$S = \{x | x \epsilon R, \ -3 < x < 4\}$

  a. R is a set of integers t, such that -2 is less than or equal to t and t is less than or equal to 4.
  b. P is a set of natural numbers r, such that 4 is less than r and r is less than 7.
  c. T is the set of real numbers y, such that y is greater than -6.
  d. V is the set of integers r, such that 2 is less than or equal to r and r is less than or equal to 3.
  e. G is the set of real numbers s, such that s is less than 5 or s is greater than 6.

f. D is the set of natural numbers n, such that 7 is less than n and n is less than 9.

g. Q is the set of integers t, such that -7 is less than t and t is less than -4.

15. Classify as true or false.

a. $-3 \not< 5$

b. $4 \geq -2$

c. $3 \leq 7$

d. $|-3| \neq |3|$

e. $|-7| > 8$

f. $\left|\dfrac{-1}{-3}\right| < \left|\dfrac{1}{1+2}\right|$

g. $|7.6 - 8.2| = |8.2 - 7.6|$

h. $|-2||-3| = |-2 \cdot (-3)|$

16. For each of the following, we have found an equivalent equation in standard form. State the properties involved in moving from one step to another.

a.
$$4y = -5x + 3$$
$$4y \overset{(1)}{=} 3 + (-5x)$$
$$4y + 5x \overset{(2)}{=} 3 + (-5x) + 5x$$
$$4y + 5x \overset{(3)}{=} 3 + [5x + (-5x)]$$
$$4y + 5x \overset{(4)}{=} 3 + 0$$
$$4y + 5x \overset{(5)}{=} 3$$
$$5x + 4y \overset{(6)}{=} 3$$

b.
$$3(2y - 4x) = -7$$
$$3 \cdot 2y + 3(-4x) \overset{(1)}{=} -7$$
$$6y - 12x \overset{(2)}{=} -7$$
$$-12x + 6y \overset{(3)}{=} -7$$

17. Tell whether each of the following is true for all replacements of the variables.

a. $\dfrac{4z}{2z} = 2, \quad (z \neq 0)$

b. $|x - y| = |y - x|$

c. $|xy| = |x| \cdot |y|$

d. $-|xx| = x \cdot (-x)$

e. $|x| \geq x$

f. $|x + y| = |-x| + |-y|$

g. $-(y - x) = -x - y$

h. $(s - t)(x - y) = -(t - s)(x - y)$

i. $-[-x] + (-x) = 0$

j. $(xy)(-z) = -x(yz)$

k. $15x - [16x - (11x + 3)] = 10x - 3$

l. $-\dfrac{-t}{s} = \dfrac{t}{s},\quad (s \neq 0)$

n. $\dfrac{r + 5t}{-2} = -\dfrac{r}{2} - \dfrac{5}{2}t$

m. $\dfrac{t}{-y} = \dfrac{-t}{y},\quad (y \neq 0)$

o. $\frac{4}{3}(5x - 6) = \frac{20}{3}x - 8$

18. Write a simpler equivalent expression for each of the following:

a. $\frac{3}{2}x + 4 - \frac{5}{2}y + \frac{1}{2}x + 2 + (-\frac{3}{2}y)$ **c.** $(-3)(-x)(-\frac{1}{3})$

b. $3x - 5x + (-2\frac{1}{3}x) - 5\frac{2}{3}x + 9x$ **d.** $(7x - \frac{2}{7}x) \div \frac{3}{4}$

19. Find the value of each of the following expressions for the designated replacements of the variables.

a. $\dfrac{x + 3y}{y - (-5y)};\ -3$ for x; 5 for y

b. $3x(y - x);\ -4$ for x; -2 for y

c. $\dfrac{2 - 3(k - r)}{3t};\ 2$ for k; -3 for r; 4 for t

d. $\dfrac{(-6) \cdot (3a - 4d)}{5d};\ 3$ for a; -4 for d

20. Classify each of the following as either a monomial, a binomial, or a trinomial (all letters are variables).

a. $4x + y$ **e.** $25abc$ **i.** $ab - ac$
b. $2m$ **f.** $\frac{1}{2}x + \frac{1}{3}y + \frac{1}{4}z$ **j.** $2t - u$
c. -4 **g.** 1.9 **k.** x
d. $x - y - z$ **h.** $4 + 12x$ **l.** $2.6n$

21. Prove each of the following:

a. $\forall_m \forall_n\ 3mn - 7mn = -4mn$

b. $\forall_x \forall_y\ 4x + 3y - 2x - y = 2x + 2y$

c. $\forall_{a \neq 0} \forall_{b \neq 0}\ \dfrac{\frac{1}{a}}{-\frac{1}{b}} = -\dfrac{b}{a}$

22. True or false?

a. $\dfrac{\frac{1}{2}}{\frac{1}{3}} = \frac{2}{3}$

b. $\forall_x\ \dfrac{\frac{x}{5}}{\frac{1}{2}} = \dfrac{x}{10}$

c. $\forall_a \forall_b\ \dfrac{\frac{a + b}{2}}{4} = \dfrac{8}{a + b},\quad (a + b \neq 0)$

d. $\forall_m \forall_n \ \dfrac{\dfrac{m+n}{2}}{\dfrac{m-n}{2}} = \dfrac{m-n}{m+n}, \quad (m+n \neq 0,\ m-n \neq 0)$

e. $\forall_a \forall_b \forall_c \forall_d \ \dfrac{1+\dfrac{a}{b}}{1+\dfrac{c}{d}} = \dfrac{(a+b)d}{(c+d)b}, \left(\dfrac{a}{b} \neq -1, \dfrac{c}{d} \neq -1,\ (c+d)b \neq 0\right)$

23. On the number line, graph the solution set of each inequality. The universal set is the set of all real numbers.

a. $A = \{b\,|\,b < -1\}$
b. $C = \{d\,|\,d \geq 2\frac{1}{2}\}$
c. $E = \{f\,|\,-5 \leq f < 2\}$

d. $G = \{h\,|\,h \neq 4\}$
e. $I = \{k\,|\,k < -2 \text{ or } k \geq 1\frac{1}{2}\}$

24. For each expression, write an expression equivalent to it and containing no parentheses.

a. $3(x+y)$
b. $-2(4-a)$
c. $(-6)\left(\dfrac{x-n}{3}\right)$

d. $(4m - 12n)(\frac{1}{4})$
e. $(a+b)(a-b)$
f. $(3-2u)(3+2u)$
g. $(a+b-c)(a+b+c)$

25. Solve each equation.

a. $n + 4 = 26$
b. $x + 12 = 9$
c. $4 - y = 3$
d. $4a + 3 = 26$
e. $1 + 7k = 8$
f. $\dfrac{3}{y} = -6$
g. $\dfrac{x+3}{2} = 4$
h. $\dfrac{3-2t}{5} = -1$

i. $|y| = 7$
j. $|x - 3| = 9$
k. $|4y + 3| = 19$
l. $3 - 2|m| = 1$
m. $3(x - 5) = 6$
n. $-2(4 - 2s) = 3$
o. $2(x + 2) = -3(3 - 2x)$
p. $\dfrac{3t-1}{2} = \dfrac{1-t}{3}$
q. $\dfrac{-(x-5)}{4} + 2 = \dfrac{2x-3}{2} + 1$

26. Determine the solution set for each inequality. The universe is the set of real numbers.

a. $n - 6 > 2$
b. $2x - 2 < 1$
c. $3y + 4 < y - 7$
d. $m > 4m - \frac{1}{2}$
e. $\dfrac{p-2}{3} > 6$

f. $\dfrac{2r-2}{7} < r + 11$
g. $|w + 2| > 0$
h. $|v - 6| < 0$

27. True or false?

a. $-4 \not< -5$ **d.** $|3-6| < |6-3|$ **g.** $|-3| \not> |3|$

b. $0 \not> -1$ **e.** $5 \le |-5|$

c. $|-6| \ne -6$ **f.** $9 > |-10|$ **h.** $\dfrac{2-3}{2} < \dfrac{3-2}{2}$

28. Solve each problem.

a. Multiplying a number by 5 and adding 20 to the product gives 5 for the result. What is the number?

b. Jim is 5 years older than Tom. Six years ago Jim was twice as old as Tom. How old is Jim?

c. Each leg of an isosceles triangle has the same measure as a side of a square. The base of the triangle is 5 inches long. What is the measure of each side of the square, if the triangle and the square have the same perimeter?

d. Miss Dollars has $24.00 in dimes and half-dollars. If she has three times as many fifty-cent coins as ten-cent coins, how many of each does she have?

e. A shelf contains 220 books. If the number of science books is $1\frac{1}{2}$ times the number of mathematics books, and the number of fiction books is twice the number of science books, how many books of each of the three kinds are there on the shelf?

BIBLIOGRAPHY

Felix, Lucienne (translated by Julius H. Hlavaty and Fancille H. Hlavaty) *The Modern Aspects of Mathematics.* New York: Basic Books, Inc., 1960. pp. 23-31.

School Mathematics Study Group. *Applied Mathematics in the High School.* Studies in Mathematics, Volume X. Stanford: Stanford University, 1963.

School Mathematics Study Group. *Mathematical Methods in Science.* Studies in Mathematics, Volume XI. Stanford: Stanford University, 1963.

Vergara, William C. *Mathematics in Everyday Things.* New York: The New American Library, 1959.

Whitehead, Alfred North. *An Introduction to Mathematics.* New York: Oxford University Press, 1958. pp. 14-38.

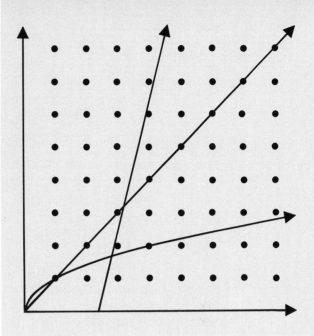

CHAPTER 9

Systems of Equations and Inequalities

EQUATIONS IN TWO VARIABLES

So far you have been studying equations with one variable. Now we shall consider equations with two variables. Let us consider the following example.

$$x + 2y = 5$$

The variables in this equation are x and y. In order to obtain true statements, we shall replace the variables x and y by numerals. We agree that the two variables may be replaced by names for the same number or for two different numbers.

We pick any number whatsoever for one variable, say x. Replacing x by, say 1, we have

$$1 + 2y = 5$$

Then solving for y we get

$$1 + 2y = 5$$
$$2y = 4$$
$$y = 2$$

Thus 1 for x, 2 for y, gives us

$$1 + 2 \cdot 2 = 5$$

which is a true statement.

Now let us use $\frac{1}{2}$ for x

$$\frac{1}{2} + 2y = 5$$
$$2y = 4\frac{1}{2}$$
$$y = 2\frac{1}{4}$$

$\frac{1}{2}$ for x and $2\frac{1}{4}$ for y, gives us

$$\frac{1}{2} + 2 \cdot 2\frac{1}{4} = 5$$
$$\frac{1}{2} + 4\frac{1}{2} = 5$$

which also is a true statement.

Thus, the pairs $(1, 2)$, that is, 1 for x, 2 for y
and $(\frac{1}{2}, 2\frac{1}{4})$, that is, $\frac{1}{2}$ for x, $2\frac{1}{4}$ for y

satisfy the equation $x + 2y = 5$.

There are many more number pairs which satisfy the equation above. Some of these are

$$(-1, 3) \qquad (4, \tfrac{1}{2}) \qquad (-2, 3\tfrac{1}{2}) \qquad (1.5,\ 1.75) \qquad (-4, 4\tfrac{1}{2})$$

Make appropriate replacements in the equation $x + 2y = 5$ to see that each of these number pairs satisfies the equation. Keep in mind that the first number listed is for x, the second for y.

Would you be able to find ten more number pairs which satisfy this equation? Given plenty of time, how many number pairs satisfying this equation would you be able to find?

EXERCISES

Each equation below has two variables. Next to each equation, there are listed three real number pairs. For each pair, tell whether or not it satisfies the equation.

1. $a + b = 7$; (a, b): $(6, 1)$; $(-10, 3)$; $(6.99, .1)$

2. $2m - 4n = 2$; (m, n): $(0, \frac{1}{2})$; $(0, -\frac{1}{2})$; $(4, 2\frac{1}{2})$

3. $\frac{1}{2}p + 3r = -4$; (p, r): $(2, 1)$; $(0, -\frac{4}{3})$; $(-2, -1)$

4. $1.7s - 3.6t = 1.5$; (s, t): $(-.2, 0)$; $(3, 1)$; $\left(0, -\dfrac{1.5}{3.6}\right)$

5. $3w = 2n + 4$; (n, w): $(0, -2)$; $(-2, 0)$; $(-5, -2)$

6. $3 - (2x + y) = 0$; (x, y): $(1, 2)$; $(\frac{3}{2}, 0)$; $(0, 0)$

7. $\frac{d-2}{5} = \frac{u+3}{4}$; (d,u): $(2,-3)$; $\left(0, -\frac{23}{5}\right)$; $\left(-4, \frac{3}{4}\right)$

8. $5(v+6z) = \frac{1}{2}(3v+9z)$; (v,z): $(0,0)$; $(51,-7)$; $(-7,51)$

9. $|m+2n| = 3$; (m,n): $(1,1)$; $(-1,-1)$; $(-\frac{1}{2},\frac{1}{2})$

10. $\frac{1}{2} \cdot |x+w| = \frac{1}{3} \cdot |x-w|$; (x,w): $(0,0)$; $(6,-\frac{6}{5})$; $(6,-30)$

11. $|x| - y = |x-y|$; (x,y): $(0,0)$; $(11,2)$; $(1,5)$

12. $2a = 3 \cdot |b| - 1$; (a,b): $(0,\frac{1}{3})$; $(0,-\frac{1}{3})$; $(-4,-3)$

More about equations with two variables

You learned that an equation of the form $Ax + By = C$ has many number pairs which satisfy it.

The equation $3x + 2y = 7$ is of such form. This equation is obtained from $Ax + By = C$ by replacing A by 3, B by 2, and C by 7. Upon replacement of A, B, and C by various numerals we obtain many different equations.

If either A or B is replaced by 0, an equation is obtained which has one variable in it. For example

$$0 \text{ for } A, \; -5 \text{ for } B, \; 6 \text{ for } C: \qquad -5y = 6$$
$$1 \text{ for } A, \; 0 \text{ for } B, \; 0 \text{ for } C: \qquad x = 0$$

The set of replacements which does not result in an equation with at least one variable is

$$0 \text{ for } A \text{ and } 0 \text{ for } B$$

What is the result of such replacements? What can you tell about the resulting equation?

An equation with two variables is not always in the form $Ax + By = C$. For example, the equation $2y = 3(x-5) + 12 - 5y$ is *not* in this form. We can find, however, an equation which is equivalent to the above and which is of the form $Ax + By = C$. Study the way it is done below and state the property involved at each step.

Example:
$$2y = 3x - 15 + 12 - 5y$$
$$2y + 5y = 3x - 3 - 5y + 5y$$
$$7y = 3x - 3$$
$$7y - 3x = 3x - 3 - 3x$$
$$-3x + 7y = -3$$
$$(-1)(-3x + 7y) = (-1)(-3)$$
$$3x - 7y = 3$$
$$3x + (-7)y = 3$$

In the development above, we have shown many details. With some practice, you will be able to "skip" some steps. You should not be too hasty in skipping steps, however, especially when you are not sure of yourself.

The last equation, $3x + (-7)y = 3$, is of the form $Ax + By = C$, where A is replaced by 3, B by -7, and C by 3. We shall call this form *the standard form of a linear equation in two variables*.

The equation $3x - 7y = 3$ is equivalent to $3x + (-7y) = 3$.

EXERCISES

For each equation below, find an equivalent equation in standard form. At each point you should be prepared to justify what you do by the appropriate property.

In the example, not every step is shown. If you are unsure of any of the steps, fill in the intermediate steps.

Example:

$$3 - 7y + 3x = 6(x - y) + 3y$$
$$3 - 7y + 3x = 6x - 6y + 3y$$
$$3 - 7y + 3x = 6x - 3y$$
$$3 - 7y + 3x - 6x = 6x - 3y - 6x$$
$$3 - 7y - 3x = -3y$$
$$3 - 7y - 3x + 3y = -3y + 3y$$
$$3 - 4y - 3x = 0$$
$$3 - 4y - 3x - 3 = 0 - 3$$
$$-4y - 3x = -3$$
$$-3x + (-4)y = -3$$

1. $x = y + 7$

2. $2x = -3 - 8y$

3. $-5(x + y) = 17$

4. $3x = 2(y + 6)$

5. $-5(2x + y) = -3(x - 2)$

6. $-10(x - 3y) = 2y - 3x + 6$

7. $6(y - 6x) + 17 = 13 - 4(x + 10y)$

8. $\dfrac{y - x}{y + x} = 3$

9. $\dfrac{2x - 3}{3y + 7} = -9$

10. $\dfrac{3}{5} = \dfrac{6x - y + 15}{3x + 7y - 1}$

11. $\dfrac{x + 3}{5} = \dfrac{y - 1}{2}$

12. $\dfrac{1}{2x + 1} = \dfrac{2}{3y + 4}$

13. $\dfrac{2y - 3}{-2} = \dfrac{-3x - 1}{-3}$

14. $\dfrac{-5}{-y + 7} = \dfrac{2}{-4x - 3}$

15. $\dfrac{3(x - 1)}{5} = \dfrac{2(2y + 7)}{9}$

16. $\dfrac{-4}{3 - y} = \dfrac{-3}{5x - 2}$

THE COORDINATE PLANE AND ORDERED NUMBER PAIRS

You may have already seen that an equation of the form $Ax + By = C$ has many number pairs which satisfy it. For example, in the system of real numbers, each of the number pairs $(1, 1)$, $(7, 5)$, $(-\frac{1}{2}, 0)$, $(-6, -\frac{11}{3})$, $(0, \frac{1}{3})$ satisfies the equation

$$2x - 3y = -1 \quad \text{(Check to see that this is so.)}$$

You will recall that, at the beginning of this course, we established a one-to-one correspondence between numbers and points on the number line. Now we shall establish a one-to-one correspondence between real *number pairs* and the *points in the plane*.

To do this, we take two number lines — it is customary to take one horizontal and one vertical line — that cross each other at their zero points. The point where the lines meet is called the *origin*. The surface on which the points are located is called a *plane*.

Now we can assign to each point a number pair and to each number pair we can assign a point. It is the usual practice to assign number pairs as in the figure below. The first number in the number pair is called the "first component," and the second number, the "second component." We are now ready to make an agreement by which a one-to-one correspondence between number pairs and points will be established.

Consider the number pair $(4, 2)$. To find the point corresponding to this pair, we shall agree that the first number tells us the number of units we are to move from the origin to the right or to the left — positive number, to the right; negative number, to the left. The second number, then, tells us how many units to move up or down — positive number, up; negative number, down.

Thus, $(4, 2)$ means move 4 units to the right, 2 units up. The point thus obtained is the point A in the figure on page 263. Do you see that there is only *one* point corresponding to the number pair $(4, 2)$?

Examine the figure on page 263 to see how the points corresponding to the following number pairs were located.

$(2, 4)$	$(\frac{1}{2}, 6\frac{1}{3})$	$(0, 2\frac{1}{2})$	$(-2, 5)$
$(-1, -4)$	$(0, -3\frac{1}{3})$	$(-4, -1)$	$(5, -2)$
$(7, -5\frac{1}{3})$	$(3.5, -3.6)$	$(6\frac{1}{2}, 0)$	

What are the coordinates of the origin?

If we should agree that the form of the number pair names is (x, y), then we could refer to the horizontal line by the name "x-axis," and to the vertical line by the name "y-axis."

Each real number pair has exactly one point corresponding to it. The numbers in the pair are the *coordinates* of that point. The first number is called the *first coordinate* or *abscissa* and the second number is called the *second coordinate* or *ordinate*.

For example, in the number pair $(4, 2)$, 4 is the abscissa of the point corresponding to $(4, 2)$ and 2 is the ordinate of that point. The abscissa is called x-coordinate, and the ordinate is called y-coordinate.

It is important to note that the numbers in a number pair cannot be interchanged. For example, do you see that $(4, 2)$ and $(2, 4)$ have two different points corresponding to them? We call such number pairs *ordered number pairs*. Thus in $(4, 2)$, 4 is the first number, and 2 is the second number. In $(2, 4)$, 2 is the first number, and 4 is the second number, and $(4, 2) \neq (2, 4)$.

The plane in which we locate points corresponding to given ordered number pairs is called "the coordinate plane" or "the Cartesian plane," after the name of the French mathematician Descartes who first introduced the idea. The two axes superimposed on the plane are referred to as the *rectangular coordinate system*.

EXERCISES

1. Make a coordinate system on a sheet of paper and locate points corresponding to the following ordered number pairs. Label points as in the diagram on page 263.

a. $(4, 1)$	**e.** $(-1, 2)$	**i.** $(2, -4.5)$
b. $(1, 4)$	**f.** $(0, 0)$	**j.** $(6, 0)$
c. $(3\frac{1}{2}, 3\frac{1}{2})$	**g.** $(-3\frac{1}{2}, -4)$	**k.** $(-7\frac{1}{2}, 0)$
d. $(0, 7)$	**h.** $(0, -1\frac{1}{2})$	**l.** $(0, -3)$

2. In the coordinate system below, the points are named by capital letters of our alphabet. List each letter on your paper, and next to it write the name of the ordered number pair corresponding to the point. (The exercise is done for point *A*.)

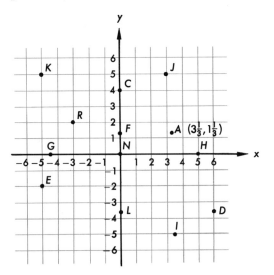

3. You have probably observed that the two axes of the rectangular coordinate system divide the plane into four sets. It is customary to name these parts as below.

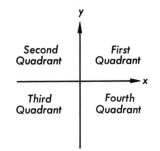

Thus, we can say that the point corresponding to the ordered number pair (1, 175), for example, belongs to the first quadrant. The points *on* the *x*-axis, or *on* the *y*-axis do *not* belong to any quadrant.

Tell to which quadrant each of the points corresponding to the ordered number pairs below belongs.

a. $(-16, -137)$

b. $(1007, -2)$

c. $(10, 1000)$

d. $(-.007, 137.99)$

e. $(\frac{13}{29}, -.003)$

f. $(-111, -3)$

g. $(-37, -678)$

h. $(-\frac{1}{3}, 99)$

    i. (127, 12)   **n.** (1027, −368)
    j. (−13, 13)   **o.** (11, −11)
    k. (13, −13)   **p.** (2006, 2006)
    l. (−128, 378)   **q.** ($|-17|$, $|-1389|$)
    m. (−998, 998)   **r.** ($|\frac{1}{2}|$, $|-\frac{1}{2}|$)

4.   Examine your answers in exercise **3.** What can you tell about the coordinates of points in the first quadrant?   In the second quadrant? In the third quadrant?   In the fourth quadrant?

5.   What can you tell about the coordinates of the points on the x-axis? On the y-axis?

6.   Complete each statement. Use diagram at the right.

$Q_2 =$ Second Quadrant $Q_1 =$ First Quadrant

$Q_3 =$ Third Quadrant $Q_4 =$ Fourth Quadrant

    a. $Q_1 \cap Q_2 = ?$

    b. $(Q_1 \cap Q_2) \cap Q_3 = ?$

    c. $(Q_1 \cap Q_2) \cap (Q_3 \cap Q_4) = ?$

    d. $(Q_1 \cup Q_2) \cup (Q_3 \cup Q_4) \cup (X \cup Y) = ?$

    e.   The intersection of the x-axis and y-axis $= ?$

GRAPHS OF LINEAR EQUATIONS IN TWO VARIABLES

You have seen that an equation of the form

$$Ax + By = C$$

where A, B, and C may have as replacements the real numbers (A and B are not both 0), has many ordered number pairs which satisfy it.   Now you also know that to each ordered number pair there corresponds exactly one point in a coordinate plane.   The points are *graphs* of the ordered number pairs.

    Let us consider the following equation.

$$2x + 5y = -3$$

Its solution set can be described as $\{(x, y) \mid 2x + 5y = -3\}$.   This is read "the set of all ordered number pairs x and y for which $2x + 5y = 3$." Here are some ordered number pairs (x, y) which satisfy this equation.

    (1, −1); (−4, 1); (0, −$\frac{3}{5}$); (11, −5); (3.5, −2); (6, −3)

Let us locate the graphs of these number pairs on the coordinate system below.

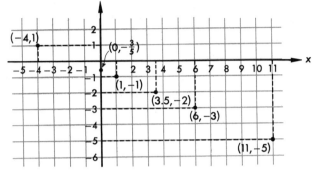

If you try to fit an edge of a ruler to these points, you will notice that they line up pretty well along the edge. As a matter of fact, later in your study of mathematics you will be able to prove that the graph of the equation $2x + 5y = -3$ is a straight line. Moreover, you will be able to *prove* that the graph of any equation of the form $Ax + By = C$, where the replacement set of A, B, and C is the set of real numbers (A and B not both 0), is a straight line. For now, we will *assume* that it is so. In fact, let us agree on the following two properties concerning straight lines.

■ *Line Property* 1
   In the system of real numbers the graph of every equation of the form $Ax + By = C$ is a straight line (A and B are not both 0).

■ *Line Property* 2
   There is only one straight line which contains two given points.

According to property one the graph of the equation $2x + 5y = -3$ is a straight line.
   According to the second property we need to locate only two points whose coordinates satisfy the equation $2x + 5y = -3$ in order to locate the graph of this equation. In practice, however, it is a good idea to locate three points as a check.

EXERCISES

Graph the following sets. Use the set of real numbers as the replacement set for both x and y.

1. $\{(x, y) \,|\, x + y = 6\}$
2. $\{(x, y) \,|\, 2x + 3y = -2\}$
3. $\{(x, y) \,|\, 4x - 5y = 10\}$
4. $\{(x, y) \,|\, x = y + 1\}$

5. $\{(x, y)\,|\,3x = 4 - 7y\}$

6. $\{(x, y)\,|\,5(x + 3) = 2(y - 1)\}$

7. $\{(x, y)\,|\,-2(3 - 2x) = 3(1 + 3y)\}$

8. $\{(x, y)\,|\,-6x + 4 = -11y\}$

9. $\{(x, y)\,|\,\frac{x}{3} + y = -5\}$

10. $\{(x, y)\,|\,5 + \frac{4}{3}x = -7y\}$

11. $\{(x, y)\,|\,-4y + 3x = 7\}$

12. $\{(x, y)\,|\,2x - 5 = -13y\}$

SOLVING SYSTEMS OF EQUATIONS BY GRAPHING

In the previous section, you learned to graph a linear equation in two variables. Since the graph of such an equation is a straight line and since two points determine a line, you needed to determine only two ordered number pairs which satisfy the equation. The two points corresponding to these number pairs determine the line.

Let us consider the equation.

$$3x - 4y = 12$$

In order to find ordered real number pairs satisfying the equation, let us first replace x by 0.

$$3 \cdot 0 - 4y = 12$$
$$-4y = 12$$
$$y = -3$$

Thus, $(0, -3)$ should be one pair which satisfies the equation. To check

$$3 \cdot 0 - 4(-3) = 0 - (-12) \text{ or } 12$$

so we know that $(0, -3)$ does, in fact, satisfy the equation.

Now let us replace y by 0.

$$3x - 4 \cdot 0 = 12$$
$$3x = 12$$
$$x = 4$$

Thus, $(4, 0)$ should be another pair which satisfies the equation. To check

$$3 \cdot 4 - 4 \cdot 0 = 12 - 0 \text{ or } 12$$

Let us locate points corresponding to the ordered number pairs $(0, -3)$ and $(4, 0)$ and draw a picture of the line through them. This line is the graph of the equation

$$3x - 4y = 12$$

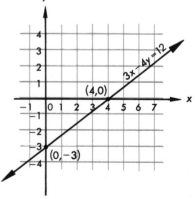

It is customary to call the distances from the origin along the x-axis and y-axis *intercepts*. Thus, the distance from $(0, 0)$ to $(4, 0)$ on the graph of $3x - 4y = 12$ is the *x-intercept* and the distance from $(0, 0)$ to $(0, -3)$ is the *y-intercept*.

It is often more convenient to locate the intercepts than to find any other two points. The two intercepts, of course, determine a line except under one special set of conditions. (What are these conditions?)

We can follow this procedure because every number pair that satisfies the equation names a point on its graph *and* every point on the graph has coordinates that satisfy the equation.

Now we are ready to consider pairs of linear equations in two variables. Each of these equations has a straight line for its graph. Thus, the graph of the two equations consists of two straight lines; and two straight lines in the same plane either intersect in one point or do not intersect at all, or else the lines are not distinct. In the last case we have two equivalent equations, that is, two equations for the same line. What do we call two lines which do not intersect?

Consider the following system of two linear equations in two variables.

$$-x + 2y = 5$$
$$3x - 2y = -13$$

Below are graphs of these two equations. Examine the graphs to see how they were obtained.

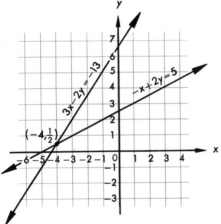

From the graph we find that the first and second coordinates of the point in which the two lines intersect are -4 and $\frac{1}{2}$, respectively. Since this point is on both lines, its coordinates must satisfy both equations; that is, since this number pair is a member of each set of number pairs specified by the equations, it is an element of their intersection — and we know the lines can intersect in no more than one point.

Let us check. In the first equation

$$-4 \text{ for } x; \quad \tfrac{1}{2} \text{ for } y$$
$$-(-4) + 2 \cdot \tfrac{1}{2} = 4 + 1 \text{ or } 5$$

Therefore $(-4, \tfrac{1}{2})$ satisfies the first equation.

In the second equation

$$-4 \text{ for } x; \quad \tfrac{1}{2} \text{ for } y$$
$$3(-4) - 2 \cdot \tfrac{1}{2} = -12 - 1 \text{ or } -13$$

Therefore $(-4, \tfrac{1}{2})$ satisfies the second equation.

Thus we have a way of finding the ordered number pair which satisfies two equations in two variables. The set $\{(-4, \tfrac{1}{2})\}$ is the solution set of the system of the two equations.

$$-x + 2y = 5$$
$$3x - 2y = -13$$

EXERCISES

For each pair of equations below, do the following:

   i. Graph the solution set of each equation.

   ii. List the coordinates of the point of intersection of the two graphs as an ordered pair of real numbers.

   iii. Check to see whether the coordinates of the point of intersection satisfy both equations in the pair.

Example: $2x + y = -4; \quad 3y = 5x - 1$

i.

ii. $(-1, -2)$

iii. CHECK: Remember, you must check both equations.

-1 for x; -2 for y

$2x + y$	$= -4$		$3y$	$= 5x - 1$
$2(-1) + (-2)$	-4		$3(-2)$	$5(-1) - 1$
$-2 + (-2)$			-6	$-5 - 1$
-4				-6

1. $x + y = 4$
    $2x - y = 2$

2. $3x + 2y = 10$
    $-x + 6y = 0$

3. $3x - y = -1$
    $x - 2y = 8$

4. $\quad 2x = 2y + 1$
    $x + 2y = 8$

5. $7y = x - 4$
    $x = y - 10$

6. $-2 - 3x = 4y$
    $\quad\quad y = -x$

7. $y = x - 1$
    $2y = 2x + 2$

8. $6x = 2y - 7$
    $2y = 13x$

9. $x = y$
    $y = -x$

10. $x = 0$
    $x = y$

11. $y = 0$
    $x = -y$

12. $-x = -y$
    $x = -2$

13. $x = 4$
    $y = -2$

More about graphing equations

In the previous section, you learned to find the coordinates of a point common to two straight lines. The two lines were graphs of two linear equations each in two variables. You found that the coordinates of the common point satisfied both equations. The ordered number pair corresponding to the common point was the solution set of the given system of equations.

Consider now the following system of two equations in two variables.

$$2x + y = -1$$
$$2y = -2 - 4x$$

Let us find two ordered number pairs which satisfy the first equation and two pairs which satisfy the second equation.

First equation: $(-1, 1)$; $(4, -9)$
Second equation: $(1, -3)$; $(-3, 5)$

Examine the graph at the top of the next page.

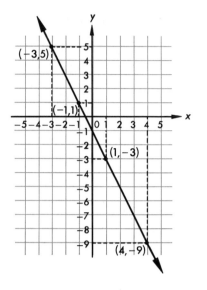

From the graph, you observe that each of the pairs of points determines the same line; that is, both equations are equations for the same line. Let us examine more closely the two equations.

$$2x + y = -1$$
$$2y = -2 - 4x$$

We shall use equation properties to attempt to get the second equation from the first. In doing this, we shall not fill in all of the steps. If you are not certain about any of the steps, you should fill in the details for yourself.

$$2x + y = -1$$
$$2x + y - 2x = -1 - 2x$$
$$y = -1 - 2x$$
$$2y = 2(-1 - 2x)$$
$$2y = -2 - 4x$$

Thus we see that the two original equations are equivalent and their graphs are the same line. Such a pair of equations is called

a dependent system of two linear equations in two variables

Now consider the following pair of equations.

$$x + 2y = 3$$
$$2x + 4y = -2$$

The first equation is satisfied by, say

$$(-1, 2) \text{ and } (5, -1)$$

The second equation is satisfied by, say

$$(1, -1) \text{ and } (-1, 0)$$

Now, study the graph at the right.

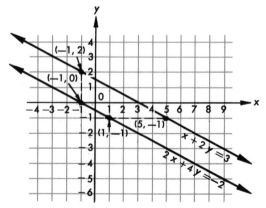

From the graph it appears that the two lines do not intersect. They are, therefore, parallel lines. Parallel lines are lines in the same plane which do not intersect no matter how far extended. In that case there would be no intersection point. If it is true that the two lines have no common point, then it is also true that there is no number pair which satisfies both equations.

It can easily be seen that the equation

$$x + 2y = -1$$

is equivalent to the equation

$$2x + 4y = -2$$

which is our second equation. Therefore, we can use the pair of equations

$$x + 2y = 3$$
$$x + 2y = -1$$

in place of the original pair. But we see that in this pair of equations we want $x + 2y$ to yield 3 and -1 for the same replacements of x and y. This is not possible.

We can conclude, then, that the equations

$$x + 2y = 3$$
$$2x + 4y = -2$$

have no common solutions. Such a pair of equations is called

an inconsistent system of two linear equations in two variables

A pair of linear equations in two variables having exactly one number pair satisfying both equations is called

an independent system of two linear equations in two variables

EXERCISES

For each pair of equations on page 276, do the following:

    i. Graph the solution set of each equation.

    ii. Tell whether the system is independent, dependent, or inconsistent.

    iii. In the case of an independent system, determine the solution set and check. In the case of a dependent or inconsistent system, use equation properties to prove your decision.

Example:
$$x + 2y = -1$$
$$2x + 4y = 4$$

i.

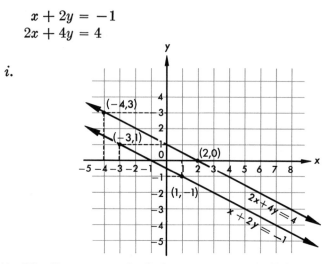

ii. The lines as graphed above appear parallel. In that case, the system is inconsistent.

iii. Let us take the second equation and obtain an equation equivalent to it.

$$2x + 4y = 4$$
$$\tfrac{1}{2}(2x + 4y) = \tfrac{1}{2} \times 4$$
$$x + 2y = 2$$

Thus, we now have the pair of equations

$$x + 2y = -1$$
$$x + 2y = 2$$

There are no ordered pairs of numbers which will satisfy both of these equations, since they lead to the conclusion that $-1 = 2$. Therefore, this system of equations is an inconsistent system.

Since the equation

$$x + 2y = 2$$

is equivalent to the equation

$$2x + 4y = 4$$

we can conclude that the original system

$$x + 2y = -1$$
$$2x + 4y = 4$$

is an inconsistent system.

Example: $-m + 3n = 7$
$2m + 4n = 16$

i.

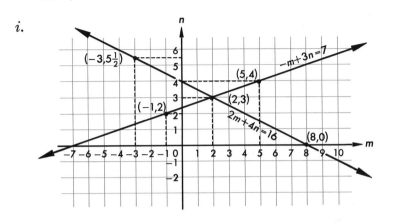

ii. The system is independent.

iii. $(2, 3)$

CHECK: 2 for m; 3 for n (we must check both equations)

$-m + 3n$	$=$	7
$-2 + 3 \cdot 3$		7
$-2 + 9$		
7		

$2m + 4n$	$=$	16
$2 \cdot 2 + 4 \cdot 3$		16
$4 + 12$		
16		

Example: $z = 4 - w$
$2w + 2z = 8$

i.

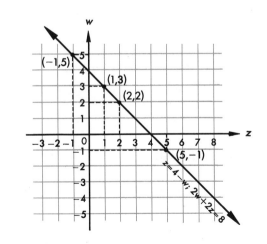

ii. The system is a dependent system.

iii. Finding equivalent equations to $z = 4 - w$ gives us

$$w + z = 4$$
$$2(w + z) = 2 \cdot 4$$
$$2w + 2z = 8$$

Thus, the first equation is equivalent to the second, and we are convinced that the system is dependent.

1. $u + v = 2$
    $2u + 5v = 7$
2. $2x = 3 - 5y$
    $10y = 6 - 4x$
3. $-s = 2t - 4$
    $4t + 2s = 1$
4. $\frac{1}{2}k + \frac{1}{3}m = -6$
    $k + m = -15$
5. $2n + 5 = r$
    $-3r = -15 - 6n$

6. $7 - 3p = 4t$
    $2t + 1.5p = 17$
7. $x = -y$
    $x = y$
8. $2t - 3u = 1$
    $3t - 2u = 1$
9. $2(a - 2b) = 3$
    $2b - a = 1$
10. $5w - 4v = 6$
    $3 + 2v = 2.5w$

GRAPHING EQUATIONS AND INEQUALITIES

The idea of a one-to-one correspondence between ordered pairs of real numbers and the points in the coordinate plane is very important in the study of equations and inequalities. Equations and inequalities are open sentences in which the number replacements which produce true statements are called *solution sets*. The sets from which we may choose replacements for the variables are called *universal sets*. The open sentences serve as the *selectors* of the number pairs for the solution set. The universal set may be the set of real numbers, integers, or any set we choose.

From the correspondence between number pairs and points in the coordinate plane we view the open sentence

$$x + y = 4$$

as the selector of a set of points corresponding to the solution set. We indicate this set as

$$\{(x, y) \,|\, x + y = 4\}$$

We read this as "the set of ordered real number pairs (x, y) for which $x + y = 4$." We say that the graph of $\{(x, y) \,|\, x + y = 4\}$ is the graph of $x + y = 4$.

Usually, we will choose the first members and the second members of the ordered pairs from the universe of real numbers, but we may restrict our choice to any set desired.

It is clear that

$$A = \{(x, y) \mid x \in R \text{ and } y \in R,\ x + y = 4\} \text{ and}$$
$$B = \{(x, y) \mid x \in I \text{ and } y \in I,\ x + y = 4\}$$

are different sets. We agree, as before, to associate the first components with the points on the horizontal axis, and the second components with the points on the vertical axis. The graph of set A is given below.

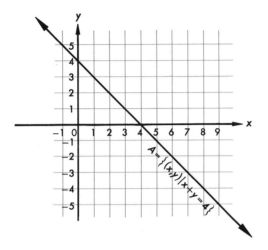

Consider another set

$$C = \{(s, t) \mid s \in R \text{ and } t \in R,\ s \geq t\}$$

A graph of this set is

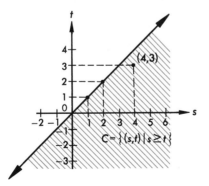

Note that the graph of the set of points which belong to C extends indefinitely. Do you see that every point in the shaded area belongs to the set C? For example, $(4, 3) \in C$, because $4 \geq 3$. Check a few more points in the shaded area to see whether they belong to C.

Do the points which make up the straight line, the boundary of the set, belong to the set? Why?

Let us now graph the set $M = \{(u, v) \mid |u| > -v\}$ if the replacement set for u and v is the set of real numbers.

First, let us name a few number pairs which belong to this set. Remember that for each pair in the set, the absolute value of the first member in the set must be greater than the opposite of the second member.

$$(5, 1) \in M \text{ because } |5| > -1$$
$$(3, 17) \in M \text{ because } |3| > -17$$
$$(5, -4) \in M \text{ because } |5| > -(-4) \text{ or } 5 > 4$$
$$\text{but } (5, -6) \notin M. \text{ Why?}$$
$$(0, 255) \in M \text{ because } |0| > -255$$
$$\text{but } (0, -1) \notin M. \text{ Why?}$$

From these examples, it is becoming clear that, if the second member of the pair is any positive number, then the first member may be any non-negative number.

Observe that

$$(4, -3) \in M, \text{ because } |4| > -(-3)$$
$$\text{but } (4, -5) \notin M, \text{ because } |4| \not> -(-5)$$

Now we can begin to make the graph. It is good practice first to identify the graph of

$$\{(u, v) \mid |u| = -v\}$$

Here are a few pairs which belong to this set. (See graph below.)

$$(3, -3), \ (2, -2), \ (-2, -2), \ (-1, -1), \ (0, 0)$$

Do you see that every pair belonging to $\{(u, v) \mid |u| = -v\}$ has for its second member a non-positive number? Explain why this is so.

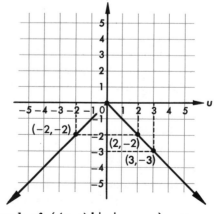

Above is the graph of $\{(u, v) \mid |u| = -v\}$

Now we are in a position to graph the set

$$M = \{(u, v) \mid |u| > -v\}$$

Do you see that only the points
in the shaded regions belong to the
set? Does $(0, 0)$ belong to M? Do the
boundaries (dashed lines) belong to
M? Does $(1, -2)$ belong to M?

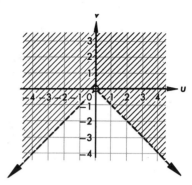

Example:

Graph the set $T = \{(m, n) \mid m + n < 1\}$ if the replacement set for m and n is the set of integers.
Here are a few pairs which belong to T.

$(-7, 7)$ because $-7 + 7 < 1$
$(-2, 1)$ because $-2 + 1 < 1$
$(-2, 2)$ because $-2 + 2 < 1$
$(0, -5)$ because $0 + (-5) < 1$
$(8, -8)$ because $8 + (-8) < 1$

but $(-2, 3) \notin T$ because $-2 + 3 \not< 1$

Are you beginning to see the relationship between the
first number and the second number in each pair which
makes a pair belong to T?
Let us first graph the set $\{(m, n) \mid m + n = 1\}$.
Here are some pairs that belong to this set: $(-4, 5)$;
$(-3, 4)$; $(-2, 3)$; $(-1, 2)$; $(0, 1)$; $(1, 0)$; $(2, -1)$; $(3, -2)$;
$(4, -3)$.

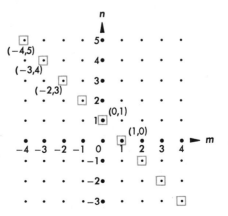

No doubt you notice that the points belonging to the graph of $\{(m, n)\,|\,m + n = 1\}$ make up a "line." It is not the ordinary line you are used to when the replacement set is the set of real numbers. Since we have only integers, we have a "dot line." How far does this "line" extend?

Now here is the graph of $T = \{(m, n)\,|\,m + n < 1\}$.

In the graph above, the points of the boundary are circled. Do they belong to T? Why? Do all the points marked $\boxed{\cdot}$ belong to T? How far does the graph extend?

EXERCISES

1.   Graph each of the following sets. The replacement set of the variable in each case is the set of real numbers.

a. $X = \{(a, b)\,|\,a + 2b = 3\}$

b. $Y = \{(c, d)\,|\,c = 5d - 4\}$

c. $A = \left\{(m, n)\,\Big|\,\dfrac{m}{n} = 1\right\}$

d. $B = \{(x, y)\,|\,2x > y\}$

e. $C = \{(p, q)\,|\,2q + 3 < 2p\}$

f. $D = \{(r, t)\,|\,|r| < t\}$

g. $E = \{(s, r)\,|\,|s| > |r|\}$

h. $M = \{(g, h)\,|\,g + h \neq 4\}$

i. $P = \{(u, v)\,|\,u \geq v - 1\}$

2.   Graph each of the following sets.

a. $G = \{(x, y)\,|\,x \in I \text{ and } y \in I,\ x + 3 > y\}$

b. $H = \{(r, s)\,|\,r \in N \text{ and } s \in N,\ 3r + 3 = s\}$

c. $K = \{(w, v)\,|\,w \in R \text{ and } v \in R,\ w < v + 3\}$

d. $T = \{(m, p)\,|\,m \in I \text{ and } p \in I,\ m + p \geq -4\}$

3.   Graph the sets in exercise **1**, using the set of integers as the universal set for the first and second components of the ordered pairs.

4.   If the universal set from which we choose the first and second components of the ordered pairs is the set $\{1, 2, 3, 4, 5\}$, graph the following sets.

a. $G = \{(x, y) \mid x + y < 4\}$ **c.** $L = \{(x, y) \mid y + 2 \geq x\}$
b. $K = \{(x, y) \mid y > x + 2\}$ **d.** $T = \{(x, y) \mid y \geq x\}$

GRAPHING MORE COMPLICATED SENTENCES

When you solved systems of two equations with two variables by means of graphs, you looked for the *intersection* of the two sets. If the intersection was the empty set, you knew that the two equations had no common solution.

Let us now consider sentences which involve both equations and inequalities.

Example: *i.* Graph the set

$$A = \{(m, n) \mid m = n \ or \ -1 < m < 3\}$$

The replacement set of m and n is the set of real numbers. To obtain the graph, we will consider the two sets separately.

$$B = \{(m, n) \mid m = n\}$$
$$C = \{(m, n) \mid -1 < m < 3\}$$

Graphs of the two sets are below.

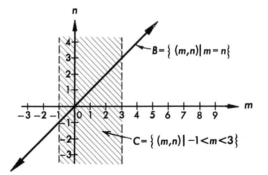

Do the vertical lines which make up the boundaries of the set C belong to C? Why? How is this fact indicated in the graph? Now the set

$$A = \{(m, n) \mid m = n \ or \ -1 < m < 3\}$$

is the *union* of the sets B and C. Why? Use the graph above to describe the graph of the union of B and C.

Example: *ii.* Let us consider another example

$$X = \{(p, q)\,|\,p \leq 2 \ and \ 2 \leq |q| < 5\}$$

where the replacement set of p and q is the set of real numbers.

The two sets involved here are

$$Y = \{(p, q)\,|\,p \leq 2\}$$
$$Z = \{(p, q)\,|\,2 \leq |q| < 5\}$$

Let us graph both sets on the same coordinate system.

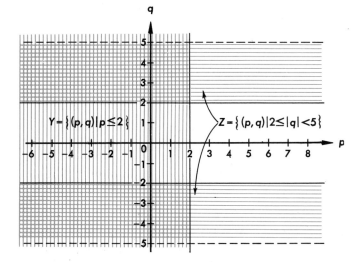

Does the boundary of the graph of the set Y belong to the graph? How is this fact indicated in the graph?

Do the boundaries of the graph of Z belong to the set? Why? How is this fact indicated in the graph?

Now we need to identify the graph of

$$X = \{(p, q)\,|\,p \leq 2 \ and \ 2 \leq |q| < 5\}$$

To do this, we find the points which belong to *both* sets Y and Z; that is, we find the *intersection* of the sets Y and Z. The picture of the set X is that part of the graph which is shaded with both kinds of shadings. Describe in detail the boundaries of the graph of X.

Of what geometric figures does the graph of X remind you?

Example: *iii.* Now let us graph the set

$$M = \{(s, t)\,|\,|s| \leq 2 \text{ and } |t| \geq 3\}$$

where the replacement set of s and t is the set of real numbers.

Again we have two sets to graph.

$$A = \{(s, t)\,|\,|s| \leq 2\}$$

In the set A only the first coordinate s has a restriction on it ($|s| \leq 2$). Since nothing is said about t, t can assume all values in the specified replacement set.

$$B = \{(s, t\,|\,|t| \geq 3\}$$

Here there is a restriction on t but no restrictions on s; therefore, s can assume all values in the replacement set. Here is the graph of both sets on one coordinate system.

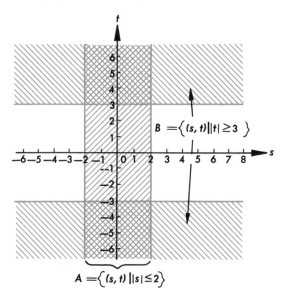

Note that the graph of A consists of one part. The graph of B has two separate parts.

Now $M = A \cap B$. Why? Thus, the graph of M is the set of points common to the graphs of A and B. (Explain.)

Identify the parts of the graph which consist of points common to A and B. This is the graph of M.

Example: iv. Now, let us graph M when the replacement set of s and t is the set of integers.

Each point which belongs to $A = \{(s, t) \mid |s| \leq 2\}$ is marked like this $\odot$.   Points which belong to $B = \{(s, t) \mid |t| \geq 3\}$ are marked like this $\boxed{\cdot}$.   Points which are marked like this $\boxed{\odot}$ belong to *both* A and B; that is, to the intersection of A and B.   And $A \cap B = M = \{(s, t) \mid |s| \leq 2 \text{ and } |t| \geq 3\}$.

How far does the graph of M extend? What would be the graph of M if the replacement set of s and t were the set of natural numbers? To what quadrant would this graph be confined?

EXERCISES

1.   Graph each of the following sets using the set of real numbers as the universal set for first and second components.

a. $A = \{(x, y) \mid x + y = 7 \text{ or } x < 3\}$

b. $B = \{(m, n) \mid m < 2 \text{ or } n < 2\}$

c. $C = \{(r, t) \mid |r| > 4 \text{ or } r + t < 2\}$

d. $D = \{(s, w) \mid -3 \leq s \leq 2 \text{ or } 1 < w < 5\}$

e. $E = \{(z, u) \mid z + u < 2 \text{ or } z - u > 5\}$

f. $F = \{(a, b) \mid 0 < |a + b| < 1 \text{ or } |a| < 3\}$

g. $G = \{(c, d) \mid |c| > |d| \text{ or } c = d\}$

h. $H = \{(p, r) \mid 2p + r < 1 \text{ or } p > 0\}$

  i. $K = \{(u, t) \mid 0 \le |u| \le 1 \text{ or } 0 \le |t| \le 1\}$
  j. $L = \{(k, m) \mid 0 \le |k + m| \le 1 \text{ or } |k| = |m|\}$

2. In each problem in exercise **1**, replace the word *or* by *and* and identify the graph of each sentence thus obtained.

3. Graph the sets in exercise **1**, using the set of integers as the universal set from which to choose the first and second components of the ordered pairs.

VOCABULARY

Use each of the following correctly in a sentence. Numerals in the parentheses refer to pages where these words were used. If you are not sure of the meaning of any word, turn to the indicated page and refresh your memory.

abscissa (264)

Cartesian plane (264)

coordinate (264)

coordinate plane (264)

dependent system (272)

first component (263)

graph (266)

inconsistent system (273)

independent system (273)

inequality (276)

intercepts (269)

intersection (281)

Line Properties (267)

ordinate (264)

origin (263)

parallel lines (273)

plane (263)

quadrant (265)

rectangular coordinate system (264)

second component (263)

selector (276)

standard form (262)

system of equations (269)

union (281)

x-axis (264)

x-coordinate (264)

x-intercept (269)

y-axis (264)

y-coordinate (264)

y-intercept (269)

PROPERTIES

■   *Line Property 1*
    In the set of real numbers the graph of every equation of the form $Ax + By = C$ is a straight line (A and B are not *both* zero).

■   *Line Property 2*
    There is only one straight line which contains two given points.

REVIEW EXERCISES

1. In each of the following, there is given a series of equivalent equations. For each numbered step, state the property or properties used.

a.
$$3x = -5 - 9y$$
$$3x \overset{(1)}{=} -5 + (-9y)$$
$$3x + 9y \overset{(2)}{=} -5 + (-9y) + 9y$$
$$3x + 9y \overset{(3)}{=} -5 + 0$$
$$3x + 9y \overset{(4)}{=} -5$$

b.
$$3(x - y) - 3 = -7$$
$$3x - 3y - 3 \overset{(1)}{=} -7$$
$$3x + (-3y) + (-3) \overset{(2)}{=} -7$$
$$3x + (-3y) + (-3) + 3 \overset{(3)}{=} -7 + 3$$
$$3x + (-3y) + 0 \overset{(4)}{=} -7 + 3$$
$$3x + (-3y) \overset{(5)}{=} -7 + 3$$
$$3x + (-3y) \overset{(6)}{=} -4$$

c.
$$5y + 3 = -6x$$
$$5y + 3 + 6x \overset{(1)}{=} -6x + 6x$$
$$5y + (3 + 6x) \overset{(2)}{=} (-6 + 6) \cdot x$$
$$5y + (6x + 3) \overset{(3)}{=} 0 \cdot x$$
$$5y + (6x + 3) \overset{(4)}{=} 0$$
$$5y + (6x + 3) + (-3) \overset{(5)}{=} 0 + (-3)$$
$$5y + 6x + [3 + (-3)] \overset{(6)}{=} -3$$
$$5y + 6x + 0 \overset{(7)}{=} -3$$
$$5y + 6x \overset{(8)}{=} -3$$
$$6x + 5y \overset{(9)}{=} -3$$

d.
$$2(y + 7) = 5(x - 3)$$
$$2y + 14 \overset{(1)}{=} 5x - 15$$
$$2y + 14 \overset{(2)}{=} 5x + (-15)$$
$$2y + 14 \overset{(3)}{=} (-15) + 5x$$
$$2y + 14 + (-5x) \overset{(4)}{=} (-15) + 5x + (-5x)$$
$$2y + 14 + (-5x) \overset{(5)}{=} (-15) + 0$$
$$2y + [14 + (-5x)] \overset{(6)}{=} -15$$
$$2y + [(-5x) + 14] \overset{(7)}{=} -15$$
$$[2y + (-5x)] + 14 \overset{(8)}{=} -15$$
$$[2y + (-5x)] + 14 + (-14) \overset{(9)}{=} -15 + (-14)$$
$$[2y + (-5x)] + 0 \overset{(10)}{=} -15 + (-14)$$
$$2y + [-5x + 0] \overset{(11)}{=} -15 + (-14)$$
$$2y + (-5x) \overset{(12)}{=} -15 + (-14)$$
$$-5x + 2y \overset{(13)}{=} -15 + (-14)$$
$$-5x + 2y \overset{(14)}{=} -29$$

2. For each equation, find an equivalent equation in standard form. Then solve for x.

Example:

$$5y + 2x + 3 = 6x + 3y - 8$$
$$5y + 2x + 3 + (-3) = 6x + 3y + (-8) + (-3)$$
$$2x + 5y = 6x + 3y + (-11)$$
$$2x + 5y + (-3y) = 6x + 3y + (-11) + (-3y)$$
$$2x + 2y = 6x + (-11)$$
$$2x + 2y + (-6x) = 6x + (-11) + (-6x)$$
$$-4x + 2y = -11$$

This equation is in standard form of a linear equation in two variables.

Now, to solve for x

$$-4x + 2y = -11$$
$$-\tfrac{1}{4}(-4x + 2y) = -\tfrac{1}{4} \cdot (-11)$$
$$x - \tfrac{1}{2}y = \tfrac{11}{4}$$
$$x = \tfrac{1}{2}y + \tfrac{11}{4}$$

The last equation has x expressed in terms not containing x.

a. $4x + 3y = 3x + 6$

b. $7y - 13 = 5x - 3y$

c. $17 + 14y = 6x - 11 - 5y$

d. $3(x - y) + 17 = 7 + 2x$

e. $8(x + y) - 5y = 6x + 8$

f. $14 - 6(2x + 3) = 7x - 3(y + 1)$

g. $17x - 6y + 4 - 6y + 4x = 21 + 5(x - y) - 6x$

h. $13(x - 3y) + 5(2y - x) + 4 = 7(7 + y) - 3x$

i. $5(y + 2x) - 3x + 14 = 5(x - 3y) + 17$

j. $\dfrac{3(x + 4)}{y - 5} = 5$

k. $\dfrac{2y + x}{x - y} = -3$

3. Graph the following:

a. $B = \{(x, y) \,|\, x \,\epsilon\, R \text{ and } y \,\epsilon\, R, \; x \geq 0 \text{ and } y \geq 0\}$

b. $C = \{(x, y) \,|\, x \,\epsilon\, R \text{ and } y \,\epsilon\, R, \; x \leq 0 \text{ and } y \leq 0\}$

c. $D = \{(x, y) \,|\, x \,\epsilon\, R \text{ and } y \,\epsilon\, R, \; x \leq 2 \text{ and } y \leq 2\}$

d. $E = \{(x, y) \,|\, x \,\epsilon\, R \text{ and } y \,\epsilon\, R, \; x + y = 5 \text{ and } y \geq 2\}$

e. $F = \{(x, y) \,|\, x \in R \text{ and } y \in R, x > y\}$

f. Graph the sets in **a** through **e** choosing x and y from the universe of integers.

g. Graph the sets **a** through **e** letting $U = \{-1, 0, 1, 2, 3, 4, 5\}$.

4. Graph the solution sets of the following:

a. $-2x + y = -6$ 　　　**b.** $\quad x - 3 = -5y$
$\quad\;\; x - 3y = 4$ 　　　　　　　　$\quad 5y - 2y = 4$

c. In what quadrant does the intersection lie in **a**? in **b**?

5. For each pair of equations below, do the following:

    i. Graph the solution set for each equation.

    ii. Tell whether the system is independent, dependent, or inconsistent.

a. $x + 3y = 7$ 　　　　　　**c.** $5x + 3 = -2y$
$\quad\; 3x + 4 = -9y$ 　　　　　　　$\quad 4y + 6 = -10x$

b. $5x + 9 = -3y$
$\quad\; 5y + 4 = -2x$

6. Graph each of the following:

a. $B = \{(x, y) \,|\, x \in R \text{ and } y \in R, x + y \geq 5 \text{ or } x > 2\}$

b. $G = \{(r, s) \,|\, r \in I \text{ and } s \in I, r \geq s \text{ and } r + s = 7\}$

c. $K = \{(w, v) \,|\, w \in R \text{ and } v \in R, |w| + 2 = v\}$

7. Solve each of the following problems.

Example:　　*i.* Find three consecutive positive integers such that seven times the third integer diminished by two times the second integer equals forty-seven more than twice the third integer.

Let x be the first integer; then $x + 1$ is the second and $x + 2$ is the third integer.

    Is $7(x + 2)$ a correct expression for seven times the third integer?

    Is $2(x + 1)$ a correct expression for two times the second integer?

    Is $7(x + 2) - 2(x + 1)$ a correct expression for seven times the third integer diminished by two times the second integer?

    Is $2(x + 2) + 47$ a correct expression for forty-seven more than twice the third integer?

We write this equation for the problem.

$$7(x + 2) - 2(x + 1) = 2(x + 2) + 47$$

Solve:
$$7x + 14 - 2x - 2 = 2x + 4 + 47$$
$$5x + 12 = 2x + 51$$
$$3x = 39$$
$$x = 13$$
$$x + 1 = 14$$
$$x + 2 = 15$$

The three consecutive integers are 13, 14, and 15.

CHECK: seven times the third integer $= 7 \times 15$ or 105

two times the second integer $= 2 \times 14$ or 28

twice the third integer $= 2 \times 15$ or 30

Now since 105 diminished by 28 is equal to 77 and 47 plus 30 is equal to 77 and since 14, 15, and 16 are three positive consecutive integers, the solution checks.

Example: *ii.* A car traveled for three hours at a certain speed. Then, it traveled for five more hours at a speed which was nine miles per hour less than twice the speed at which it traveled the first three hours. The entire distance covered was 423 miles. Find the speed of the car during the three-hour and the five-hour period.

Let r be the speed in miles per hour of the car during the first three hours of travel.

Is $3r$ a correct expression for the distance covered in the three-hour period?

Is $2r - 9$ a correct expression for the speed during the five-hour period?

Is $5(2r - 9)$ a correct expression for the distance covered during the five-hour period?

Now we write this equation.

$$3r + 5(2r - 9) = 423$$
Solve:
$$3r + 10r - 45 = 423$$
$$13r - 45 = 423$$
$$13r = 468$$
$$r = 36$$

The car traveled at 36 m.p.h. for 3 hours; then it traveled at 63 m.p.h. for 5 hours.

CHECK: The distance covered in 3 hours at 36 m.p.h. is 108 miles.
The distance covered in 5 hours at 63 m.p.h. is 315 miles.
And $108 + 315 = 423$

a. Find three consecutive integers such that ten times the second integer plus three times the third integer is 72 more than six times the first integer.

b. Find three consecutive integers such that twelve times the third integer diminished by three times the second integer is 83 more than four times the third integer.

c. Find three consecutive even integers such that the sum of five times the smallest integer and six times the second integer equals 126 less than three times the third integer.

d. A freight train left New York City at 7 a.m. traveling 40 miles per hour. At 9 a.m. a passenger train left the same station traveling at 50 miles per hour. After how many hours will the passenger train overtake the freight train?

CHAPTER TEST

1. For each of the following equations, find an equivalent equation in standard form.

a. $-3y + \dfrac{5}{2} = -4x$ **b.** $\dfrac{-2x + 3}{5y + 7} = -2$

2. Graph the following sets on the number line.

a. $G = \{w \,|\, w \in I, \, -4 \le w < 5\}$

b. $H = \{r \,|\, r \in R, \, r > 2 \text{ and } r \le 5\}$

c. $K = \{x \,|\, x \in U, \, 4 < x < 7\}, \; U = \{1, 2, 3, 4, 5, 6, 7\}$

d. $T = \{y \,|\, y \in R, \, y < -5 \text{ or } y > 3\}$

e. $V = \{x \,|\, x \in R, \, x > -4 \text{ and } x < -4\}$

3. Locate the points in the coordinate plane corresponding to the following number pairs.

a. $(-3, -7)$ **c.** $(-11, 3)$ **e.** $(0, -3)$
b. $(9, 5)$ **d.** $(4, -9)$ **f.** $(6, 0)$

4. If $B = \{(x, y) \,|\, x \in R \text{ and } y \in R, \, x + y \ge 5\}$, classify each of the following as true or false.

a. $(1, 4) \in B$ **b.** $(2, -3) \in B$ **c.** $(4, 2) \in B$

5. Let $G = \{(x, y) \mid x \in R \text{ and } y \in R, x \geq 0 \text{ and } y \leq 0\}$

    a. Describe in words the graph of G.

    b. True or false?

        i. $(5, -2) \in G$

       ii. $(0, 0) \in G$

      iii. $(175, 6) \in G$

       iv. $(-1106, 299) \in G$

        v. $(-12, -3709) \in G$

6. For each pair of equations, *i.* graph the solution set, and *ii.* tell whether the system of equations is independent, dependent, or inconsistent.

    a. $-3y + 5 = -7x$
         $2x + 5 = -3y$

    b. $-6x + 2 = 4y$
         $-2y = 2(3 + 1.5x)$

    c. $\dfrac{x + 2y}{3} = 2x + 1$

        $2y = 5x + 3$

7. Let $U = \{-3, -2, -1, 0, 1\}$. Graph the following:

    a. $\{(x, y) \mid x \in U \text{ and } y \in U, x > -2 \text{ and } y < -1\}$

    b. $\{(x, y) \mid x \in U \text{ and } y \in U, x \geq y\}$

8. Replace each of the variables below to obtain ordered number pairs which satisfy the equation $3x - 2y = -1$.

    a. $(2, y)$ **b.** $(x, -3)$ **c.** $(-4, y)$ **d.** $(x, 5)$

9. Choose a letter in place of a number name and write an expression for each of the following:

    a. Eleven less than one-third of a number

    b. Seven more than the square of a number

    c. Difference of two numbers multiplied by their sum

    d. Square of a number plus the cube of another number

10. Find three consecutive integers such that the sum of the smallest integer, twice the second integer, and three times the third integer is seventy less than nine times the smallest integer.

11. Find three consecutive odd integers such that the sum of seven times the largest, three times the next integer, and two times the smallest equals 91 more than nine times the smallest integer.

12. Car A travels 10 m.p.h. faster than car B. A travels 320 miles in the same time that B travels 240 miles. What is the average speed of each car?

13. Two small planes leave cities 970 miles apart and travel toward each other. One plane's average speed is 40 m.p.h. greater than that of the other plane. If they meet in two and one-half hours, determine the speed of each plane.

BIBLIOGRAPHY

Committee on the Undergraduate Program, Mathematical Association of America. *Universal Mathematics, Part I, Functions and Limits.* University of Kansas, 1954. pp. 67-85.

Glenn, William H., and Johnson, Donovan A. *Adventures in Graphing.* St. Louis: Webster Publishing Company, 1961.

Heimer, R. T.; Kocher, F.; and Lottes, J. J. *A Program in Contemporary Algebra.* Book 3, Equations and Inequalities in Two Variables. New York: Holt, Rinehart and Winston, Inc., 1963.

Nichols, Eugene D.; Kalin, Robert; and Garland, E. Henry. *Introduction to Coordinate Geometry* (A Programed Unit). New York: Holt, Rinehart and Winston, Inc., 1963.

Nichols, Eugene D.; Heimer, Ralph T.; and Garland, E. Henry. *Modern Intermediate Algebra.* New York: Holt, Rinehart and Winston, Inc., 1965. Chapter 10.

Ore, Oystein. *Graphs and Their Uses.* New York: The L. W. Singer Company, 1963.

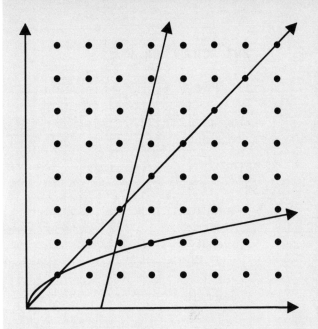

CHAPTER 10

Solution Sets of Systems of Equations

APPROXIMATIONS TO SOLUTIONS OF SYSTEMS

You learned that an independent system of two linear equations in two variables has one ordered pair of numbers for its solution set. Let us graph the two lines given by the following equations.

$$4x - 3y = 2$$
$$-3x + 7y = -10$$

In making the graph, we shall use the following pairs for the respective equations.

$$(2, 2) \text{ and } (-1, -2) \text{ for } 4x - 3y = 2$$
$$(-6, -4) \text{ and } (1, -1) \text{ for } -3x + 7y = -10$$

Check to see that the pairs satisfy the respective equations. Now study the graph on the next page.

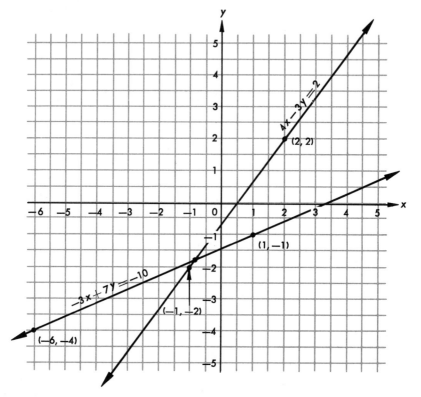

Examination of the graph reveals that the point of intersection of the two lines has coordinates somewhere in the neighborhood of $(-1, -2)$. It is difficult, however, to tell from the graph the *exact* coordinates of the point of intersection. In other words, it is difficult to tell the solution set of the system of equations from the graph. However, it is important to realize that graphing will always yield an approximation to the solution set, and the method is often an easy way to do a rough check.

We must develop a way to determine the solution sets of systems of equations without having to make graphs. You will learn some methods which will enable you to find the exact solutions of any independent systems of linear equations in two variables.

SOLVING SYSTEMS OF EQUATIONS BY COMPARISON

We shall now illustrate one method of determining the exact solutions of a system of equations without making graphs.

Example: Solve the system of two linear equations in two variables on the top of page 295.

$$x - 4y = -4$$
$$3x + 2y = -5$$

We first find two equations each of the form $x = My + N$, one equivalent to the first equation, and the other equivalent to the second equation.

$$x - 4y = -4$$
$$x = 4y - 4$$
$$x = 4y + (-4)$$

$$3x + 2y = -5$$
$$3x = -2y - 5$$
$$x = \frac{-2y - 5}{3}$$
$$x = -\tfrac{2}{3}y - \tfrac{5}{3}$$
$$x = -\tfrac{2}{3}y + (-\tfrac{5}{3})$$

Now, if each of the above equations is to be satisfied by the same pair of numbers, then the following must be true.

$$-\tfrac{2}{3}y + (-\tfrac{5}{3}) = 4y + (-4)$$
$$-\tfrac{2}{3}y - \tfrac{5}{3} = 4y - 4$$
$$\frac{-2y - 5}{3} = 4y - 4$$

Let us solve the last equation.

$$-2y - 5 = 3(4y - 4)$$
$$-2y - 5 = 12y - 12$$
$$-2y - 12y = -12 + 5$$
$$-14y = -7$$

$$y = \tfrac{-7}{-14}$$
$$y = \tfrac{1}{2}$$

We now replace y by $\tfrac{1}{2}$ in the first of the two original equations.

$$3x + 2 \cdot \tfrac{1}{2} = -5$$
$$3x + 1 = -5$$
$$3x = -6$$
$$x = -\tfrac{6}{3}$$
$$x = -2$$

Thus the pair $(-2, \tfrac{1}{2})$ should satisfy both equations.

CHECK: Note that it is important to check *both* equations.

$x - 4y = -4$		$3x + 2y$	$=$	-5
$-2 - 4 \cdot \frac{1}{2}$	-4	$3 \cdot (-2) + 2 \cdot \frac{1}{2}$		-5
$-2 - 2$		$-6 + 1$		
-4		-5		

The pair $(-2, \frac{1}{2})$ satisfies each equation. Thus, the solution set of the given system of equations is $\{(-2, \frac{1}{2})\}$.

The method which we just used in determining the roots or the solution set of the system may be called the *comparison method*. Why is this name a sensible one for this method?

Let us use the comparison method in determining the solution set of the system we graphed on page 294.

$$4x - 3y = 2$$
$$-3x + 7y = -10$$

Solving each equation for x

$$4x - 3y = 2 \qquad\qquad -3x + 7y = -10$$
$$4x = 3y + 2 \qquad\qquad -3x = -7y - 10$$
$$x = \frac{3y + 2}{4} \qquad\qquad 3x = 7y + 10$$
$$x = \frac{7y + 10}{3}$$

Comparing and solving for y

$$\frac{3y + 2}{4} = \frac{7y + 10}{3}$$
$$3(3y + 2) = 4(7y + 10)$$
$$9y + 6 = 28y + 40$$
$$9y - 28y = 40 - 6$$
$$-19y = 34$$
$$y = -\frac{34}{19}$$

Instead of substituting $-\frac{34}{19}$ for y in one of the original equations and solving for x, we can use the comparison method also in determining the value of x.

Solving each equation for y

$$4x - 3y = 2 \qquad\qquad -3x + 7y = -10$$
$$-3y = -4x + 2 \qquad\qquad 7y = 3x - 10$$
$$3y = 4x - 2 \qquad\qquad y = \frac{3x - 10}{7}$$
$$y = \frac{4x - 2}{3}$$

Comparing and solving for x

$$\frac{4x - 2}{3} = \frac{3x - 10}{7}$$
$$7(4x - 2) = 3(3x - 10)$$
$$28x - 14 = 9x - 30$$
$$28x - 9x = 14 - 30$$
$$19x = -16$$
$$x = -\frac{16}{19}$$

Thus, the pair $(x, y) = (-\frac{16}{19}, -\frac{34}{19})$ should satisfy the system.

CHECK:

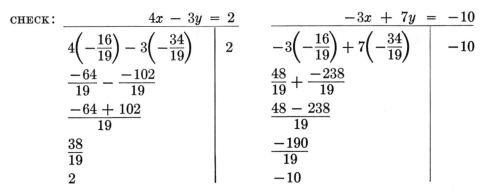

Thus, $\{(-\frac{16}{19}, -\frac{34}{19})\}$ *is the solution set of the system*

$$4x - 3y = 2$$
$$-3x + 7y = -10$$

Do you see why it was difficult to read the solution from the graph?

EXERCISES

1. Using the comparison method, solve each of the following systems of equations and check. Make a record of your answers and save it for later problems.

a. $x = -y + 4$
   $x = y - 2$

b. $y = x - 1$
   $y = 2x$

c. $2m = n + 3$
   $3m = n + 3$

d. $s + t = -6$
   $s - t = 2$

e. $\frac{1}{2}h + k = 2$
   $2h - 3k = 1$

f. $\frac{1}{3}k + \frac{1}{2}m = 0$
   $k + m = 2$

g. $2m - 3t = 3$
   $4m - t = 1$

h. $2k + s = -2$
   $s + k = -1$

i. $x + y = 3$
$\ x - y = -2$
j. $3m = \frac{1}{2}n + 3$
$\ n = 2 - m$
k. $2p - 2r = 1$
$\ p = 7r - 3$
l. $\dfrac{u + w}{3} = 2u$
$\ 2w = 7u + \frac{5}{2}$

m. $2a + b = 1$
$\ b = 3 - a$
n. $-4s = -3t + 1$
$\ 3 = s - t$
o. $7.5c - 3d = 5$
$\ 4d = 3c - 6$
p. $v + t = 3v - t + 6$
$\ 7 - t = 8 + v$

2. Using x for the first number and y for the second number, write an expression for each of the following:

a. the sum of twice the first number and three times the second number

b. the difference between one-half of the second number and one-third of the first number

c. the product of the sum of the first number and the second number and the difference between the first number and the second number

d. one-half of the first number subtracted from four times the second number

e. one-third of the sum of the first and second numbers

f. twice the difference between the second and the first numbers

g. the product of the quotient of the first number and the second number and the sum of the two numbers

h. square of the sum of the first and second numbers

3. A number is doubled and 1 is added to the result. The same result is obtained when multiplying this number by 4 and adding 7 to the result. What is this number?

4. Diminishing the product of a number and 2 by 4 gives the same result as dividing the product of the number and 6 by 7. What is this number?

5. There are three consecutive integers such that the product of the second and the largest integer exceeds the product of the smallest and the second integer by 26. What are the integers?

6. There are four consecutive integers such that the product of the two largest integers exceeds the product of the two smallest integers by 70. What are the integers?

SOLVING SYSTEMS OF EQUATIONS BY SUBSTITUTION

We shall now illustrate another method of solving systems of two linear equations in two variables, in which graphing is not required. Consider the system

$$2x - y = 1$$
$$x + 4y = -3$$

We solve the second equation for x.

$$x + 4y = -3$$
$$x = -4y - 3$$

Now we *substitute* $-4y - 3$ in place of x in the first equation.

$$2x - y = 1$$
$$2(-4y - 3) - y = 1$$

Solve for y

$$2(-4y - 3) - y = 1$$
$$-8y - 6 - y = 1$$
$$-9y = 7$$
$$y = -\frac{7}{9}$$

We found above that $x = -4y - 3$. Substituting $-\frac{7}{9}$ for y in this equation

$$x = -4\left(-\frac{7}{9}\right) - 3$$
$$= \frac{28}{9} - 3$$
$$= \frac{28 - 27}{9}$$
$$= \frac{1}{9}$$

Now we check whether the pair $(x, y) = (\frac{1}{9}, -\frac{7}{9})$ satisfies each of the equations in the system

$2x - y$	$=$	1
$2(\frac{1}{9}) - (-\frac{7}{9})$		1
$\frac{2}{9} + \frac{7}{9}$		
$\frac{9}{9}$		
1		

$x + 4y$	$=$	-3
$\frac{1}{9} + 4(-\frac{7}{9})$		-3
$\frac{1}{9} - \frac{28}{9}$		
$-\frac{27}{9}$		
-3		

Thus, $\{(\frac{1}{9}, -\frac{7}{9})\}$ is the solution set of the system

$$2x - y = 1$$
$$x + 4y = -3$$

Note that we first solved the *second* equation for x. This was the easiest thing to do because the coefficient here is 1.

The method we used in solving this system is different from the comparison method. It is called the *substitution method*. How would you justify this name?

EXERCISES

1. Using the substitution method, solve each of the systems of equations given in exercises **1a-1p,** pages 297 and 298.

2. Solve, using the substitution method.

a. $3x - 2y = 12$
     $4x - 5y = 16$

b. $3y - 2 = x$
     $4x - 3 = y$

3. Solve each problem.

Example: In a two-digit numeral, the number represented by the units digit is three greater than the number represented by the tens digit. The number named by reversing the digits in the numeral is twenty less than twice the original number. What is the number?

One Way to Solve: Let x be the tens digit. Then is $x + 3$ the units digit? Is $10x + (x + 3)$ the value of the original numeral? After reversing the digits is $x + 3$ the tens digit? Is x the units digit? Is $10(x + 3) + x$ the value of the new numeral?

An equation for this problem is

$$2[10x + (x + 3)] - 20 = 10(x + 3) + x$$

Solve: $2[10x + (x + 3)] - 20 = 10(x + 3) + x$
          $20x + 2x + 6 - 20 = 10x + 30 + x$
          $22x - 14 = 11x + 30$
          $11x = 44$
          $x = 4$

CHECK: The original number $10x + (x + 3)$ is
          $10 \cdot 4 + (4 + 3) = 47$

By reversing the digits we obtain 74. Now is it true that the new number (74) is 20 less than twice the original number (47)?

a. In a two-digit numeral the number represented by the units digit is 4 greater than the number represented by the tens digit. If the digits are interchanged, the sum of the resulting number and the original number is 154. Determine the original number.

b. In a two-digit numeral the number represented by the units digit is 2 greater than the number represented by the tens digit. A new number is formed by adding 3 to the number represented by the tens digit and subtracting 3 from the number represented by the units digit. Sixty-five less than three times the original number is equal to the new number. What was the original number?

c. The units digit in a two-digit numeral represents a number 3 greater than the number represented by the tens digit. The number is 39 more than twice the sum of the numbers represented by the two digits. What is the number?

SOLVING SYSTEMS OF EQUATIONS BY ADDITION

Examine the following arithmetic examples.

$$4 = 3 + 1$$
$$7 = 5 + 2$$
$$\overline{4 + 7 = (3 + 1) + (5 + 2)}$$

or $\qquad 11 = 11$

$$17 = 25 + (-8)$$
$$15\tfrac{1}{2} = 16 + (-\tfrac{1}{2})$$
$$\overline{17 + 15\tfrac{1}{2} = [25 + (-8)] + [16 + (-\tfrac{1}{2})]}$$

or $\qquad 32\tfrac{1}{2} = 32\tfrac{1}{2}$ [check the computations for yourself]

The property illustrated by these two examples is a result of the basic properties for a field. It may be stated using variables as follows:

$\forall_a \forall_b \forall_c \forall_d$, if $a = b$ and $c = d$, then $a + c = b + d$.

To state this property in the same form as the examples above, we can write

$$a = b$$
$$c = d$$
$$\overline{a + c = b + d}$$

This addition property can be used in solving systems of equations. Take,

for example, the system
$$2x - y = 3$$
$$x + 5y = 7$$

You know that every equation has many equivalent equations. We shall take the second equation above

$$x + 5y = 7$$

and find an equation which is equivalent to it, but we will choose an equivalent equation which turns out to be particularly well suited for our purpose. It will be your job to discover why we chose this particular equation.

The equation we select is $-2x + (-10y) = -14$.

Do you see that this equation is equivalent to the equation

$$x + 5y = 7?$$

Show how the equation $-2x + (-10y) = -14$ is obtained from $x + 5y = 7$.

You know that two equivalent equations have exactly the same roots; that is, the solution set of $x + 5y = 7$ is also the solution set of $-2x + (-10y) = -14$.

Let us take the first equation in our original system

$$2x - y = 3$$

and the newly obtained equation

$$-2x + (-10y) = -14$$

which is equivalent to the second equation in the original system. You know that whatever pair of numbers satisfies the system

$$2x - y = 3$$
$$-2x + (-10y) = -14$$

also satisfies the original system. Why?

Now we use the addition property stated above.

$$2x - y = 3$$
$$-2x + (-10y) = -14$$
$$\overline{(2x - y) + [-2x + (-10y)] = 3 + (-14)}$$
$$2x - y + (-2x) + (-10y) = -11$$
$$2x + (-2x) + (-y) + (-10y) = -11$$
$$0 + (-11y) = -11$$
$$-11y = -11$$
$$y = 1$$

At this point you should see why we chose the equation

$$-2x + (-10y) = -14$$

rather than some other equation. This choice led us to one equation in one variable.

Now we replace y by 1 in one of the original equations.

$$2x - y = 3$$
$$2x - 1 = 3$$
$$2x = 4$$
$$x = 2$$

Thus, the pair (2, 1) should satisfy the system of two equations we have set out to solve.

CHECK: $\quad 2x - y = 2 \cdot 2 - 1 \qquad x + 5y = 2 + 5 \cdot 1$
$$\qquad\qquad\qquad = 4 - 1 \qquad\qquad\qquad\; = 2 + 5$$
$$\qquad\qquad\qquad = 3 \qquad\qquad\qquad\qquad\; = 7$$

The solution set of this system of equations is $\{(2, 1)\}$.

The method shown above is called the *addition method*. How would you justify this name?

EXERCISES

1. Using the addition method, solve each of the systems of equations in exercises **1a–1p**, pages 297 and 298.

2. Solve each of the systems of equations below by *each* of the three methods you have just studied.

a. $m + n = 0$
$\quad\; m - n = 2$

b. $2x - y = 0$
$\quad\; 2x + y = -4$

c. $\quad 3s = 2 - r$
$\quad -2r = 4s + 2$

d. $2v = 4w + 1$
$\quad\;\; v = w$

e. $7t - \frac{1}{2}u = 2$
$\quad\;\; -2t = u + 4$

f. $5y = 3z$
$\quad\; 2z = 3z + .1$

g. $\dfrac{x + y}{3} = 2$

$\quad \dfrac{x - y}{2} = -1$

h. $10h - 6m = 2h + 1$
$\qquad\quad 2h = 12m + 9$

i. $6p - 7q = 3$
$\quad\;\; q + 1 = 1$

j. $\dfrac{2x + 4y}{-3} = -4y - x$

$\qquad -x = 4y + 1$

3.   Solve each problem.

Example: Mr. Jones is pouring two different cement slabs.   The area of slab A is 693 sq. ft. greater than the area of slab B.   Slab A is four times as long as it is wide.   Slab B is nine feet longer than slab A.   The width of slab B is twelve feet less than the width of slab A.   Determine the length and the width of each cement slab.

Let x be the width of slab A.   Then $4x$ is the length of slab A.   Why?

Is $4x + 9$ the correct expression for the length of slab B?   Why or why not?   Is $x - 12$ the correct expression for the width of slab B?   Why or why not?

Area of slab A: $4x \cdot x$.

Area of slab B: $(4x + 9)(x - 12)$.

Now we can write an equation for the problem.

$$4x^2 = (4x + 9)(x - 12) + 693$$

Solve $4x^2 = 4x^2 - 48x + 9x - 108 + 693$

$$0 = -39x + 585$$
$$39x = 585$$
$$x = 15$$

Thus, we found the width of slab A to be 15 feet.   Then the length of slab A is 60 feet, the length of slab B is 3 feet, and the width of slab B is 69 feet.

Area of slab A: 15×60 or 900 sq. ft.

Area of slab B: 3×69 or 207 sq. ft.

Thus, the answers meet the conditions of the problem.

a.   In two square figures the side of a square is 5 ft. longer than the side of the other square.   The area of the square with the longer sides is 153 sq. ft. greater than the area of the other square. Find the length of the sides of each square.

b.   The difference of the squares of two consecutive integers is 39. Find the integers.

c.   Mr. Woody cut out two pieces of wood in the shape of rectangles. In piece A, the length was five times the width.   In piece B, the width was 4 inches less than the length of piece A, and the length was 2 inches more than the width of piece A.   The areas of both rectangles are the same.   Find the dimensions of each rectangle.

d.   The length of a rectangle is 3 in. longer than its width.   A square whose side is as long as the length of the rectangle has an area 48 sq. in. greater than the area of the rectangle.   Find the dimensions of the rectangle.

PROBLEMS LEADING TO SYSTEMS OF EQUATIONS

To know how to solve systems of equations is helpful in solving many types of problems. Consider, for example, the following problem.

Example: The sum of two numbers is 121. The sum of twice one of the numbers and three times the other number is 17. What are the two numbers?

If one number is a and the other b, then we have the following two equations.

$$a + b = 121$$
$$2a + 3b = 17$$

We can use any one of the methods we know to solve this system of equations. Let us use the substitution method.

From the first equation

$$a + b = 121, \text{ we obtain}$$
$$a = 121 - b$$

Replacing a by $121 - b$ in the second equation

$$2(121 - b) + 3b = 17$$
$$242 - 2b + 3b = 17$$
$$242 + b = 17$$
$$b = 17 - 242$$
$$b = -225$$

Now replacing b by -225 in the first equation (if you wish, you may replace b by -225 in the second equation instead)

$$a + (-225) = 121$$
$$a = 121 + 225$$
$$a = 346$$

Thus, the numbers are 346 and -225.

CHECK: The sum is $346 + (-225)$ or 121.
Twice the first number is 2×346 or 692.
Three times the second number is $3 \times (-225)$ or -675.
The sum of twice the first and three times the second is $692 + (-675)$ or 17.
Thus, we know that the two numbers we are after are 346 and -225.

EXERCISES

Write a system of equations to fit each problem and solve the system. Check the roots of the system in the original problem.

1. The sum of two numbers is 12. Their difference is 14. What are the numbers?

2. A and B are supplementary angles. Twice the measure of A is equal to $\frac{2}{3}$ of the measure of B. Compute the measures of A and B.

3. Sally's father is three times as old as Sally is. Five years ago her father was five times as old as she was then. How old is Sally and how old is her father?

4. The length of a rectangle is 5 inches longer than its width. Its perimeter is 26 inches. How long is the side of the square whose area is equal to the area of the rectangle?

5. Twelve oranges and nine grapefruit cost $1.02. Twenty oranges and four grapefruit cost $1.04. What is the price of each?

6. The total number of businesses which failed in 1963 and 1964 was 29,460. If there were 460 more failures in 1964 than in 1963, how many businesses failed in each of the two years?

7. The number named by the units digit of a certain number is 1 more than twice the number named by the tens digit. When the digits are interchanged, the resulting number is 2 more than twice the original number. What is the number?

8. A school received a shipment of algebra and geometry books costing $558.75. There were 25 more algebra books than geometry books. How many algebra and how many geometry books did the school purchase, if an algebra book costs $2.55 and a geometry book $2.95.

9. One angle of a triangle measures twice as large as another angle. The sum of the degree measures of the two angles is 115. Compute the degree measure of all three angles.

10. In a parallelogram, the measure of one angle is $\frac{2}{5}$ of the measure of the adjacent angle. What are the measures of the angles of this parallelogram?

11. The sum of the lengths of two line segments is 7 inches. If the length of the shorter line segment is tripled, the resulting segment is 1 inch shorter than the longer segment. Find the measure of each segment.

12. The length of each leg of an isosceles triangle is $2\frac{1}{2}$ times the length of the base. What is the length of each side of the triangle if the perimeter is 38 inches?

13. Eight cans of sardines and five cans of pears cost $2.61. Three cans of sardines and seven cans of pears cost $2.67. What is the cost of each can of sardines and each can of pears?

14. The product of four and the sum of two numbers is equal to 140. The difference of the larger and the smaller number is 13. What are the two numbers?

15. Mrs. Partying bought a certain number of pounds of $.29 candy and a certain number of pounds of $.49 candy for a party. She paid $2.92 for all the candy. If she had bought twice the number of pounds of the cheaper candy and five times the number of pounds of the more expensive candy, she would have had 25 lbs. of candy. How many pounds of each kind of candy did she buy?

16. Two ounces of perfume A and three ounces of perfume B cost $73. An ounce of perfume A costs $22.75 more than an ounce of perfume B. What is the cost of one ounce of each perfume?

17. The combined ages of Tim and Jack are 26 years. Three times Tim's age is 10 more than Jack's age. How old is each of them?

18. Mr. Kaufblend blended 10 lbs. of cheap coffee with 5 lbs. of expensive coffee. The cost of the 15 lb. blend was $19.70. Had he used 10 lbs. of the expensive coffee and 5 lbs. of the cheap coffee, the 15 lb. blend would have cost $24.70. What was the price of each kind of coffee?

19. The perimeter of a rectangle is equal to 34 in. If its width is doubled and the length increased by 3 in., the new rectangle is created with the perimeter of 50 in. What is the width and the length of the first rectangle?

20. The length of a rectangle is 2 more than 4 times the measure of a side of a square. The width of the rectangle is one-fourth of the measure of the side of the square. If the perimeter of the rectangle is equal to 68 in., determine the measure of a side of the square.

VOCABULARY

Use each of the following correctly in a sentence. Numerals in the parentheses refer to pages where these words were used. If you are not sure of the meaning of any word, turn to the indicated page and refresh your memory.

Addition method (301)
Comparison method (294)
Substitution method (299)
Systems of equations (293)

REVIEW EXERCISES

1. **a.** Using the comparison method, solve the system of equations.
$$x = \frac{y}{2} + 1$$
$$x = 2y - 3$$

   b. Explain why the comparison method is convenient to use for this system.

2. **a.** Using the substitution method, solve the system of equations.
$$x = y - 2$$
$$5x - y = 1$$

   b. Explain why the substitution method is convenient to use for this system.

3. **a.** Using the addition method, solve the system of equations.
$$5x - 3y = 7$$
$$x + 3y = 5$$

   b. Explain why the addition method is convenient to use for this system.

4. Solve each system of equations using any method you wish.

   a. $3x + y = 5$
       $x - y = 1$

   b. $m = -n$
       $10m - n = 33$

   c. $\dfrac{p + r}{2} = \dfrac{1}{4}$
       $r - 2p = 0$

   d. $3z = -2w$
       $\dfrac{6z + 10w}{3} = 2w$

   e. $5r = t - 5$
       $t + r = -1$

   f. $3u + w = 25$
       $\dfrac{u + w}{5} = -1$

   g. $3t + 5v = -15$
       $5v - t = 31$

   h. $x + u = 100$
       $50x - u = 100x - 149$

5. Make a system of equations to fit each problem, solve the system, and check the solution in the given problem.

   a. The sum of two numbers is 16. Their difference is 18. What are the two numbers?

b. If one of two numbers is multiplied by 12, a number which is 16 less than the second number is obtained. If the second number is 20 times the first number, what are the two numbers?

c. The perimeter of a rectangle is 21.4 inches. Twice the width is .2 inches less than the length. What are the dimensions of the rectangle?

d. A rectangle and a square have equal perimeters. The length of the rectangle is 2 inches more than a side of the square. The length of the rectangle is 4 inches more than its width, and the area of the square is equal to 9 sq. in. What are the dimensions of each figure?

e. A number is $\frac{1}{3}$ of the sum of itself and another number. What are the two numbers if the first number is 1 less than twice the second number?

f. In a triangle, the sum of the measures of two angles is 51°. If the measure of one of these angles is decreased by 11°, its measure will equal the measure of the other angle. What is the measure of each of the three angles of the triangle?

g. The length of an altitude of a triangle whose area is 64 sq. in. is one-half the length of the base. What is the length of the altitude and of the base?

h. A line segment 25 inches long is divided into three parts. Part A is three times as long as Part B, and the length of Part B is $\frac{3}{5}$ of the length of Part C. How long is each part?

i. Two bicyclists start out from the same point on a circular track with a radius of 60 feet. Bicyclist A rides at a speed of 9 mph and bicyclist B at a speed of 12 mph. If they started out riding in opposite directions, how long will it take them to meet?

j. The difference between the measures of two complementary angles is 1°. What is the measure of each of the two angles?

k. Mike's age 10 years ago was seven times Ted's age. Five years ago Mike's age was twice Ted's age. How old is each now?

l. Mrs. Housewife has two different size measuring spoons. Six spoonfuls of the large spoon and two spoonfuls of the small spoon of flour give 5 lbs. of flour; fifteen spoonfuls of the large spoon and ten spoonfuls of the small spoon give 14 lbs. of flour. What is the pound capacity of each spoon?

CHAPTER TEST

1. Solve each problem.

    a. The width of a rectangle is 20% less than the length. Compute the width and the length if the perimeter is 342 feet.
    b. The sum of two numbers is 21. Three times the smaller number subtracted from the larger number gives 3. What are the two numbers?
    c. Tommy is three times as old as Nancy. Four years ago he was eleven times as old as Nancy was then. How old is Tommy?
    d. Three is $\frac{5}{2}$ of what number?
    e. A grocer mixes a certain number of pounds of 15¢ candy with some 12¢ candy. He obtains 32 pounds of mixed candy which sells for \$4.44. How many pounds of each kind of candy did he use?

2. Determine the solution set of each system of equations. Use any method you wish.

    a. $m + n = 3$
        $m - n = -4$

    b. $3(v + 2u) = 7(3u - 2v)$
        $4v - 5(2v - u) = 5v + 4(v - 3u)$

    c. $15x + 4z = 11$
        $x + z = 0$

    d. $p = 3r - 7$
        $r = 3p - 1$

    e. $2x - y = \frac{1}{2}$
        $3x + 2y = -\frac{1}{4}$

    f. $w + z = w - z$
        $2w + 3z = 6$

3. Check each of the following ordered number pairs (x, y) to see whether it satisfies the equation $2x - 3y = -7$.

    a. $(0, \frac{3}{7})$
    b. $(-\frac{7}{2}, 0)$
    c. $(-3, \frac{1}{3})$
    d. $(-\frac{1}{2}, 2)$
    e. $(8, -3)$
    f. $(-2, -1)$

4. a. On a coordinate system, graph the following system of equations.

    $$5x - y = 4$$
    $$2 + y = -3x$$

    b. Read the solution of this system from the graph as accurately as you can.
    c. Now solve the system using one of the methods which does not involve a graph.
    d. Check the solution you obtained in part c.

5. **a.** Using the comparison method, solve the system

$$y = 2x - 1$$
$$y = 3x + 4$$

   b. Check the solution you obtained in part **a**.

6. **a.** Using the addition method, solve the system

$$2x - 3y = 9$$
$$-5x + 3y = 0$$

   b. Check the solution you obtained in part **a**.

7. **a.** Using the substitution method, solve the system

$$x = 2y - 3$$
$$4x + 2y = 7$$

   b. Check the solution you obtained in part **a**.

BIBLIOGRAPHY

Adler, Irving. *The New Mathematics*. New York: The John Day Company, 1958. pp. 125-147.

Nichols, Eugene D.; Heimer, Ralph T.; and Garland, E. Henry. *Modern Intermediate Algebra*. New York: Holt, Rinehart and Winston, Inc., 1965. Chapter 10.

Nichols, Eugene D.; Kalin, Robert; and Garland, E. Henry. *Introduction to Coordinate Geometry* (A Programed Unit). New York: Holt, Rinehart and Winston, Inc., 1963.

School Mathematics Study Group. *Intermediate Mathematics*. New Haven: Yale University Press, 1961. Chapter 7.

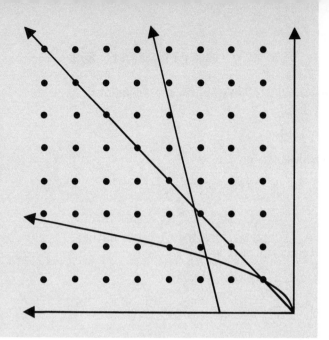

CHAPTER 11

Exponents and Radicals

EXPONENT, BASE, POWER AND PRODUCT OF POWERS

According to agreement, 3×3 and 3^2 name the same number; that is, $3 \times 3 = 3^2$. Read "3^2" as "the square of three" or "three squared" or "the second power of three." Similarly, $4 \times 4 \times 4$ and 4^3 name the same number, that is, $4 \times 4 \times 4 = 4^3$. Read "$4^3$" as "the cube of four" or "four cubed" or "the third power of four." Write $2 \times 2 \times 2 \times 2 \times 2$ using this abbreviated form. How would you read the abbreviated form that you wrote?

In 3^2, the 2 is called an *exponent* and the 3 is called a *base*.

$$3^2 \leftarrow \text{exponent}$$
$$\uparrow$$
$$\text{base}$$

The entire symbol "3^2" is called a *power*. In this case, 3^2 is the second power of 3. Since $3^2 = 9$, the second power of 3 is 9.

Using a variable and the set of real numbers as the replacement set, we can state the following:

$$\forall_x \, x^2 = x \cdot x$$
$$\forall_x \, x^3 = x \cdot x \cdot x$$
$$\forall_x \, x^4 = x \cdot x \cdot x \cdot x$$

and so on

More generally, this pattern can be stated as a definition. We will let "R" represent the set of real numbers and "N" represent the set of natural numbers.

▪ *Definition of Natural Number Exponent* $\forall_{x \in R} \, \forall_{n \in N}, \, _{n \geq 2}$
$$x^n = \underbrace{x \cdot x \cdot x \cdot \ldots \cdot x}$$

x used n times as a factor

To make this definition complete, we define x^1 as follows:

$$x^1 = x$$

This definition helps us to simplify certain multiplication problems. To discover this simplification, consider the following example.

$$2^3 \times 2^4 = (2 \times 2 \times 2) \times (2 \times 2 \times 2 \times 2)$$
$$= 2 \times 2 \times 2 \times 2 \times 2 \times 2 \times 2$$
$$= 2^7$$

Thus, $2^3 \times 2^4 = 2^7$. Observe also that $3 + 4 = 7$; thus, $2^3 \times 2^4 = 2^{3+4}$ and, in general, $\forall_x \, x^3 \cdot x^4 = x^{3+4} = x^7$.

This example illustrates the following:

▪ *The Product of Powers Property*
$\forall_{x \in R} \, \forall_{n \in N} \, \forall_{m \in N} \quad x^m \cdot x^n = x^{m+n}$

It is easy to see that this property can be extended to problems like the following:

$$x^3 \cdot x^4 \cdot x^5 = x^{3+4+5} = x^{12}$$
$$y^2 \cdot y \cdot y^2 \cdot y^6 = y^{2+1+2+6} = y^{11}$$

And in general

$$x^a \cdot x^b \cdot \ldots \cdot x^z = x^{a+b+ \, \cdots \, +z}$$

CAUTION: Observe that the product of powers property applies only to cases where the base is the same.

Why doesn't the product of powers property apply to $2^3 \times 5^2$? Verify that $2^3 \times 5^2 \neq 10^5$.

What is -2^2 equal to? Is it $(-2) \times (-2)$ which equals 4 or is it $-(2)(2)$ which equals -4? Since -2^2 is an ambiguous symbol, we must make an agreement on its meaning.

AGREEMENT: -2^2 means $-(2)(2)$ which equals -4

That is, *raising to a power comes first; taking the opposite comes second.*
What is $2 \cdot 3^2$ equal to? Is it $2 \cdot (3 \cdot 3)$ which equals $2 \cdot 9$ or 18; or is it $(2 \cdot 3)(2 \cdot 3)$ which equals $6 \cdot 6$ or 36? Since $2 \cdot 3^2$ is an ambiguous symbol, we make the following agreement on its meaning.

AGREEMENT: $2 \cdot 3^2$ means $2 \cdot (3^2)$ which equals $2 \cdot 9$ or 18

That is, *raising to a power comes first; multiplying by another factor comes second.*

EXERCISES

1. Give the simplest number name involving no exponents.

Examples: *i.* $(-7)^3 = (-7)(-7)(-7) = -343$

ii. $\left(-\frac{3}{4}\right)^2 = \left(-\frac{3}{4}\right)\left(-\frac{3}{4}\right) = \frac{9}{16}$

iii. $-6^4 = -(6 \times 6 \times 6 \times 6) = -1296$

iv. $(-6)^4 = (-6)(-6)(-6)(-6) = 1296$

a. 3^4	**j.** 10^8	**s.** $4 \cdot \left(\frac{6}{7}\right)^2$
b. $(-5)^2$	**k.** $(0.1)^2$	**t.** $(.2)^2$
c. $-(5)^2$	**l.** $(0.1)^3$	**u.** $(.05)^2$
d. $\left(-\frac{3}{4}\right)^3$	**m.** $(0.1)^4$	**v.** $(.002)^2$
e. $5 \cdot 10^2$	**n.** $(0.1)^8$	**w.** $(-2)^4(-2)^3$
f. $6 \cdot 7^2$	**o.** $\left(\frac{2}{3}\right)^5$	**x.** $\left(-\frac{1}{2}\right)^2\left(-\frac{1}{2}\right)^3\left(-\frac{1}{2}\right)^5$
g. 10^2	**p.** $(-2)^4$	**y.** $-\left(\frac{1}{3}\right)\left(\frac{1}{3}\right)^3$
h. 10^3	**q.** -2^4	**z.** $\left(-\frac{1}{3}\right)\left(-\frac{1}{3}\right)^3$
i. 10^4	**r.** $3 \cdot (-2)^4$	**a'.** $\left(-\frac{1}{5}\right)^2\left(-\frac{1}{5}\right)^2$

2. Give simpler equivalent expressions.

Examples: *i.* $x^3x^6 = x^{3+6} = x^9$

ii. $x^2y^3x^3y^4 = (x^2x^3)(y^3y^4) = x^5y^7$

iii. $xx^3y^2 = (x^1x^3)y^2 = x^4y^2$

a. x^4x^5

b. r^2r^7

c. ss^2s^3

d. $y^3y^7y^2$

e. $nn^{12}n^6$

f. xyx^3

g. $a^3b^2b^4a$

h. $mn^4mn^5m^2n$

i. $abca^2b^2c^2a^3b^3c^3$

3. Study each of the examples, then answer the questions. If you are not sure of the answers, try some additional examples of your own.

Examples: *i.* $2^3 = 2 \times 2 \times 2 = 8$

ii. $(-2)^3 = (-2)(-2)(-2) = -8$

iii. $2^4 = 2 \times 2 \times 2 \times 2 = 16$

iv. $(-2)^4 = (-2)(-2)(-2)(-2) = 16$

a. If a power has a positive number base and an odd number exponent, is the power a positive or a negative number?

b. If a power has a positive number base and an even number exponent, is the power a positive or a negative number?

c. If a power has a negative number base and an odd number exponent, is the power a positive or a negative number?

d. If a power has a negative number base and an even number exponent, is the base a positive or a negative number?

4. Just by looking at each of the following, tell whether it names a positive or a negative number.

a. 2^4

b. $(-1)^3$

c. $(-1)^{17}$

d. $(-1)^6$

e. $(-1)^4$

f. $(-17)^4$

g. $(-17)^{17}$

h. 125^4

i. 125^{23}

j. $(-125)^{37}$

k. $(-100)^{100}$

l. $(-100)^{1001}$

m. $(-2)^4(-2)^9$

n. $(-17)^4(-17)^{12}$

o. $(-100)^{97}(-100)^{98}$

The power of a power

The work done in the following examples is based on the definition of a natural number exponent and on the product of powers property. Study these examples and watch for the pattern.

$$(2^4)^3 = 2^4 \cdot 2^4 \cdot 2^4 = 2^{12} = 2^{4 \times 3}$$

$$(5^2)^4 = 5^2 \cdot 5^2 \cdot 5^2 \cdot 5^2 = 5^8 = 5^{2 \times 4}$$

$$(6^8)^2 = 6^8 \cdot 6^8 = 6^{16} = 6^{8 \times 2}$$

These examples lead us to the following pattern.

The Power of a Power Property

$$\forall_{x \in R} \ \forall_{n \in N} \ \forall_{m \in N} \ (x^n)^m = x^{nm}$$

EXERCISES

1. Give simpler equivalent expressions which have only one exponent by using the power of a power property.

Examples: *i.* $(x^3)^5 = x^{3 \cdot 5} = x^{15}$

ii. $(16^2)^7 = 16^{2 \cdot 7} = 16^{14}$

iii. $[(-2)^3]^4 = (-2)^{3 \cdot 4} = (-2)^{12} = 2^{12}$

iv. $[(-2)^3]^3 = (-2)^{3 \cdot 3} = (-2)^9 = -2^9$

a. $(r^2)^4$ **d.** $[(-5)^3]^7$ **g.** $[(-\frac{1}{3})^4]^2$

b. $(a^5)^2$ **e.** $[(-5)^7]^3$ **h.** $[(-3.5)^5]^{20}$

c. $[(-x)^3]^5$ **f.** $[(-\frac{1}{3})^2]^4$ **i.** $(x^1)^{17}$

2. Prove:

Theorem 1 $\forall_{x \in R} \ \forall_{n \in N} \ \forall_{m \in N} \ (x^n)^m = (x^m)^n$

3. Just by looking at each of the following, tell whether it names a positive or a negative number.

a. $[(-1)^3]^5$ **d.** $[(-2.65)^{15}]^{15}$ **f.** $[-(-3)^4]^5$

b. $[(-1)^{12}]^3$ **e.** $[-(3)^4]^5$ **g.** $[-(-3)^4]^6$

c. $[(-1)^3]^{12}$ [CAUTION: $-(3)^4 \neq (-3)^4$]   **h.** $[-(-1)^5]^5$

The power of a product

We shall again use the definition of a natural number exponent and other basic properties to arrive at another property involving exponents.
Study these examples and watch for the pattern.

$(3 \times 4)^2 = (3 \times 4) \times (3 \times 4) = (3 \times 3) \times (4 \times 4) = 3^2 \times 4^2$
$(5 \times 7)^3 = (5 \times 7) \times (5 \times 7) \times (5 \times 7)$
$\qquad = (5 \times 5 \times 5) \times (7 \times 7 \times 7) = 5^3 \times 7^3$
$(9 \times 6)^4 = (9 \times 6) \times (9 \times 6) \times (9 \times 6) \times (9 \times 6)$
$\qquad = (9 \times 9 \times 9 \times 9) \times (6 \times 6 \times 6 \times 6) = 9^4 \times 6^4$

These examples illustrate the following:

■ *The Power of a Product Property*
$\forall_{x \in R} \ \forall_{y \in R} \ \forall_{n \in N} \ (xy)^n = x^n y^n$

EXERCISES

1. For each of the following, compute answers in each of two ways:

    i. multiply first, then raise to a power

    ii. apply the power of a product property

Examples: *i.* $(5 \times 3)^2$;   *i.* $(5 \times 3)^2 = 15^2 = 225$

                              ii. $(5 \times 3)^2 = 5^2 \times 3^2 = 25 \times 9 = 225$

        ii. $[(-2)(-3)]^4$;   *i.* $[(-2)(-3)]^4 = 6^4 = 1296$

                              ii. $[(-2)(-3)]^4 = (-2)^4(-3)^4$

                                          $= 16 \times 81 = 1296$

   a. $(2 \times 6)^2$ **e.** $[(-1)(-1)]^{13}$ **i.** $[(-1) \times .1]^2$

   b. $[(-1) \times 4]^2$ **f.** $[(-3)(-5)]^2$ **j.** $[(-\frac{3}{4})(-\frac{1}{2})]^3$

   c. $[(-1) \times 3]^3$ **g.** $[10 \times (-4)]^3$ **k.** $[(-1)(-1)(-1)]^{125}$

   d. $[(-1)(-1)]^{12}$ **h.** $(\frac{1}{2} \times \frac{1}{3})^4$ **l.** $[(-2)(-3)(-4)]^2$

2. Write simpler equivalent expressions using the appropriate properties of powers.

Examples: *i.* $[(-x)y]^5 = (-x)^5 y^5 = -x^5 y^5$

        ii. $(a^2 b^3)^6 = (a^2)^6 (b^3)^6 = a^{12} b^{18}$

      iii. $[(-1)x]^4 = (-1)^4 x^4 = 1 \cdot x^4 = x^4$

      iv. $[(-1) \cdot y]^3 = (-1)^3 \cdot y^3 = -1 \cdot y^3 = -y^3$

   a. $(3r)^2$ **e.** $[(-3)a]^4$ **i.** $(3^2 m^3 n)^2$

   b. $(4xy)^2$ **f.** $[(-3)a]^5$ **j.** $[(-1)^5 x^3 y^2]^4$

   c. $[(-3)a]^2$ **g.** $(5m^3)^4$ **k.** $[(-.2)^2(-a)^2(-b)]^3$

   d. $[(-3)a]^3$ **h.** $[(-3)xt]^5$ **l.** $[(-m)(-n)^2(-p)^3]^4$

3. Prove: **a.** $\forall_x [(-1) \cdot x]^2 = x^2$

           b. $\forall_x [(-1) \cdot x]^3 = -x^3$

4. Prove: **a.** $\forall_x (-x)^4 = x^4$

           b. $\forall_x (-x)^5 = -x^5$

5. True or false? For all real numbers x and y

   a. $3x^2 = 9x^2$ **g.** $(-3x)^3 = -27x^3$

   b. $(3x)^2 = 9x^2$ **h.** $-(3x)^3 = -27x^3$

   c. $(-3x)^2 = 9x^2$ **i.** $3(xy)^2 = 3x^2 y^2$

   d. $-3x^2 = 9x^2$ **j.** $(3xy)^2 = 3x^2 y^2$

   e. $-(3x)^2 = -9x^2$ **k.** $(-3xy)^2 = -9x^2 y^2$

   f. $-(3x)^2 = 9x^2$ **l.** $-3(xy)^2 = -3x^2 y^2$

6.   True or false?

a. $[5(-3)]^2 = 5(3)^2$

b. $[(-5)(-3)]^2 = (-5)^2(-3)^2$

c. $[(-5)(-3)]^2 = (25)(9)$

d. $[5(-2)]^3 = 5(-2)^3$

e. $[5(-2)]^3 = 5^3 2^3$

f. $[(-5)(-2)]^3 = (-5)^3(-2)^3$

g. $[(-5)^3(-2)^3] = -(5^3 \cdot 2^3)$

h. $[(-5)^3(-2)^3] = 5^3 \cdot 2^3$

The power of a quotient

In raising a quotient to a natural number power, we again make use of the definition of the natural number exponent.

$$\left(\frac{x}{y}\right)^n = \underbrace{\frac{x}{y} \cdot \frac{x}{y} \cdot \ldots \cdot \frac{x}{y}}_{n \text{ factors}} = \frac{\overbrace{x \cdot x \cdot \ldots \cdot x}^{n \text{ factors}}}{\underbrace{y \cdot y \cdot \ldots \cdot y}_{n \text{ factors}}} = \frac{x^n}{y^n}$$

Thus, we have derived

■   *The Power of a Quotient Property*

$$\forall_{x \in R} \ \forall_{y \in R, \ y \neq 0} \ \forall_{n \in N} \ \left(\frac{x}{y}\right)^n = \frac{x^n}{y^n}$$

Why did we state that $y \neq 0$?

EXERCISES

1.   For each natural number n and for each real number $y \neq 0$, what is the value of $\left(\dfrac{0}{y}\right)^n$? Of $\dfrac{0^n}{y^n}$?

2.   Give equivalent expressions using the power of a quotient property. Simplify wherever possible.

a. $\left(\dfrac{a}{b}\right)^4$

b. $\left(\dfrac{-x}{y}\right)^2$

c. $\left(\dfrac{-x}{y}\right)^3$

d. $\left[\dfrac{(-2)m}{n}\right]^4$

e. $\left[\dfrac{(-x)^2(-y)}{-3}\right]^3$

f. $\left[\dfrac{(-p)^2(-r)^3}{-s}\right]^4$

g. $\left[\dfrac{(-3c^2d)^2}{2a}\right]^3$

h. $\left[\dfrac{(r^2t^3)^5}{(-2)x^3(-y)^4}\right]^3$

i. $\left[\dfrac{(-2r^4)^2}{(-3xy^3)}\right]^4$

j. $\left[\dfrac{(-2)^2(-2)^3(-x)(-y)^3}{(-3)^2(-3)^3(-a)^2(-b)^4}\right]^2$

The quotient of powers

How can $3^5 \div 3^2$ be simplified? Observe the following procedure to see how it is done.

$$3^5 \div 3^2 = \frac{3^5}{3^2} = \frac{3 \times 3 \times 3 \times 3 \times 3}{3 \times 3} = 3 \times 3 \times 3 = 3^3$$

Observe also that $5 - 2 = 3$.

Proceed as in the example above to verify that each statement below is true.

$$\frac{2^6}{2^2} = 2^4 \qquad \frac{5^6}{5^2} = 5^4 \qquad \frac{2^5}{2^2} = 2^3 \qquad \frac{3^4}{3} = 3^3$$

Instead of working with numbers, we can use a variable.

$$\forall_x \; \frac{x^5}{x^2} = \frac{x \cdot x \cdot x \cdot x \cdot x}{x \cdot x} = x \cdot x \cdot x = x^3, \quad (x \neq 0)$$

We shall assume that a divisor is in no case equal to 0, even if we do not explicitly state it in each case.

EXERCISES

For each of the following, give a simplified equivalent expression.

Examples:

i. $\dfrac{y^4}{y} = \dfrac{y \cdot y \cdot y \cdot y}{y} = y \cdot y \cdot y = y^3$

ii. $\dfrac{x^3 y^4}{x y^2} = \dfrac{x \cdot x \cdot x \cdot y \cdot y \cdot y \cdot y}{x \cdot y \cdot y} = x \cdot x \cdot y \cdot y = x^2 y^2$

iii. $\dfrac{15 a^4 b^3}{3 a^2 b} = \dfrac{15}{3} \; \dfrac{a \cdot a \cdot a \cdot a \cdot b \cdot b \cdot b}{a \cdot a \cdot b}$

$\qquad = 5 \; a \cdot a \cdot b \cdot b = 5 a^2 b^2$

iv. $\dfrac{(x + y)^3}{(x + y)^2} = \dfrac{(x + y)(x + y)(x + y)}{(x + y)(x + y)} = x + y$

1. $\dfrac{x^5}{x}$

2. $\dfrac{y^{17}}{y^4}$

3. $\dfrac{a^3}{a}$

4. $\dfrac{c^6}{c^2}$

5. $\dfrac{c^2 m^3}{cm}$

6. $\dfrac{14 y^3}{2y}$

7. $\dfrac{18 x^3 y^2}{3 x y^2}$

8. $\dfrac{-15 r^7 s^5}{-3 r^2 s^2}$

9. $\dfrac{-48 r^5 s^7}{-3 r^2 s}$

10. $\dfrac{-3 m^3 s^2}{ms}$

11. $\dfrac{(x + y)^5}{(x + y)^2}$

12. $\dfrac{(a - b)^3 (c + d)^{12}}{(a - b)(c + d)^7}$

All of the problems you worked on the preceding page point to the following property for natural number exponents.

■ *The Quotient of Powers Property*

$$\forall_{x \in R, \ x \neq 0} \ \forall_{b \in N} \ \forall_{a \in N} \ \frac{x^b}{x^a} = x^{b-a}, \quad (b > a)$$

Note that we imposed some limitations on b and a: they must be natural numbers and b must be greater than a. We will now extend this property to allow a and b to be any integers. This more general property will include cases when $a = b$ and $b < a$.

First consider the following examples.

$$\frac{2^3}{2^3} \qquad\qquad \frac{3^4}{3^4} \qquad\qquad \frac{(-3)^2}{(-3)^2} \qquad\qquad \frac{4^6}{4^6}$$

The first example may be computed in the following manner.

$$\frac{2^3}{2^3} = \frac{2 \cdot 2 \cdot 2}{2 \cdot 2 \cdot 2} = 1$$

Compute the other three examples in a similar way.

Also, you may think of each of these examples as a non-zero number divided by itself, which, of course, is equal to 1. Thus

$$\frac{2^3}{2^3} = 1 \qquad \frac{3^4}{3^4} = 1 \qquad \frac{(-3)^2}{(-3)^2} = 1 \qquad \frac{4^6}{4^6} = 1$$

or in general

■ $$\forall_{x \in R, \ x \neq 0} \ \forall_{m \in I, \ m > 0} \ \frac{x^m}{x^m} = 1 \qquad (I \text{ is the set of integers.})$$

If we agree that the quotient of powers property is to apply to the case $a = b$, then we obtain another interesting result.

$$\frac{x^a}{x^a} = x^{a-a} = x^0 = 1$$

Justify each step in the above. Thus we have the

■ *Zero Power Property*

$$\forall_{x \in R, \ x \neq 0} \ x^0 = 1$$

What about the meaning of a negative number exponent? For example, what does 2^{-2} mean?

To answer this question, we examine the expression $2^2 \cdot 2^{-2}$. If $x^a \cdot x^b = x^{a+b}$ is to hold, we have

$$2^2 \cdot 2^{-2} = 2^{2+(-2)} = 2^0 = 1$$

From our study of number fields, we recall that if the product of two numbers is 1, each number is the reciprocal of the other. Thus, since

$$2^2 \cdot 2^{-2} = 1 \text{ and } 2^2 \cdot \frac{1}{2^2} = 1 \quad \text{then } 2^{-2} = \frac{1}{2^2}$$

Generally, if $c^x \cdot c^{-x} = c^{x+(-x)} = c^0 = 1$ where $c \neq 0$ is to be true, it must hold that c^{-x} is the reciprocal of c^x

or
$$c^{-x} = \frac{1}{c^x}$$

Hence, $3^{-4} = \frac{1}{3^4}$, $(-2)^{-3} = \frac{1}{(-2)^3}$, $5^{-2} = \frac{1}{5^2}$, $4^{-3} = \frac{1}{4^3}$, and $\left(\frac{1}{3}\right)^{-2} = 3^2$

are all true statements.

We now proceed to show that for all real numbers $c \neq 0$, and all integers x and y, $\frac{c^x}{c^y} = c^{x-y}$.

$\frac{c^x}{c^y}$ may be expressed as $c^x \cdot \frac{1}{c^y}$

$$\frac{c^x}{c^y} = c^x \cdot \frac{1}{c^y} = c^x \cdot c^{-y} = c^{x+(-y)} = c^{x-y}$$

And thus we have a more generalized property (see page 320).

■ *The Quotient of Powers Property (For Integer Exponents)*

$$\forall_{c \in R, \; c \neq 0} \; \forall_{x \in I} \; \forall_{y \in I} \quad \frac{c^x}{c^y} = c^{x-y}$$

EXERCISES

For each of the following, give a simplified equivalent expression containing only *positive* exponents.

Examples: i. $\dfrac{4^{-3} \cdot 4^7}{4^2} = \dfrac{4^{-3+7}}{4^2} = \dfrac{4^4}{4^2} = 4^2$

ii. $\dfrac{(-2)^5 \cdot (-2)^{-2}}{(-2)^{-6}} = \dfrac{(-2)^{5-2}}{(-2)^{-6}} = \dfrac{(-2)^3}{(-2)^{-6}}$

$= (-2)^{3-(-6)} = (-2)^9 = -2^9$

iii. $\dfrac{r^{-2} \cdot r^7}{r^2} = \dfrac{r^{-2+7}}{r^2} = \dfrac{r^5}{r^2} = r^3$

$$iv. \quad \frac{k^{-3} \cdot t^7}{t^9 \cdot k^{-8}} = \frac{k^{-3}}{k^{-8}} \cdot \frac{t^7}{t^9} = k^{-3-(-8)} \cdot t^{7-9}$$

$$= k^5 \cdot t^{-2} = k^5 \cdot \frac{1}{t^2} = \frac{k^5}{t^2}$$

$$v. \quad \frac{(m+n)^{-3}(m-n)^5}{(m+n)^{-2}(m-n)^{-1}} = (m+n)^{-3-(-2)}(m-n)^{5-(-1)}$$

$$= (m+n)^{-1}(m-n)^6 = \frac{(m-n)^6}{m+n}$$

1. $\dfrac{5^9 \cdot 5^{-4}}{5^3}$

2. $\dfrac{10^3 \cdot 10^{-7}}{10^5}$

3. $\dfrac{(\frac{1}{3})^2(\frac{1}{3})^{-4}}{(\frac{1}{3})^{-2}(\frac{1}{3})^{-5}}$

4. $\dfrac{(1.5)^3(1.5)^4}{(1.5)^{10}}$

5. $\dfrac{x^3x^4}{x^2}$

6. $\dfrac{m^3m^2}{m^9}$

7. $\dfrac{m^{-2}n^3}{m^{-7}n^4}$

8. $\dfrac{-2k^{-2}m^{-1}}{4k^3}$

9. $\dfrac{20r^4s^{-4}}{5r^{-1}s^{-3}}$

10. $\dfrac{(a+b)^6}{(a+b)^9}$

11. $\dfrac{(x+y)^4(x-y)^3}{(x+y)^5(x-y)^{-2}}$

12. $\dfrac{(5+m)^3(3-n)^{-4}}{(3-n)^{-12}}$

13. $\dfrac{(12a+b)(c+d)}{-4(a+b)^3(c+d)^4}$

14. $\dfrac{3x(z+y)^{-6}(s+t)^{-2}}{y(z+y)(s+t)}$

15. $\dfrac{(x+y+z)^3}{(x+y+z)^6}$

16. $\dfrac{12(a+b)^{-2}(a+b+c)^4}{-6(a+b)^4(a+b+c)^{-3}}$

Study the following true statements and look for a pattern.

$$5 \times 2^{-3} = 5 \times \frac{1}{2^3} = \frac{5}{2^3}; \text{ hence, } 5 \times 2^{-3} = \frac{5}{2^3}$$

$$7 \times 3^{-2} = 7 \times \frac{1}{3^2} = \frac{7}{3^2}; \text{ hence, } 7 \times 3^{-2} = \frac{7}{3^2}$$

$$-3 \times 4^{-4} = -3 \times \frac{1}{4^4} = \frac{-3}{4^4}; \text{ hence, } -3 \times 4^{-4} = \frac{-3}{4^4}$$

These statements suggest the following theorem.

Theorem 2 $\forall_{a \in R} \; \forall_{b \in R, \; b \neq 0} \; \forall_{c \in I, \; c > 0} \; a \cdot b^{-c} = \dfrac{a}{b^c}$

Proof $\quad a \cdot b^{-c} = a \cdot \dfrac{1}{b^c}$ Why?

$\qquad\qquad\qquad = \dfrac{a}{b^c}$ Why?

EXERCISES

Write an equivalent expression which contains no negative exponents by making use of Theorem 2.

1. $3x^{-2}$

2. $-2t^{-4}$

3. $5x^2r^{-3}$

4. $-4x^{-2}m$

5. $2(x+y)^{-3}$

6. $-3(t+2)^2(x-4)^{-7}$

7. $8 \cdot 2^{-3}$

8. $8 \cdot 2^{-4}$

9. $3a^{-2}bc^{-4}$

10. $6xyz^{-2}$

11. $6x(yz)^{-2}$

12. $-6(xyz)^{-2}$

Study the following true statements and look for a pattern.

$$\frac{5}{2^{-3}} = 5 \times \frac{1}{2^{-3}} = 5 \times 2^3; \text{ hence, } \frac{5}{2^{-3}} = 5 \times 2^3$$

$$\frac{7}{3^{-2}} = 7 \times \frac{1}{3^{-2}} = 7 \times 3^2; \text{ hence, } \frac{7}{3^{-2}} = 7 \times 3^2$$

$$\frac{-3}{4^{-4}} = -3 \times \frac{1}{4^{-4}} = -3 \times 4^4; \text{ hence, } \frac{-3}{4^{-4}} = -3 \times 4^4$$

These statements suggest the following theorem.

Theorem 3 $\forall_{a \in R} \ \forall_{b \in R, \ b \neq 0} \ \forall_{c \in I, \ c > 0} \ \dfrac{a}{b^{-c}} = ab^c$

Proof $\dfrac{a}{b^{-c}} = a \cdot \dfrac{1}{b^{-c}}$ Why?

$= a \cdot b^c$ Why?

EXERCISES

1. Write an equivalent expression which contains no negative exponents by making use of Theorem 3.

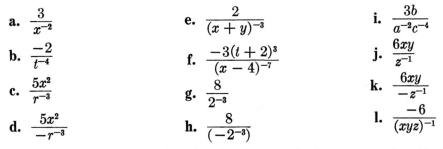

a. $\dfrac{3}{x^{-2}}$

b. $\dfrac{-2}{t^{-4}}$

c. $\dfrac{5x^2}{r^{-3}}$

d. $\dfrac{5x^2}{-r^{-3}}$

e. $\dfrac{2}{(x+y)^{-3}}$

f. $\dfrac{-3(t+2)^3}{(x-4)^{-7}}$

g. $\dfrac{8}{2^{-3}}$

h. $\dfrac{8}{(-2^{-3})}$

i. $\dfrac{3b}{a^{-2}c^{-4}}$

j. $\dfrac{6xy}{z^{-1}}$

k. $\dfrac{6xy}{-z^{-1}}$

l. $\dfrac{-6}{(xyz)^{-1}}$

2. For each expression, write the simplest equivalent expression that does not contain negative exponents. Note as a consequence of the two previous theorems, the following are pairs of equivalent expressions.

Examples: *i.* $\dfrac{x^{-2}y^{-3}}{a^{-7}b^{-6}}$ and $\dfrac{a^7b^6}{x^2y^3}$ *iii.* $\dfrac{x^{-2}y^3}{a^{-7}b^{-6}}$ and $\dfrac{a^7b^6y^3}{x^2}$

   ii. $\dfrac{x^2y^{-3}}{a^{-7}b^6}$ and $\dfrac{x^2a^7}{y^3b^6}$ *iv.* $\dfrac{x^2y^3}{a^{-7}b^{-6}}$ and $x^2y^3a^7b^6$

a. $\dfrac{3x^{-2}}{a^{-3}b^2}$

b. $\dfrac{-3x^2}{a^3b^{-2}}$

c. $\dfrac{2x^{-2}}{a^{-3}b^{-2}}$

d. $\dfrac{12m^2}{4t^{-3}}$

e. $\dfrac{2x^{-6}}{8y^4}$

f. $\dfrac{2x^{-6}}{-8y^{-4}}$

g. $\dfrac{(x+y)^{-3}(m+t)^2}{5r^{-2}}$

h. $\dfrac{7^{-2}}{x^{-2}}$

i. $\dfrac{7^{-2}}{-x^{-2}}$

j. $\dfrac{-7^{-2}}{-x^{-2}}$

k. $\dfrac{-x^{-2}}{-y^{-3}}$

l. $\dfrac{-(x-y)^{-3}}{-(a+b)^{-4}}$

SQUARE ROOT

Let us consider the following equation.

$$x^2 = 36$$

The solution set of this equation is $\{6, -6\}$, since "$6^2 = 36$" and "$(-6)^2 = 36$" are both true statements. Furthermore, there are only two numbers each of which squared gives 36.

Thus the equation $x^2 = 36$ or its equivalent equation $x^2 - 36 = 0$ has two solutions: 6 and -6, which are opposites. Since $6 \times 6 = 36$, we call 6 a *square root* of 36. Also, since $(-6)(-6) = 36$, we call -6 a *square root* of 36. Thus, 36 has two square roots: one a *positive* number, the other a *negative* number. To distinguish between the two square roots, we shall call the *positive* square root of 36

the *principal* square root of 36

A short name for the principal square root of 36 is $\sqrt{36}$. Since the other square root of 36 is the opposite of the principal square root, it is $-\sqrt{36}$ or simply -6. Thus

$$(\sqrt{36})^2 = 36 \qquad\qquad (-\sqrt{36})^2 = 36$$

AGREEMENT: Whenever we use $\sqrt{x}$ ($x \geq 0$) we shall mean the *principal* square root of x.

According to the agreement, $\sqrt{10}$ is a positive number. Is the statement "$3 < \sqrt{10} < 4$" concerning $\sqrt{10}$ true? $-\sqrt{10}$ is a negative number. Is the statement "$-4 < -\sqrt{10} < -3$" concerning $-\sqrt{10}$ true?

You noticed that we made sure that in $\sqrt{x}$, x must be non-negative. The following argument will show why this is necessary.

> The $\sqrt{x}$ is a real number which multiplied by itself results in x. Suppose x is negative.
>
> Then some number multiplied by itself gives a negative number for the product.
>
> But each real number is either positive or negative or 0:
> the product of a pair of positive numbers is a positive number
> the product of a pair of negative numbers is a positive number
> $0 \times 0 = 0$
>
> Therefore, there is no real number which multiplied by itself results in a product which is a negative number.

In later study of algebra you will learn about numbers whose squares are negative numbers.

We shall now use the various properties of real numbers to work with expressions involving square roots. Let us first observe a pattern in the following examples.

$$\sqrt{4} \cdot \sqrt{9} = 2 \cdot 3 = 6; \text{ also } \sqrt{4 \cdot 9} = \sqrt{36} = 6$$
$$\text{therefore, } \sqrt{4} \cdot \sqrt{9} = \sqrt{4 \cdot 9}$$
$$\sqrt{4} \cdot \sqrt{16} = 2 \cdot 4 = 8; \text{ also } \sqrt{4 \cdot 16} = \sqrt{64} = 8$$
$$\text{therefore, } \sqrt{4} \cdot \sqrt{16} = \sqrt{4 \cdot 16}$$
$$\sqrt{4} \cdot \sqrt{25} = 2 \cdot 5 = 10; \text{ also } \sqrt{4 \cdot 25} = \sqrt{100} = 10$$
$$\text{therefore, } \sqrt{4} \cdot \sqrt{25} = \sqrt{4 \cdot 25}$$
$$\sqrt{4} \cdot \sqrt{36} = 2 \cdot 6 = 12; \text{ also } \sqrt{4 \cdot 36} = \sqrt{144} = 12$$
$$\text{therefore, } \sqrt{4} \cdot \sqrt{36} = \sqrt{4 \cdot 36}$$

Since $\sqrt{0} = 0$, we also have $\sqrt{0} \cdot \sqrt{0} = \sqrt{0 \cdot 0}$

We shall now state the theorem suggested by this pattern and prove it.

Theorem 4 Product of Square Roots

$$\forall_{x\in R,\ x\geq0}\ \forall_{y\in R,\ y\geq0}\quad \sqrt{xy} = \sqrt{x}\,\sqrt{y}$$

Proof $\sqrt{x} \geq 0$ and $\sqrt{y} \geq 0$, therefore $\sqrt{x}\,\sqrt{y} \geq 0$

$$(\sqrt{x}\,\sqrt{y})^2 = (\sqrt{x}\,\sqrt{y})(\sqrt{x}\,\sqrt{y})$$

$$= (\sqrt{x}\,\sqrt{x})(\sqrt{y}\,\sqrt{y}) = xy$$

$$\sqrt{xy} \geq 0 \text{ and } \sqrt{xy}\,\sqrt{xy} = xy$$

Since xy is the square of the non-negative number $\sqrt{x}\,\sqrt{y}$ and also of the non-negative number $\sqrt{xy}$,

$$\sqrt{xy} = \sqrt{x}\,\sqrt{y}.$$

Theorem 4 is sometimes referred to as "Distributivity of Square Root over Multiplication." An extension of this theorem to the nth root is

Theorem 5 $\forall_{x\in R,\ x\geq0}\ \forall_{y\in R,\ y\geq0}\ \forall_{n\in N}\quad \sqrt[n]{xy} = \sqrt[n]{x}\,\sqrt[n]{y}$

Simplify each of the following:

Examples:

i. $\sqrt{48} = \sqrt{16 \times 3} = \sqrt{16}\,\sqrt{3} = 4\sqrt{3}$

ii. $\sqrt{75} = \sqrt{25 \times 3} = \sqrt{25}\,\sqrt{3} = 5\sqrt{3}$

iii. $\sqrt{7} \times \sqrt{6} \times \sqrt{5} = \sqrt{7 \times 6} \times \sqrt{5}$
$$= \sqrt{42} \times \sqrt{5} = \sqrt{210}$$

iv. $\sqrt[3]{16} = \sqrt[3]{8 \times 2} = \sqrt[3]{8} \times \sqrt[3]{2} = 2\sqrt[3]{2}$

v. $\sqrt[4]{30{,}000} = \sqrt[4]{10{,}000} \times \sqrt[4]{3} = 10\sqrt[4]{3}$

vi. $\sqrt{7} \times \sqrt{6} \times \sqrt{77} \times \sqrt{22}$

$$= \sqrt{7} \times (\sqrt{2} \times \sqrt{3}) \times (\sqrt{7} \times \sqrt{11}) \times (\sqrt{2} \times \sqrt{11})$$

$$= (\sqrt{7} \times \sqrt{7}) \times (\sqrt{2} \times \sqrt{2}) \times (\sqrt{11} \times \sqrt{11}) \times \sqrt{3}$$

$$= 7 \times 2 \times 11 \times \sqrt{3} = 154\sqrt{3}$$

vii. $\forall_{t\geq0}\ \sqrt{t^9} = \sqrt{t^8 \cdot t} = \sqrt{t^8} \cdot \sqrt{t} = t^4\sqrt{t}$

$viii.$ $\forall_x \sqrt[3]{8x^4} = \sqrt[3]{(8x^3) \cdot (x)} = \sqrt[3]{8x^3} \cdot \sqrt[3]{x} = 2x\sqrt[3]{x}$

$ix.$ $\forall_{x\geq0}$ $\forall_{y\geq0}$ $\forall_{z\geq0}$ $\sqrt[4]{16x^3y^4z^4} = \sqrt[4]{16y^4z^4} \cdot \sqrt[4]{x^3} = 2yz\sqrt[4]{x^3}$

EXERCISES

Simplify each of the following:

1. $\sqrt{98}$

2. $\sqrt{44}$

3. $\sqrt{99}$

4. $\sqrt{242}$

5. $\sqrt{450}$

6. $\sqrt{243}$

7. $\sqrt{80}$

8. $\sqrt{63}$

9. $\sqrt{4} \cdot \sqrt{3}$

10. $\sqrt{12} \cdot \sqrt{9}$

11. $\sqrt{7} \cdot \sqrt{11}$

12. $\sqrt{50}$

13. $\sqrt{18}$

14. $3\sqrt{2} \cdot 3\sqrt{32}$

15. $3\sqrt{5} \cdot 3\sqrt{32}$

16. $\sqrt[3]{27}$

17. $\sqrt[3]{24}$

18. $\sqrt[3]{-24}$

19. $\sqrt{125}$

20. $\sqrt{3} \cdot \sqrt{6}$

21. $\sqrt[3]{7} \cdot \sqrt[3]{7} \cdot \sqrt[3]{7}$

22. $\sqrt[3]{7} \ \sqrt[3]{7}$

23. $\sqrt{30} \cdot \sqrt{10} \cdot \sqrt{3}$

24. $\sqrt{27} \cdot \sqrt{12} \cdot \sqrt{18} \cdot \sqrt{2}$

25. $\sqrt[5]{32}$

26. $\sqrt[5]{64}$

27. $\sqrt{3} \ (\sqrt{3} + \sqrt{5})$

28. $2 \ (\sqrt{6} + 7)$

29. $\sqrt{3} \ (\sqrt{2} - \sqrt{5})$

30. $-\sqrt{7} \ (\sqrt{5} - \sqrt{6})$

31. $\sqrt{5} \ (3\sqrt{5} + 2\sqrt{5})$

32. $\sqrt{r^5}$

33. $4\sqrt{2} \cdot 5\sqrt{3}$

34. $\sqrt[4]{z^9}$

35. $\sqrt[3]{-27s^7}$

36. $\sqrt{.25t^5}$

37. $\sqrt{5x} \cdot \sqrt{5x^2}$

38. $\sqrt[3]{2x} \cdot \sqrt[3]{4x^2}$

39. $\sqrt[3]{48r^2s^4}$

40. $\sqrt[3]{9x} \cdot \sqrt[3]{9x^3}$

Now observe a pattern in the following examples.

$$\frac{5}{\sqrt{5}} = \frac{5\sqrt{5}}{\sqrt{5} \cdot \sqrt{5}} = \frac{5\sqrt{5}}{5} = \sqrt{5}$$

$$\frac{21}{\sqrt{21}} = \frac{21\sqrt{21}}{\sqrt{21} \cdot \sqrt{21}} = \frac{21\sqrt{21}}{21} = \sqrt{21}$$

$$\frac{30}{\sqrt{30}} = \frac{30\sqrt{30}}{\sqrt{30} \cdot \sqrt{30}} = \frac{30\sqrt{30}}{30} = \sqrt{30}$$

The theorem suggested by the examples on page 327 and its proof are as follows:

Theorem 6 $\forall_{x \in R, \, x>0} \quad \dfrac{x}{\sqrt{x}} = \sqrt{x}$

Proof $\dfrac{x}{\sqrt{x}} = \dfrac{\sqrt{x}\,\sqrt{x}}{\sqrt{x}} = \sqrt{x}$

EXERCISES

Simplify each of the following:

Examples: i. $\dfrac{5}{\sqrt{5}} = \dfrac{\sqrt{5}\,\sqrt{5}}{\sqrt{5}} = \sqrt{5}$

ii. $\dfrac{3\sqrt{7}}{\sqrt{3}} = \dfrac{\sqrt{3}\,\sqrt{3}\,\sqrt{7}}{\sqrt{3}} = \sqrt{3}\,\sqrt{7} = \sqrt{21}$

1. $\dfrac{2}{\sqrt{2}}$ 4. $\dfrac{9}{\sqrt{3}}$ 7. $\dfrac{2}{\sqrt{2}} \cdot \dfrac{7}{\sqrt{7}}$

2. $\dfrac{11}{\sqrt{11}}$ 5. $\dfrac{10}{\sqrt{5}}$ 8. $\dfrac{5\sqrt{17}}{\sqrt{5}} \cdot \dfrac{10}{\sqrt{10}}$

3. $\dfrac{5\sqrt{7}}{\sqrt{5}}$ 6. $\dfrac{10\sqrt{3}}{\sqrt{5}}$ 9. $\dfrac{443}{\sqrt{443}}$

The following are examples involving quotients of square roots.

$$\frac{\sqrt{9}}{\sqrt{4}} = \frac{3}{2}; \text{ also } \sqrt{\frac{9}{4}} = \frac{3}{2}; \text{ therefore } \frac{\sqrt{9}}{\sqrt{4}} = \sqrt{\frac{9}{4}}$$

$$\frac{\sqrt{25}}{\sqrt{16}} = \frac{5}{4}; \text{ also } \sqrt{\frac{25}{16}} = \frac{5}{4}; \text{ therefore } \frac{\sqrt{25}}{\sqrt{16}} = \sqrt{\frac{25}{16}}$$

$$\frac{\sqrt{25}}{\sqrt{4}} = \frac{5}{2}; \text{ also } \sqrt{\frac{25}{4}} = \frac{5}{2}; \text{ therefore } \frac{\sqrt{25}}{\sqrt{4}} = \sqrt{\frac{25}{4}}$$

This pattern suggests the following theorem.

Theorem 7 (Quotient of Square Roots)

$$\forall_{x \in R, \ x \geq 0} \ \forall_{y \in R, \ y > 0} \quad \sqrt{\frac{x}{y}} = \frac{\sqrt{x}}{\sqrt{y}}$$

Proof $\quad \sqrt{y} \cdot \sqrt{\dfrac{x}{y}} = \sqrt{y \cdot \dfrac{x}{y}} = \sqrt{x}$

Hence, $\sqrt{y} \cdot \sqrt{\dfrac{x}{y}} = \sqrt{x}$ and $\sqrt{\dfrac{x}{y}} = \dfrac{\sqrt{x}}{\sqrt{y}}$

An extension of this theorem to the nth root is

Theorem 8 $\quad \forall_{x \in R, \ x \geq 0} \ \forall_{y \in R, \ y > 0} \ \forall_{n \in N} \quad \sqrt[n]{\dfrac{x}{y}} = \dfrac{\sqrt[n]{x}}{\sqrt[n]{y}}$

Simplify each of the following:

Examples: i. $\dfrac{\sqrt{55}}{\sqrt{11}} = \sqrt{\dfrac{55}{11}} = \sqrt{5}$

ii. $\sqrt{\dfrac{98}{3}} = \dfrac{\sqrt{98}}{\sqrt{3}} = \dfrac{\sqrt{49}\sqrt{2}}{\sqrt{3}}$

$$= \dfrac{7\sqrt{2}}{\sqrt{3}} = \dfrac{7\sqrt{2}\sqrt{3}}{\sqrt{3}\sqrt{3}} = \dfrac{7\sqrt{6}}{3}$$

The name $\dfrac{7\sqrt{6}}{3}$ is frequently preferred to $\dfrac{7\sqrt{2}}{\sqrt{3}}$, since it is much easier to compute a rational number approximation to this irrational number when starting with $\dfrac{7\sqrt{6}}{3}$. Changing from $\dfrac{7\sqrt{2}}{\sqrt{3}}$ to $\dfrac{7\sqrt{2}\cdot\sqrt{3}}{\sqrt{3}\sqrt{3}}$ and then to $\dfrac{7\sqrt{6}}{3}$ is an example of what is called "rationalizing the denominator."

Simplify each of the following:

Examples: i. $\dfrac{\sqrt{56}}{\sqrt{11}} = \dfrac{\sqrt{4 \times 14}}{\sqrt{11}} = \dfrac{2\sqrt{14}}{\sqrt{11}}$

$$= \dfrac{2\sqrt{14}\cdot\sqrt{11}}{\sqrt{11}\cdot\sqrt{11}} = \dfrac{2\sqrt{154}}{11}$$

ii. $\forall_{x \neq 0} \ \sqrt[3]{\dfrac{-27}{x^6}} = \dfrac{\sqrt[3]{-27}}{\sqrt[3]{x^6}} = \dfrac{-3}{x^2}$

EXERCISES

Simplify each of the following. Express your answer in one of the forms: a, $\dfrac{a}{d}$, $\sqrt[n]{b}$, $\dfrac{\sqrt[n]{b}}{d}$, or $\dfrac{a\sqrt[n]{b}}{d}$ for some integers a, b, and d, such that b has no perfect nth root and a and d have no common factor different from 1.

1. $\dfrac{\sqrt{27}}{\sqrt{3}}$

2. $\dfrac{\sqrt{45}}{\sqrt{3}}$

3. $\dfrac{\sqrt{28}}{\sqrt{2}}$

4. $\dfrac{\sqrt{98}}{\sqrt{7}}$

5. $\dfrac{\sqrt{7}}{\sqrt{3}}$

6. $\dfrac{1}{\sqrt{6}}$

7. $\dfrac{1}{\sqrt{7}}$

8. $\dfrac{1}{\sqrt{9}}$

9. $\dfrac{1}{\sqrt{3}}$

10. $\sqrt{\dfrac{1}{3}}$

11. $\dfrac{1}{\sqrt{17}}$

12. $\sqrt{\dfrac{1}{17}}$

13. $\dfrac{\sqrt{2} \cdot \sqrt{3}}{\sqrt{6}}$

14. $\dfrac{\sqrt{5} \cdot \sqrt{14}}{\sqrt{7} \cdot \sqrt{2}}$

15. $\dfrac{\sqrt{5} \cdot \sqrt{14}}{\sqrt{7} \cdot \sqrt{5}}$

16. $\dfrac{\sqrt[3]{21}}{\sqrt[3]{3}}$

17. $\dfrac{\sqrt[5]{48}}{\sqrt[5]{12}}$

18. $\dfrac{\sqrt[5]{64}}{\sqrt[5]{2}}$

19. $\sqrt[3]{\dfrac{-27}{x^6 y^3}}$

20. $\dfrac{\sqrt{98}}{7\sqrt{2}}$

21. $\dfrac{\sqrt[3]{125}}{\sqrt[3]{8}}$

22. $\dfrac{\sqrt[3]{64}}{\sqrt[3]{8}}$

23. $\dfrac{\sqrt{64}}{3\sqrt{32}}$

24. $\dfrac{\sqrt{4x^2}}{\sqrt{x^3}}$

25. $\dfrac{\sqrt[3]{64}}{\sqrt[3]{16}}$

By using the distributive properties for multiplication over addition or subtraction and previous theorems, we are able to perform other simplifications. Study each of the following examples.

Simplify each of the following:

Examples: i. $6\sqrt{3} + 8\sqrt{3} = (6 + 8)\sqrt{3}$
$$= 14\sqrt{3}$$

ii. $3\sqrt{48} + 4\sqrt{18} = 3(\sqrt{16} \cdot \sqrt{3}) + 4(\sqrt{6} \cdot \sqrt{3})$
$$= 3 \cdot 4\sqrt{3} + 4\sqrt{6} \cdot \sqrt{3}$$
$$= 12\sqrt{3} + 4\sqrt{6}\sqrt{3}$$
$$= (12 + 4\sqrt{6})\sqrt{3}$$

iii. $\sqrt{3}\,(2+\sqrt{3}) = (\sqrt{3}\cdot 2) + (\sqrt{3}\cdot\sqrt{3})$
$$= 2\sqrt{3} + 3$$

iv. $(2+\sqrt{3})\cdot(\sqrt{5}+4) = \boxed{(2+\sqrt{3})}\cdot(\sqrt{5}+4)$

$$= \boxed{(2+\sqrt{3})}\cdot\sqrt{5} + \boxed{(2+\sqrt{3})}\cdot 4$$

$$= (2\sqrt{5}) + (\sqrt{3}\cdot\sqrt{5}) + (2\cdot 4) + (\sqrt{3}\cdot 4)$$

$$= 2\sqrt{5} + \sqrt{15} + 8 + 4\sqrt{3}$$

v. $(3\sqrt{3}+\sqrt{5})\cdot(3\sqrt{3}-\sqrt{5})$

$$= \boxed{(3\sqrt{3}+\sqrt{5})}\cdot(3\sqrt{3}-\sqrt{5})$$

$$= \boxed{(3\sqrt{3}+\sqrt{5})}\cdot(3\sqrt{3})$$

$$-\boxed{(3\sqrt{3}+\sqrt{5})}\cdot\sqrt{5}$$

$$= (3\sqrt{3}\cdot 3\sqrt{3}) + (\sqrt{5}\cdot 3\sqrt{3})$$

$$- (3\sqrt{3}\cdot\sqrt{5}) - (\sqrt{5}\cdot\sqrt{5})$$

$$= (9\cdot 3) + 3\sqrt{15} - 3\sqrt{15} - 5 \; = 27 - 5 \; = 22$$

EXERCISES

Simplify each of the following:

1. $5\sqrt{2}+7\sqrt{2}$

2. $16\sqrt{7}-5\sqrt{7}$

3. $3\sqrt{11}-12\sqrt{11}$

4. $3\sqrt{6}+\sqrt{6}+7\sqrt{6}$

5. $2\sqrt{3}+5\sqrt{3}+6\sqrt{7}-2\sqrt{7}$

6. $4\sqrt{7}+2\sqrt{5}+3\sqrt{7}+4\sqrt{5}$

7. $3\sqrt{6}-\sqrt{6}$

8. $2\sqrt{2}+\sqrt{2}$

9. $\sqrt{8}+\sqrt{2}$

10. $3\sqrt{8}+7\sqrt{2}$

11. $\sqrt{48}+\sqrt{96}$

12. $\sqrt{2}\left(\dfrac{2\sqrt{5}}{\sqrt{2}}+\dfrac{2\sqrt{7}}{\sqrt{8}}\right)$

13. $\dfrac{\sqrt{20}}{\sqrt{2}}(\sqrt{10}+\sqrt{5})$

14. $\dfrac{\sqrt{90}}{\sqrt{3}}(\sqrt{30}-\sqrt{2})$

15. $\dfrac{\sqrt{21}}{\sqrt{3}}(\sqrt{5}+\sqrt{7})$

16. $(5\sqrt{3}+\sqrt{10})(\sqrt{3}-4)$

17. $(\tfrac{1}{2}\sqrt{2}+\tfrac{1}{3}\sqrt{3})(\tfrac{1}{4}\sqrt{2}+\tfrac{1}{5}\sqrt{3})$

18. $(\sqrt{2}+\sqrt{3})(\sqrt{2}-\sqrt{3})$

19. $(\sqrt{7}+\sqrt{3})(\sqrt{7}-\sqrt{3})$

20. $(\sqrt{6}+\sqrt{8})(\sqrt{6}-\sqrt{8})$

21. $(3\sqrt{5}+\sqrt{2})(3\sqrt{5}-\sqrt{2})$

22. $(4\sqrt{7}-\sqrt{5})(4\sqrt{7}+\sqrt{5})$

23. $(3\sqrt{2}-\sqrt{5})^2$

24. $(3-\sqrt{2})^2-(\sqrt{2}-3)^2$

RATIONAL NUMBER EXPONENTS

In the patterns involving exponents, we limited ourselves to natural number exponents. We now assume that all of the properties and theorems stated in this chapter are also true for *rational* number exponents. Thus, according to the product of powers property

$$\forall_{x \geq 0}\ x^{\frac{1}{2}} \cdot x^{\frac{1}{2}} = x^{\frac{1}{2} + \frac{1}{2}} = x^1 = x$$
$$\text{Also } \forall_{x \geq 0}\ \sqrt{x}\ \sqrt{x} = \sqrt{x^2} = x$$
$$\text{Since } \forall_{x \geq 0}\ \sqrt{x}\ \sqrt{x} = x \text{ and } x^{\frac{1}{2}} \cdot x^{\frac{1}{2}} = x$$

we have
$$\sqrt{x} = x^{\frac{1}{2}} \text{ for all real numbers } x \geq 0$$

We now examine $\sqrt{x^2}$ for $x < 0$. For example, what is $\sqrt{(-3)^2}$ equal to? Agreeing that raising to a power comes first, we have

$$\sqrt{(-3)^2} = \sqrt{9} = 3 = |-3|$$
$$\sqrt{(-4)^2} = \sqrt{16} = 4 = |-4|$$
$$\sqrt{(-7)^2} = \sqrt{49} = 7 = |-7|$$

We extend the pattern and conclude that

$$\forall_x \sqrt{x^2} = |x|$$

EXERCISES

1. Give a number name which does not contain a square root sign ($\sqrt{}$) for each of the following:

Example: $\sqrt{(-2)^2} = |-2| = 2$

a. $\sqrt{(-5)^2}$	**c.** $\sqrt{3^2}$	**e.** $\sqrt{(-.7)^2}$
b. $\sqrt{(-\frac{1}{2})^2}$	**d.** $\sqrt{6^2}$	**f.** $\sqrt{(\frac{1}{3})^2}$

In the development of further patterns, we shall restrict ourselves to principal roots.

$$\text{Since}\quad \forall_{x \in R}\ \sqrt[3]{x}\ \sqrt[3]{x}\ \sqrt[3]{x} = x$$

$$\text{and}\quad \forall_x\ x^{\frac{1}{3}} \cdot x^{\frac{1}{3}} \cdot x^{\frac{1}{3}} = x$$

$$\text{we have}\quad \forall_{x \in R}\ \sqrt[3]{x} = x^{\frac{1}{3}}$$

$$\text{Similarly,}\quad \forall_{x \in R,\ x \geq 0}\ \sqrt[4]{x}\ \sqrt[4]{x}\ \sqrt[4]{x}\ \sqrt[4]{x} = x$$

$$\text{and}\quad \forall_{x \geq 0}\ x^{\frac{1}{4}} \cdot x^{\frac{1}{4}} \cdot x^{\frac{1}{4}} \cdot x^{\frac{1}{4}} = x$$

$$\text{Therefore,}\quad \forall_{x \in R,\ x = 0}\ \sqrt[4]{x} = x^{\frac{1}{4}}$$

More generally

■ *Definition* $\forall_{x \in R,\ x \geq 0}\ \forall_{n \in N}\ \sqrt[n]{x} = x^{\frac{1}{n}}$

Since $\forall_{x \in R,\ x \geq 0}\ \forall_{m \in N}\ (x^{\frac{1}{n}})^n = x^{\frac{1}{n} \cdot n} = x$, we have

■ *Definition* $\forall_{x \in R,\ x \geq 0}\ \forall_{n \in N}\ (\sqrt[n]{x})^n = x$

In order to simplify communication, we introduce a few names in connection with roots.

We call: $\sqrt[n]{x}$ a *radical*

$\sqrt[n]{}$ a *radical sign*

x in $\sqrt[n]{x}$ a *radicand*

n in $\sqrt[n]{x}$ an *index*

It is interesting to note what happens when a radicand is a negative number. Observe that $(-2)(-2) = 4$; $(-2)(-2)(-2) = -8$. More generally, an even number of negative factors produces a positive product; an odd number of negative factors produces a negative product. Because of this, $\sqrt[3]{-8} = -2$, but $\sqrt{-4}$ is not found among the real numbers. Why?

We conclude that

■ $\forall_{x \in R,\ x < 0}\ \forall_{n \in N,\ n \text{ odd}}\ \sqrt[n]{x}$ is a negative number

■ $\forall_{x \in R,\ x < 0}\ \forall_{n \in N,\ n \text{ even}}\ \sqrt[n]{x}$ is not a real number

EXERCISES

1. Label each statement as either true or false.

   a. $5^{\frac{1}{2}} = \sqrt{5}$

   b. $(-3)^{\frac{1}{3}} = \sqrt[3]{-3}$

   c. $4^{\frac{1}{6}} = \sqrt[6]{4}$

   d. In $\sqrt[3]{-4}$, 3 is the radicand

   e. In $\sqrt[3]{-4}$, -4 is the radicand

   f. In $\sqrt[5]{2}$, 5 is the index

   g. In $\sqrt{3}$, 2 is the index

   h. $5^{\frac{1}{2}}$ is a radical

   i. $\sqrt[12]{-10}$ is not a real number

   j. $\sqrt[13]{-10}$ is not a real number

   k. $\sqrt[20]{5}$ is not a real number

   l. $\sqrt[19]{5}$ is not a real number

   m. $2^{\frac{1}{3}} \cdot 2^{\frac{1}{3}} = 2^{\frac{2}{3}}$

   n. $(-6)^{\frac{1}{5}}(-6)^{\frac{1}{5}}(-6)^{\frac{1}{5}} = (-6)^{\frac{3}{5}}$

Observe now a pattern emerging from the examples on the top of the next page.

i. Since $4^{\frac{1}{3}} = \sqrt[3]{4}$ and $4^{\frac{1}{3}} \cdot 4^{\frac{1}{3}} = 4^{\frac{1}{3}+\frac{1}{3}} = 4^{\frac{2}{3}}$

and $\sqrt[3]{4} \cdot \sqrt[3]{4} = \sqrt[3]{4 \cdot 4} = \sqrt[3]{4^2}$

it follows that $4^{\frac{2}{3}} = \sqrt[3]{4^2}$

ii. Since $5^{\frac{1}{4}} = \sqrt[4]{5}$ and $5^{\frac{1}{4}} \cdot 5^{\frac{1}{4}} \cdot 5^{\frac{1}{4}} = 5^{\frac{1}{4}+\frac{1}{4}+\frac{1}{4}} = 5^{\frac{3}{4}}$

and $\sqrt[4]{5} \cdot \sqrt[4]{5} \cdot \sqrt[4]{5} = \sqrt[4]{5 \cdot 5 \cdot 5} = \sqrt[4]{5^3}$

it follows that $5^{\frac{3}{4}} = \sqrt[4]{5^3}$

iii. Since $9^{\frac{1}{5}} = \sqrt[5]{9}$ and $9^{\frac{1}{5}} \cdot 9^{\frac{1}{5}} \cdot 9^{\frac{1}{5}} = 9^{\frac{1}{5}+\frac{1}{5}+\frac{1}{5}} = 9^{\frac{3}{5}}$

and $\sqrt[5]{9} \cdot \sqrt[5]{9} \cdot \sqrt[5]{9} = \sqrt[5]{9 \cdot 9 \cdot 9} = \sqrt[5]{9^3}$

it follows that $9^{\frac{3}{5}} = \sqrt[5]{9^3}$

The pattern suggested by these examples is

Theorem 9 $\forall_{x \in R,\ x>0} \ \forall_{m \in N} \ \forall_{n \in N} \quad \sqrt[n]{x^m} = x^{\frac{m}{n}}$

Now observe the following examples which lead to another pattern.

i. $\sqrt[3]{8^2} = \sqrt[3]{64} = 4$

and $(\sqrt[3]{8})^2 = (2)^2 = 4$

Hence, $\sqrt[3]{8^2} = (\sqrt[3]{8})^2$

ii. $\sqrt[4]{16^2} = \sqrt[4]{256} = 4$

and $(\sqrt[4]{16})^2 = (2)^2 = 4$

Hence, $\sqrt[4]{16^2} = (\sqrt[4]{16})^2$

The theorem suggested by these examples is

Theorem 10 $\forall_{x \in R,\ x \geq 0} \ \forall_{m \in N} \ \forall_{n \in N} \quad \sqrt[n]{x^m} = (\sqrt[n]{x})^m$

Proof $\sqrt[n]{x^m} = x^{\frac{m}{n}} = x^{m \cdot \frac{1}{n}} = x^{\frac{1}{n} \cdot m} = (\sqrt[n]{x})^m$

Study the examples below which illustrate the use of the concepts introduced above.

Examples: i. $81^{\frac{3}{4}} = \sqrt[4]{81^3} = (\sqrt[4]{81})^3 = 3^3 = 27$

ii. $\sqrt{9x^3} = \sqrt{9x^2 \cdot x}$

$= \sqrt{9} \cdot \sqrt{x^2} \cdot \sqrt{x}$

$= 3 \cdot |x| \cdot \sqrt{x}$

$= 3x\sqrt{x}$, since x must be non-negative

iii. $\sqrt[3]{\dfrac{27}{125x^3}} = \dfrac{\sqrt[3]{27}}{\sqrt[3]{125x^3}} = \dfrac{\sqrt[3]{27}}{\sqrt[3]{125} \cdot \sqrt[3]{x^3}} = \dfrac{3}{5x},\quad (x \neq 0)$

$iv.$ $\sqrt{(x-1)^3} = \sqrt{(x-1)^2(x-1)}$
$\qquad\qquad = \sqrt{(x-1)^2} \cdot \sqrt{x-1}$
$\qquad\qquad = |x-1| \cdot \sqrt{x-1}$
$\qquad\qquad = (x-1)\sqrt{x-1}, \quad (x \geq 1)$

$v.$ $\sqrt{(x-y)^4} = \sqrt{(x-y)^2 \cdot (x-y)^2}$
$\qquad\qquad = \sqrt{(x-y)^2} \cdot \sqrt{(x-y)^2}$
$\qquad\qquad = |x-y| \cdot |x-y|$
$\qquad\qquad = (x-y)(x-y)$

Why can we say that

$$\forall_x \forall_y \ |x-y| \cdot |x-y| = (x-y)(x-y)?$$

$vi.$ $\sqrt{\sqrt{81}} = \sqrt{9} = 3$

$vii.$ $\sqrt[3]{-8y^3} = \sqrt[3]{-8} \cdot \sqrt[3]{y^3}$
$\qquad\qquad = -2y$

$viii.$ $\sqrt{32x^4} = \sqrt{32} \cdot \sqrt{x^4}$
$\qquad\qquad = \sqrt{16 \cdot 2} \cdot \sqrt{x^4}$
$\qquad\qquad = \sqrt{16} \cdot \sqrt{2} \cdot \sqrt{x^4}$
$\qquad\qquad = 4 \cdot \sqrt{2} \cdot x^2$
$\qquad\qquad = 4x^2\sqrt{2}$

EXERCISES

1. For each of the following write an equivalent symbol using a radical sign.

a. $z^{\frac{1}{3}}$

c. $d^{\frac{3}{4}}$

e. $3y^{\frac{4}{3}}$

b. $r^{\frac{2}{3}}$

d. $2x^{\frac{1}{2}}$

f. $r^{\frac{2}{5}}$

2. For each of the following, write an equivalent symbol using fractional exponents.

a. $\sqrt{3}$

d. $\sqrt[4]{r^3}$

g. $\sqrt[3]{(x+y)^2}$

b. $\sqrt[3]{11}$

e. $\sqrt[7]{t^3}$

h. $\sqrt{(r-t)^3}$

c. $\sqrt[5]{x^2}$

f. $\sqrt[5]{x^8}$

i. $\sqrt[3]{(a+b+c)^4}$

3. Give the simplest name involving no exponents for each of the following.

a. 3^{-3}

c. $4^{-\frac{1}{2}}$

e. $4^{-\frac{3}{2}}$

b. 53^0

d. 3^{-1}

f. $(-3)^{-2}$

g. $\dfrac{4^{-2}}{6^0}$

h. $3 \cdot 3^{-3}$

i. $16 \cdot 8^{-\frac{1}{3}}$

j. $\dfrac{6}{4^{-2}}$

k. $16^{\frac{1}{2}} \cdot 4^{-\frac{1}{2}}$

l. $\dfrac{3}{25^{-\frac{1}{2}}}$

m. $25^{-\frac{5}{2}}$

n. $(\frac{3}{4})^{-2}$

o. $(\frac{25}{16})^{-\frac{1}{2}}$

p. $32 \cdot 2^{-5}$

q. $5^{-1} \cdot 5^{-3} \cdot 5^4$

r. $\dfrac{7^{-2}}{7^{-3}}$

s. $125^{\frac{2}{3}}$

t. $27^{\frac{4}{3}}$

u. $8^{-\frac{2}{3}}$

4. Simplify. Do not use a negative exponent or a radical sign.

a. $x^{\frac{3}{2}} \cdot x^{\frac{1}{2}}$

b. $y^{\frac{1}{3}} \cdot y^{\frac{1}{4}}$

c. $d^{\frac{4}{3}} \cdot d^{\frac{1}{2}}$

d. $r^{\frac{7}{3}} \cdot r^{-\frac{1}{3}}$

e. $\dfrac{x^{\frac{2}{3}}}{x^{\frac{1}{3}}}$

f. $\dfrac{3y}{y^{\frac{2}{3}}}$

g. $\dfrac{s^3}{s^{\frac{1}{3}}}$

h. $\dfrac{r^{\frac{5}{6}}}{r^{\frac{1}{3}}}$

i. $\dfrac{p^{\frac{1}{3}}}{p^{\frac{1}{2}}}$

5. Simplify.

a. $(x^4 y^2)^{\frac{3}{2}}$

b. $\left(\dfrac{125y^4}{216y^{-1}}\right)^{\frac{1}{3}}$

c. $\left(\dfrac{9x^{-3}}{4z^2}\right)^{\frac{1}{2}}$

d. $(125y^9)^{\frac{1}{3}}$

e. $\dfrac{x^{-2}y^5}{x^5 y^{-2}}$

f. $(36x^{-2})^{-\frac{1}{2}}$

g. $(x^{\frac{3}{4}} y^{\frac{4}{3}})^3$

h. $(r^{\frac{2}{3}} s^{\frac{1}{3}})^3$

i. $\dfrac{(z^4 y^{\frac{3}{4}})^4}{r^{\frac{5}{4}}}$

j. $(x^{-3})^{-\frac{1}{3}}$

k. $(16r^2 t^3)^{\frac{3}{4}}$

l. $(a^{-2} \cdot b^{-3})^{-\frac{1}{6}}$

6. Express the following in simplest form using only positive exponents and no radical signs.

a. $\dfrac{-x^{-2}}{2}$

b. $\dfrac{r^{-2}s^{-3}}{t^2}$

c. $\dfrac{x^{-\frac{4}{3}}}{x}$

d. $\dfrac{r^{-\frac{3}{4}}}{3}$

e. $\dfrac{7}{-6s^{-2}}$

f. $\dfrac{(x+y)^{-2}}{3}$

g. $\dfrac{5}{(r-t)^{-3}}$

h. $rs^{-3} + r^{-2}s$

i. $3^{-1}cy^{-2}$

j. $2^{-4}dx^{-3}y^{-4}$

RADICAL EQUATIONS

If an equation contains a variable under a radical sign, we call it a *radical equation*. For example

$$\sqrt{x} - 1 = 2$$

is a radical equation. To determine solutions of radical equations, we will make use of the following:

■ $\forall_{x \epsilon R} \, \forall_{y \epsilon R} \, \forall_{n \epsilon N}$ if $x = y$, then $x^n = y^n$

Here are two examples in which this principle is illustrated.

$$\text{if } 4 = 3 + 1, \text{ then } 4^3 = (3 + 1)^3$$
$$\text{if } -2 = 3 - 5, \text{ then } (-2)^5 = (3 - 5)^5$$

Some radical equations are solved for you below.   Study these solutions and observe what caution you must exercise when solving radical equations.

Example: i. $\sqrt{x} - 1 = 2$

$\sqrt{x} = 3$

$(\sqrt{x})^2 = 3^2$

$x = 9$; the solution set *seems* to be $\{9\}$

CHECK:

$\sqrt{x} - 1$	$=$	2
$\sqrt{9} - 1$		2
$3 - 1$		
2		$\{9\}$ *is* the solution set

Example: ii. $\sqrt{y + 3} = \sqrt{3y - 5}$

$(\sqrt{y + 3})^2 = (\sqrt{3y - 5})^2$

$y + 3 = 3y - 5$

$8 = 2y$

$y = 4$; the solution set *seems* to be $\{4\}$

CHECK:

$\sqrt{y + 3}$	$=$	$\sqrt{3y - 5}$
$\sqrt{4 + 3}$		$\sqrt{3 \cdot 4 - 5}$
$\sqrt{7}$		$\sqrt{12 - 5}$
$\sqrt{7}$		$\sqrt{7}$ $\{4\}$ *is* the solution set

Example: iii. $2\sqrt{z} + 5 = 1$

$2\sqrt{z} = -4$

$(2\sqrt{z})^2 = (-4)^2$

$4z = 16$

$z = 4$; the solution set *seems* to be $\{4\}$

CHECK:

$$\begin{array}{c|c} 2\sqrt{z} + 5 = 1 \\ \hline 2\sqrt{4} + 5 & 1 \\ 2\cdot 2 + 5 & \\ 9 & \end{array}$$ but since $9 = 1$ is false, $\{4\}$ is *not* the solution set

The solution set of $2\sqrt{z} + 5 = 1$ in the set of real numbers is ϕ. Note that the equation $2\sqrt{z} = -4$ and its equivalent equation $\sqrt{z} = -2$ require that the principal square root of a number be -2. Since the principal square root of any non-negative real number is a non-negative number, this equation has no real number solution.

You should note also that the technique used above in solving radical equations leads to new equations which may or may not be equivalent to the equation with which we started. In the first two examples, we obtained equivalent equations, but in the third example, the final equation $(z = 4)$ was not equivalent to the original equation $(2\sqrt{z} + 5 = 1)$.

Sometimes this technique leads to a so-called "quadratic equation," for example

$$\sqrt{x} + x = 1$$
$$\sqrt{x} = 1 - x$$
$$(\sqrt{x})^2 = (1 - x)^2$$
$$x = 1 - 2x + x^2$$
$$x^2 - 3x + 1 = 0$$

The last equation is a *quadratic* equation because it is of the form $ax^2 + bx + c = 0$, where a, b, and c are real numbers. You will learn to solve such equations in the next chapter.

EXERCISES

1. Determine the solution sets.

a. $\sqrt{n} = 2$

b. $\sqrt{x} - 1 = 1$

c. $2\sqrt{y} + 4 = 20$

d. $4\sqrt{z} - 1 = 24$

e. $9\sqrt{s} - 40 = 18$

f. $5 + 4\sqrt{t} = 30$

g. $\dfrac{\sqrt{x} + 1}{3} = 4$

h. $\sqrt{2p} = 10$

i. $\sqrt{2r - 4} = 2$

j. $\sqrt{3s - 2} = 25$

k. $\sqrt{\dfrac{x - 1}{3}} = 2$

l. $\sqrt{2y + 3} = \sqrt{y - 1}$

m. $\sqrt{1 - 2z} = \sqrt{5z + 15}$

n. $\sqrt{\dfrac{2n + 3}{3}} = \sqrt{\dfrac{n - 1}{2}}$

o. $\sqrt{\dfrac{2}{s - 3}} = \sqrt{\dfrac{1}{2s + 1}}$

p. $\sqrt[3]{2x} = 2$

q. $\sqrt[3]{s} + 1 = 4$ **s.** $\sqrt[3]{3t} + 2 = -1$

r. $\sqrt[3]{2y} - 1 = 3$ **t.** $\sqrt[3]{m} + 1 = -2$

2. Determine a negative number whose square decreased by 2 is equal to 1.

3. A number is multiplied by 2 and 5 is added to the product; the square root of the result is equal to 3. What was the original number?

4. A number is increased by 1; the square root of the sum is divided by 2 resulting in 2. What was the original number?

SCIENTIFIC NOTATION

What you learned in this chapter can be used to simplify the problem of dealing with very large or very small numbers. The scientists, in particular, must constantly deal with such numbers.

For examples of large and small numbers with which the scientists deal, consider the following:

The light-year is the distance traveled by light in the course of one year: 1 light-year = 6,000,000,000,000 miles.

The most accurate measures of the speed of light show this speed to be 29,979,300,000 cm. per sec.

The distance of the earth from the sun is about 93,000,000 miles.

The mass of the sun is 2,000,000,000,000,000,000,000,000,000 tons.

The sun emits every second 3,900,000,000,000,000,000,000,000,000, 000,000 ergs of electromagnetic radiation. (One erg is the amount of work required to raise $\frac{1}{981}$ of a gram vertically through one centimeter.)

The wavelength of the longest x-rays is .0000001 cm.

The wavelength of γ-rays is .0000000002 cm.

Radar waves have photon energy of .00000000000000000002 erg.

Writing such numerals as those above is extremely unwieldy. We shall now attempt to show some of the numbers above as the product of

a number between 1 and 10

and

the appropriate integer power of 10.

When a number is shown in this way, it is said to be given in *scientific notation*.

Examples: *i.* Show the light-year, given in miles, in scientific notation.

$6,000,000,000,000 = 6 \times 10^{12}$

Thus, 1 light-year = 6×10^{12} miles.

ii. Show the wavelength of the longest x-rays, given in centimeters, in scientific notation.

$$.0000001 = \frac{1}{10^7} = 10^{-7}$$

Thus, this wavelength is 1×10^{-7} cm.

EXERCISES

1. For each number, give its name in scientific notation.

Examples: *i.* $352.6 = 3.526 \times 10^2$

ii. $.0215 = \frac{2.15}{10^2} = 2.15 \times 10^{-2}$

a. 65.3   **d.** 20.01   **g.** .0021
b. 309.27   **e.** .2   **h.** .000126
c. 126.302   **f.** .317   **i.** .00000091

2. Give each of the following in scientific notation.

a. the speed of light in cm. per sec.
b. the distance of the earth from the sun in miles
c. the mass of the sun in tons
d. the number of ergs the sun emits every second in the form of electromagnetic radiation
e. the wavelength of γ-rays
f. the photon energy of radar waves in ergs.

3. Using the appropriate properties of exponents, simplify each of the following:

Examples: *i.* $10^4 \times 10^3 \times 10^{-5} = 10^7 \times 10^{-5} = 10^2$

ii. $\dfrac{10^3 \times 10^4 \times 10^{-2}}{10^5 \times 10^{-3}} = \dfrac{10^7 \times 10^{-2}}{10^2} = \dfrac{10^5}{10^2} = 10^3$

iii. $\dfrac{5.6 \times 10^3 \times 10^{-5}}{10^4 \times 10} = 5.6 \times \dfrac{10^{-2}}{10^5} = 5.6 \times 10^{-7}$

a. $10^3 \times 10^6 \times 10^{-5}$

b. $10^5 \times 10^{-3} \times 10^3$

c. $10^2 \times 10^{-5} \times 10^4$

d. $\dfrac{10^5 \times 10^{-3}}{10^2}$

e. $\dfrac{10^6 \times 10^{-8}}{10^{-3}}$

f. $\dfrac{10^3 \times 10^{-4}}{10^2 \times 10^{-5}}$

g. $\dfrac{10^{-3} \times 10^{-5}}{10^{-6} \times 10}$

h. $\dfrac{10^{-2} \times 10^5 \times 10^{-3}}{10^4 \times 10^{-6}}$

i. $10^{-2} \div 10^5$

j. $(4 \times 10^6) \times (2.1 \times 10^{-4})$

k. $(4.12 \times 10^4) \times (2 \times 10^3)$

l. $(6.12 \times 10^4) \times (2 \times 10^3)$

m. $(3.13 \times 10^{-3}) \times (2 \times 10^{-2})$

n. $\dfrac{4.66 \times 10^7}{2 \times 10^3}$

o. $\dfrac{(4 \times 10^5) \times (17 \times 10^2)}{8 \times 10^4}$

p. $\dfrac{(14.7 \times 10^2) \times (12 \times 10^5)}{(4 \times 10^{-1}) \times (7 \times 10^4)}$

4. Solve each problem.

   a. The wavelength of the visible blue light is 4.5×10^{-5} cm. How many wavelengths should be put together to obtain 1 cm.?

   b. If the speed of light is 2.99793×10^{10} cm. per sec., what is the speed in kilometers per sec.? [Give the answer in scientific notation. HINT: 1 cm. $= 10^{-5}$ kilometers.]

   c. The speed of sound at sea level is approximately 760 mph. Give this speed in feet per second written in scientific notation. [HINT: 1 mile $= 5.28 \times 10^3$ feet; 1 hour $= 3.6 \times 10^3$ seconds.]

   d. It was estimated that, among stars, the formation of planetary systems similar to ours takes place in 1 out of 100 stars. If there are 10^{11} stars in our galaxy, how many of them possess planetary systems?

   e. It is estimated that, if all matter were spread out uniformly, the radius of curvature of the universe would be 1.1×10^{10} light-years. How many miles is this? [Give the answer in scientific notation.]

   f. Give, in scientific notation, the number of seconds in a year. [HINT: 1 year $= 365$ days.]

   g. Spaceships travel at speeds of 18,000 mph. How many feet per second is this?

VOCABULARY

Use each of the following correctly in a sentence. Numerals in the parentheses refer to pages where these words were used. If you are not sure of the meaning of any word, turn to the indicated page and refresh your memory

base (312)

exponent (312)

index (333)

power (312)

power of a power (315)

power of a product (316)

power of a quotient (318)

principal square root (324)

product of powers (313)

product of square roots (325)

quotient of powers (319)

quotient of square roots (328)

radical (333)

radical equation (337)

radical sign (333)

radicand (333)

scientific notation (339)

square root (324)

zero power (320)

DEFINITIONS, PROPERTIES, AND THEOREMS

■ *Definition of Natural Number Exponent*

$$\forall_{x \in R} \forall_{n \in N, \, n \geq 1} \quad x^n = \underbrace{x \cdot x \cdot x \cdot \ldots \cdot x}_{x \text{ is used } n \text{ times as a factor}}$$

■ *Definition* $\forall_{x \in R, \, x \geq 0} \forall_{n \in N}$ $\sqrt[n]{x} = x^{\frac{1}{n}}$

■ *Definition* $\forall_{x \in R, \, x \geq 0} \forall_{n \in N}$ $(\sqrt[n]{x})^n = x$

■ *The Product of Powers Property* $\forall_{x \in R} \forall_{n \in N} \forall_{m \in N}$ $x^m \cdot x^n = x^{m+n}$

■ *The Power of a Power Property* $\forall_{x \in R} \forall_{n \in N} \forall_{m \in N}$ $(x^n)^m = x^{nm}$

■ *The Power of a Product Property* $\forall_{x \in R} \forall_{y \in R} \forall_{n \in N}$ $(xy)^n = x^n y^n$

■ *The Power of a Quotient Property* $\forall_{x \in R} \forall_{y \in R, \, y \neq 0} \forall_{n \in N}$ $\left(\dfrac{x}{y}\right)^n = \dfrac{x^n}{y^n}$

■ *The Quotient of Powers Property*

$$\forall_{x \in R, \, x \neq 0} \forall_{b \in N} \forall_{a \in N} \quad \dfrac{x^b}{x^a} = x^{b-a} \quad (b > a)$$

■ *Zero Power Property* $\forall_{x \in R, \, x \neq 0}$ $x^0 = 1$

■ *The Quotient of Powers Property (For Integer Exponents)*

$$\forall_{c \in R, \, c \neq 0} \forall_{x \in I} \forall_{y \in I} \quad \dfrac{c^x}{c^y} = c^{x-y}$$

Theorem 1 $\forall_{x \in R} \forall_{n \in N} \forall_{m \in N}$ $(x^n)^m = (x^m)^n$

Theorem 2 $\forall_{a \in R} \forall_{b \in R, \, b \neq 0} \forall_{c \in I}$ $a \cdot b^{-c} = \dfrac{a}{b^c}$

Theorem 3 $\forall_{a \in R} \forall_{b \in R, \, b \neq 0} \forall_{c \in I}$ $\dfrac{a}{b^{-c}} = ab^c$

Theorem 4   Product of Square Roots

$$\forall_{x \in R, \, x \geq 0} \forall_{y \in R, \, y \geq 0} \quad \sqrt{xy} = \sqrt{x} \sqrt{y}$$

Theorem 5 $\forall_{x \in R, \, x \geq 0} \forall_{y \in R, \, y \geq 0} \forall_{n \in N}$ $\sqrt[n]{xy} = \sqrt[n]{x} \sqrt[n]{y}$

Theorem 6 $\forall_{x \in R, \, x \geq 0}$ $\dfrac{x}{\sqrt{x}} = \sqrt{x}$

Theorem 7   Quotient of Square Roots

$$\forall_{x \in R, \, x \geq 0} \forall_{y \in R, \, y > 0} \quad \sqrt{\dfrac{x}{y}} = \dfrac{\sqrt{x}}{\sqrt{y}}$$

Theorem 8 $\forall_{x \in R, \, x \geq 0} \forall_{y \in R, \, y > 0} \forall_{n \in N}$ $\sqrt[n]{\dfrac{x}{y}} = \dfrac{\sqrt[n]{x}}{\sqrt[n]{y}}$

Theorem 9 $\forall_{x \in R,\ x \geq 0} \forall_{m \in N} \forall_{n \in N}$ $\sqrt[n]{x^m} = x^{\frac{m}{n}}$

Theorem 10 $\forall_{x \in R,\ x \geq 0} \forall_{m \in N} \forall_{n \in N}$ $\sqrt[n]{x^m} = (\sqrt[n]{x})^m$

REVIEW EXERCISES

1. Simplify.

  a. $2s^{\frac{1}{2}} \cdot s^{\frac{3}{2}}$

  b. $x^{\frac{5}{3}} \div x^{\frac{1}{3}}$

  c. $r^{\frac{1}{6}} \cdot r^{\frac{1}{3}}$

  d. $x^{-3} \cdot x^7$

  e. $12y^{-4} \div (3y^{-2})$

  f. $\dfrac{r^{-\frac{2}{3}}}{r^{\frac{1}{3}}}$

  g. $\dfrac{7x^3}{\frac{1}{x^2}}$

  h. $(36y^6x^2)^{\frac{1}{2}}$

2. Give equivalent expressions containing only positive exponents.

  a. $\dfrac{4x^2}{x^{-5}}$

  b. $\dfrac{5}{x^{-2}}$

  c. $\dfrac{x^{-2}}{x^{-4}}$

  d. $\dfrac{ab^{-2}}{m^2n^{-4}}$

  e. $\dfrac{a^{-3}b^{-4}}{x^{-2}y^{-3}}$

  f. $\dfrac{(x-y)^{-2}(x+y)^{-3}}{(x-y)^4(x+y)^{-7}}$

3. Give equivalent expressions containing fractional exponents.

  a. $\sqrt{r}$

  b. $\sqrt[5]{s}$

  c. $\sqrt[3]{x^2}$

  d. $\sqrt[5]{(x-3)^2}$

  e. $\sqrt[3]{y^2}$

  f. $\sqrt[4]{r^3}$

  g. $\sqrt{x^5}$

  h. $\sqrt[3]{(y-x)^7}$

  i. $\sqrt[7]{(y-x)^3}$

4. True or False?

  a. $(1.2^3)^2 = (1.2)^5$

  b. $\forall_{r \neq 0} \dfrac{r^2 \cdot r^3}{r^{-5}} = 1$

  c. $\sqrt[3]{2} = 2^{-3}$

  d. $(\frac{3}{5})^3 = \frac{9}{15}$

  e. $(\frac{1}{2})^{-1} = 2$

  f. $\sqrt{\dfrac{3}{5}} = \dfrac{\sqrt{15}}{5}$

  g. $\sqrt[5]{-32} = -2$

  h. $\sqrt[3]{27} = 9$

  i. $(16)^{\frac{5}{4}} = 64$

  j. $\forall_x\forall_y (16x^4y^2)^{\frac{1}{2}} = 8x^2y$

  k. $\sqrt{6} \cdot \sqrt{3} = 3\sqrt{2}$

  l. $\dfrac{\sqrt{56}}{\sqrt{14}} = 2$

  m. $\sqrt{27} = 3\sqrt{3}$

n. $(2\sqrt{3} + \sqrt{2}) \cdot (\sqrt{3} - \sqrt{2}) = 4 - \sqrt{6}$
o. $4\sqrt{8} + \sqrt{2} = 8\sqrt{2} + \sqrt{2} = 9\sqrt{2}$
p. $\sqrt[3]{48} + \sqrt[3]{6} = 2\sqrt[3]{6} + \sqrt[3]{6} = 3\sqrt[3]{6}$
q. $(3\sqrt{4})^2 = 36$

5. Give equivalent expressions containing a radical sign.

   a. $r^{\frac{2}{3}}$

   b. $[(2s)^2]^{\frac{1}{3}}$

   c. $\left(\dfrac{3t}{2}\right)^{\frac{4}{3}}$

   d. $(-5x)^{-\frac{1}{3}}$

6. Determine the real number solution sets.

   a. $x^2 = 144$
   b. $x^3 = -64$
   c. $x^{-3} = \frac{1}{27}$
   d. $3x^2 = 108$
   e. $-x^3 = 216$
   f. $\dfrac{x^3}{x^5} = 64$

7. Determine the real number solution sets.

   a. $\sqrt{2x} = 1$
   b. $\sqrt{3y - 2} = -1$
   c. $\sqrt{z - 10} = 6$
   d. $\sqrt{n + 1} = \sqrt{3n - 7}$
   e. $\sqrt{\dfrac{2 - 3m}{3}} = \sqrt{\dfrac{m + 1}{4}}$
   f. $\sqrt{\dfrac{2}{3t - 1}} = \sqrt{\dfrac{3}{t + 4}}$

8. For each number, give its name in scientific notation.

   a. 75.6
   b. 3052.12
   c. .79
   d. .018
   e. .0008
   f. .0000059

9. Using the appropriate properties of exponents, simplify each of the following:

   a. $10^3 \times 10^{-1} \times 10^5$
   b. $10^9 \div 10^5$
   c. $10^{-3} \div 10^7$
   d. $10^{-3} \div 10^{-4}$
   e. $10^{-8} \div 10^{-5}$
   f. $\dfrac{10^5 \times 10^{-2}}{10^8 \times 10^4}$
   g. $\dfrac{10^{-8} \times 10^2}{10^7 \times 10^{-3}}$
   h. $\dfrac{10^3 \times 10^2 \times 10^{-7}}{10^{-2} \times 10^2 \times 10^{-9}}$

10. The U. S. Saturn C-1 flew along a ballistic trajectory which took it over 65 miles at a maximum speed of 3744 miles per hour. Give the maximum speed in feet per second. [Use scientific notation for computations.]

CHAPTER TEST

1. Simplify.

a. $3\sqrt{11} - 6\sqrt{11}$

b. $\sqrt[3]{24} - \sqrt[3]{16}$

c. $\sqrt[3]{3x} \cdot \sqrt[3]{9x^2}$

d. $\sqrt[4]{81xy^4z^3}$

e. $(125x^6)^{\frac{1}{3}}$

f. $(16y^{-4})^{-\frac{1}{2}}$

g. $\dfrac{r^{\frac{1}{2}}}{r^{\frac{1}{3}}}$

h. $(2\sqrt{5} - 2)(\sqrt{5} - 3)$

2. Give equivalent expressions containing fractional exponents.

a. $\sqrt[4]{x^3}$

b. $\sqrt[5]{(xy)^3}$

c. $\sqrt[3]{2x^5}$

d. $\sqrt[3]{\dfrac{x^2}{y^2}}$

e. $\sqrt[7]{\dfrac{a^8}{b^9}}$

3. Give equivalent expressions containing a radical sign.

a. $x^{\frac{1}{3}}y^{\frac{2}{3}}$

b. $(3xy)^{\frac{5}{3}}$

c. $r^{\frac{3}{2}}$

d. $\left(\dfrac{x^2}{2}\right)^{\frac{1}{3}}$

e. $\left(\dfrac{a^2}{b^2}\right)^{\frac{1}{4}}$

4. Give equivalent expressions containing only positive exponents.

a. $3x^3 \cdot x^{-\frac{2}{3}}$

b. $\dfrac{3}{x^{-5}}$

c. $\dfrac{x^{-\frac{2}{3}}}{4}$

d. $\dfrac{2}{\dfrac{1}{x^{-2}}}$

e. $\dfrac{3x^3y^{-2}}{x^{-\frac{5}{3}}}$

5. Determine the real number solution sets.

a. $x^3 = 27$

b. $x^5 = -32$

c. $x^4 = 81$

d. $x^{-2} = \frac{1}{4}$

e. $5x^3 = 40$

f. $x^{-3} = 8$

6. True or False?

a. $\sqrt[3]{-8} = 2$

b. $(16)^{\frac{1}{4}} = 2$

c. $(2^2)^2 = 8$

d. $(\frac{2}{3})^3 = \frac{8}{27}$

e. $\forall_x \sqrt[3]{x^2} = x^{\frac{3}{2}}$

f. $\sqrt{45} = 3\sqrt{15}$

g. $(\frac{1}{2})^{-2} = 4$

h. $\forall_x\forall_y (4x^2y)^3 = 12x^6y^3$

i. $(6\sqrt{3})^2 = 108$

j. $\dfrac{\sqrt{39}}{\sqrt{3}} = \sqrt{13}$

k. $(3\sqrt{5} - 1)^2 = 46 - 6\sqrt{5}$

l. $\sqrt{72} = 6\sqrt{2}$

m. $\bigvee_{x=0} \dfrac{2}{x^{-3}} = 2x^3$

n. $\bigvee_s (3s^3)^2 = 9s^6$

o. $\bigvee_{x=0} \bigvee_{y=0} 16y^3x^5 \div (2yx^2) = 8y^3x$

p. $\bigvee_{r=0} r^{\frac{2}{5}} \cdot r^{-\frac{1}{5}} = r^{\frac{3}{5}}$

q. $\bigvee_{x=0} \dfrac{x^{-3}}{x^2} = x^{-5}$

r. $\dfrac{2}{\sqrt{2}} = \dfrac{2\sqrt{2}}{2} = \sqrt{2}$

7. Simplify.

a. $\dfrac{36xy^3z^3}{\frac{1}{3}y^{-2}z^2}$

b. $\dfrac{7x^5}{x^{-3}}$

c. $(81x^3y^4)^{\frac{1}{2}}$

d. $r^{\frac{3}{2}} \cdot r^{\frac{2}{3}}$

e. $\dfrac{x^{-6}}{\frac{1}{x^2}}$

f. $\dfrac{r^{\frac{7}{3}}}{r^{-2}}$

8. Determine the real number solution sets.

a. $\sqrt{5x} = 1$

b. $\sqrt{4t} = -2$

c. $\sqrt{5 - 2s} = 5$

d. $\sqrt{3 - y} = \sqrt{2y - 3}$

e. $\sqrt{\dfrac{5 + 4m}{5}} = \sqrt{\dfrac{3m - 1}{3}}$

f. $\sqrt{\dfrac{1}{1 + x}} = \sqrt{\dfrac{3}{2x - 1}}$

9. For each number, give its name in scientific notation.

a. 3.49   b. .83   c. .09   d. .000364

10. Using the appropriate properties of exponents, simplify each of the following:

a. $10^6 \times 10^{-2} \times 10^{-1}$

b. $10^{-4} \div 10^{-3}$

c. $10^{-5} \div 10^{-8}$

d. $\dfrac{10^3 \times 10^{-5}}{10^2}$

e. $\dfrac{10^{-3} \times 10^{-5} \times 10^4}{10^4 \times 10^{-3} \times 10^2}$

CUMULATIVE REVIEW EXERCISES

These exercises are designed for your review of the basic ideas in Chapters 9 through 11.

1. For each equation, find an equivalent equation in standard form.

   a. $5x - 7y + 1 = x - 9y + 6$

   b. $-2(2x-3y) + 4 = 3 + 4(x-9y)$

   c. $\dfrac{5(2x + y)}{3(-3y + x)} = 4$

   d. $\dfrac{4(x - y)}{3} = \dfrac{-5(2y - 3x)}{-7}$

   e. $\dfrac{3x - 2y}{2} + 4 = \dfrac{y - 2x}{3} - 2$

2. Using the set of real numbers as the universe, graph each of the following:

   a. $A = \{(x, y) \mid x + 2 \ge y\}$

   b. $B = \{(x, y) \mid x \ge -2 \text{ and } y < 1\}$

   c. $C = \{(x, y) \mid 2x - y = 3 \text{ and } y \ge -1\}$

   d. $D = \{(x, y) \mid 3x + 2y = 1 \text{ and } x + y = 0\}$

   e. $E = \{(x, y) \mid x > 0 \text{ or } y \le 2\}$

   f. $F = \{(x, y) \mid x + y = 1 \text{ or } x = -2\}$

3. For each system of equations

   i. graph the solution set for each equation

   ii. tell whether the system is independent, dependent, or inconsistent

   a. $2x + y = 3$
       $\dfrac{12 - 4y}{2} = 4x$

   b. $4x = 3 - y$
       $2y + 8x = -3$

   c. $2x + y = 2$
       $-3y + x = 1$

   d. $4x + y = 0$
       $\dfrac{2y + 3x}{5} = 1$

4. Below there are given six pairs of equations. For each graph identify one pair of equations represented by the graph.

a. $y - 4x = -2$
$x + 4y = 12$

b. $x + y = -2$
$x - 2y = 1$

c. $y - 3x = 4$
$3x - y = -1$

d. $y - x = -2$
$2(x - y) = 4$

e. $4x - y = 2$
$x + y = 1$

f. $3x - y = 4$
$y - 3x = 2$

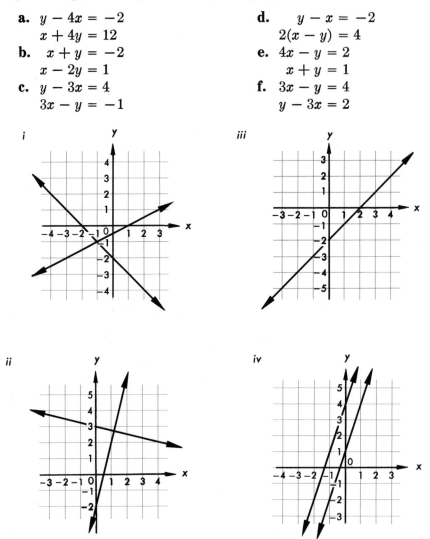

5. The sum of twice the first number plus one-half times the second number is 6. Twice the sum of the two numbers is 27. What are the two numbers?

6. Two trains are traveling toward each other. They travel for 5 hours before meeting. During that time, they cover a total distance of 485 miles. If one train averages 45 miles per hour, what is the average speed of the second train?

7. Find the solutions set of each system of equations.

a. $2x - 3y = 12$
$y - x = -4$

b. $4(m + n) = 0$
$3(m - n) = 3$

c. $\dfrac{-2s + t}{6} = 1$
$t - s = 3$

d. $2(2r + s) + 1 = 3(s - r) - 12$
$\dfrac{1}{r + s} = \dfrac{5}{2r + 3s}$

8. Mary has a total of eighty five-cent stamps and eight-cent stamps, the total value of which is $4.30. How many stamps of each type does she have?

9. In rectangle A the length is 6 in. greater than the width. In rectangle B, the length is three times the width. If the rectangles have the same perimeter and if the width of rectangle B is twice the width of rectangle A, determine the length and the width of each rectangle.

10. The sum of a number represented by two-digits and the new number named by interchanging the two digits is 121, and the difference of the two numbers is 45. What is the number?

11. The difference between the measures of two supplementary angles is 22. What is the measure of each angle?

12. Susan is 6 years older than Jane. Eight years ago Susan was seven times as old as Jane. How old is each girl?

13. A grocer mixes x lb. of 29¢ candy with y lb. of 24¢ candy to make 18 lb. of mixture selling for $4.82. How many pounds of each kind of candy did he use?

14. For the replacements of variables for which each expression is defined, tell whether it is true or false.

a. $-3a^{\frac{1}{2}}a^{\frac{5}{2}} = -3a^3$

b. $y^{\frac{3}{2}} \div y^{\frac{1}{2}} = y^2$

c. $\dfrac{x^{-\frac{1}{2}}}{\dfrac{1}{x^{\frac{1}{2}}}} = x$

d. $(16m^2n^8)^2 = 16^2m^4n^{10}$

e. $\dfrac{s^{-2}}{s^{-3}} = s$

f. $\dfrac{(m + n)^{-2}}{(m + n)^3} = (m + n)^{-5}$

g. $\sqrt[3]{r^2} = r^{\frac{2}{3}}$

h. $(t^2)^4 = t^6$

i. $\sqrt{x} + \sqrt{y} = \sqrt{x+y}$ **l.** $\sqrt{u} + \sqrt[3]{v} = \sqrt[5]{uv}$

j. $\sqrt{\dfrac{s}{t}} = \dfrac{\sqrt{s}}{\sqrt{t}}$ **m.** $\left(\dfrac{a}{b}\right)^3 = \dfrac{a^3}{b^{-3}}$

k. $\sqrt{mn} = \sqrt{m}\sqrt{n}$ **n.** $\sqrt[3]{a} + \sqrt[3]{a} = \sqrt[6]{a}$

15. Determine the real number solution sets.

    a. $y^2 = 81$ **c.** $4n^2 = 196$

    b. $m^5 = -\frac{1}{32}$ **d.** $\dfrac{x}{x^3} = 121$

16. Determine the real number solution sets.

    a. $\sqrt{2y+1} = 3$

    b. $\sqrt{\dfrac{18 - \frac{1}{2}m}{4}} = 2$ **c.** $\sqrt{\dfrac{1}{8+m}} = \sqrt{\dfrac{2}{2-5m}}$

17. For each number, give its name in scientific notation.

    a. 365.7   **c.** .09

    b. .83   **d.** .00076

18. Simplify each of the following:

    a. $10^4 \times 10^{-3} \times 10^5$

    b. $10^5 \div 10^{12}$ **f.** $\dfrac{10^{-7} \times 10^3}{10^5 \times 10^{-5}}$

    c. $10^{-2} \div 10^{-5}$

    d. $10^{-9} \div 10^{-3}$ **g.** $\dfrac{10^2 \times 10^3 \times 10^{-6}}{10^{-8} \times 10^7 \times 10^2}$

    e. $\dfrac{10^{-3} \times 10^2}{10^4}$

BIBLIOGRAPHY

Committee on the Undergraduate Program, Mathematical Association of America. *Universal Mathematics, Part I, Functions and Limits.* University of Kansas, 1954. pp. 336-337.

Heimer, R. T.; Kocher, F.; and Lottes, J. J. *A Program in Contemporary Algebra.* Book 5, Exponents, Radicals, and Quadratic Equations. New York: Holt, Rinehart and Winston, Inc., 1963.

Nichols, E. D.; Heimer, R. T.; and Garland, E. H. *Modern Intermediate Algebra.* New York: Holt, Rinehart and Winston, Inc., 1965. Chapter 2.

Odom, Mary Margaret, and Nichols, Eugene D. (Consulting Editor). *Introduction to Exponents* (A Programed Unit). New York: Holt, Rinehart and Winston, Inc., 1964.

School Mathematics Study Group. *Applied Mathematics in the High School.* Studies in Mathematics, Volume X. Stanford: Stanford University, 1963. pp. 31-75.

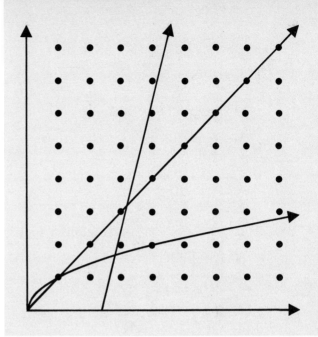

CHAPTER 12

Factoring, Polynomials, and Quadratic Equations

MULTIPLICATION OF TWO BINOMIALS

To find the product $(x + 2)(x + 5)$, we use the distributive and commutative properties to produce the following equivalent expressions.

$$\boxed{(x+2)}\ (x+5) = \boxed{(x+2)}\cdot x + \boxed{(x+2)}\cdot 5$$
$$= x^2 + 2x + 5x + 10$$
$$= x^2 + 7x + 10$$

Also $\qquad \boxed{(x-6)}\ (x+4) = \boxed{(x-6)}\cdot x + \boxed{(x-6)}\cdot 4$

$$= x^2 - 6x + 4x - 24$$
$$= x^2 - 2x - 24$$

Similarly $\boxed{(3x-7)}\ (2x-5) = \boxed{(3x-7)}\cdot 2x - \boxed{(3x-7)}\cdot 5$

$$= 6x^2 - 29x + 35$$

351

EXERCISES

Find the products.

1. $(x + 4)(x + 2)$
2. $(y + 7)(y + 9)$
3. $(x - 2)(x + 4)$
4. $(v - 3)(v - 6)$
5. $(y + 7)(y - 3)$
6. $(z - 8)(z + 5)$
7. $(x - 3)(x + 4)$
8. $(2x + 3)(x + 4)$
9. $(3x + 5)(x + 2)$
10. $(x + 7)(4x + 5)$
11. $(6y + 4)(3y - 1)$
12. $(5t - 2)(3t + 1)$
13. $(3r - 4)(2r - 3)$
14. $(7t - 3)(6t + 4)$
15. $(5x - 2)(x + 1)$
16. $(2x + 4)(x - 3)$
17. $(3x - 1)(x + 2)$

18. $(x - 5)(2x + 3)$
19. $(2x - 1)(3x + 4)$
20. $(6x - 7)(x + 3)$
21. $(2x + 2)(2x + 2)$
22. $(3x - 2)(3x + 2)$
23. $(5x + 2)(5x + 2)$
24. $(6x + 3)(6x - 3)$
25. $(5x - 1)(x - 3)$
26. $(3x + 3)(3x - 3)$
27. $(4x + 1)(2x - 1)$
28. $(3x + 7)(x - 1)$
29. $(9x + 7)(9x - 7)$
30. $(\frac{1}{2}u + 3)(u - 2)$
31. $(\frac{3}{4}a - \frac{1}{2})(\frac{1}{2}a + \frac{1}{3})$
32. $(\frac{1}{3}n - \frac{1}{4})(\frac{2}{5}n - \frac{1}{6})$
33. $(1.5m + 2)(2.5m - 1)$
34. $(1.6s - 1)(3s + 1)$

Patterns in the multiplication of binomials

If you examine thoughtfully the exercises you worked above, you should discover some interesting patterns. For example, in the first illustration we used, we found that $(x + 2)(x + 5)$ and $x^2 + 7x + 10$ are equivalent expressions. We refer to $x + 2$ and $x + 5$ as *factors* of $x^2 + 7x + 10$, because

$$(x + 2)(x + 5) = x^2 + 7x + 10$$

This is similar to the situation in arithmetic where we call 5 and 3 factors of 15, because $5 \times 3 = 15$.

Now observe the following:

$$2 \times 5 = 10$$
$$(x + 2)(x + 5) = x^2 + 7x + 10$$
$$2 + 5 = 7$$

$$-3 \times 6 = -18$$
$$[y + (-3)](y + 6) = y^2 + 3y - 18$$
$$-3 + 6 = 3$$

$$(-2) \times (-5) = 10$$
$$[z + (-2)][z + (-5)] = z^2 - 7z + 10$$
$$-2 + (-5) = -7$$

It appears that the pattern

$$\forall_a \forall_b \ (x + a)(x + b) = x^2 + (a + b)x + a \cdot b$$

holds for every replacement of a and b by real number names.

Let us prove that this pattern is true.

$$\boxed{(x + a)} \ (x + b)$$

$$= \boxed{(x + a)} \cdot x + \boxed{(x + a)} \cdot b \quad \text{LDPMA}$$
$$= x^2 + x \cdot a + x \cdot b + a \cdot b \quad \text{RDPMA and CPM}$$
$$= x^2 + x(a + b) + a \cdot b \quad \text{LDPMA}$$
$$= x^2 + (a + b)x + a \cdot b \quad \text{CPM}$$

Thus, we have established

Theorem 1 $\forall_a \forall_b \ (x + a)(x + b) = x^2 + (a + b)x + ab$

Here are some instances of this theorem.

Examples: i. $(x + 3)(x + 39)$
$$= x^2 + (3 + 39) \cdot x + 3 \times 39$$
$$= x^2 + 42x + 117$$

ii. $[x + (-15)](x + 20)$
$$= x^2 + (-15 + 20)x + (-15) \times 20$$
$$= x^2 + 5x - 300$$

iii. $[x + (-7)][x + (-9)]$
$$= x^2 + [-7 + (-9)]x + (-7)(-9)$$
$$= x^2 + (-16)x + 63$$
$$= x^2 - 16x + 63$$

This theorem should enable you to write down quickly the product of two factors like those above.   The second and third examples can be shown as

$$(x - 15)(x + 20)$$
$$= x^2 + (-15 + 20)x - 15 \times 20$$
$$= x^2 + 5x - 300$$

and

$$(x - 7)(x - 9)$$
$$= x^2 - (7 + 9)x + 7 \times 9$$
$$= x^2 - 16x + 63$$

EXERCISES

1. Supply reasons for the steps in the proof of the following theorems.

Theorem 2 $\forall_a \forall_b \ (x - a)(x + b) = x^2 + (-a + b)x - a \cdot b$

Proof $\boxed{(x - a)}\ (x + b)$

$= \boxed{(x - a)} \cdot x + \boxed{(x - a)} \cdot b$

$= x^2 - a \cdot x + x \cdot b - a \cdot b$

$= x^2 - a \cdot x + b \cdot x - a \cdot b$

$= x^2 + (-a) \cdot x + b \cdot x - a \cdot b$

$= x^2 + (-a + b)x - a \cdot b$

Theorem 3 $\forall_a \forall_b \ (x - a)(x - b) = x^2 - (a + b)x + a \cdot b$

Proof $\boxed{(x - a)}\ (x - b)$

$= \boxed{(x - a)} \cdot x - \boxed{(x - a)} \cdot b$

$= x^2 - a \cdot x - x \cdot b + a \cdot b$

$= x^2 - a \cdot x - b \cdot x + a \cdot b$

$= x^2 + (-a) \cdot x + (-b) \cdot x + a \cdot b$

$= x^2 + [-a + (-b)]x + a \cdot b$

$= x^2 + [-(a + b)]x + a \cdot b$

$= x^2 - (a + b)x + a \cdot b$

2. Give the products without performing any computations in writing.

a. $(x + 1)(x + 2)$ **n.** $(r - 2)(r - 105)$

b. $(u + 3)(u + 6)$ **o.** $(y - 5)(y - 5)$

c. $(n + 7)(n + 11)$ **p.** $(t - 2)(t - 2)$

d. $(y + 2)(y + 25)$ **q.** $(w - 5)(w + 5)$

e. $(c + 12)(c + 8)$ **r.** $(a + 10)(a - 10)$

f. $(a + 9)(a + 9)$ **s.** $(s - 12)(s + 12)$

g. $(c - 1)(c + 3)$ **t.** $(h - 20)(h + 20)$

h. $(m - 6)(m + 15)$ **u.** $(k - 20)(k - 20)$

i. $(p + 5)(p - 4)$ **v.** $(w + 20)(w + 20)$

j. $(r + 2)(r - 50)$ **w.** $(x - 1.5)(x + 3)$

k. $(m - 2)(m - 3)$ **x.** $(t + 2.5)(t + 4)$

l. $(d - 3)(d - 20)$ **y.** $(u - \frac{1}{4})(u - \frac{1}{2})$

m. $(n - 11)(n - 10)$ **z.** $(r - 2.6)(r - 2.5)$

FACTORING TRINOMIALS OF THE FORM $x^2 + px + q$

The theorem $(x + a)(x + b) = x^2 + (a + b)x + a \cdot b$, which we proved in the last section, is quite helpful in factoring trinomials. Our problem now will be to start with a trinomial and find two factors whose product is that trinomial. That is, we start with

$$x^2 + (a + b)x + a \cdot b$$

and will have to find

$$(x + a) \text{ and } (x + b)$$

such that

$$x^2 + (a + b)x + a \cdot b = (x + a)(x + b)$$

Suppose, we have the trinomial

$$x^2 + 13x + 22$$

To find its factors, the problem reduces to finding replacements for a and b for which

$$a + b = 13 \text{ and } a \cdot b = 22$$

To do this, we shall resort mostly to trial and error and common sense Some intelligent guessing will help. What two integers have the sum 13 and product 22? Answer: 11 and 2. Thus

$$x^2 + 13x + 22 = (x + 11)(x + 2)$$

Examples: i.   What are the factors of $m^2 - 5m + 4$?

To answer this, we must answer the question "What two numbers have the sum -5 and the product 4?"
Answer: -1 and -4
Therefore, $m^2 - 5m + 4 = (m - 1)(m - 4)$

ii.   Factor $y^2 + 10y - 24$
We need to answer the question "What two numbers have the sum 10 and the product -24?"
Answer: -2 and 12
Therefore, $y^2 + 10y - 24 = (y - 2)(y + 12)$

iii.   Factor $m^2 - 6m - 7$
What two numbers have the sum -6 and the product -7?
Answer: 1 and -7
Therefore, $m^2 - 6m - 7 = (m + 1)(m - 7)$

iv. Factor $s^2 - \frac{1}{6}s - \frac{1}{6}$

What two numbers have the sum $-\frac{1}{6}$ and the product $-\frac{1}{6}$? (It takes a little more searching here!)

Answer: $-\frac{1}{2}$ and $\frac{1}{3}$.

Therefore, $s^2 - \frac{1}{6}s - \frac{1}{6} = (s - \frac{1}{2})(s + \frac{1}{3})$

EXERCISES

Factor each of the following:

1. $x^2 + 5x + 6$
2. $p^2 + 10p + 16$
3. $z^2 + 15z + 36$
4. $a^2 + 10a + 9$
5. $n^2 + 9n + 14$
6. $s^2 + 16s + 15$
7. $t^2 + 2t - 3$
8. $x^2 + x - 30$
9. $r^2 + r - 12$
10. $b^2 + b - 72$
11. $c^2 + 3c - 10$
12. $u^2 + 4u - 45$
13. $m^2 - m - 6$
14. $n^2 - 3n - 4$
15. $p^2 - 5p - 14$
16. $v^2 - 5v - 50$
17. $d^2 - 5d - 24$
18. $c^2 - 9c - 10$
19. $e^2 - 3e + 2$
20. $g^2 - 15g + 14$
21. $h^2 - 15h + 56$
22. $w^2 - 13w + 22$
23. $k^2 - 17k + 30$
24. $m^2 - 6m + 9$
25. $n^2 - 10n + 25$
26. $y^2 - 8y + 16$
27. $r^2 + 6r + 9$
28. $t^2 + 10t + 21$
29. $n^2 + 8n - 9$
30. $z^2 - 5z - 24$

31. $t^2 - 4t + 4$
32. $x^2 + 10x + 25$
33. $x^2 + 8x - 33$
34. $r^2 - 7r + 6$
35. $r^2 - 8r + 16$
36. $k^2 - 15k + 56$
37. $x^2 - 5x - 14$
38. $y^2 + 14y + 48$
39. $z^2 - 7z - 44$
40. $t^2 + 8t - 9$
41. $r^2 - 14r + 48$
42. $x^2 + 14x + 49$
43. $y^2 + 6y - 16$
44. $t^2 - 6t - 27$
45. $x^2 + x - 12$
46. $z^2 - z - 30$
47. $k^2 + k - 56$
48. $r^2 - 49$
49. $s^2 - 4s - 21$
50. $t^2 - 36$
51. $x^2 + 7x - 18$
52. $y^2 - 25$
53. $r^2 - 100$
54. $a^2 - 625$
55. $t^2 - 196$
56. $h^2 - 289$
57. $n^2 - 144$
58. $n^2 - 1225$
59. $n^2 - 2025$
60. $s^2 - 2500$

Factoring trinomials of the form $ax^2 + bx + c$

In order to learn to factor polynomials like $3x^2 + 13x + 4$, let us further examine multiplication of binomials. Observe the following:

$$3x \cdot x = 3x^2$$

$$(3x + 1)\ (x + 4) = 3x^2 + 13x + 4$$

$$1 \cdot 4$$

The diagram shows how we obtain $3x^2$ and 4 in the product. Now examine the following diagram.

$$(3x + 1)\ (x + 4) = 3x^2 + 13x + 4$$

$$1 \cdot x = x \qquad x + 12x = 13x$$

$$3x \cdot 4 = 12x$$

Now, if we are faced with the problem of factoring $3x^2 + 13x + 4$, we shall look for

two monomials whose product is $3x^2$ ($3x$ and x)
two numbers whose product is 4, but
the two numbers must be such that one of them multiplied by x plus the other multiplied by $3x$ result in $13x$ (1 and 4; $1 \cdot x + 4 \cdot 3x = 13x$).

Before doing some examples, let us agree that the coefficients a, b, and c in $ax^2 + bx + c$ are integers and that resulting binomial factors have integers for their coefficients. Thus, we will consider factoring over the set of integers. This is the case with the example

$$3x^2 + 13x + 4 = (3x + 1)(x + 4)$$

The coefficients in the trinomial are 3, 13, and 4. Are these all integers? The coefficients in the first binomial factor $(3x + 1)$ are 3 and 1; and the coefficients in the second binomial factor $(x + 4)$ are 1 and 4. Are these integers?

Examples: i. Factor $3y^2 + 10y + 8$ over the set of integers.
Two monomials with integral coefficients whose product is $3y^2$ are $3y$ and y. Let's jot down parts of the binomial factors. $(3y + d)(y + e)$

Now what two integers will give 8 for their product? Let's try 1 and 8.
$$(3y + 1)(y + 8) = 3y^2 + 25y + 8$$
$$\uparrow$$
we need 10 here

Let's try the factors $(3y + 8)$ and $(y + 1)$.
$(3y + 8)(y + 1) = 3y^2 + 11y + 8$
$$\uparrow$$
we need 10 here

So, 1 and 8 are not the numbers we are seeking.
Let's try 2 and 4.
$(3y + 2)(y + 4) = 3y^2 + 14y + 8$
$$\uparrow$$
we need 10 here
What about the factors $(3y + 4)$ and $(y + 2)$?
$(3y + 4)(y + 2) = 3y^2 + 10y + 8$
And we finally succeeded in obtaining the factors we need.

ii. Factor $6x^2 + 7x + 2$ over the set of integers.
After trying several alternatives on the side, we find
$6x^2 + 7x + 2 = (2x + 1)(3x + 2)$.
Multiply the two binomials to see that the product is the desired trinomial.

iii. Factor $15a^2 + 7a - 2$ over the set of integers.
Several tries lead to $15a^2 + 7a - 2 = (5a - 1)(3a + 2)$.
Multiply the two binomials to verify that the product is equal to $15a^2 + 7a - 2$.

iv. Factor $9m^2 - 30m + 24$ over the set of integers.
We find that $9m^2 - 30m + 24 = (3m - 4)(3m - 6)$
Perform the multiplication to verify this.

v. Factor $-6x^2 + 14x - 4$ over the set of integers.
A few tries lead to $-6x^2 + 14x - 4 = (-3x + 1)(2x - 4)$.

EXERCISES

Factor each trinomial over the set of integers.

1. $2n^2 + 5n + 2$

2. $3a^2 + 5a + 2$

3. $5x^2 + 11x + 2$

4. $3s^2 + 8s + 4$

5. $2t^2 + 11t + 12$

6. $6m^2 + 11m + 5$

7. $5u^2 + 6u + 1$

8. $6x^2 + 5x + 1$

9. $6c^2 + 11c + 3$

10. $6r^2 + 13r + 6$

11. $10v^2 + 17v + 3$

12. $9d^2 + 46d + 5$

13. $12h^2 + 13h + 3$

14. $21k^2 + 10k + 1$

15. $15p^2 + 11p + 2$

16. $2x^2 + 3x - 2$

17. $3a^2 + 20a - 7$

18. $4m^2 + 13m - 12$

19. $5r^2 + 11r - 12$

20. $6s^2 + 29s - 5$

21. $6t^2 + t - 2$

22. $3x^2 - 14x - 5$

23. $5n^2 - 19n - 4$

24. $6u^2 - 11u - 7$

25. $6y^2 - 13y - 5$

26. $2a^2 + 5a - 3$

27. $13m^2 + 11m - 2$

28. $6d^2 - 5d - 21$

29. $10x^2 + 19x - 15$

30. $20n^2 + n - 12$

31. $2k^2 - 5k + 2$

32. $5h^2 - 17h + 6$

33. $7s^2 - 31s + 12$

34. $6v^2 - 7v + 2$

35. $21y^2 - 29y + 10$

36. $10p^2 - 27p + 18$

37. $12r^2 - 13r + 3$

38. $20a^2 - 56a + 15$

39. $6x^2 - 31x + 40$

40. $6u^2 - 23u + 7$

41. $15v^2 - 51v + 18$

42. $6n^2 - 35n + 50$

43. $-x^2 - 5x + 14$

44. $-3m^2 + 7m - 2$

45. $-2a^2 - 5a - 2$

46. $-15t^2 + 11t + 12$

47. $-12s^2 - 25s + 7$

48. $x^2 + 11x + 24$

49. $2y^2 + 15y + 7$

50. $12a^2 + 25a + 12$

51. $3m^2 + 20m - 7$

52. $15t^2 - 26t + 8$

53. $18m^2 + 61m - 7$

54. $4k^2 - 32k + 55$

55. $12s^2 - 37s + 28$

56. $10 + 11y + y^2$

[HINT: First write an equivalent expression of the form $ax^2 + bx + c$.]

57. $14c + 8c^2 - 9$

58. $-2x^2 + 12 - 5x$

59. $21n^2 + 21 - 58n$

60. $-12y^2 + 14 - 13y$

FINDING COMMON FACTORS

In the expression $3xy + 4xz$ we notice that $3xy$ and $4xz$ have a common factor. We can use a distributive property and obtain the following:
$$3xy + 4xz = x(3y + 4z)$$
Thus we have a binomial $3xy + 4xz$ and an expression which is equivalent to it and which is the product of x and $3y + 4z$. Thus, x and $3y + 4z$ are factors of $3xy + 4xz$.

Here are a few more examples of the same kind. Study them thoughtfully.

Example:
$$3rt^2 + 7ts = (3rt) \cdot t + 7s \cdot t$$
$$= (3rt + 7s) \cdot t$$
Thus, t and $3rt + 7s$ are factors of $3rt^2 + 7ts$.

We may also factor a single term from a trinomial.

Examples: i. $2xy^2 + 5x^2y + 3xt = (2y^2)x + (5xy)x + (3t) \cdot x$
$$= (2y^2 + 5xy + 3t) \cdot x$$

ii. $6rt + 3ts = (2r) \cdot 3t + s \cdot (3t) = (2r + s) \cdot 3t$

iii. $5xy - 10x^2z = 5xy + (-10x^2z)$
$$= y \cdot 5x - (2xz) \cdot 5x$$
$$= (y - 2xz) \cdot 5x$$
Thus, $(y - 2xz)$ and $5x$ are factors of $5xy - 10x^2z$.

Did you discover that an important part of such factoring is to determine the largest factor common to all terms in a given expression?

Study the next examples to see how this kind of factoring is useful in finding simpler expressions equivalent to the given fractional expressions, such as $\dfrac{8x + 12}{4x - 20}$. In such cases we shall assume, without stating it, that those replacements for the variables which lead to undefined symbols are excluded. For example, in $\dfrac{8x + 12}{4x - 20}$ the replacement set for x is the set of real numbers except 5 for x, since then $\dfrac{8x + 12}{4x - 20}$ becomes $\dfrac{52}{0}$, which does not name any number.

Examples: i. $\dfrac{8x + 12}{4x - 20} = \dfrac{4(2x + 3)}{4(x - 5)} = \dfrac{2x + 3}{x - 5}$

ii. $\dfrac{6xy - 21x^2}{3x^2y + 9x} = \dfrac{3x(2y - 7x)}{3x(xy + 3)} = \dfrac{2y - 7x}{xy + 3}$

iii. $\dfrac{2x^2 - 3x - 2}{3x^2 - 5x - 2} = \dfrac{(2x + 1)(x - 2)}{(3x + 1)(x - 2)} = \dfrac{2x + 1}{3x + 1}$

EXERCISES

1. Factor each of the following:

a. $3rt + 6s$

b. $4cr + 5cz$

c. $6xt + 9ts$

d. $3xy^2 + 5xy$

e. $7rt + 9t^2y$

f. $4xy + 8x^2r$

g. $5xy + 10xz + 15x^2y$

h. $13 + 39x$

i. $5x^2 + 7x$

j. $y^3 + 3y^2 + 2y$

k. $25y^2z + 10y^3x$

l. $2xy + 4x^2y + 6x^2y^2$

m. $2xy + 4xt + 6t$

n. $7x - 3xy$

o. $14xy + 15xy^2 + 13x^2z$

p. $5 - 15t$

q. $6 - 9xy + 3z$

r. $3x^3 - 5x^2 - 2xy^2$

s. $5z^2y + 10yx^2 - 15zx$

t. $16rt - 4tx$

u. $8x^2y^3 - 2xy$

v. $9rt^3 - 3rt^2$

w. $xyz^2 - x^2yz + x^2yz^2$

x. $3xy - 4yz^2 + 4yx^2$

y. $9rs^2 - 6st$

z. $14xy^2 + 7x^2y - 21x^2y$

[HINT: Be sure to factor completely.]

a'. $2x^2 + 4x - 6$

b'. $3x^2 + 3x - 90$

c'. $4r^2 + 24r + 36$

d'. $5m^2 + 40m - 45$

2. Find equivalent expressions by factoring and simplifying. In each case, replacements of the variables which lead to undefined symbols are excluded.

a. $\dfrac{3a + 6}{9a + 3}$

b. $\dfrac{7m + 14}{14m - 7}$

c. $\dfrac{4 - 6t}{2t - 8}$

d. $\dfrac{2xy + 4x}{6x^2 + 8x^2y}$

e. $\dfrac{16a^2b^2 - 4ab}{a^2b^2 + ab}$

f. $\dfrac{27mn + 9m^2}{18m^2 + 9m}$

g. $\dfrac{25a^2 + 5a}{5a - 10ab}$

h. $\dfrac{7m^2n^2 - 28mn}{7mn}$

i. $\dfrac{k^2 + 2k - 3}{2k^2 + 11k + 15}$

j. $\dfrac{2s^2 + 11s - 6}{-2s^2 + 7s - 3}$

k. $\dfrac{3u^2 - 13u - 10}{6u^2 + u - 2}$

l. $\dfrac{-a^2 + 4a + 21}{-2a^2 + 15a - 7}$

SOLVING QUADRATIC EQUATIONS

Some time ago you learned to solve linear equations. That is, you learned a way of finding a replacement for x in $cx + b = 0$ so that a true statement resulted.

We shall now be concerned with a problem of finding a replacement for x in $ax^2 + bx + c = 0$ to result in a true statement. The factoring which you have learned will be of great help here. Consider the equation $x^2 + 8x + 12 = 0$. An equation of the form $ax^2 + bx + c = 0$ is called a *quadratic* equation.

You know that $x^2 + 8x + 12 = (x + 6)(x + 2)$, so this equation is equivalent to the equation $(x + 6)(x + 2) = 0$. The last equation can be worded as follows:

The product of two numbers, $x + 6$ and $x + 2$, is zero.

Recall that the only way to obtain zero as a result of multiplying two numbers is to multiply a non-zero number by 0 or to multiply 0 by itself.

Thus $(x + 6)(x + 2) = 0$ means $x + 6 = 0$ or $x + 2 = 0$.

Now, $x + 6 = 0$ when x is replaced by -6, and
$x + 2 = 0$ when x is replaced by -2.

It appears, then, that the solution set of the equation $x^2 + 8x + 12 = 0$ is $\{-6, -2\}$, that is, the solution set consists of two members, -6 and -2. Or, the equation $x^2 + 8x + 12 = 0$ has two roots, -6 and -2.

Let us check to make sure that these two numbers are indeed the roots of this equation.

-6 for x			-2 for x	
$x^2 + 8x + 12$	$= 0$		$x^2 + 8x + 12$	$= 0$
$(-6)^2 + 8(-6) + 12$	0		$(-2)^2 + 8(-2) + 12$	0
$36 + (-48) + 12$			$4 + (-16) + 12$	
$-12 + 12$			$-12 + 12$	
0			0	

Example: What is the solution set of the equation $3m^2 - 12 = 0$? An equation which is equivalent to $3m^2 - 12 = 0$ is $3m^2 = 12$; and $3m^2 = 12$ is equivalent to $m^2 = 4$. But the last equation is simply this: a number squared is 4. What is the number? You know that there are two such numbers: 2 and -2. Thus, the solution set of $3m^2 - 12 = 0$ is $\{-2, 2\}$.

CHECK:

-2 for m			2 for m	
$3m^2 - 12$	$= 0$		$3m^2 - 12$	$= 0$
$3(-2)^2 - 12$	0		$3 \cdot 2^2 - 12$	0
$3 \cdot 4 - 12$			$3 \cdot 4 - 12$	
$12 - 12$			$12 - 12$	
0			0	

Here is another way to find the roots of this equation.

$$3m^2 - 12 = 0$$
$$3(m^2 - 4) = 0$$
$$m^2 - 4 = 0 \quad \text{(Why?)}$$
$$(m - 2)(m + 2) = 0 \quad \text{(Why?)}$$
$$m - 2 = 0 \qquad\qquad m + 2 = 0$$
$$m = 2 \qquad\qquad m = -2$$

The solution set is $\{2, -2\}$.

Thus you see that the solutions of quadratic equation can be found in different ways.

EXERCISES

Find the solution sets, and check.

1. $x^2 + x - 6 = 0$
2. $r^2 + 4r - 5 = 0$
3. $t^2 - 30 = t$
4. $x^2 + 5x = 14$
5. $y^2 - 16y + 48 = 0$
6. $63 - 16x = -x^2$
7. $s^2 + 8s + 16 = 0$
8. $10x + x^2 = -16$
9. $18 = -3r + r^2$
10. $11x = x^2 + 30$
11. $42 + x - x^2 = 0$
12. $x^2 - 7x = -12$
13. $10 - 3x - x^2 = 0$

14. $10x - 28 = -2x^2$
15. $2t - t^2 = -15$
16. $3x^2 - 12x = 135$
17. $24 - 16t = -2t^2$
18. $-2x^2 - 4x - 2 = 0$
19. $-12x - 32 = x^2$
20. $2x^2 + 32 = 16x$
21. $-2x^2 - 18x = 28$
22. $r^2 + 7r - 8 = 0$
23. $-s^2 + 10s = 16$
24. $t^2 - 16 = 0$
25. $x^2 - 25 = 0$
26. $2r^2 = 72$

PATTERNS IN SQUARING BINOMIALS

Let us square a few binomials and look for patterns.

$$(x + 3)^2 = x^2 + 6x + 9$$
$$(x + 5)^2 = x^2 + 10x + 25$$
$$(x + 25)^2 = x^2 + 50x + 625$$
$$(x - 4)^2 = x^2 - 8x + 16$$
$$(x - 7)^2 = x^2 - 14x + 49$$
$$(x - \tfrac{1}{2})^2 = x^2 - x + \tfrac{1}{4}$$
$$(x - 1.3)^2 = x^2 - 2.6x + 1.69$$

Now take a good look at the examples above. Does the following pattern describe correctly all of the examples?

$$(x + a)^2 = x^2 + 2 \cdot a \cdot x + a^2$$

Trinomials like

$$x^2 + 6x + 9$$
$$x^2 + 10x + 25$$
$$x^2 + 50x + 625$$

are called *perfect squares* because they result from squaring binomials.

EXERCISES

1. Replace the a, b, or c with numerals to obtain true statements.

a. $(x - 2)^2 = x^2 + b \cdot x + 4$

b. $(x + 5)^2 = x^2 + 10x + c$

c. $(x + 4)^2 = x^2 + b \cdot x + 16$

d. $(x - 1)^2 = x^2 - 2x + c$

e. $(x + a)^2 = x^2 + 4x + 4$

f. $(x - \frac{3}{2})^2 = x^2 + b \cdot x + \frac{9}{4}$

g. $(r + \frac{3}{4})^2 = r^2 + \frac{3}{2}r + c$

h. $(t - a)^2 = t^2 - \frac{4}{3}t + \frac{4}{9}$

i. $(z + a)^2 = t^2 + b \cdot x + \frac{25}{9}$

j. $(r - a)^2 = r^2 - 12r + c$

k. $(x + \frac{4}{7})^2 = x^2 + b \cdot x + \frac{16}{49}$

l. $(x - \frac{3}{4})^2 = x^2 + b \cdot x + c$

m. $(y - a)^2 = y^2 - \frac{6}{5}y + c$

n. $(z + a)^2 = z^2 + b \cdot z + \frac{36}{49}$

o. $(t - a)^2 = t^2 - 16t + c$

p. $(x + a)^2 = x^2 + b \cdot x + 81$

2. In each case, replace the c with a numeral to obtain an expression which is a perfect square.

Example: $x^2 + c \cdot x + 9$

If c is replaced by 6, we have $x^2 + 6x + 9$, which is equivalent to $(x + 3)^2$.

a. $x^2 + cx + 4$

b. $y^2 - 10y + c$

c. $z^2 + cz + \frac{9}{4}$

d. $x^2 - 6x + c$

e. $r^2 + \frac{3}{2}r + c$

f. $x^2 + cx + \frac{36}{49}$

g. $t^2 + \frac{5}{3}t + c$

h. $s^2 + \frac{8}{5}s + c$

i. $x^2 - cx + \frac{4}{9}$

j. $t^2 - \frac{7}{8}t + c$

k. $x^2 - cx + \frac{1}{9}$

l. $x^2 - .2x + c$

PERFECT SQUARES AND QUADRATIC EQUATIONS

Suppose you are asked to find the solution set of the equation

$$(y + 5)^2 = 36$$

You may reason as follows: Some number, $y + 5$, squared gives me. There are two such numbers: 6 and -6. Therefore

$$y + 5 = 6 \text{ or } y + 5 = -6$$
$$y = 1 \qquad y = -11$$

So, the solution set of $(y + 5)^2 = 36$ should be $\{1, -11\}$.

CHECK: 1 for y

$(y + 5)^2$	$=$	36
$(1 + 6)^2$		36
6^2		
36		

-11 for y

$(y + 5)^2$	$=$	36
$(-11 + 5)^2$		36
$(-6)^2$		
36		

Now note that
$$(y + 5)^2 = 36$$
$$y^2 + 10y + 25 = 36$$
$$y^2 + 10y - 11 = 0$$
are all equivalent equations.

Suppose that, instead of being given the equation $(y + 5)^2 = 36$, you were given its equivalent equation
$$y^2 + 10y - 11 = 0$$
You probably would factor the latter as follows:
$$(y - 1)(y + 11) = 0$$
and immediately find the solution set to be $\{1, -11\}$.

There is another way to attack this problem. Suppose we start with $y^2 + 10y - 11 = 0$ and arrive at $(y + 5)^2 = 36$. One way to do this would be to reason along these lines.
$$y^2 + 10y - 11 = 0$$
To get a trinomial which is a perfect square, we should have $y^2 + 10y + 25$ since $(y + 5)^2 = y^2 + 10y + 25$. But $y^2 + 10y + 25$ is *not* equivalent to $y^2 + 10y - 11$. We can do the following, however.
$$(y^2 + 10y + 25) - 36 = y^2 + 10y - 11$$
or
$$(y + 5)^2 - 36 = y^2 + 10y - 11$$
Thus the equation now becomes
$$(y + 5)^2 - 36 = 0$$
and we can solve it in the way we have done above.

The process of arriving at $(y + 5)^2 - 36$ as an equivalent expression to $y^2 + 10y - 11$ is called *completing the square*.

Example: Find the solution set of $(y + 5)^2 = 17$
$$y + 5 = \sqrt{17} \qquad \text{or} \qquad y + 5 = -\sqrt{17}$$
$$y = -5 + \sqrt{17} \qquad \text{or} \qquad y = -5 - \sqrt{17}$$
The solution set of the equation $(y + 5)^2 = 17$ should be
$$\{-5 + \sqrt{17}, -5 - \sqrt{17}\}$$

CHECK:

$-5 + \sqrt{17}$ for y

$(y + 5)^2$	$= 17$
$(-5 + \sqrt{17} + 5)^2$	17
$(-5 + 5 + \sqrt{17})^2$	
$(\sqrt{17})^2$	
17	

$-5 - \sqrt{17}$ for y

$(y + 5)^2$	$= 17$
$(-5 - \sqrt{17} + 5)^2$	17
$(-5 + 5 - \sqrt{17})^2$	
$(-\sqrt{17})^2$	
17	

EXERCISES

1. Find the solution sets and check.

a. $(x - 2)^2 = 5$ f. $(x + 4)^2 = 5$

b. $(r - 6)^2 = 8$ g. $(x + \frac{5}{3})^2 = 7$

c. $(t + 1)^2 = 7$ h. $(s - 5)^2 = 6$

d. $(s - 3)^2 = 2$ i. $(x + \frac{2}{5})^2 = 3$

e. $(v - \frac{3}{2})^2 = 11$ j. $(y + 2)^2 = 13$

2. For each of the following, obtain an equivalent expression by completing the square.

Examples: i. $x^2 + 6x + 5$

$x^2 + 6x + 9$ is a perfect square
because $x^2 + 6x + 9 = (x + 3)^2$
$$x^2 + 6x + 5 = x^2 + 6x + (9 - 4)$$
$$= (x^2 + 6x + 9) - 4$$
$$= (x + 3)^2 - 4$$

ii. $r^2 + 12r$

$r^2 + 12r + 36$ is a perfect square
because $r^2 + 12r + 36 = (r + 6)^2$
$$r^2 + 12r = r^2 + 12r + (36 - 36)$$
$$= (r^2 + 12r + 36) - 36$$
$$= (r + 6)^2 - 36$$

iii. $3x^2 + 7x - 6 = 3(x^2 + \frac{7}{3}x - 2)$

Now we shall work with $x^2 + \frac{7}{3}x - 2$
$x^2 + \frac{7}{3}x + \frac{49}{36}$ is a perfect square
because $x^2 + \frac{7}{3}x + \frac{49}{36} = (x + \frac{7}{6})^2$
$$x^2 + \frac{7}{3}x - 2 = x^2 + \frac{7}{3}x + (\frac{49}{36} - \frac{121}{36})$$
$$= (x^2 + \frac{7}{3}x + \frac{49}{36}) - \frac{121}{36}$$
$$= (x + \frac{7}{6})^2 - \frac{121}{63}$$
$$3(x^2 + \frac{7}{3}x - 2) = 3[(x + \frac{7}{6})^2 - \frac{121}{36}]$$
$$= 3(x + \frac{7}{6})^2 - \frac{121}{12}$$

a. $x^2 + 4x + 1$ f. $a^2 + 7a - 18$

b. $y^2 - 2y + 3$ g. $h^2 + 2h + 30$

c. $t^2 + 2t - 6$ h. $z^2 - 7z - 29$

d. $m^2 + m + 2$ i. $p^2 - 13p$

e. $n^2 + 10n + 26$ j. $x^2 + 4x$

k. $s^2 + 11s$

l. $y^2 + 2y - 10$

m. $2x^2 + 4x + 6$

n. $2m^2 + 6m + 9$

o. $3x^2 + 12x - 1$

p. $3n^2 + 8n + 10$

q. $4x^2 - x - 2$

r. $5t^2 + 3t - 1$

3. Find the solution sets by completing the square.

Example: i. $x^2 + 4x + 1 = 0$

$x^2 + 4x + 4$ is a perfect square

because it is equal to $(x + 2)^2$

$$x^2 + 4x + 1 = x^2 + 4x + (4 - 3)$$
$$= (x^2 + 4x + 4) - 3$$
$$= (x + 2)^2 - 3$$

$$(x + 2)^2 - 3 = 0$$
$$(x + 2)^2 = 3$$

$x + 2 = \sqrt{3}$ or $x + 2 = -\sqrt{3}$

$x = -2 + \sqrt{3}$ or $x = -2 - \sqrt{3}$

CHECK: $-2 + \sqrt{3}$ for x

$$x^2 + 4x + 1 \quad = \quad 0$$

$(-2 + \sqrt{3})^2 + 4(-2 + \sqrt{3}) + 1$	0
$(4 - 4\sqrt{3} + 3) + (-8) + 4\sqrt{3} + 1$	
$7 - 8 + 1$	
$-1 + 1$	
0	

$-2 - \sqrt{3}$ for x

$$x^2 + 4x + 1 \quad = \quad 0$$

$(-2 - \sqrt{3})^2 + 4(-2 - \sqrt{3}) + 1$	0
$4 + 4\sqrt{3} + 3 + (-8) + (-4\sqrt{3}) + 1$	
$4 + 3 + (-8) + 4\sqrt{3} + (-4\sqrt{3}) + 1$	
$7 + (-8) + 1$	
$-1 + 1$	
0	

The solution set is $\{-2 + \sqrt{3}, -2 - \sqrt{3}\}$

Example: ii. $y^2 + 2y = 0$

$y^2 + 2y + 1$ is a perfect square

because it is equal to $(y + 1)^2$

$$y^2 + 2y = y^2 + 2y + (1 - 1)$$
$$= (y^2 + 2y + 1) - 1$$
$$= (y + 1)^2 - 1$$

$$(y + 1)^2 - 1 = 0$$
$$(y + 1)^2 = 1$$
$$y + 1 = 1 \quad \text{or} \quad y + 1 = -1$$
$$y = 0 \quad \text{or} \quad y = -2$$

CHECK:

0 for y		-2 for y	
$y^2 + 2y$	$= \quad 0$	$y^2 + 2y$	$= \quad 0$
$0^2 + 2 \cdot 0$	0	$(-2)^2 + 2 \cdot (-2)$	0
$0 + 0$		$4 + (-4)$	
0		0	

The solution set is $\{0, -2\}$.

Example: *iii.* $2m^2 + 3m - 1 = 0$

$$2m^2 + 3m - 1 = 2(m^2 + \tfrac{3}{2}m - \tfrac{1}{2})$$

$m^2 + \tfrac{3}{2}m + \tfrac{9}{16}$ is a perfect square

because it is equal to $(m + \tfrac{3}{4})^2$

$$m^2 + \tfrac{3}{2}m - \tfrac{1}{2} = m^2 + \tfrac{3}{2}m + (\tfrac{9}{16} - \tfrac{17}{16})$$
$$= (m^2 + \tfrac{3}{2}m + \tfrac{9}{16}) - \tfrac{17}{16}$$
$$= (m + \tfrac{3}{4})^2 - \tfrac{17}{16}$$
$$2(m^2 + \tfrac{3}{2}m - \tfrac{1}{2}) = 2[(m + \tfrac{3}{4})^2 - \tfrac{17}{16}]$$
$$= 2(m + \tfrac{3}{4})^2 - \tfrac{17}{8}$$
$$2(m + \tfrac{3}{4})^2 - \tfrac{17}{8} = 0$$
$$2(m + \tfrac{3}{4})^2 = \tfrac{17}{8}$$
$$(m + \tfrac{3}{4})^2 = \tfrac{17}{16}$$

$$m + \tfrac{3}{4} = \sqrt{\tfrac{17}{16}} \qquad \text{or} \qquad m + \tfrac{3}{4} = -\sqrt{\tfrac{17}{16}}$$

$$m + \frac{3}{4} = \frac{\sqrt{17}}{4} \qquad \text{or} \qquad m + \frac{3}{4} = \frac{-\sqrt{17}}{4}$$

$$m = \frac{-3 + \sqrt{17}}{4} \qquad \text{or} \qquad m = \frac{-3 - \sqrt{17}}{4}$$

CHECK: $\dfrac{-3 + \sqrt{17}}{4}$ for m

$$2m^2 + 3m - 1 \quad = \quad 0$$

$$2\left(\frac{-3 + \sqrt{17}}{4}\right)^2 + 3\left(\frac{-3 + \sqrt{17}}{4}\right) - 1 \quad \Big| \quad 0$$

$$2 \cdot \frac{9 - 6\sqrt{17} + 17}{16} + 3\left(\frac{-3 + \sqrt{17}}{4}\right) - \frac{4}{4}$$

$$\frac{26 - 6\sqrt{17}}{8} + \frac{-9 + 3\sqrt{17}}{4} - \frac{4}{4}$$

$$\frac{13 - 3\sqrt{17}}{4} + \frac{-9 + 3\sqrt{17}}{4} - \frac{4}{4}$$

$$\frac{13 - 3\sqrt{17} - 9 + 3\sqrt{17} - 4}{4}$$

$$\frac{(13 - 9 - 4) + (-3\sqrt{17} + 3\sqrt{17}}{4}$$

$$\frac{0}{4}$$

$$0$$

$$\frac{-3 - \sqrt{17}}{4} \text{ for } m$$

$$2m^2 + 3m - 1 \quad = \quad 0$$

$$2\left(\frac{-3 - \sqrt{17}}{4}\right)^2 + 3\left(\frac{-3 - \sqrt{17}}{4}\right) - 1 \qquad 0$$

$$2 \cdot \frac{9 + 6\sqrt{17} + 17}{16} + \frac{-9 - 3\sqrt{17}}{4} - 1$$

$$\frac{26 + 6\sqrt{17}}{8} + \frac{-9 - 3\sqrt{17}}{4} - 1$$

$$\frac{13 + 3\sqrt{17}}{4} + \frac{-9 - 3\sqrt{17}}{4} - 1$$

$$\frac{13 + 3\sqrt{17} - 9 - 3\sqrt{17} - 4}{4}$$

$$\frac{(13 - 9 - 4) + (3\sqrt{17} - 3\sqrt{17})}{4}$$

$$\frac{0}{4}$$

$$0$$

The solution set is $\left\{\dfrac{-3 + \sqrt{17}}{4}, \quad \dfrac{-3 - \sqrt{17}}{4}\right\}$.

a. $x^2 + 16x + 20 = 0$

b. $y^2 + 8y + 3 = 0$

c. $z^2 + 10z + 15 = 0$

d. $m^2 + 4m + 1 = 0$

e. $x^2 + 8x = 0$

f. $p^2 - 5p = 0$

g. $x^2 + 3x + 2 = 0$

h. $n^2 + 5n - 1 = 0$

i. $s^2 + 2s + 1 = 0$

j. $t^2 - 7t - 2 = 0$

k. $3x^2 + 4x - 1 = 0$

l. $6x^2 + 11x + 4 = 0$

m. $2x^2 - x - 21 = 0$

n. $6x^2 - x - 2 = 0$

o. $5x^2 - 2x = 3$

p. $-2x^2 - 4x + 6 = 0$

q. $3r^2 + 27r + 42 = 0$

r. $6s^2 - 29s - 5 = 0$

s. $2t^2 + 11t + 5 = 0$

t. $5x^2 + 9x - 3 = 0$

u. $7x^2 + 3x - 5 = 0$

v. $5x^2 - 7x + 2 = 0$

w. $2x^2 - 3x - 6 = 0$

x. $-3n^2 - n + 1 = 0$

y. $16t^2 + 16t - 16 = 0$

THE QUADRATIC FORMULA

We have stated on page 361 that equations of the form
$$ax^2 + bx + c = 0,$$
where a, b and c are real numbers and $a \neq 0$, are called quadratic equations.

As we have seen, completing the square is one method of dertermining roots of a quadratic equation. Let us employ this method to determine the roots of $ax^2 + bx + c = 0$, where a, b and c are real numbers and $a \neq 0$.

$$a\left(x^2 + \frac{b}{a}x\right) + c = 0$$

$$a\left[x^2 + \frac{b}{a}x + \left(\frac{b^2}{4a^2}\right) + \left(-\frac{b^2}{4a^2}\right)\right] + c = 0$$

$$a\left[\left(x^2 + \frac{b}{a}x + \frac{b^2}{4a^2}\right) + \left(-\frac{b^2}{4a^2}\right)\right] + c = 0$$

$$a\left[\left(x + \frac{b}{2a}\right)^2\right] + \left(-\frac{b^2}{4a}\right) + c = 0$$

$$a\left(x + \frac{b}{2a}\right)^2 + \left(-\frac{b^2}{4a}\right) + \frac{4ac}{4a} = 0$$

$$a\left(x + \frac{b}{2a}\right)^2 + \left(-\frac{b^2 - 4ac}{4a}\right) = 0$$

$$a\left(x + \frac{b}{2a}\right)^2 = \frac{b^2 - 4ac}{4a}$$

$$\left(x + \frac{b}{2a}\right)^2 = \frac{b^2 - 4ac}{4a^2}$$

$$x + \frac{b}{2a} = \sqrt{\frac{b^2 - 4ac}{4a^2}} \text{ or } x + \frac{b}{2a} = -\sqrt{\frac{b^2 - 4ac}{4a^2}}$$

$$x = \frac{-b}{2a} + \sqrt{\frac{b^2 - 4ac}{4a^2}} \text{ or } x = \frac{-b}{2a} + \left(-\sqrt{\frac{b^2 - 4ac}{4a^2}}\right)$$

These may be simplified to

$$x = \frac{-b}{2a} + \frac{\sqrt{b^2 - 4ac}}{2a} = \frac{-b + \sqrt{b^2 - 4ac}}{2a} \text{ and}$$

$$x = \frac{-b}{2a} - \frac{\sqrt{b^2 - 4ac}}{2a} = \frac{-b - \sqrt{b^2 - 4ac}}{2a}$$

Thus, the roots of the equation $ax^2 + bx + c = 0$, (a, b, c real numbers and $a \neq 0$) are

$$\frac{-b + \sqrt{b^2 - 4ac}}{2a} \text{ and } \frac{-b - \sqrt{b^2 - 4ac}}{2a}$$

This is called the *quadratic formula* and is written as

$$x = \frac{-b \pm \sqrt{b^2 - 4ac}}{2a}$$

Now study the following examples to see how convenient the quadratic formula is when solving quadratic equations.

Example: Determine the roots of the equation

$$x^2 + 6x + 3 = 0$$

This equation is obtained from $ax^2 + bx + c = 0$ by replacing a by 1, b by 6, and c by 3.
Therefore we shall make the same replacements in the quadratic formula.

$$x = \frac{-b + \sqrt{b^2 - 4ac}}{2a}$$

$$= \frac{-6 + \sqrt{6^2 - 4 \cdot 1 \cdot 3}}{2 \cdot 1} = \frac{-6 + \sqrt{36 - 12}}{2}$$

$$= \frac{-6 + \sqrt{24}}{2} = \frac{-6 + \sqrt{4 \cdot 6}}{2} = \frac{-6 + 2\sqrt{6}}{2}$$

$$x = -3 + \sqrt{6}$$

It is easy to see that the second root is $-3 - \sqrt{6}$.

CHECK: $-3 + \sqrt{6}$ for x

$$
\begin{array}{r|r}
x^2 + 6x + 3 & = \quad 0 \\
\hline
(-3 + \sqrt{6})^2 + 6(-3 + \sqrt{6}) + 3 & 0 \\
9 - 6\sqrt{6} + 6 - 18 + 6\sqrt{6} + 3 & \\
(9 + 6 - 18 + 3) + (-6\sqrt{6} + 6\sqrt{6}) & \\
15 - 18 + 3 & \\
-3 + 3 & \\
0 &
\end{array}
$$

$-3 - \sqrt{6}$ for x

$$
\begin{array}{c|c}
x^2 + 6x + 3 & = \quad 0 \\
\hline
(-3 - \sqrt{6})^2 + 6(-3 - \sqrt{6}) + 3 & 0 \\
9 + 6\sqrt{6} + 6 + (-18 - 6\sqrt{6}) + 3 & \\
9 + 6 + 6\sqrt{6} - 18 - 6\sqrt{6} + 3 & \\
(9 + 6 - 18 + 3) + (6\sqrt{6} - 6\sqrt{6}) & \\
15 - 18 + 3 & \\
-3 + 3 & \\
0 &
\end{array}
$$

Thus, the solution set of $x^2 + 6x + 3 = 0$ is

$$\{ -3 + \sqrt{6}, \ -3 - \sqrt{6} \}$$

Do you see that both roots of this equation are irrational numbers?

It is possible to have quadratic equations whose solution set in the universe of real numbers is the empty set. Consider, for example, this very simple quadratic equation

$$x^2 = -2$$

This equation may be turned into the question

What real number squared results in -2?

You know that real numbers consist of positive numbers, negative numbers, and zero. You also know that every positive number squared is a positive number, every negative number squared is a positive number, and zero squared is zero. So, there is no real number whose square is a negative number. Thus, the equation $x^2 = -2$ has no root in the universe of real numbers.

Later in your study of algebra you will learn about new numbers (not in the set of real numbers) whose squares may be negative numbers. For now we shall say that such equations have the empty set for their solution set.

Example: Find the solution set of the equation

$$3x^2 - 5x - 7 = 0$$

This equation is obtained from $ax^2 + bx + c = 0$ by replacing a by 3, b by -5, and c by -7.

$$x = \frac{-b + \sqrt{b^2 - 4ac}}{2a} = \frac{5 + \sqrt{(-5)^2 - 4 \cdot 3 \cdot (-7)}}{2 \cdot 3}$$

$$= \frac{5 + \sqrt{25 + 84}}{6} = \frac{5 + \sqrt{109}}{6}$$

The second root is $\dfrac{5 - \sqrt{109}}{6}$

The solution set is $\left\{ \dfrac{5 + \sqrt{109}}{6}, \ \dfrac{5 - \sqrt{109}}{6} \right\}$

EXERCISES

Determine the roots of the following equations using the quadratic formula.

1. $x^2 - 3x - 5 = 0$
2. $x^2 + 6x - 3 = 0$
3. $x^2 + 8x + 5 = 0$
4. $x^2 - 6x - 1 = 0$
5. $3x^2 - 2x - 7 = 0$
6. $-2x^2 + 8x + 5 = 0$
7. $3x^2 + 5x = 0$
8. $-6x^2 + 11 = 0$
9. $3x^2 + 9x - 5 = 0$
10. $7x^2 + 2x - 2 = 0$

11. $3x^2 - 5x - 8 = 0$
12. $x^2 + 7x = -4$
13. $2x^2 - 6 = -5x$
14. $-8x - 3 = 5x^2$
15. $-4x^2 + 2x + 3 = 0$
16. $x(3x + 1) = 5(3 - x)$
17. $6(x + 4) = x(x - 3)$
18. $5(4 - x) = 7x(x + 2)$
19. $-4(x + 3) = 5x(4 - x)$
20. $3(2 + x) = -2x(3 - x)$

THE DISCRIMINANT

For the quadratic equation $ax^2 + bx + c = 0$, the expressions

$$\dfrac{-b + \sqrt{b^2 - 4ac}}{2a} \quad \text{and} \quad \dfrac{-b - \sqrt{b^2 - 4ac}}{2a}$$

give you a way of determining the roots.

We have said that many quadratic equations do not have roots among the real numbers. With a little thought we will see that it is not necessary to try to solve a quadratic equation to discover that it has no roots in the real number system.

The part $\sqrt{b^2 - 4ac}$ in the expression which gives you the roots is a clue to the answer.

If $b^2 - 4ac$ is a positive number, then

$$\dfrac{-b + \sqrt{b^2 - 4ac}}{2a} \quad \text{and} \quad \dfrac{-b - \sqrt{b^2 - 4ac}}{2a}$$

are two different real numbers and thus the equation has two real roots.

If $b^2 - 4ac$ is 0, then each of

$$\dfrac{-b + \sqrt{b^2 - 4ac}}{2a} \quad \text{and} \quad \dfrac{-b - \sqrt{b^2 - 4ac}}{2a}$$

yields $\dfrac{-b}{2a}$, and thus, the equation has one real root.

If $b^2 - 4ac$ is a negative number, then $\sqrt{b^2 - 4ac}$ does not exist among real numbers and the equation has no roots in the real number system.

The expression $b^2 - 4ac$ is given the name of *discriminant* and is abbreviated by the Greek letter Δ [read: delta].

▪ $\Delta > 0$; two real roots

▪ $\Delta = 0$; one real root

▪ $\Delta < 0$; no real roots

Let us now describe the nature of the roots of some quadratic equations by just examining the discriminant.

Examples: i. $3x^2 + 5x + 1 = 0$
$\Delta = b^2 - 4ac = 5^2 - 4 \cdot 3 \cdot 1 = 25 - 12 = 13$
$\Delta > 0$, therefore the equation has two real roots. Solve the equation to see that it is so.

ii. $x^2 + 2x + 1 = 0$
$\Delta = b^2 - 4ac = 2^2 - 4 \cdot 1 \cdot 1 = 4 - 4 = 0$
$\Delta = 0$, therefore the equation has one real root. Solve the equation to see that it is so.

iii. $x^2 + 5x + 20 = 0$
$\Delta = b^2 - 4ac = 5^2 - 4 \cdot 1 \cdot 20 = 25 - 80 = -55$
$\Delta < 0$, therefore the equation has no real roots. Solve the equation to see that it is so.

EXERCISES

Without solving the equations, tell whether they have two real roots, one real root, or no real roots.

1. $y^2 + y - 1 = 0$

2. $2m^2 - m + 1 = 0$

3. $17x^2 + 5x - 10 = 0$

4. $n^2 + n + 1 = 0$

5. $3p^2 - \frac{1}{2}p - \frac{1}{4} = 0$

6. $s^2 - 2s - 3 = 0$

7. $t^2 = t - 7$

8. $z = 2z^2 + 5$

9. $5u - \frac{3}{4}u^2 = \frac{1}{2}$

10. $2w = -3w^2$

11. $3 = -r + \frac{1}{2}r^2$

12. $1.5x^2 - 2.5x + 3.5 = 0$

13. $\dfrac{y^2 - y}{6} = 7$

14. $\dfrac{n(n - 1)}{n} = 15$

15. $(t - 1)(t - 2) = 4$

USING EQUATION PROPERTIES

In Chapter 7 you learned the equation property for multiplication

$$\forall_x \, \forall_y \, \forall_{y=0} \ x = y \text{ if and only if } xz = yz$$

An example of the use of this property is

$$\tfrac{1}{2}x + 5 = 4$$
$$(\tfrac{1}{2}x + 5) \cdot 2 = 4 \cdot 2$$
$$x + 10 = 8$$

The equations $x + 10 = 8$ and $\tfrac{1}{2}x + 5 = 4$ are equivalent equations, because they have the same solution set. It is $\{-2\}$.

In the illustration above we used the number 2 as a multiplier. As long as you use a non-zero real number as a multiplier, you will get an equivalent equation.

When using as a multiplier a polynomial involving a variable, the situation is quite different. Let us see what may happen.

$$3x = 10$$

using x as a multiplier,
$$(3x)x = 10x$$
$$3x^2 = 10x$$
$$3x^2 - 10x = 0$$
$$x(3x - 10) = 0$$

The solution set of the original equation $3x = 10$ is $\{\tfrac{10}{3}\}$. The solution set of the equation $x(3x - 10) = 0$ is $\{0, \tfrac{10}{3}\}$. Thus, the two equations are *not* equivalent, because they have different solution sets.

You must also exercise caution when squaring. For example, the following statement is true

$$\forall_x \, \forall_y, \text{ if } x = y, \text{ then } x^2 = y^2$$

But the statement

$$\forall_x \, \forall_y, \text{ if } x^2 = y^2, \text{ then } x = y$$

is *not* true. Here is an example to prove that it is false.

$$(-3)^2 = 3^2 \text{ is true}$$
$$\text{but} \quad -3 = 3 \text{ is false}$$

If you start out with an equation, say, $x - 1 = 5$, and obtain a new equation $(x - 1)^2 = 25$, the new equation is not equivalent to the first. The equation $x - 1 = 5$ has for its solution set $\{6\}$. The solution set of the equation $(x - 1)^2 = 25$ is $\{-4, 6\}$.

Whenever you perform operations like those above, you must compare the solution set of the new equation with that of the original equation before deciding whether the derived equation is equivalent to the original equation.

EXERCISES

For each pair of equations do the following:

 i. tell how the second equation in the pair is obtained from the first

 ii. find the solution set of each equation

 iii. state whether the equations are equivalent

1. $x = -5$; $x^2 = -5x$

2. $\dfrac{1}{x+1} = 3$; $3x + 3 = 1$

3. $2n = -3$; $4n^2 = 9$

4. $\dfrac{y^2 - 1}{y + 1} = 3$; $y - 1 = 3$

5. $\dfrac{1}{s^2} = 1$; $\dfrac{1}{s} = 1$

6. $2t + 5 = 11$; $4t^2 + 20t + 25 = 121$

7. $\sqrt{u} = 7$; $u = 49$

8. $\sqrt{m-1} = 11$; $m - 1 = 121$

9. $\sqrt{z^2 + 4} = -12$; $z^2 + 4 = 144$

10. $\sqrt{\dfrac{v}{4}} = -\dfrac{1}{2}$; $\dfrac{v}{4} = \dfrac{1}{4}$

USING QUADRATIC EQUATIONS

There are many problems which lead to quadratic equations. The roots of the equations may provide answers to these problems. Some problems may be solved by the use of quadratic equations, but they may be so simple that you can "guess" at the answers. For example, consider this problem:

I thought of a number. The square of the number is 36. What number did I think of?

You no doubt. quickly answer: 6 or -6.

It would be wasteful to go through the following:

$$x^2 = 36$$
$$x^2 - 36 = 0$$
$$(x - 6)(x + 6) = 0$$
$$x - 6 = 0; \; x = 6$$
$$\text{or } x + 6 = 0; \; x = -6$$

Therefore, I thought of 6 or -6.

But there are problems in which it is extremely difficult to "guess" the answer. In such cases, the ability to solve quadratic equations is very helpful.

Example: *i.* The product of one less than a certain number and two less than three times this number is 14. Determine the given number.

If we let x stand for this number, we have

$$(x - 1)(3x - 2) = 14$$
$$x \cdot 3x - x \cdot 2 - 3x + 2 = 14$$
$$3x^2 - 2x - 3x + 2 = 14$$
$$3x^2 - 5x + 2 = 14$$
$$3x^2 - 5x - 12 = 0$$

This is in the form $ax^2 + bx + c = 0$; thus the roots are given by

$$\frac{-b + \sqrt{b^2 - 4ac}}{2a} \quad \text{and} \quad \frac{-b - \sqrt{b^2 - 4ac}}{2a}$$

In our problem, a is 3, b is -5, and c is -12.

One root: $\dfrac{-(-5) + \sqrt{(-5)^2 - 4(3)(-12)}}{2(3)}$

$$= \frac{5 + \sqrt{169}}{6} = \frac{5 + 13}{6} = \frac{18}{6} = 3$$

Second root: $\dfrac{5 - 13}{6} = \dfrac{-8}{6} = -\dfrac{4}{3}$

The solution set of the equation is $\{3, -\frac{4}{3}\}$.

Let's check the first root.
>One less than a number: $3 - 1 = 2$
>Two less than three times this number:
>$$3 \times 3 - 2 = 7$$
>The product: $2 \times 7 = 14$

Thus, 3 is indeed one solution.

What about $-\frac{4}{3}$?
>One less than a number: $-\frac{4}{3} - 1 = -2\frac{1}{3}$
>Two less than three times this number:
>$$-\frac{4}{3} \times 3 - 2 = -6$$
>The product: $-2\frac{1}{3} \times (-6) = 14$

Thus, $-\frac{4}{3}$ is also a solution.

Example: *ii.* The sum of the square of a certain negative integer and 6 times the integer is 16. Determine the integer.

$$x^2 + 6x = 16$$
$$x^2 + 6x - 16 = 0$$

One root: $\dfrac{-6 + \sqrt{36 - 4(-16)}}{2}$

$$= \frac{-6 + \sqrt{36 + 64}}{2} = \frac{-6 + \sqrt{100}}{2}$$

$$= \frac{-6 + 10}{2} = \frac{4}{2} = 2$$

Second root: $\dfrac{-6 - 10}{2} = \dfrac{-16}{2} = -8$

CHECK: First root:
    the square: $2^2 = 4$
    six times the number: $6 \times 2 = 12$
    sum: $4 + 12 = 16$

Although the number 2 seems to check, we reject this answer because in the problem it is stated that we are seeking a *negative* integer.
Second root:
    the square: $(-8)^2 = 64$
    six times the number: $6 \times (-8) = -48$
    sum: $64 + (-48) = 16$

We accept -8 as the only solution of this problem.

Example: *iii.* An altitude of a triangle is 6 inches longer than the corresponding base. The area of the triangle is $13\frac{1}{2}$ square inches. Determine the length of this altitude and base.
Let x be the measure of the base in inches. Then the measure of the altitude is $(x + 6)$ inches. The area of the triangle is $\frac{1}{2} \cdot x \cdot (x + 6)$ square inches. We have the equation

$$\tfrac{1}{2}x(x + 6) = 13\tfrac{1}{2}$$
$$\tfrac{1}{2}x^2 + 3x = 13\tfrac{1}{2}$$
$$x^2 + 6x = 27$$
$$x^2 + 6x - 27 = 0$$

One root: $\dfrac{-6 + \sqrt{36 - 4(-27)}}{2}$

$$= \frac{-6 + \sqrt{36 + 108}}{2} = \frac{-6 + \sqrt{144}}{2}$$

$$= \frac{-6 + 12}{2} = \frac{6}{2} = 3$$

Second root: $\dfrac{-6 - 12}{2} = \dfrac{-18}{2} = -9$

Since we are here concerned with the measure of line segments, we must reject the negative number.

Thus, the length of the base is 3 inches and that of the altitude, 9 inches.

Check to see that you obtain the correct area.

EXERCISES

Solve each problem.

1. If the length of a rectangle exceeds its width by 12 inches and the area is 28 square inches, determine the length and the width of the rectangle.

2. The product of one greater than a given integer and nine less than two times the integer is equal to -12. Determine the given integer.

3. If the measure of one leg of a right triangle is 5 units less than the measure of the other leg and the area of the triangle is 18 square units, determine

    a. the measure of each leg

    b. the measure of the hypotenuse

4. The length of the pictured rectangular solid is one unit more than its width. Its height is equal to its width. Its total area is $\frac{13}{4}$ square units. Determine the measures of the edges.

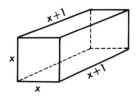

5. If the perimeter of a rectangle is 72 inches and its area is 155 square inches, determine the length and the width of the rectangle.

6. If one subtracts 11 from the number of square inches in the area of a square, he would get twice the number of inches in the perimeter. Determine the measure of the side of the square.

7. Each of three consecutive integers is squared. The three results are added and the sum 29 is obtained. What are the three integers?
[HINT: Let x, $x + 1$, $x + 2$ denote the three integers].

8. In the diagram at the right, if the area enclosed by the large rectangle is twice the area of the small rectangle, compute the width of the shaded strip.

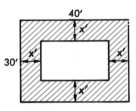

9. A certain negative number added to the square of the number results in 3.75. What is the number? What is the positive number that meets this condition?

10. The measures of the legs of a right triangle are 3 inches and 2 inches. Compute the measure of the hypotenuse.

11. In a right triangle, the measure of the first leg is one inch greater than the measure of the second leg. The measure of the hypotenuse is 3 inches greater than the measure of the first leg. Determine the measures of the three sides.

12. The area of a square is 13 square inches. Compute the measure of a diagonal of the square.

13. The measure of one of the two parallel sides of an isosceles trapezoid is 4 inches greater than the measure of the other side. If the measure of the shorter of the two parallel sides is 12 inches and the area of the trapezoid is 42 square inches, compute the perimeter of the trapezoid.

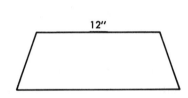

14. The sum of a number and its reciprocal is equal to $2\sqrt{2}$. What is the number?

15. In a right triangle the measure of the hypotenuse is 1 inch greater than the measure of one of its legs and 2 inches greater than the measure of the other leg. Determine the measure of each side of this triangle.

16. The equation $d = st - 16t^2$ gives the vertical distance d in feet that an object is from the starting point t seconds after being projected vertically upward with the beginning speed of s feet per second. How long will it take an object to reach a height of 616 feet above the starting point, if it is projected vertically upward at the speed of 200 feet per second?

17. Solve the equation $d = st - 16t^2$ for t in terms of d and s. From this solution state the relation between d and s for which t has *one* value.

18. Five hundred pine seedlings were planted in rows, so that the number of seedlings in each row was five greater than the number of rows. How many rows were there?

19. The sum of the squares of two consecutive positive integers is 313. What are the two integers?

20. The difference between the square of a positive integer and the square of one-half of that integer is 192. What is the integer?

MORE FACTORING

Recall that $x^2 - y^2 = (x + y)(x - y)$ yields true statements for all replacements of the variables. We speak of $x^2 - y^2$ as the difference of two squares. Many expressions may be put in this general form, which enables us to factor them readily.

Also, some polynomials may be factored by noting terms which have a common binomial factor.

For example, to factor the expression

$$a(x - y) + b(x - y)$$

we apply a distributive property to yield

$$a(x - y) + b(x - y) = (a + b)(x - y)$$

Thus $(a + b)$ and $(x - y)$
are factors of $a(x - y) + b(x - y)$

Example: i. Factor $bx + by - cx - cy$
We observe that the expression is equivalent to $b(x + y) - c(x + y)$ which in turn is equivalent to $(b - c)(x + y)$.
Thus, $bx + by - cx - cy = (b - c)(x + y)$

Example: ii. Factor $x^2 - 4x + 4 - 25y^2$
We observe that the first three terms may be grouped together and viewed as a perfect square, and that the last term is also a perfect square.
$(x^2 - 4x + 4) - 25y^2$ is equivalent to $(x - 2)^2 - (5y)^2$
Thus, we have the expression in the form of the difference of two squares.
Hence
$$(x - 2)^2 - (5y)^2 = [(x - 2) - (5y)][x - 2) + (5y)]$$
$$= (x - 5y - 2)(x + 5y - 2)$$

Sometimes quite a bit of regrouping and simplifying is needed to get an expression into the form of the difference of two squares.

Example: *iii.*   Factor $r^2 - x^2 + t^2 - 2rt + 2xy - y^2$

We regroup to produce an equivalent expression.
$$(r^2 - 2rt + t^2) - x^2 + 2xy - y^2$$
Next we obtain
$$(r^2 - 2rt + t^2) - (x^2 - 2xy + y^2)$$
This is in the form of the difference of two squares
$$(r - t)^2 - (x - y)^2$$
which is equivalent to
$$[(r - t) - (x - y)][(r - t) + (x - y)]$$
$$= (r - t - x + y)(r - t + x - y)$$

Thus, $(r - t - x + y)$ and $(r - t + x - y)$ are the factors of $r^2 - x^2 + t^2 - 2rt + 2xy - y^2$.

Binominals and trinomials can frequently be factored by first finding equivalent expressions in the form of the difference of two squares.

In factoring the expression
$$x^4 + x^2 + 1$$
we note that the expression is nearly a perfect square. We know that $x^4 + 2x^2 + 1$ is a perfect square, and we are aware that zero is the only number which may be added without changing the value of the expression. Since $x^2 + (-x^2)$ is equivalent to zero it may be added to get the equivalent expression
$$x^4 + x^2 + 1 = x^4 + x^2 + 1 + [(x^2) + (-x^2)]$$
The last expression is equivalent to
$$(x^4 + 2x^2 + 1) - x^2 = (x^2 + 1)^2 - x^2$$
$$= [(x^2 + 1) + x][(x^2 + 1) - x]$$
$$= (x^2 + x + 1)(x^2 - x + 1)$$
Thus, $x^2 + x + 1$ and $x^2 - x + 1$ are factors of $x^4 + x^2 + 1$ and we have
$$x^4 + x^2 + 1 = (x^2 + x + 1)(x^2 - x + 1)$$

Example: *iv.*   Factor $x^4 - 12x^2y^2 + 16y^4$

Observe first that
$$x^4 - 8x^2y^2 + 16y^4$$
is a perfect square. Why?

Of course, this expression is not equivalent to the given expression. To obtain an equivalent expression we must add $-4x^2y^2$.

$$(x^4 - 8x^2y^2 + 16y^4) - (4x^2y^2) = x^4 - 12x^2y^2 + 16y^4$$

We now have the difference of two squares.

$$(x^2 - 4y^2)^2 - (2xy)^2$$

which is equivalent to

$$[(x^2 - 4y^2) + 2xy][(x^2 - 4y^2) - 2xy]$$

or $$(x^2 + 2xy - 4y^2)(x^2 - 2xy - 4y^2)$$

Thus
$$x^4 - 12x^2y^2 + 16y^4 = (x^2 + 2xy - 4y^2)(x^2 - 2xy - 4y^2)$$

Example: v. Multiply $(x + y)(x^2 - xy + y^2)$

$$= (x + y) \cdot x^2 - (x + y)(xy) + (x + y) \cdot y^2$$
$$= x^3 + x^2y - x^2y - xy^2 + xy^2 + y^3$$
$$= x^3 + y^3$$

Thus, $x^3 + y^3$ has as its factors $x + y$ and $x^2 - xy + y^2$

or $$x^3 + y^3 = (x + y)(x^2 - xy + y^2)$$

Example: vi. Multiply $(x - y)(x^2 + xy + y^2)$

$$= (x - y) \cdot x^2 + (x - y) \cdot (xy) + (x - y) \cdot y^2$$
$$= x^3 - x^2y + x^2y - xy^2 + xy^2 - y^3$$
$$= x^3 - y^3$$

Thus, $x^3 - y^3$ has as its factors $x - y$ and $x^2 + xy + y^2$

or $$x^3 - y^3 = (x - y)(x^2 + xy + y^2)$$

The last two examples are helpful in understanding how to factor expressions which are the sum or difference of two cubes. The next two examples illustrate how to factor such expressions.

Examples: vii. Factor $8x^3 + 27$
We observe that $8x^3 + 27$ is of the form $A^3 + B^3$
$$8x^3 + 27 = (2x)^3 + (3)^3$$
$$= (2x + 3)[(2x)^2 - (2x)(3) + (3)^2]$$
$$= (2x + 3)(4x^2 - 6x + 9)$$

viii. Factor $x^6 - y^6$
We note that $x^6 - y^6$ is of the form $A^3 - B^3$
$$x^6 - y^6 = (x^2)^3 - (y^2)^3$$
$$= (x^2 - y^2)[(x^2)^2 + (x^2)(y^2) + (y^2)^2]$$
$$= (x^2 - y^2)(x^4 + x^2y^2 + y^4)$$

Any expression which is the sum or the difference of two cubes may be factored by this method.

EXERCISES

Factor each of the following:

1. $cr + dr + ct + dt$
2. $16r^2 - 9t^2 + 4r - 3t$
3. $x^4 - 3x^2 + 1$
4. $8y^3 - 125x^3$
5. $y^2 - 6y$
6. $x^2 - 4x + 4 - 25y^2$
7. $(r + s)^2 + 2(r + s) + 1$
8. $x^6 + 8$
9. $16x^2 - 81y^2$
10. $9cy^2 - d^2c$
11. $y^5 - 4y$
12. $\frac{1}{8}y^3 - \frac{1}{27}x^3$
13. $7x^2 + 42xy + 63y^2$
14. $2x^2 - 9y - 18 + yx^2$
15. $y(x + 2) + r(x + 2)$
16. $r^2 - 2rt + t^2 - x^2 + 2xy - y^2$
17. $9x^4 + 5x^2 + 1$
18. $r^2t - rt^2$
19. $9 - 81z^4$
20. $8y^3 - 1$
21. $3x^3 + 24$
22. $r^2st - r^3 - s^2t + rs$

23. $4z^2 - (x + 3)^2$
24. $x^2 + 2ry - y^2 - r^2$
25. $z^4 - 7z^2 + 1$
26. $c^2r - r + c^2t - t$
27. $4 - x^2 - 2xy - y^2$
28. $cr + cs - dr - ds$
29. $9x^4 + 11x^2 + 4$
30. $r^3 + 3r^2 - (r + 3)$
31. $x^2 + y - x - y^2$
32. $tw + vx - vw - tx$
33. $(x^2 - 6x + 9) - z^2$
34. $x^2 - y^2 + x + y$
35. $15 + (x + y) - 6(x + y)^2$
36. $81x^4 + 64y^4$
37. $x^4 - y^4$
38. $r(y - x) + t(x - y)$
39. $s^2 - (t^2 + 4t + 4)$
40. $x^4 - 7x^2 + 1$
41. $cz^2 - c - z^2 + 1$
42. $w^2 - r^2 - z^2 + 2rz$
43. $9x^3 - 18x^2r + 9rx^2$
44. $y^8 - z^8$
45. $z^4 + z^2 + 1$

POLYNOMIALS

Each of the following is a polynomial.

(1) $2x^3 + 3x^2 - x + 3$
(2) $4x^4 - x^2 + 3x - 4$
(3) $3x^2 - 5x + 1$
(4) $4x^5 - 3x^2 + x + 2$
(5) $-x + 3$
(6) -2

■ Any expression of the general form $a_rx^r + a_{r-1}x^{r-1} + \cdots + a_1x + a_0$ with $a_r \neq 0$ is called a *polynomial* of degree r in x.

NOTE: $a_0, a_1 \cdots, a_r$ are read "a sub-zero, a sub-one, $\cdots$, a sub-r."

The letter variables a_0, a_1, $\cdot \cdot \cdot$, a_r are replaceable by real number names, and r is a positive integer. Of course, for the polynomial to be of degree r, a_r cannot be zero.

■ a_r, a_{r-1}, $\cdot \cdot \cdot$, a_1, a_0 are called *coefficients*.

In (1) on page 384 the degree of the polynomial is three. Here a_3 is replaced by 2, a_2 by 3, a_1 by -1 and a_0 by 3.

In (2) the degree of the polynomial is four, and the replacements for the coefficients are

4 for a_4　　　0 for a_3　　-1 for a_2　　3 for a_1　　-4 for a_0

We shall use the symbols $P(x)$, $Q(x)$, and so on as symbols for polynomials in x. If $P(x)$ stands for a polynomial in x, $P(3)$ is the number which results when we replace all occurrences of x in the polynomial with 3.

Examples:　　　*i.* in (1), $P(3) = 2(3)^3 + 3(3)^2 - 3 + 3 = 81$

　　　　　　　ii. in (3), $P(2) = 3(2)^2 - 5(2) + 1 = 3$

　　　　　　　iii. in (5), $P(-1) = -(-1) + 3 = 4$

In adding polynomials, we make use of the properties of operations. Study the examples below to see how it is done.

Examples:　　*i.* $(4x^5 - 3x^2 + x + 2) + (-x + 3)$
$$= 4x^5 - 3x^2 + (x - x) + (2 + 3)$$
$$= 4x^5 - 3x^2 + 0 + 5$$
$$= 4x^5 - 3x^2 + 5$$

　　ii. $(3x^2 - 5x + 1) - (-x + 3)$
$$= 3x^2 - 5x + 1 + x - 3$$
$$= 3x^2 + (-5x + x) + (1 - 3)$$
$$= 3x^2 - 4x - 2$$

In multiplying polynomials we again make use of our properties. Can you name the properties used in each step?

Example:　　　　$(-x + 3)(3x^2 - 5x + 1)$
$$= (-x + 3) \cdot 3x^2 - (-x + 3)(5x) + (-x + 3) \cdot 1$$
$$= -3x^3 + 9x^2 + 5x^2 - 15x - x + 3$$
$$= -3x^3 + 14x^2 - 16x + 3$$

Thus, if we let

$$P(x) = -x + 3 \quad \text{and} \quad Q(x) = 3x^2 - 5x + 1$$
$$\text{then } P(x) \cdot Q(x) = -3x^3 + 14x^2 - 16x + 3$$

EXERCISES

If $P(x) = 5x^3 - 4x^2 + 2x - 1$, $Q(x) = 2x^2 - 3x + 3$,   and $F(x) = 5x - 3$, determine

1. $P(-1);\ P(0);\ P(3)$
2. $Q(0);\ Q(1);\ Q(-1)$
3. $F(2);\ F(-3);\ F(-2)$
4. $P(x) + Q(x)$
5. $F(x) + Q(x)$

6. $F(x) + P(x)$
7. $P(x) - F(x)$
8. $P(x) - Q(x)$
9. $F(x) \cdot Q(x)$
10. $Q(x) \cdot P(x)$

DIVISION OF POLYNOMIALS

When dividing one number by another, we can show the result in different ways. For example, in dividing 7 by 2, we can show the result as follows:

$$\tfrac{7}{2} = 3, \text{ remainder } 1 \quad \text{or} \quad 7 = 3 \cdot 2 + 1$$

Here are a few more examples shown in the same way.

$$\tfrac{9}{4} = 2, \text{ remainder } 1 \quad \text{or} \quad 9 = 4 \cdot 2 + 1$$
$$\tfrac{11}{3} = 3, \text{ remainder } 2 \quad \text{or} \quad 11 = 3 \cdot 3 + 2$$
$$\tfrac{14}{5} = 2, \text{ remainder } 4 \quad \text{or} \quad 14 = 5 \cdot 2 + 4$$
$$\tfrac{16}{3} = 5, \text{ remainder } 1 \quad \text{or} \quad 16 = 3 \cdot 5 + 1$$
$$\tfrac{17}{6} = 2, \text{ remainder } 5 \quad \text{or} \quad 17 = 6 \cdot 2 + 5$$

To show the pattern of each example above, we may write

$$\frac{c}{d} = q, \text{ remainder } r \quad \text{or} \quad c = dq + r$$

Observe that it is true for each example that

$$0 \leq r < d$$

When dividing polynomials, the same pattern appears.

$$\frac{c(x)}{d(x)} = q(x), \text{ remainder } r(x)$$
$$\text{or} \qquad c(x) = d(x) \cdot q(x) + r(x)$$

The degree of $r(x)$ is less than the degree of $d(x)$. Of course, $r(x)$ may be equal to 0 or be of degree 0, that is, $r(x)$ may be equal to some non-zero real number.

To divide one polynomial by another, it is important to arrange both the dividend and divisor in order of descending powers of the variable. For example, to divide $x - 12 + x^2$ by $-3 + x$, we write the dividend as $x^2 + x - 12$ and the divisor as $x - 3$.

$$
\begin{array}{r}
x + 4 \\
x - 3 \overline{\smash{\big)}\ x^2 + x - 12}
\end{array}
$$

4x divided by x
x^2 divided by x

$x^2 - 3x$ ◄——— x multiplied by $(x - 3)$
$4x - 12$ ◄——— $(x^2 - 3x)$ subtracted from $(x^2 - x - 12)$
$4x - 12$ ◄——— 4 multiplied by $(x - 3)$
0 ◄——— $(4x - 12)$ subtracted from $(4x - 12)$

The quotient is $(x + 4)$ and the remainder is 0. Thus, we have

$$x^2 + x - 12 = (x - 3)(x + 4)$$

Multiply $(x - 3)$ by $(x + 4)$ to see whether you obtain $x^2 + x - 12$. Study two more examples which are worked out for you.

Example: i.

$$
\begin{array}{r}
x^2 + x - 3 \\
x + 5 \overline{\smash{\big)}\ x^3 + 6x^2 + 2x - 4} \\
\underline{x^3 + 5x^2} \\
x^2 + 2x - 4 \\
\underline{x^2 + 5x} \\
-3x - 4 \\
\underline{-3x - 15} \\
11
\end{array}
$$

The quotient is $x^2 + x - 3$ and the remainder is 11. Thus, $x^3 + 6x^2 + 2x - 4 = (x^2 + x - 3)(x + 5) + 11$. Perform the operations on the right of "=" to verify this.

Example: ii. In dividing $(3x^3 + 2x - 5)$ by $(x + 2)$, we need to be aware that the coefficient of x^2 in $3x^3 + 2x - 5$ is 0.

$$
\begin{array}{r}
3x^2 - 6x + 14 \\
x + 2 \overline{\smash{\big)}\ 3x^3 + 0 \cdot x^2 + 2x - 5} \\
\underline{3x^3 + 6x^2} \\
-6x^2 + 2x \\
\underline{-6x^2 - 12x} \\
14x - 5 \\
\underline{14x + 28} \\
-33
\end{array}
$$

Thus, $3x^3 + 2x - 5 = (3x^2 - 6x + 14)(x + 2) + (-33)$. Perform the operations on the right of "=" to verify this.

EXERCISES

Divide the following:

1. $(x^2 + 7x + 18) \div (x + 9)$
2. $(2r^3 - 5r^2 - 3r + 3) \div (r + 2)$
3. $(x^2 - 8x + 9) \div (x - 4)$
4. $(x^3 - y^3) \div (x - y)$
5. $(x^3 - 64) \div (x + 4)$
6. $(9r^3 + 11r + 8) \div (3r - 2)$
7. $(4y^3 - 8y^2 - 9y + 7) \div (2y - 3)$
8. $(r^6 - 13r^3 + 42) \div (r^3 - 7)$
9. $(t^2 - 17t + 60) \div (t - 12)$
10. $(-15x^3 - 19x^2 - 30x - 8) \div (3x^2 + 5x - 4)$

THEOREMS

Theorem 1 $\forall_a \forall_b \forall_x \ (x + a)(x + b) = x^2 + (a + b)x + ab$

Theorem 2 $\forall_a \forall_b \ (x - a)(x + b) = x^2 + (-a + b)x - a \cdot b$

Theorem 3 $\forall_a \forall_b \ (x - a)(x - b) = x^2 - (a + b)x + a \cdot b$

VOCABULARY

Use each of the following correctly in a sentence. Numerals in the parentheses refer to pages where these words were used. If you are not sure of the meaning of any word, turn to the indicated page and refresh your memory.

coefficient (385)

common factor (359)

completing the square (365)

degree of a polynomial (384)

discriminant (374)

factor (352)

perfect square (364)

polynomial (384)

quadratic equation (361)

quadratic formula (371)

remainder (386)

squaring binomials (363)

REVIEW EXERCISES

1.   Find the products.

    a. $3(x + 3)$

    b. $5(m - 7)$

    c. $x(x - 9)$

    d. $(n + 3)(n + 4)$

    e. $(s - 4)(s + 6)$

    f. $(t - 7)(t - 2)$

    g. $(2u + 1)(3u + 4)$

    h. $(3u - 1)(4u + 2)$

i. $(4k - 3)(7k - 4)$ **k.** $(\frac{1}{3}x - 2)(\frac{1}{2}x + 3)$
j. $(-2y + 1)(y - 6)$ **l.** $(1.5u - 1)(2.6y - 2)$

2. Factor.

a. $3x^2 + 6x$ **h.** $27m^3 - 8n^3$
b. $5m + 15m^2$ **i.** $9m^2 - 30mn + 25n^2$
c. $t^2 + 2t + 1$ **j.** $(3t + s)(m + n) + (3t + s)(m - n)$
d. $6m^2 - m - 1$ **k.** $6x^2 + 7x + 2$
e. $a(x - y) + b(x - y)$ **l.** $4x^2 + x - 3$
f. $7(2x + 5) + 3(2x + 5)$ **m.** $3k^2 - 17k + 20$
g. $9y^2 - 16z^2$ **n.** $-2t^2 - 5t - 3$

3. Find equivalent expressions by factoring and simplifying. In each case, replacements of the variables which lead to undefined symbols are excluded.

a. $\dfrac{4a + 6}{12a + 14}$ **e.** $\dfrac{6k^2 + 7k - 3}{3k^2 + 2k - 1}$

b. $\dfrac{5x - 10}{10x - 5}$ **f.** $\dfrac{s^2 + 4s + 3}{s^2 + 3s + 2}$

c. $\dfrac{3xy + 9x}{6xy - 3x}$ **g.** $\dfrac{nk + 3n + k + 3}{nm + 4n + m + 4}$

d. $\dfrac{x^2 - 2x - 3}{2x^2 + 3x + 1}$ **h.** $\dfrac{ac + 4a - 2c - 8}{ak - a - 2k + 2}$

4. Solve each quadratic equation by factoring.

a. $x^2 - 6x + 5 = 0$ **g.** $-6x^2 - 19x + 7 = 0$
b. $x^2 - 4x - 21 = 0$ **h.** $-8x^2 - 18x + 35 = 0$
c. $x^2 + 7x + 10 = 0$ **i.** $x^2 - 4 = 0$
d. $2x^2 - 7x - 4 = 0$ **j.** $4x^2 - 9 = 0$
e. $12x^2 - 11x - 5 = 0$ **k.** $4x^2 - 4x + 1 = 0$
f. $15x^2 - 14x - 8 = 0$ **l.** $9x^2 + 12x + 4 = 0$

5. Determine the solution sets by the use of the quadratic formula.

a. $x^2 - 8x + 15 = 0$ **d.** $12x^2 + 11x + 2 = 0$
b. $2x^2 + 5x - 3 = 0$ **e.** $15x^2 + 7x - 2 = 0$
c. $6x^2 - x - 1 = 0$ **f.** $14x^2 + 5x - 1 = 0$

6. Compute the discriminant and tell whether each equation has two real roots, one real root, or no real roots.

a. $x^2 + 3x + 4 = 0$ **d.** $2x^2 + x + 1 = 0$
b. $x^2 + x + 1 = 0$ **e.** $-x^2 + 3x - 4 = 0$
c. $3x^2 - x - 2 = 0$ **f.** $x^2 + 2x + 1 = 0$

7. Solve each problem.

    a. The altitude of a triangle is six inches longer than its base and the area of the triangle is 13.5 square inches. Determine the measure of the base and altitude.

    b. The product of a number decreased by 3 and the same number increased by 1 is 2. What is the number? How many such numbers are there?

    c. A triangle has a base twice as long as the altitude. The area is 30.25 sq. in. Compute the length of the base and altitude. How many different triangles with these dimensions are there?

    d. A number squared is equal to that number increased by 12. What is the number? How many such numbers are there?

    e. The sum of the squares of two consecutive positive integers is equal to 113. What are the two integers?

    f. The sum of a number and its reciprocal is equal to $\frac{1}{2} + \frac{3}{2}\sqrt{3}$. What is the number?

8. Given the polynomials

$$P(x) = 4x^5 - x^4 + x^2 - 2 \qquad R(x) = x + 1$$
$$Q(x) = x^2 - 1 \qquad\qquad S(x) = x - 1$$

determine each of the following:

    a. $P(1)$

    b. $Q(-3)$

    c. $R(-\frac{7}{9})$

    d. $S(\sqrt{2})$

    e. $P(x) \cdot Q(x)$

    f. $P(x) \div Q(x)$

    g. $Q(x) \cdot R(x)$

    h. $Q(2) \cdot S(-3)$

    i. $\dfrac{Q(-9)}{S(-2)}$

    j. $P(1) \cdot Q(-1) \cdot R(0) \cdot S(2)$

CHAPTER TEST

1. Solve each problem.

    a. An airplane is flying at a certain number of miles per hour. If this number is doubled and added to the square of the speed, 436,920 is obtained. What is the speed of the plane?

    b. A classroom is a rectangle 25 ft. by 40 ft. Compute the length of a diagonal to two decimal places.

2. Factor each of the following:

    a. $2x + 14$

    b. $7y - 21$

    c. $n^2 + 7n + 6$

    d. $m^2 + 7m - 18$

e. $k^2 - 10k + 24$
f. $6s^2 + 11s + 3$
g. $8a^2 + 2a - 1$
h. $3t^2 - 23t + 14$
i. $3ax - 6ay$

j. $16a^2 - 25b^2$
k. $4r^2 - 4rs + s^2$
l. $3a(2x - y) - 2b(y - 2x)$
m. $8p^3 + 27r^3$
n. $64k^3 - 27m^3$

3. Given the polynomials

$$P(x) = 2x^3 - x^2 + x - 2$$
$$\text{and} \quad Q(x) = x - 1$$

determine each of the following:

a. $P(1)$
b. $Q(\sqrt{2})$
c. $P(x) + Q(x)$

d. $P(x) - Q(x)$
e. $P(x) \cdot Q(x)$
f. $P(x) \div Q(x)$

4. Find the products.

a. $3(2n - 7)$
b. $(x + 3)(x - 2)$
c. $(2m - 1)(3m + 4)$

d. $(-3s + 1)(2s - 3)$
e. $(2 - 5t)(t + 1)$
f. $(1 - 4x)(4x - 1)$

5. True or false for all replacements of variables for which the expressions are defined?

a. $\dfrac{2x + 12}{4x - 2} = \dfrac{x + 6}{x - 1}$

b. $\dfrac{x + 7}{x - 1} = -7$

c. $\dfrac{ax + ay}{bx + by} = \dfrac{a}{b}$

d. $\dfrac{x^2 - 1}{x - 1} = x - 1$

e. $\dfrac{n^2 - 1}{n^2 + 2n + 1} = \dfrac{n - 1}{n + 1}$

f. $\dfrac{k^2 + k + 1}{k^2 + 2k - 3} = \dfrac{2}{3}$

6. Solve each quadratic equation using any method you wish.

a. $x^2 + x - 2 = 0$

b. $x^2 = x + 12$

c. $2 = 5x^2 + x$

d. $\dfrac{x + 4}{x + 9} = \dfrac{x}{3x - 1}$

e. $\dfrac{x + 1}{x + 3} + 2 = \dfrac{x + 2}{x + 1} + \dfrac{1}{3}$

7. Without solving, tell whether the following equations have two real roots, one real root, or no real roots.

a. $x = -x^2 - 1$

b. $\dfrac{y}{y - 1} = y + 2$

c. $2z = 3z^2 + 8$

d. $\frac{1}{2} + m + 2m^2 = 3m$
e. $t(t + 1) = 3t(2 - 4t)$

f. $\dfrac{u + 2}{2u + 3} = \dfrac{3u + 4}{4u + 5}$

BIBLIOGRAPHY

Nichols, E. D.; Heimer, R. T.; and Garland, E. H. *Modern Intermediate Algebra*. New York: Holt, Rinehart and Winston, Inc., 1965. Chapters 3 and 8.

Sawyer, W. W. *A Concrete Approach to Abstract Algebra*. San Francisco: W. H. Freeman and Company, 1959. Chapters 2 and 4.

Sawyer, W. W. *Mathematician's Delight*. Baltimore: Penguin Books, 1956. Chapter 15.

Sawyer, W. W. *Prelude to Mathematics*. Baltimore: Penguin Books, 1959. Chapters 3 and 4.

School Mathematics Study Group. *First Course in Algebra*. New Haven: Yale University Press, 1961. pp. 493-510.

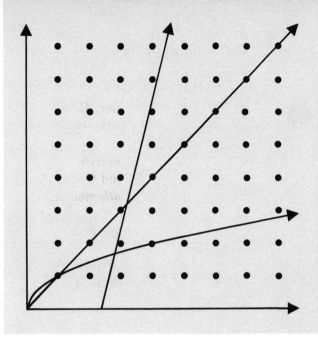

CHAPTER 13

Relations and Functions

INTRODUCTION

We have studied open sentences of the type

$$2x - 9 = 13$$
$$|r| \leq 9$$
$$3s + 5 > 17$$

in which the variables hold places for numerals. The numerals which are chosen as replacements name the elements of a set called the universal set or the universe.

We use the letter U in referring to a universal set.

An open sentence like

$$2x - 9 = 13$$

partitions a chosen universe into two subsets. One of the subsets contains the elements for which $2x - 9 = 13$ results in false statements. The other subset of U contains elements for which $2x - 9 = 13$ yields true statements. We call this latter subset the solution set of the given open sentence.

If the set of positive integers is chosen as the universal set, the following sentences have the solution sets listed on the right.

i. $2x - 9 = 13$ $\{x \mid x = 11\}$, or $\{11\}$

ii. $|r| \leq 9$ $\{r \mid 1 \leq r \leq 9\}$, or $\{1, 2, 3, 4, 5, 6, 7, 8, 9\}$

iii. $3s + 5 > 17$ $\{s \mid s > 4\}$, or $\{5, 6, 7, 8, \ldots\}$

Recall that each number can be associated with a point on the number line. The above sets can be graphed then as follows:

If the universal set were chosen to be the set of non-negative real numbers, the same open sentences have the solution sets listed on the right below.

i. $2x - 9 = 13$ $\{x \mid x = 11\}$

ii. $|r| \leq 9$ $\{r \mid 0 \leq r \leq 9\}$

iii. $3s + 5 > 17$ $\{s \mid s > 4\}$

The graphs now are as follows:

EXERCISES

1.   Use the set of negative integers as the universal set and name the members of the solution sets of the open sentences in exercises **a-f** below.

a. $2x + 2 = 14$

b. $2 < |m| \leq 4$

c. $|y| \leq 1$

d. $|n + 1| < 2$

e. $1 < 2r + 3 < 9$

f. $\dfrac{3t - 2}{t} < 10$

2.   Graph the solution set in each of exercises **1a-1f** on a number line.

3.   Describe the solution set in each of exercises **1a-1f** if the universal set is the set of all real numbers. Graph each set.

Ordered pairs

Suppose the universal set is the set of non-negative integers less than 4, that is

$$U = \{0, 1, 2, 3\}$$

We form the set of all ordered pairs of numbers which belong to U

(0, 0)	(1, 0)	(2, 0)	(3, 0)
(0, 1)	(1, 1)	(2, 1)	(3, 1)
(0, 2)	(1, 2)	(2, 2)	(3, 2)
(0, 3)	(1, 3)	(2, 3)	(3, 3)

This set of all ordered pairs of numbers from U is called the *Cartesian Set* of U. It is written $U \times U$ and read: U cross U. You learned earlier that every *ordered* pair of numbers has one point in the coordinate plane associated with it. The graph of $U \times U$, where $U = \{0, 1, 2, 3\}$ is given at the right. The number pairs are (x, y) with x and y belonging to U.

Now let the universal set, U, be the set of all real numbers for which $0 \leq U \leq 3$. The graph of $U \times U$ is the graph of all ordered number pairs (x, y) for which

$$0 \leq x \leq 3 \text{ and } 0 \leq y \leq 3$$

This set can be described as follows:

$$U \times U = \{(x, y) \mid x \in U \text{ and } y \in U, 0 \leq x \leq 3 \text{ and } 0 \leq y \leq 3\}$$

The graph of the set is at the right. What is the graph of $U \times U$ where U is the set of all real numbers?

EXERCISES

Graph the Cartesian Set of U, where U is

1. $\{0, 1, 2\}$
2. $\{2, 4, 6\}$
3. $\{5\}$
4. the set of integers less than 1 and greater than -4
5. the set of real numbers less than or equal to 0 and greater than or equal to $-1\frac{1}{2}$
6. the set of real numbers less than -2 and greater than or equal to -5 [Describe clearly the boundary of the graph.]

OPEN SENTENCES WITH TWO VARIABLES

You have already worked with open sentences containing two variables. Here are examples of such sentences

$$x - 5 = y$$
$$2x - 3y = 5$$
$$x + 5 < y$$
$$|x| + |y| = 7$$

Suppose we decide to use the set $U = \{0, 1, 2, 3, 4, 5, 6, 7, 8\}$ as the universal set. We can find all pairs (x, y) where x and y are members of U which yield true statements upon replacement in the sentences above.

For example, the solution set of $x - 5 = y$ is

$$\{(x, y) \mid x \in U \text{ and } y \in U \text{ and } x - 5 = y\}$$

The members of this set are $(5, 0)$, $(6, 1)$, $(7, 2)$, $(8, 3)$.

Of course, the solution set is a subset of $U \times U$. The open sentence $x - 5 = y$ selects a subset of $U \times U$, which is the solution set of this sentence.

The solution set of the sentence $2x - 3y = 5$ is

$$\{(x, y) \mid x \in U \text{ and } y \in U \text{ and } 2x - 3y = 5\}$$

It has only two members, $(4, 1)$ and $(7, 3)$.

Here are the members of the solution set of $x + 5 < y$

$$(0, 6) \qquad (0, 7) \qquad (0, 8) \qquad (1, 7) \qquad (1, 8) \qquad (2, 8)$$

The members of the solution set of $|x| + |y| = 7$ are

$$(0, 7) \qquad (1, 6) \qquad (2, 5) \qquad (3, 4) \qquad (4, 3) \qquad (5, 2) \qquad (6, 1) \qquad (7, 0)$$

Examine the graphs of these four sets. In each, $U \times U$ is the Cartesian set of $U = \{0, 1, 2, 3, 4, 5, 6, 7, 8\}$.

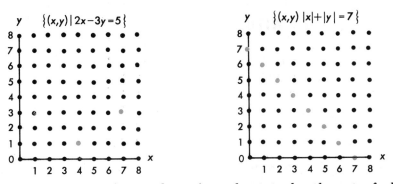

Suppose now we choose the universal set to be the set of all real numbers. Examine the graphs below to see whether you agree with them.

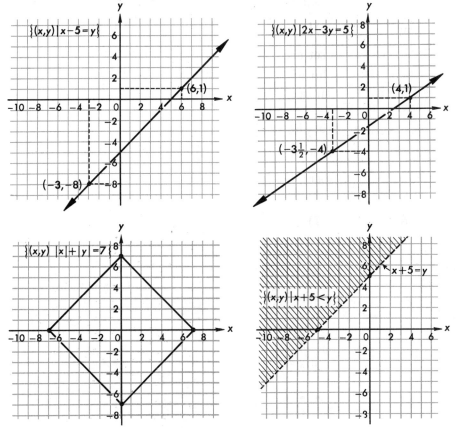

Notice that on the shaded graph every point on the marked side of the line belongs to $\{(x, y) \mid x \in U$ and $y \in U$ and $x + 5 < y\}$; and the line $x + 5 = y$, itself does not belong to the set. Why? Do you see that the choice of the universal set makes a great deal of difference as to what solution set you obtain for a given open sentence?

EXERCISES

1. Let $U = \{-3, -2, -1, 0, 1, 2\}$. Name the members of the solution sets of the following open sentences.

a. $x + y = 0$ **d.** $2x - y = -1$
b. $x \not< y$ **e.** $2x \geq y + 1$
c. $|x| = |y|$ **f.** $|x| + |y| \leq 2$

2. Graph each of the solution sets you obtained in exercises **1a-1f**.
3. Graph each of the solution sets of open sentences in exercises **1a-1f** if the universal set is the set of all real numbers.

RELATIONS AND FUNCTIONS

You have seen, given a set U, that $U \times U$ is a set of ordered number pairs. A set of ordered pairs of things is called a *relation*. Of course, we are particularly interested in ordered pairs of numbers.

Thus, every one of the sets

$$\{(5, 0), (6, 1), (7, 2)\ (8, 3)\}$$
$$\{(4, 1), (7, 3)\}$$
$$\{(0, 6), (0, 7), (0, 8), (1, 7), (2, 8)\}$$
$$\{(0, 7), (1, 6), (2, 5), (3, 4), (4, 3), (5, 2), (6, 1), (7, 0)\}$$

is a relation.

The set of the first coordinates of a relation is called the *domain of the relation*. Thus, for the first relation above, the domain is $\{5, 6, 7, 8\}$. What are the domains of the other relations?

The set of the second coordinates of a relation is called the *range of the relation*. The range of the first relation above is $\{0, 1, 2, 3\}$. What are the ranges of the other relations?

Now let us consider the universe $U = \{0, 1, 2\}$.
The graph of $U \times U$ is at the right.

$U \times U = \{(0, 0), (0, 1), (0, 2), (1, 0), (1, 1),$
$\qquad\qquad (1, 2), (2, 0), (2, 1), (2, 2)\}$

Now consider the following four subsets of $U \times U$.

(K) $\{(0, 1), (1, 1), (2, 2)\}$ (L) $\{(1, 1), (2, 2)\}$ (M) $\{(1, 1), (2, 1), (2, 2)\}$ (N) $\{(1, 2), (1, 1)\}$

Can you see how the subsets K and L differ from the subsets M and N?

Note that in K each member of the domain $D = \{0, 1, 2\}$ is paired with only *one* member of the range $R = \{1, 2\}$. The same is true in L.

Now examine M; 2, which is a member of the domain, is paired once with 1 and another time with 2. Thus the pairs $(2, 1)$ and $(2, 2)$ belong to subset M. Is the situation similar in the case of N? Relations like K and L are called *functions*.

> Thus, a *function* is a *relation* in which no member of the domain has more than one member of the range associated with it.

We usually associate the first components of the ordered pairs with the horizontal axis and the second components with the vertical axis. A relation is a function if and only if no vertical line intersects or touches the graph of the relation in more than one point. This is sometimes called the vertical line test for a function.

EXERCISES

1. Given the universal set $U = \{0, 1, 2, 3, 4, 5, 6, 7, 8\}$, graph each of the following relations. List the members of the domain and range.

Example: *i.* Relation: $\{(1, 3), (2, 5), (2, 2)\}$

Domain: $\{1, 2\}$
Range: $\{2, 3, 5\}$

Example: *ii.* Relation: $\{(x, y) \mid 2x > y\}$

Domain: $\{1, 2, 3, 4, 5, 6, 7, 8\}$
Range: $\{0, 1, 2, 3, 4, 5, 6, 7, 8\}$

The ordered pairs of this relation are listed at the top of the next page.

The following pairs belong to the relation $\{(x, y) \mid 2x < y\}$.

$(1, 0)$, $(1, 1)$, $(2, 0)$, $(2, 1)$, $(2, 2)$, $(2, 3)$, $(3, 0)$,
$(3, 1)$, $(3, 2)$, $(3, 3)$, $(3, 4)$, $(3, 5)$, $(4, 0)$, $(4, 1)$,
$(4, 2)$, $(4, 3)$, $(4, 4)$, $(4, 5)$, $(4, 6)$, $(4, 7)$, $(5, 0)$,
$(5, 1)$, $(5, 2)$, $(5, 3)$, $(5, 4)$, $(5, 5)$, $(5, 6)$, $(5, 7)$,
$(5, 8)$, $(6, 0)$, $(6, 1)$, $(6, 2)$, $(6, 3)$, $(6, 4)$, $(6, 5)$,
$(6, 6)$, $(6, 7)$, $(6, 8)$, $(7, 0)$, $(7, 1)$, $(7, 2)$, $(7, 3)$,
$(7, 4)$, $(7, 5)$, $(7, 6)$, $(7, 7)$, $(7, 8)$, $(8, 0)$, $(8, 1)$,
$(8, 2)$, $(8, 3)$, $(8, 4)$, $(8, 5)$, $(8, 6)$, $(8, 7)$, $(8, 8)$

a. $\{(x, y) \mid y = x - 6\}$

b. $\{(x, y) \mid y < x\}$

c. $\{(x, y) \mid y \geq x\}$

d. $\{(x, y) \mid 2x + y = 5\}$

e. $\{(x, y) \mid x + y < 5\}$

f. $\{(x, y) \mid y = x^2\}$

g. $\{(x, y) \mid y = 2 \mid x \mid\}$

h. $\{(x, y) \mid y \neq x\}$

i. $\{(x, y) \mid 2x + y > 4\}$

j. $\{(x, y) \mid y = 3\}$

k. $\{(x, y) \mid x = 4\}$

l. $\{(x, y) \mid \mid x \mid = \mid y \mid\}$

2. Do exercises **1 (a-l)** for the universal set

$$U = \{-6, -5, -4, -3, -2, -1, 0, 1, 2, 3, 4, 5, 6,\}$$

3. Do exercises **1 (a-l)** for the universal set

$$U = \text{the set of all real numbers}$$

4. For exercises **3 (a-l)** tell which relations are functions.

5. Given $U = \{0, 1, 2, 3\}$,

   a. List the pairs which belong to $A = \{(x, y) \mid y < x\}$
   b. Graph $U \times U$
   c. Graph the set A
   d. List the members of the domain of A and of the range of A

6. Given $U = \{-3, -2, -1, 0, 1, 2, 3\}$, graph each of the following:

   a. $U \times U$

   b. $\{(x, y) \mid y = 2x\}$

   c. $\{(x, y) \mid y < x\}$

   d. $\{(x, y) \mid \mid y \mid + \mid x \mid = 3\}$

   e. $\{(x, y) \mid y = -2\}$

   f. $\{(x, y) \mid y = 3x - 1\}$

   g. $\{(x, y) \mid x + y \leq -3\}$

   h. $\{(x, y) \mid \mid x \mid = 2\}$

   i. Tell which relations in **(b-h)** are functions.

7. Graph the relations in exercise **6** if the universal set is the set of real numbers.

8.   Each graph below is a graph of a relation in $U \times U$, where

$$U = \{0, 1, 2, 3, 4\}$$

For each relation
      i. tell whether it is a function
     ii. list its members
    iii. list the members of the domain and range

Example:

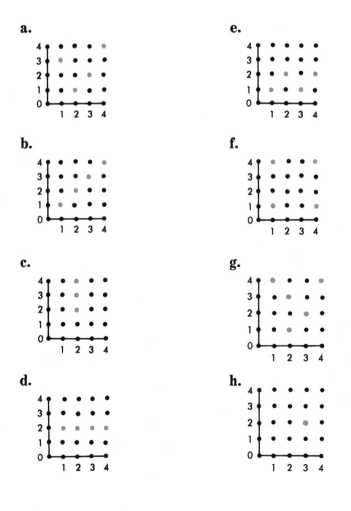

   i. not a function

  ii. $\{(1, 1), (2, 2), (3, 1), (3, 4)\}$

 iii. Domain: $\{1, 2, 3\}$

       Range: $\{1, 2, 4\}$

a.

b.

c.

d.

e.

f.

g.

h.

9. If U is the set of all real numbers, the graph of $U \times U$ is the entire plane.   For each graph below, tell whether it is a graph of a function.

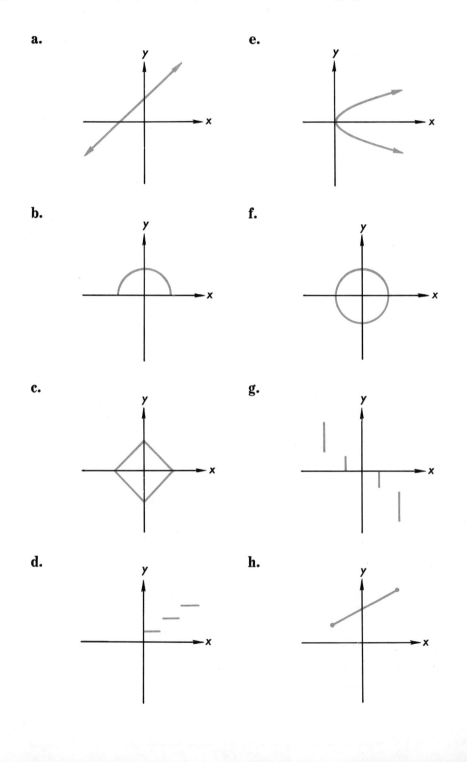

a.

b.

c.

d.

e.

f.

g.

h.

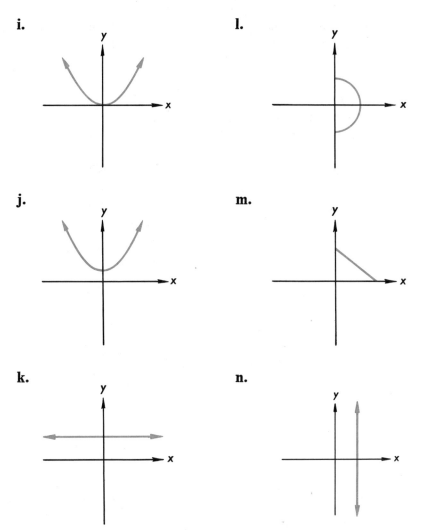

i.

l.

j.

m.

k.

n.

10. For each of the following relations, tell whether it is a function.

    a. {(2, 1), (3, 1), (4, 2), (6, 7)}
    b. {(3, 3), (4, 5), (6, 9), (7, 1), (5, 4)}
    c. {(3, 3), (4, 7), (8, 9), (3, 5), (1, 2)}
    d. {(2, 8), (6, 1), (7, 6), (3, 2), (4, 4), (5, 3)}
    e. {(1, 1), (2, 1), (3, 1), (4, 1), (5, 1), (6, 1)}
    f. {(1, 1), (2, 1), (1, 3), (1, 4), (1, 5), (1, 6)}
    g. {(3, 7), (7, 3), (8, 5), (5, 8), (9, 2), (3, 5)}
    h. {(1, 5), (1, 7), (3, 9), (8, 2), (6, 5)}
    i. {(2, 1), (5, 3), (4, 4), (8, 2)}
    j. {(6, 6)}

11. Using set A as the domain and set B as the range, list the members of $A \times B$, and graph $A \times B$. Then use B as the domain and A as the range and graph $B \times A$.

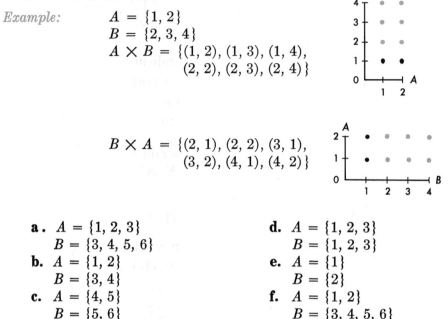

Example: $A = \{1, 2\}$
              $B = \{2, 3, 4\}$
              $A \times B = \{(1, 2), (1, 3), (1, 4),$
                          $(2, 2), (2, 3), (2, 4)\}$

$B \times A = \{(2, 1), (2, 2), (3, 1),$
            $(3, 2), (4, 1), (4, 2)\}$

a. $A = \{1, 2, 3\}$
    $B = \{3, 4, 5, 6\}$
b. $A = \{1, 2\}$
    $B = \{3, 4\}$
c. $A = \{4, 5\}$
    $B = \{5, 6\}$

d. $A = \{1, 2, 3\}$
    $B = \{1, 2, 3\}$
e. $A = \{1\}$
    $B = \{2\}$
f. $A = \{1, 2\}$
    $B = \{3, 4, 5, 6\}$

INVERSES

If $U = \{0, 1, 2, 3, 4,\}$, the relation $G = \{(2, 1), (3, 2), (4, 3)\}$ is a subset of $U \times U$.

The graph of G is at the right.
The domain of this relation is

$\{2, 3, 4\}$

and the range is

$\{1, 2, 3\}$

Now we take the relation
    $H = \{(1, 2), (2, 3), (3, 4)\}$
The graph of this relation is at the right.

How is relation H related to G?   The coordinates of each pair in H are obtained by interchanging the coordinates in the pairs in G. Thus, if $(2, 1) \epsilon G$, then $(1, 2) \epsilon H$.

H is called an *inverse* of G. If H is an inverse of G, is it true that G is an inverse of H? What is an inverse of the inverse of G?

If we graph both G and H on the same set of axes, we can observe an interesting relationship between their graphs. The line segments which con-nect the corresponding points of the

graphs of a relation and its inverse are perpendicular to the line $x = y$ and they are bisected by the line; that is, the graph of a relation is a *reflection* of its inverse with respect to the line $x = y$.

If we interchange the first and second coordinates in each ordered pair of a function, we obtain the *inverse of the function.*

Examine the graphs of the two functions and their inverses below. We will use the symbol K' for the inverse of K, A' for the inverse of A, and so on.

$A = \{(1, 1), (2, 3), (4, 2)\}$ $A' = \{(1, 1), (3, 2), (2, 4)\}$

Domain $= \{1, 2, 4\}$ Domain $= \{1, 2, 3\}$
Range $= \{1, 2, 3\}$ Range $= \{1, 2, 4\}$

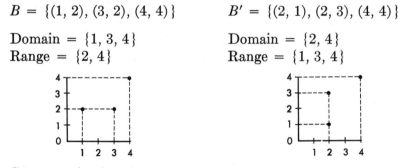

What do you notice about the domain of A and the range of A'? The range of A and the domain of A'?

Do you see that A is a function and A' is also a function?

$B = \{(1, 2), (3, 2), (4, 4)\}$ $B' = \{(2, 1), (2, 3), (4, 4)\}$

Domain $= \{1, 3, 4\}$ Domain $= \{2, 4\}$
Range $= \{2, 4\}$ Range $= \{1, 3, 4\}$

Compare the domain of B and the range of B'; the range of B and the domain of B'.

Do you notice that in this case, B is a function, but B' is *not* a function?

$C = \{(1, 2), (1, 3), (2, 2)\}$ $C' = \{(2, 1), (3, 1), (2, 2)\}$

Domain = $\{1, 2\}$ Domain = $\{2, 3\}$
Range = $\{2, 3\}$ Range = $\{1, 2\}$

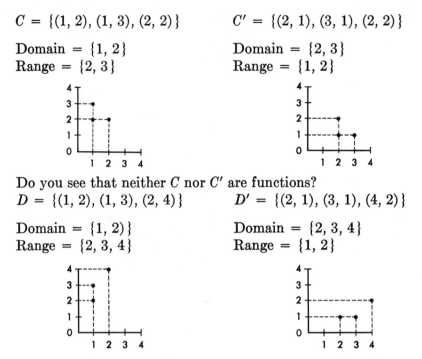

Do you see that neither C nor C' are functions?

$D = \{(1, 2), (1, 3), (2, 4)\}$ $D' = \{(2, 1), (3, 1), (4, 2)\}$

Domain = $\{1, 2)\}$ Domain = $\{2, 3, 4\}$
Range = $\{2, 3, 4\}$ Range = $\{1, 2\}$

Do you see that D is *not* a function, but D' *is* a function?

What conclusions can you draw from the examples above?

How can you tell by examining a function whether its inverse is a function?

Now let us take the set of all real numbers as the universal set. In this universal set, consider the function

$$E = \{(x, y)\,|\,y = x + 3\}$$

Its graph is as follows:

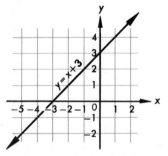

To obtain the inverse of E, we interchange x and y in the equation. Thus

$$E' = \{(x, y)\,|\,x = y + 3\}$$
$$= \{(x, y)\,|\,y = x - 3\}$$

Here is a graph of E'.

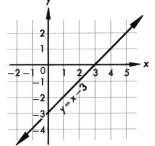

On a sheet of graph paper, graph E and E' on the same axes. Then graph the line $x = y$. Does it appear that the graph of E' is a reflection of the graph of E with respect to the graph of $x = y$?

Here is another pair of graphs of a function and its inverse. The universal set is the set of real numbers.

$$F = \{(x, y) \,|\, y = 2x\}$$
$$F' = \{(x, y) \,|\, x = 2y\} = \{(x, y) \,|\, y = \tfrac{1}{2}x\}$$

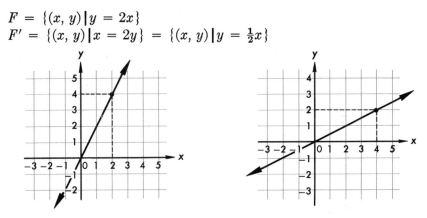

EXERCISES

1.   For each graph below, list the members of the relation. Then list the members of the inverse of the relation. Graph the inverse. List the domain and range of each relation and of its inverse. The graph of each relation is shown by red dots.

a.   **b.**   **c.**

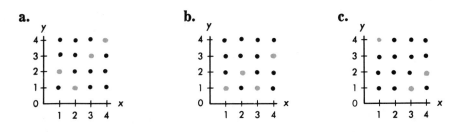

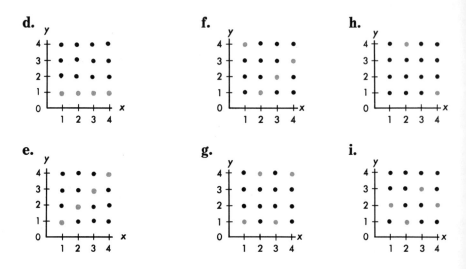

2. Taking the set of all real numbers as the universal set, graph each of the following functions. Then determine the inverse of each function and graph it.

a. $\{(x, y)\,|\,y = x + 1\}$

b. $\{(x, y)\,|\,y = x - 2\}$

c. $\{(x, y)\,|\,y = 5x\}$

d. $\{(x, y)\,|\,y = 2x + 2\}$

e. $\left\{(x, y)\,\big|\,y = \dfrac{x}{3} + 1\right\}$

f. $\left\{(x, y)\,\big|\,y = \dfrac{x}{2} - 5\right\}$

g. $\{(x, y)\,|\,2x = y - 2\}$

h. $\{(x, y)\,|\,3x = 2y + 4\}$

i. $\{(x, y)\,|\,4x - 3 = 3y + 5\}$

Naming functions

You are already familiar with the symbol (x, y) used in connection with ordered number pairs. Here, x denotes the first member of the pair, y the second member.

Frequently a function is named by the use of letters f, g, and others. For example, f may be the set of ordered pairs (x, y) for which $y = 2x$.

$$f = \{(x, y)\,|\,y = 2x\}$$

The sentence $y = 2x$ *describes* the function. Knowing this sentence, you can decide for any ordered pair whether or not it belongs to the function.

Frequently you will find that instead of writing (x, y), the symbol $(x, f(x))$ is used. The function above would then be described by

$$\{(x, f(x))\,|\,f(x) = 2x\}$$

Thus, $f(x)$ and y are being used here interchangeably.

We will call a second member of a pair belonging to a function the *value of the function.* For example, the value of the function $f(x) = 2x$ at 1 is

$$f(1) = 2 \cdot 1 = 2$$

The value of f at -1 is $f(-1) = 2 \cdot (-1) = -2$. Also

$$f(0) = 2 \cdot 0 = 0$$
$$f(3) = 2 \cdot 3 = 6$$
$$f(\tfrac{1}{2}) = 2 \cdot \tfrac{1}{2} = 1$$

Let g be the function which is defined by $g(x) = 3x + 4$. Then

$$g(0) = 3(0) + 4 = 4$$
$$g(-1) = 3(-1) + 4 = 1$$
$$g(5) = 3(5) + 4 = 19$$

Let h be the function defined by $h(x) = x^2 + 1$. Then

$$h(0) = 1$$
$$h(1) = 2$$
$$h(-1) = 2$$
$$h(-4) = 17$$
$$h(\tfrac{1}{2}) = 1\tfrac{1}{4}$$
$$h(\sqrt{2}) = 3$$

Here are a few more examples of equations that define functions.

$$f(r) = 2r$$
$$k(s) = 5s + 3$$
$$t(w) = w^2$$
$$r(v) = \frac{1}{v^2}$$
$$v(t) = 5t^2 + 3t$$
$$f(y) = 3y - 7$$
$$g(z) = |z|$$

■ **Definition of Linear Function** A *linear function* is a set of ordered pairs $(x, f(x))$ in which

$$\forall_{a \in R,\ a \neq 0}\ \forall_{b \in R}\ f(x) = ax + b$$

■ **Definition of Quadratic Function** A *quadratic function* is a set of ordered pairs $(x, f(x))$ in which

$$\forall_{a \in R,\ a \neq 0}\ \forall_{b \in R}\ \forall_{c \in R}\ f(x) = ax^2 + bx + c$$

You have already seen that a linear function has a straight line for its graph.

EXERCISES

1. For each function defined below, compute its value at 0, -1, -2, 3, $\frac{1}{2}$, $\frac{2}{3}$, and $\sqrt{2}$.

Example:
$$m(u) = 2u^2 + 5$$
$$m(0) = 5$$
$$m(-1) = 7$$
$$m(-2) = 13$$
$$m(3) = 23$$
$$m(\tfrac{1}{2}) = 5\tfrac{1}{2}$$
$$m(\tfrac{2}{3}) = 5\tfrac{8}{9}$$
$$m(\sqrt{2}) = 9$$

a. $h(y) = 3y - 7$

b. $f(v) = 2v^2 + v$

c. $m(z) = -2 + z^2 + 2z$

d. $g(x) = 3x^2 + |x|$

e. $s(x) = x - |x| + x^2$

f. $t(w) = w^3 + w^2 + 6$

2. Classify each function as a linear or a quadratic function.

a. $f(x) = 2x + 1$

b. $g(y) = 3y^2 + y - 3$

c. $h(m) = -2 + 2m$

d. $k(s) = -1 + s^2 - 3s$

e. $f(u) = -\sqrt{2} - 6u$

f. $g(t) = -1 - t - t^2$

GRAPHS OF LINEAR FUNCTIONS

We have already seen that a function whose defining equation is of the form $y = ax + b$, where a and b are real numbers, is a linear function. Its graph is a straight line.

We shall now try to discover how different replacements for a and b in $y = ax + b$ affect the graphs of linear functions.

EXERCISES

1. Graph all functions on the same coordinate system.

a. $y = x$

b. $y = 2x$

c. $y = 4x$

d. $y = \frac{1}{2}x$

e. $y = \frac{1}{4}x$

f. $y = -x$

g. $y = -2x$

h. $y = -4x$

i. $y = -\frac{1}{2}x$

j. $y = -\frac{1}{4}x$

2. How are the graphs affected by different replacements for a in $y = ax + b$, when $b = 0$?

3. Graph all functions on the same coordinate system.

a. $y = 2x$ **e.** $y = 2x - 1$
b. $y = 2x + 1$ **f.** $y = 2x - 2$
c. $y = 2x + 2$ **g.** $y = 2x - 3$
d. $y = 2x + 3$ **h.** $y = 2x - 4$

4. How are the graphs affected by different replacements for b in $y = ax + b$, when the same replacement for a is used?

5. Graph all functions on the same coordinate system.

a. $y = x + 2$ **f.** $y = -x + 2$
b. $y = 2x + 2$ **g.** $y = -2x + 2$
c. $y = 4x + 2$ **h.** $y = -4x + 2$
d. $y = \dfrac{x}{2} + 2$ **i.** $y = -\dfrac{x}{2} + 2$
e. $y = \dfrac{x}{4} + 2$ **j.** $y = -\dfrac{x}{4} + 2$

6. How are the graphs affected by different replacements for a in $y = ax + b$, while the same replacement for b (different from 0) is used?

7. Now examine all of the graphs you made. What is the relation between the replacements for b in $y = ax + b$ and the points at which the graphs intersect the y-axis?

In the exploratory exercises you observed that the replacements for a in $y = ax + b$ have something to do with the "steepness" of the graphs. This "steepness" is determined by a number called the *slope* of the graph. This number is represented by a in the equation $y = ax + b$. Thus, the slope of the graph of $y = 3x + 10$ is 3. The slope of the graph of $y = -2x - 1$ is -2. Here is a graph of $y = 3x + 10$.

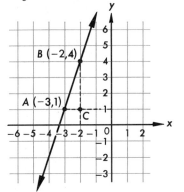

Points A and B with coordinates $(-3, 1)$ and $(-2, 4)$ respectively are on the graph of $y = 3x + 10$. The slope of this graph can be obtained if we know any two different points which belong to the graph. It is done by moving from one point to the other, first along the vertical, then along the horizontal. Moving from B to C, we cover -3 units (negative direction), then from C to A we cover -1 unit (negative direction). The slope is defined as the quotient $\dfrac{-3}{-1}$ or 3.

Let us now follow a similar procedure with the graph of $y = -2x - 1$.

Moving from point D to F, we cover -6 units (negative direction). Moving from F to E, we cover 3 units (positive direction). The quotient $\dfrac{-6}{3}$ or -2 is the slope.

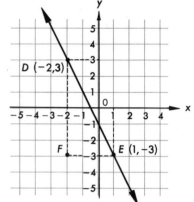

Thus, you can choose two points at random on the graph of a linear function. Knowing the coordinates of these points, you can compute the slope of the graph of the function without even knowing its defining equation.

EXERCISES

1.   Graph each of the linear functions defined below. Choose two points on each graph and compute the slope of the function.

a. $y = 3x - 7$

b. $y = -2x + 3$

c. $6x = 3y + 9$ [HINT: First find an equivalent equation of the form $y = ax + b$.]

d. $x = y - \frac{1}{2}$

e. $2x + 4y = 1$

f. $3 - \frac{1}{2}y = -x$

g. $-\frac{1}{3}x + \frac{1}{6}y = 2$

h. $3x + 2y - 4 = 0$

2.   We observed that in $y = ax + b$, a tells the slope of the graph and b tells the point at which the graph crosses the y-axis. Using these facts, graph each of the following:

a. $y = x + 1$

b. $y = 3x + 2$

c. $y = -2x + 3$

d. $y = -3x - 1$

e. $\frac{1}{2}y = 5x + 4$ (HINT: First find an equivalent equation of the form $y = ax + b$.]

f. $\frac{1}{3}y = 2x - 2$

g. $x + y = 3$

h. $2x + y = -7$

i. $4x + 2y = 2$

j. $2y - 3x = 1$

k. $4x - \frac{1}{2}y - 3 = 0$

l. $3y - 7x + 5 = 4x - y$

QUADRATIC FUNCTIONS

Each of the five following equations defines a quadratic function.

$$f(x) = x^2$$
$$g(u) = 3u^2 + 7$$
$$u(v) = -2v^2 + 5$$

$$t(w) = \frac{w^2}{2} + 2w$$
$$s(y) = -\tfrac{1}{3}y^2 + y - 3$$

Recall that, by definition, a quadratic function f is a set of ordered number pairs of the form $(x, f(x))$ where $f(x) = ax^2 + bx + c$, where a, b, and c are real numbers and $a \neq 0$.

If $f(x) = 4x^2 + 3x + 1$, then $f(2) = 4(2)^2 + 3(2) + 1 = 23$. Thus $f(2) = 23$ and the ordered pair $(2, 23)$ belongs to the function.

Suppose we want to graph the function defined by $y = 2x^2$ when the universal set is the set of integers. We choose the domain D to be $\{x \mid -2 \leq x \leq 2\}$; that is, $D = \{-2, -1, 0, 1, 2\}$. To find the range we replace x by each element of the domain.

$$f(x) = 2x^2; f(-2) = 8$$
$$f(-1) = 2$$
$$f(0) = 0$$
$$f(1) = 2$$
$$f(2) = 8$$

Thus, the following ordered pairs make up the function: $(-2, 8)$, $(-1, 2)$, $(0, 0)$, $(1, 2)$, $(2, 8)$. Its graph is given at the right.

In the universe of the real numbers, if the domain

$$D = \{x \mid -2 \leq x \leq 2\}$$

then there will be an infinite number of ordered pairs (x, y) such that $y = 2x^2$. A few of these are as follows:

$$(2, 8) \quad (0, 0) \quad (1, 2) \quad (\tfrac{1}{4}, \tfrac{1}{8}) \quad (\tfrac{3}{2}, \tfrac{9}{2})$$
$$(\tfrac{1}{2}, \tfrac{1}{2}) \quad (\tfrac{5}{4}, \tfrac{25}{8}) \quad (-\tfrac{3}{2}, \tfrac{9}{2}) \quad (-2, 8)$$

Plotting these and drawing a smooth line between successive points, we get the graph at the right. Curves of this type are called *parabolas*.

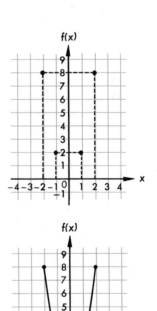

EXERCISES

1.   Let g be a function defined by $g(x) = 3x^2 - 5x + 7$. Compute each of the following:

a. $g(1)$

b. $g(3)$

c. $g(-5)$

d. $g(-\frac{1}{2})$

e. $g(1.5)$

f. $g(-2.3)$

g. $g(\sqrt{2})$

h. $g(\sqrt{3})$

i. $g\left(\dfrac{\sqrt{2}}{2}\right)$

j. $g(-\sqrt{5})$

2.   Graph the functions defined below in the universe of real numbers when the domain $D = \{x \mid -3 \leq x \leq 3\}$.

a. $y = x^2$

b. $y = 2x^2$

c. $y = 3x^2$

d. $y = 4x^2$

e. $y = -x^2$

f. $y = -2x^2$

g. $y = -3x^2$

h. $y = -4x^2$

3.   Using the domain D given in exercise **2**, graph the following functions.

a. $y = \dfrac{x^2}{2}$

b. $y = \dfrac{x^2}{4}$

c. $y = \dfrac{x^2}{8}$

d. $y = -\dfrac{x^2}{2}$

e. $y = -\dfrac{x^2}{4}$

f. $y = -\dfrac{x^2}{8}$

4.   The functions in exercises **2** and **3** are described by equations of the form $y = ax^2$. Describe the nature of the parabolas when

a. a is positive

b. a is negative

c. $|a|$ increases

5.   Graph the quadratic functions in the universe of real numbers defined by the following equations. Plot them all on the same coordinate system and use the domain $D = \{x \mid -3 \leq x \leq 3\}$.

a. $y = x^2$

b. $y = x^2 + 1$

c. $y = x^2 + 2$

d. $y = x^2 + 3$

e. $y = x^2 - 1$

f. $y = x^2 - 2$

g. $y = x^2 - 3$

6.   In exercise **5**, the equations are of the form $y = x^2 + b$. Tell how the parabolas are affected by different replacements for b.

7.   Graph the quadratic functions defined by the following equations in the universe of real numbers.   Consider the domain $D = \{x \mid -3 \le x \le 3\}$. Graph on the same coordinate system.

    a. $y = x^2$
    b. $y = x^2 + 1$
    c. $y = x^2 + 2$
    d. $y = x^2 + 3$
    e. $y = -x^2$
    f. $y = -x^2 + 1$
    g. $y = -x^2 + 2$
    h. $y = -x^2 - 1$
    i. $y = -x^2 - 2$
    j. $y = -x^2 - 3$

8.   Examine the graphs in exercise **7** in relation to their equations. Describe the relation between the numbers named by replacements of a and b in $y = ax^2 + b$ and the graphs.

9.   For each function defined below, find thirteen pairs belonging to each function by replacing x by 0, 1, -1, 2, -2, 3, -3, 4, -4, 5, -5, 6, and -6.   Plot the points.   Draw a parabola for each set of points.

    a. $f(x) = x^2 + x + 1$
    b. $g(x) = 2x^2 + x - 3$
    c. $m(x) = x^2 - 4x + 7$
    d. $n(x) = -3x^2 + 5x - 7$
    e. $s(x) = 4x^2 - 3x - 9$
    f. $t(x) = 6x^2 + 5x + 3$

VOCABULARY

Use each of the following correctly in a sentence.   Numerals in the parentheses refer to pages where these words were used.   If you are not sure of the meaning of any word, turn to the indicated page and refresh your memory.

Cartesian set (395)

domain (398)

function (399)

inverse (405)

linear function (409)

parabola (413)

partition (393)

quadratic function (409)

range (398)

reflection (405)

relation (398)

slope (411)

to select a subset (396)

value of a function (409)

vertical line test (399)

REVIEW EXERCISES

1. On a number line, graph the solution set of each of the following:

    a. $5x + 3 > 4$ **d.** $|2p| < 1$

    b. $|y| \leq 3$ **e.** $|3r + 2| \geq 3$

    c. $|m| > 5$ **f.** $|2t + 1| \leq 7$

2. Given the universal set $U = \{-1, 0, 1, 2\}$, list the ordered pairs which are members of the solution sets of the following:

    a. $x = y$ **d.** $2x > y$

    b. $|x| = |y|$ **e.** $x < 2y$

    c. $x > y$ **f.** $|x| > |y|$

3. Let the domain of each relation below be the set of real numbers. Graph each relation.

    a. $\{(x, y) | y = x\}$ **g.** $\{(x, y) | y < x\}$

    b. $\{(x, y) | y = x^2\}$ **h.** $\{(x, y) | y < x^2\}$

    c. $\{(x, y) | y = x^3\}$ **i.** $\{(x, y) | y \leq x^2\}$

    d. $\{(x, y) | y = x^4\}$ **j.** $\{(x, y) | 2x + 3 > y\}$

    e. $\{(x, y) | y > x\}$ **k.** $\{(x, y) | \frac{1}{2}y + 1 > x\}$

    f. $\{(x, y) | y > x^2\}$ **l.** $\{(x, y) | |y| = x\}$

4. For the relations given in exercise 3, tell which relations are also functions.

5. Using the set of real numbers as the universal set, graph each of the following functions. Then determine the inverse of each function and graph it.

    a. $\{(x, y) | y = 2x\}$ **c.** $\left\{(x, y) \left| \frac{x + 2}{5} = \frac{y - 1}{3}\right.\right\}$

    b. $\{(x, y) | 2y + 1 = 3x\}$ **d.** $\{(x, y) | x = y\}$

6. For each function defined below, compute its value at 0, $-\frac{1}{2}$, and $\sqrt{3}$.

    a. $f(x) = x^3$ **c.** $h(x) = \dfrac{x^2 - 1}{x + 1}$

    b. $g(x) = 2x^2 - x$ **d.** $j(x) = 4x + |x|$

7. Graph each function and its inverse. Tell the slope of each graph. The universal set is the set of real numbers.

    a. $\{(x, y) | y = 2x + 1\}$ **c.** $\{(x, y) | y = -2x + 3\}$

    b. $\{(x, y) | y = \frac{1}{3}x - 4\}$ **d.** $\{(x, y) | y = -\frac{1}{2}x - 2\}$

8. For each graph below tell whether it is a graph of a function.   Red dots show the graph.

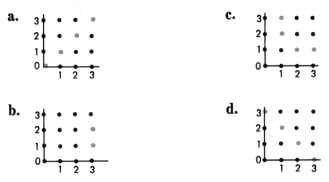

a.

c.

b.

d.

9. For each graph in exercise 8, list all of the ordered number pairs which belong to the relation.

10. For each graph below tell whether it is a graph of a function.

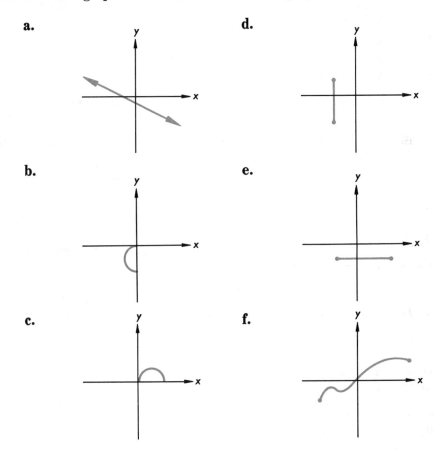

a.

d.

b.

e.

c.

f.

CHAPTER TEST

1. Graph each of the following. Tell the slope of each graph.

a. $y = 3x - 1$

c. $2x + y = -\frac{1}{2}$

b. $3y = 6x - 5$

d. $2y - 4x = 2x + y - 3$

2. For each function given below, compute its value at 0, $\sqrt{2}$, $-\frac{1}{3}$, and 0.1.

a. $f(x) = \frac{1}{2}x - 3$

c. $g(u) = \dfrac{2u + 5}{u - 1}$

b. $h(m) = |m| + 2m$

d. $j(n) = n^2 + n + 1$

3. Let $U = \{-1, -\frac{1}{2}, 0, \frac{1}{2}, 1\}$. Give the solution sets of the following open sentences.

a. $x + y = 0$

c. $2y \geq x - 1$

b. $x - y > 0$

d. $\frac{1}{2}x + \frac{1}{2} \leq y + 1$

4. For the universal set $U = \{1, 2, 3, 4, 5\}$, graph the following:

a. $\{(a, b) \,|\, a = b\}$

d. $\{(a, b) \,|\, a \leq b\}$

b. $\left\{(a, b) \,\middle|\, \dfrac{a}{2} = b\right\}$

e. $\{(a, b) \,|\, a \geq b\}$

f. $\{(a, b) \,|\, a + b < 10\}$

c. $\{(a, b) \,|\, 2a + 3b = 5\}$

5. Graph each of the sets in exercise **4** when the universal set is the set of real numbers.

6. For each set, plot the points which belong to it, given the domain $D = \{-2, -1, 0, 1, 2\}$.

a. $\{(x, y) \,|\, y = x\}$

f. $\{(x, y) \,|\, y = -x^3\}$

b. $\{(x, y) \,|\, y = -x\}$

g. $\{(x, y) \,|\, y = x^2 + 1\}$

c. $\{(x, y) \,|\, y = x^2\}$

h. $\{(x, y) \,|\, y = x^2 - 1\}$

d. $\{(x, y) \,|\, y = -x^2\}$

i. $\{(x, y) \,|\, y = 2x^2\}$

e. $\{(x, y) \,|\, y = x^3\}$

j. $\{(x, y) \,|\, y = -2x^2\}$

7. Graph each set in problem **6** when the domain is the following subset of the set of real numbers: $D = \{x \,|\, -2 \leq x \leq 2\}$.

8. For each graph below, make the graph of the inverse of the given relation.

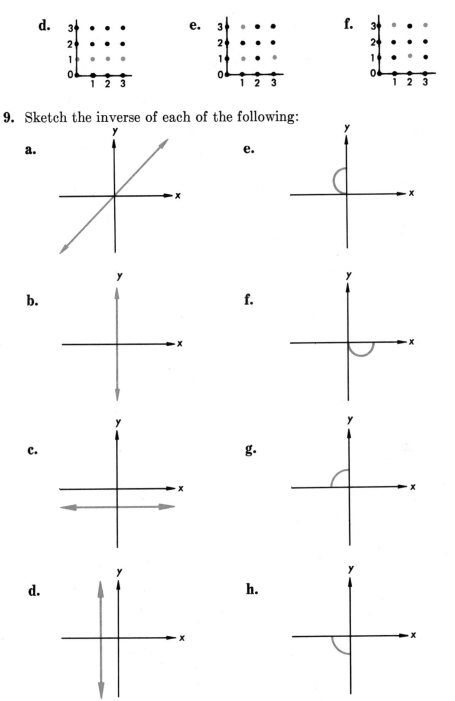

d.

e.

f.

9. Sketch the inverse of each of the following:

a.

b.

c.

d.

e.

f.

g.

h.

10. For each relation and its inverse in problems **8** and **9**, tell whether it is a function.

BIBLIOGRAPHY

Committee on the Undergraduate Program, Mathematical Association of America. *Universal Mathematics, Part I, Functions and Limits*. University of Kansas, 1954. pp. 136-182.

Nichols, Eugene D. *Pre-Algebra Mathematics*. New York: Holt, Rinehart and Winston, Inc., 1965. Chapter 15.

Nichols, Eugene D.; Heimer, R. T.; and Garland, E. Henry. *Modern Intermediate Algebra*. New York: Holt, Rinehart and Winston, Inc., 1965. Chapter 6.

School Mathematics Study Group. *Mathematics Through Science*. Stanford: Stanford University, 1963. Part II, Graphing, Equations and Linear Functions. Part III, An Experimental Approach to Functions.

Titchmarsh, E. C. *Mathematics for the General Reader*. New York: Doubleday & Company, Inc., 1959. pp. 140-151.

The University of Chicago, The College Mathematics Staff. *Concepts and Structure of Mathematics*. Chicago: The University of Chicago Press, 1954. pp. 187-300.

Whitehead, Alfred North. *An Introduction to Mathematics*. New York: Oxford University Press, 1958. pp. 107-120.

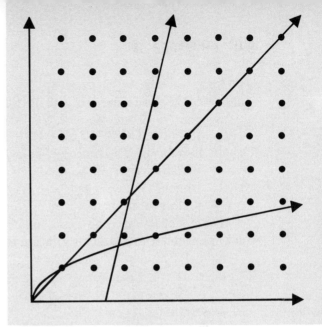

CHAPTER 14

(optional)

Numerical Trigonometry of the Right Triangle

RIGHT TRIANGLES

The word "trigonometry" is derived from Greek words which mean "triangle measurement." Thus, in this chapter we shall be concerned with the measures of sides and angles of triangles. More specifically, we shall learn to *compute* the measures of some parts of triangles when the measures of other parts are known to us.

Since we shall be working with right triangles in this chapter, let us review the meaning of some words associated with right triangles.

The longest side of a right triangle is called the *hypotenuse* (see the picture on the top of the next page). The other two sides are called the *legs*. In the picture, leg $\overline{AC}$ is said to be *adjacent* to vertex A, and the leg $\overline{BC}$ is *opposite* to vertex A.

421

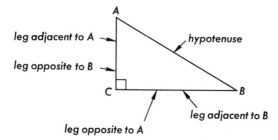

There exists an interesting relation between the measures of the sides in a right triangle. This relation is illustrated in triangle ABC below.

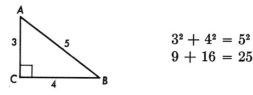

$$3^2 + 4^2 = 5^2$$
$$9 + 16 = 25$$

It is true in every right triangle that the sum of the squares of the measures of the legs is equal to the square of the measure of the hypotenuse. This relation is known as the *Pythagorean Relation*, after the name of the Greek philosopher, Pythagoras.

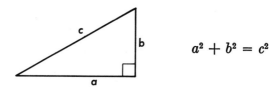

$$a^2 + b^2 = c^2$$

Thus, if we know the measures of any two sides in a right triangle, we can compute the measure of the third side. Study the examples below.

Examples: i.

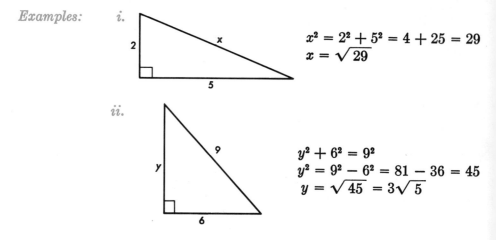

$$x^2 = 2^2 + 5^2 = 4 + 25 = 29$$
$$x = \sqrt{29}$$

ii.

$$y^2 + 6^2 = 9^2$$
$$y^2 = 9^2 - 6^2 = 81 - 36 = 45$$
$$y = \sqrt{45} = 3\sqrt{5}$$

EXERCISES

1. For the picture on the right, name each of the following:

    a. hypotenuse
    b. leg adjacent to X
    c. leg opposite to X
    d. leg adjacent to Y
    e. leg opposite to Y

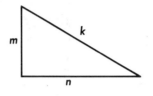

2. Compute the missing measures.

    a. $m = 5$, $n = 6$; $k = ?$
    b. $m = 3$, $k = 7$; $n = ?$
    c. $n = 1$, $k = 4$; $m = ?$
    d. $m = \sqrt{2}$, $n = 2$; $k = ?$
    e. $n = \sqrt{11}$, $k = 6$; $m = ?$

Ratios of measures of sides and trigonometric ratios

The measures of the sides of the triangle in the figure below are

$AC = 3$	$DE = 2$	$FG = 1$
$CB = 12$	$DB = 8$	$FB = 4$

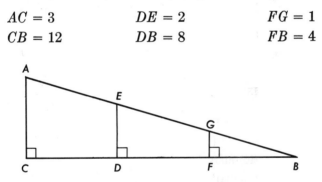

We can now compute the measures of the remaining sides of each of the triangles ABC, EBD, and GBF, using the Pythagorean Relation.

$$(AB)^2 = (AC)^2 + (CB)^2$$
$$AB = \sqrt{(AC)^2 + (CB)^2} = \sqrt{3^2 + 12^2} = \sqrt{153} = 3\sqrt{17}$$

$$(EB)^2 = (ED)^2 + (DB)^2$$
$$EB = \sqrt{(ED)^2 + (DB)^2} = \sqrt{2^2 + 8^2} = \sqrt{68} = 2\sqrt{17}$$

$$(GB)^2 = (GF)^2 + (FB)^2$$
$$GB = \sqrt{(GF)^2 + (FB)^2} = \sqrt{1^2 + 4^2} = \sqrt{17}$$

Now observe the following interesting relations.

$$\frac{AC}{CB} = \frac{3}{12} = \frac{1}{4} \qquad \frac{ED}{DB} = \frac{2}{8} = \frac{1}{4} \qquad \frac{GF}{FB} = \frac{1}{4}$$

Therefore, $\dfrac{AC}{CB} = \dfrac{ED}{DB} = \dfrac{GF}{FB}$

Thus, for each of the three triangles *the ratio of the measure of the side opposite to B to the measure of the side adjacent to B is the same.*

We relate this ratio to the degree-measure of angle B and call it

tangent of degree-measure of angle B

We write: $\tan (m \angle B) = \frac{1}{4}$

We now observe a second set of relations.

$$\frac{AC}{AB} = \frac{3}{3\sqrt{17}} = \frac{1}{\sqrt{17}} \qquad \frac{ED}{EB} = \frac{2}{2\sqrt{17}} = \frac{1}{\sqrt{17}} \qquad \frac{GF}{GB} = \frac{1}{\sqrt{17}}$$

Therefore, $\dfrac{AC}{AB} = \dfrac{ED}{EB} = \dfrac{GF}{GB}$

Thus, for each of the three triangles *the ratio of the measure of the side opposite to B to the measure of the hypotenuse is the same.*

We call this ratio

sine of degree-measure of angle B

We write: $\sin(m \angle B) = \dfrac{1}{\sqrt{17}}$

There is one more set of relations which we observe.

$$\frac{CB}{AB} = \frac{12}{3\sqrt{17}} = \frac{4}{\sqrt{17}} \qquad \frac{DB}{EB} = \frac{8}{2\sqrt{17}} = \frac{4}{\sqrt{17}} \qquad \frac{FB}{GB} = \frac{4}{\sqrt{17}}$$

Therefore, $\dfrac{CB}{AB} = \dfrac{DB}{EB} = \dfrac{FB}{GB}$

Thus, for each of the three triangles *the ratio of the measure of the side adjacent to B to the measure of the hypotenuse is the same.*

We call this ratio

cosine of degree-measure of angle B

We write: $\cos(m \angle B) = \dfrac{4}{\sqrt{17}}$

To summarize

$$\tan(m \angle X) = \frac{ZY}{XZ}$$

$$\sin(m \angle X) = \frac{ZY}{XY}$$

$$\cos(m \angle X) = \frac{ZX}{XY}$$

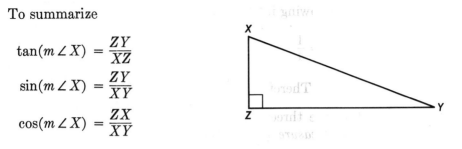

EXERCISES

1. For the triangle pictured below give the following trigonometric ratios

   a. $\sin (m \angle A)$ d. $\sin(m \angle B)$

   b. $\cos (m \angle A)$ e. $\cos(m \angle B)$

   c. $\tan(m \angle A)$ f. $\tan(m \angle B)$

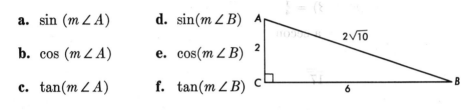

2. Using the picture of $\triangle XYZ$, give the following trigonometric ratios.

   a. $\sin 30°$ d. $\sin 60°$

   b. $\cos 30°$ e. $\cos 60°$

   c. $\tan 30°$ f. $\tan 60°$

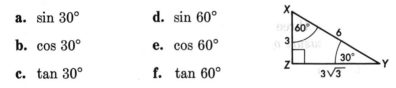

TRIGONOMETRIC RATIOS AND COMPLEMENTARY ANGLES

We recall that two angles for which the sum of their measures is 90°
are called *complementary angles*. For example, if
$$m \angle A = 35° \text{ and } m \angle B = 55°$$
then angles A and B are complementary angles, since
$$m \angle A + m \angle B = 90°.$$
We also know that the sum of the measures of the three angles in
any triangle is 180°. Since the measure of one angle in a right triangle is
90°, the sum of the measures of the two remaining angles is 90°.
We call an angle whose measure is less than 90° an *acute angle*.

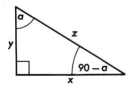

Explain why every right triangle has two
acute angles. Explain why, if the degree-
measure of one acute angle in a right triangle is a, then the degree-measure of the
second acute angle is $90 - a$.

We shall now observe an interesting relation between sine and cosine of the measures of complementary angles. As shown in the picture above, the measures of sides in a right triangle are x, y, and z; the degree-measures of acute angles are a and $90 - a$.

$$\sin(a) = \frac{x}{z} \qquad \cos(90 - a) = \frac{x}{z}$$

therefore, $\sin(a) = \cos(90 - a)$

$$\cos(a) = \frac{y}{z} \qquad \sin(90 - a) = \frac{y}{z}$$

therefore, $\cos(a) = \sin(90 - a)$

According to the first formula above, if we know that $\sin(20°) \doteq .342$, then we can conclude that $\cos(70°) \doteq .342$. According to the second formula, if we know that $\cos(25°) \doteq .906$, then we can conclude that $\sin(65°) \doteq .906$. Explain.

From the picture on the bottom of page 425, we can also reach a conclusion concerning the tangents of measures of complementary angles.

$$\tan(a) = \frac{x}{y} \qquad \tan(90 - a) = \frac{y}{x}$$

Since $\forall_{x=0} \forall_{y=0} \dfrac{x}{y} \cdot \dfrac{y}{x} = 1$, $\dfrac{x}{y}$ and $\dfrac{y}{x}$ are reciprocals of each other;

therefore, $\tan(a) \cdot \tan(90 - a) = 1$

We now introduce one more trigonometric ratio, namely the ratio obtained by dividing the measure of the side adjacent to a vertex by the measure of the side opposite to this vertex. We call this ratio *cotangent* of an angle measure. It is abbreviated *cot*.

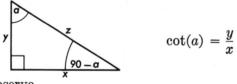

$$\cot(a) = \frac{y}{x}$$

Now observe

$$\tan(a) = \frac{x}{y} \qquad \cot(90 - a) = \frac{x}{y}$$

therefore, $\tan(a) = \cot(90 - a)$

Furthermore, since $\tan(a) = \dfrac{x}{y}$ and $\cot(a) = \dfrac{y}{x}$, we have

$$\tan(a) \cdot \cot(a) = 1$$

EXERCISES

1. For each given angle measure, tell the measure of its complementary angle.

a. 20°

b. 45°

c. 49.5°

d. 89.9°

e. ½°

f. .001°

2. One of two complementary angles measures three times greater than the other. What is the measure of each of the two angles?

3. The sum of the measure of one angle and one-half of the measure of its complementary angle is 50°. What is the measure of each of the two angles?

4. If sin (44°) ≐ .695, what is cos(46°) equal to?

5. Verify that sin(45°) = cos(45°).

6. If tan(1°) ≐ .017, what is cot(89°) equal to?

7. Verify that tan(45°) = cot(45°).

8. According to the Pythagorean Relation, $a^2 + b^2 = c^2$

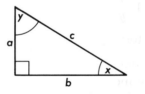

If the degree-measures of angles are as shown in the picture, we have

$$\sin(x) = \frac{a}{c} \quad \text{and} \quad \cos(x) = \frac{b}{c}$$

Therefore,

$$[\sin(x)]^2 + [\cos(x)]^2 = \left(\frac{a}{c}\right)^2 + \left(\frac{b}{c}\right)^2$$

Complete this development to prove the following theorem.

$$[\sin(x)]^2 + [\cos(x)]^2 = 1$$

9. If $\sin(30°) = \frac{1}{2}$ and $\cos(30°) = \frac{\sqrt{3}}{2}$, verify that sin(30°) and cos(30°) satisfy the theorem you proved in problem **8.**

10. Using the picture of problem **8,** prove the following:

$$\tan(x) + \cot(x) = \frac{a^2 + b^2}{ab}$$

Tables of trigonometric ratios

The table on page 450 gives the four trigonometric ratios rounded to three decimal places for angle measures from 1° to 45°.

From the table we can read directly the trigonometric ratios of any angle measure given in whole degrees from 1 to 45. For example

$$\sin(10°) \doteq .174 \qquad \tan(15°) \doteq .268$$
$$\cos(44°) \doteq .719 \qquad \cot(40°) \doteq 1.19$$

Since

$$\sin(x) = \cos(90 - x) \qquad \tan(x) = \cot(90 - x)$$

we can use the table to tell the four trigonometric ratios of angle measures between 45° and 90°. For example

$$\sin(70°) = \cos[(90 - 70)°] = \cos(20°) \doteq .940$$
$$\tan(80°) = \cot[(90 - 80)°] = \cot(10°) \doteq 5.67$$

EXERCISES

1. From the table or by the use of an appropriate formula, give the four trigonometric ratios of each of the following:

    a. 1°   **b.** 19°   **c.** 45°   **d.** 50°   **e.** 74°   **f.** 88°

2. Use the table on page 450 to find the measure of the angle whose sine is

    a. .070   **b.** .515   **c.** .276   **d.** .682

3. Tell the measure of the angle whose cosine is

    a. .777   **b.** .993   **c.** .707   **d.** .966

4. Tell the measure of the angle whose tangent is

    a. .700   **b.** .035   **c.** .754   **d.** .306

5. Tell the measure of the angle whose cotangent is

    a. 1.11   **b.** 57.3   **c.** 2.05   **d.** 9.51

6. Insert either $<$, $>$, or $=$ to obtain a true statement from each of the following:

    a. If $\sin(a) > \sin(b)$, then a ___?___ b
    b. If $\cos(a) > \cos(b)$, then a ___?___ b
    c. If $\tan(a) > \tan(b)$, then a ___?___ b
    d. If $\cot(a) > \cot(b)$, then a ___?___ b

SOLVING RIGHT TRIANGLES

With each triangle, there are associated six measures: the degree-measures of the three angles and the measures of the three sides. Given a right triangle, we immediately know one of the six measures, namely the measure of one of three angles. What is this measure? We shall see that, knowing two additional measures which include at least one side will enable us to compute the remaining measures. We say that a triangle *is solved* when all of its measures are determined.

Examples below illustrate how these computations are done. We obtain the necessary trigonometric ratios from the table on page 450.

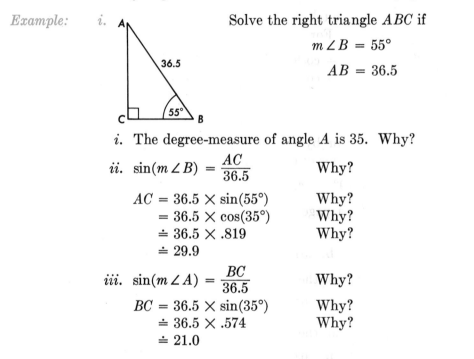

Example: i.   Solve the right triangle ABC if

$$m \angle B = 55°$$

$$AB = 36.5$$

i. The degree-measure of angle A is 35. Why?

ii. $\sin(m \angle B) = \dfrac{AC}{36.5}$ Why?

$AC = 36.5 \times \sin(55°)$ Why?
$ = 36.5 \times \cos(35°)$ Why?
$ \doteq 36.5 \times .819$ Why?
$ \doteq 29.9$

iii. $\sin(m \angle A) = \dfrac{BC}{36.5}$ Why?

$BC = 36.5 \times \sin(35°)$ Why?
$ \doteq 36.5 \times .574$ Why?
$ \doteq 21.0$

Since we now know all of the six measures, the triangle is solved.

Example: ii.   Solve the right triangle MNP if

$$PN = 2.16$$

$$PM = 5.21$$

$i.$ $\tan(m \angle M) = \dfrac{2.16}{5.21}$ Why?

$\qquad\qquad\qquad \doteq .415$

In the tangent column in the table we find that the closest degree-measure for which tangent is .415 is 23. Therefore, $m \angle M \doteq 23°$.

$ii.$ $m \angle N = 90 - m \angle M = 57°$

$iii.$ $MN = \sqrt{(5.21)^2 + (2.16)^2}$ Why?

$\qquad\qquad \doteq \sqrt{27.1 + 4.67}$

$\qquad\qquad \doteq \sqrt{31.77}$

$\qquad\qquad \doteq 5.64$

EXERCISES

1. Solve each right triangle. Determine measures of angles to the nearest whole degree and the measures of sides to two digits.

a.

d.

b.

e.

c.

f.

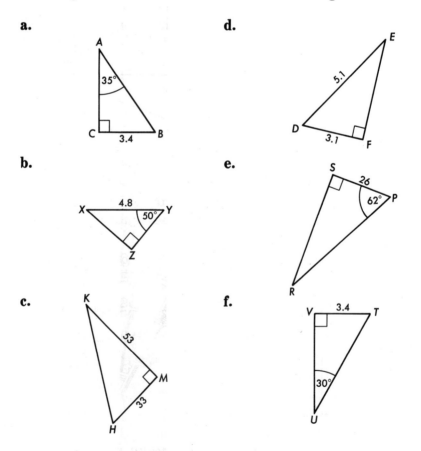

g.

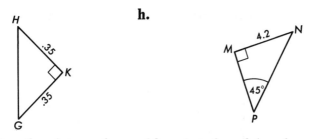

h.

2. **a.** Examine the pictures for problem **1** and explain why sine cannot have a value greater than 1.

b. Explain why tangent can have a value equal to any positive number.

FINDING DISTANCES TO INACCESSIBLE OBJECTS

Knowledge of trigonometric ratios is useful when computing distances to inaccessible objects. For example, suppose we want to compute the height of a tree without climbing the tree. Or, we want to compute distances across lakes without actually crossing the lakes.

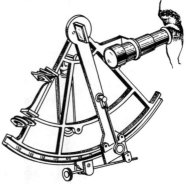

One problem which occurs in such computations is that of measuring an angle between the line of your eye level and, say, the top of a tree. This is done by means of an instrument called a *sextant* whose picture is shown here.

Example: **i.** Compute the height of the tree pictured below. Use the measures shown in the picture.

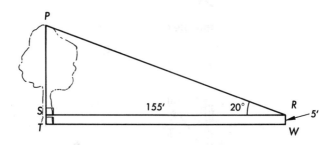

We found that the distance from where you stand (point W) to the base of the tree is 155 feet: $SR = 155$.

Using the sextant, we find that the measure of $\angle PRS$ in degrees is 20. We now compute SP.

$$\frac{SP}{155} = \tan 20° \qquad \text{Why?}$$
$$SP \doteq 155 \times .364 \qquad \text{Why?}$$
$$\doteq 56.4 \text{ feet}$$

Now we add your height (5 feet) and obtain 61.4 feet for the height of the tree.

We now illustrate how trigonometric ratios can be used to compute the distance between two points located on opposite sides of a lake.

Example: *ii.* Compute the distance between M and N on opposite sides of a lake.

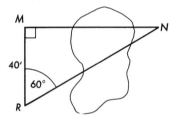

We arbitrarily pace off 40 feet from M perpendicular to $\overline{MN}$; this locates point R. We sight point N with a sextant and find the measure of angle R to be 60°. We can now compute MN.

$$\frac{MN}{MR} = \tan 60° \qquad \text{Why?}$$

$$MN = MR \times \tan 60° \qquad \text{Why?}$$
$$= 40 \times \cot 30° \qquad \text{Why?}$$
$$\doteq 40 \times 1.73$$
$$\doteq 69$$

Thus, the distance between the points M and N is approximately 69 feet.

EXERCISES

1. Make your own drawing for each problem. Compute lengths to the nearest foot and degree-measures to the nearest whole number.

   a. A ladder 50 ft. long is placed against a wall so that the foot of the ladder is 25 ft. from the wall. What is the angle between the ground and the ladder?

b. Town A is 20 miles directly south from town B. Town C is 25 miles directly east from town A. What is the angle which the line connecting towns C and B makes with the line connecting towns C and A?

c. The top of a tree is sighted from the distance of 65 feet. The angle between the horizontal line and the line from the eye to the top of the tree is 40°. How tall is the tree? [Assume that the eye and the base of the tree are on the same level.]

d. A fireman extends a ladder making a 25° angle with the horizontal line to a window 60 feet from the ground. How long is the ladder?

e. A plane flying at an altitude of 500′ shoots a rocket along a straight path making an angle of 70° with the vertical line. How long is the path of the rocket before it hits the ground?

2.   For each problem use the drawing provided and compute lengths to the nearest foot and degree-measures to the nearest whole number.

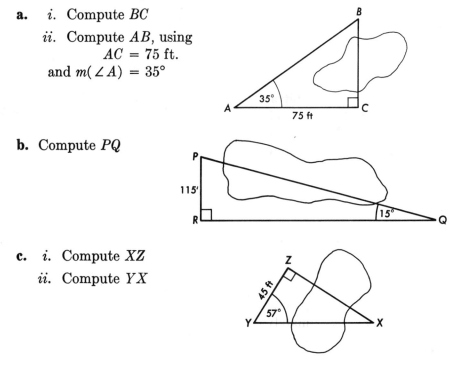

a.   *i.* Compute BC

　　ii. Compute AB, using
　　　　$AC = 75$ ft.
　　and $m(\angle A) = 35°$

b. Compute PQ

c. *i.* Compute XZ

　ii. Compute YX

d.   *i.* Compute AC

　　ii. Compute AB

　　iii. Compute BC

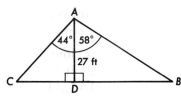

USING SIMILAR TRIANGLES

In similar triangles the measures of corresponding angles are the same and the ratios of the measures of the corresponding sides are equal.

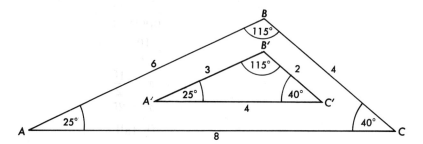

If triangles ABC and $A'B'C'$ are similar, then it follows that

$$m(\angle A) = m(\angle A')$$
$$m(\angle B) = m(\angle B')$$
$$m(\angle C) = m(\angle C')$$

$$\frac{AB}{A'B'} = \frac{BC}{B'C'} = \frac{CA}{C'A'} = 2$$

In two right triangles, if the measures of a pair of corresponding angles are equal, then there are three pairs of congruent angles. (Two angles are congruent means that they have the same measure.) See the picture.

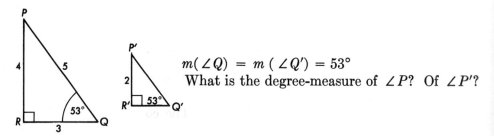

$m(\angle Q) = m(\angle Q') = 53°$
What is the degree-measure of $\angle P$? Of $\angle P'$?

In a geometry course you will prove that, if two triangles have three pairs of angles with respectively equal measures, then the two triangles are similar; that is, it follows that the ratios of the measures of their corresponding sides are equal.

Thus, in the picture above, it follows that

$$\frac{PR}{P'R'} = \frac{RQ}{R'Q'} = \frac{QP}{Q'P'}$$

We can then find that $R'Q' = 1.5$ and $Q'P' = 2.5$.

Example: A pole 10 ft. tall casts a shadow 2 ft. long. At the same time a tree casts a shadow 5 ft. long. How tall is the tree?

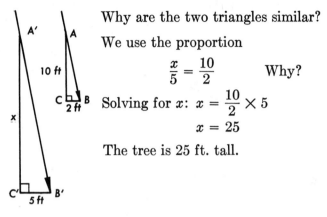

Why are the two triangles similar?

We use the proportion

$$\frac{x}{5} = \frac{10}{2} \qquad \text{Why?}$$

Solving for x: $x = \dfrac{10}{2} \times 5$

$$x = 25$$

The tree is 25 ft. tall.

EXERCISES

1.   A boy 5 ft. 3 in. tall casts a shadow 5 ft. 3 in. long. What is the height of a pole which at the same time casts a shadow 120 ft. long?

2.   How long would be a shadow cast by a tower 80 ft. tall at the time a pole 12 ft. tall casts a shadow of length 7 ft.?

3.   Triangles ABC and DEF are similar.

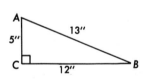

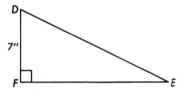

Sides $\overline{AC}$ and $\overline{DF}$ are corresponding sides. Compute the measures of $\overline{DE}$ and $\overline{EF}$.

4.   Triangles MPQ and $M'P'Q'$ are similar. The corresponding pairs of sides are

MQ and $M'Q'$ QP and $Q'P'$ MP and $M'P'$

Compute PQ and $M'P'$.

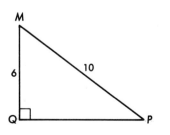

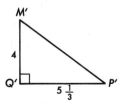

SOME SPECIAL RIGHT TRIANGLES

Here is a picture of an isosceles right triangle.

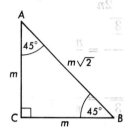

If the measure of $\overline{AC}$ is m, then the measure of $\overline{CB}$ is also m. We compute the measure of $\overline{AB}$ using the Pythagorean Relation.

$$AB = \sqrt{m^2 + m^2}$$
$$= \sqrt{2m^2}$$
$$= m\sqrt{2}$$

Now, we compute the exact values of the four trigonometric ratios for the 45° angles. Try to remember these values.

$$\sin(45°) = \frac{m}{m\sqrt{2}} = \frac{1}{\sqrt{2}} = \frac{\sqrt{2}}{2}$$

$$\cos(45°) = \frac{m}{m\sqrt{2}} = \frac{1}{\sqrt{2}} = \frac{\sqrt{2}}{2}$$

$$\tan(45°) = \frac{m}{m} = 1$$

$$\cot(45°) = \frac{m}{m} = 1$$

Now let us consider an equilateral triangle; that is, a triangle in which all sides have the same measure and each angle has the measure of 60°.

$\overline{PR}$ is the bisector of $\angle MPQ$; it is perpendicular to the base $\overline{MQ}$ and bisects it. Thus, $MR = RQ = \dfrac{n}{2}$. We use the Pythagorean Relation and compute PR.

$$PR = \sqrt{n^2 - \left(\frac{n}{2}\right)^2}$$

$$= \sqrt{n^2 - \frac{n^2}{4}}$$

$$= \sqrt{\frac{4n^2 - n^2}{4}}$$

$$= \sqrt{\frac{3n^2}{4}}$$

$$= \frac{n\sqrt{3}}{2}$$

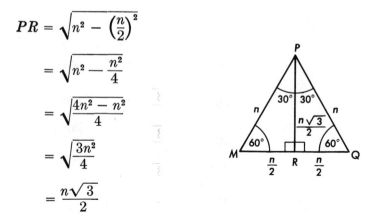

Let us now concentrate on the right triangle MPR.

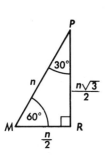

$$\sin(30°) = \dfrac{\frac{n}{2}}{n} = \dfrac{n}{2n} = \dfrac{1}{2}$$

$$\cos(30°) = \dfrac{\frac{n\sqrt{3}}{2}}{n} = \dfrac{n\sqrt{3}}{2n} = \dfrac{\sqrt{3}}{2}$$

$$\tan(30°) = \dfrac{\frac{n}{2}}{\frac{n\sqrt{3}}{2}} = \dfrac{n}{n\sqrt{3}} = \dfrac{1}{\sqrt{3}} = \dfrac{\sqrt{3}}{3}$$

Since $\cot(30°)$ is the reciprocal of $\tan(30°)$

$$\cot(30°) = \sqrt{3}$$

Since we know that $\sin(n°) = \cos[(90 - n)°]$, we have

$$\sin(60°) = \cos(30°) = \dfrac{\sqrt{3}}{2}$$

and since

$$\cos(n°) = \sin[(90 - n)°], \text{ we have}$$

$$\cos(60°) = \sin(30°) = \tfrac{1}{2}$$

and since

$$\tan(n°) = \cot[(90 - n)°], \text{ we have}$$

$$\tan(60°) = \cot(30°) = \sqrt{3}$$

Since $\cot(60°)$ is the reciprocal of $\tan(60°)$,

$$\cot(60°) = \dfrac{\sqrt{3}}{3}$$

To summarize what we found

$\sin(45°) = \dfrac{\sqrt{2}}{2}$	$\sin(30°) = \dfrac{1}{2}$	$\sin(60°) = \dfrac{\sqrt{3}}{2}$
$\cos(45°) = \dfrac{\sqrt{2}}{2}$	$\cos(30°) = \dfrac{\sqrt{3}}{2}$	$\cos(60°) = \dfrac{1}{2}$
$\tan(45°) = 1$	$\tan(30°) = \dfrac{\sqrt{3}}{3}$	$\tan(60°) = \sqrt{3}$
$\cot(45°) = 1$	$\cot(30°) = \sqrt{3}$	$\cot(60°) = \dfrac{\sqrt{3}}{3}$

Try to commit these values to your memory.

EXERCISES

Using the trigonometric ratios above, compute the measures of the indicated parts. Do not use tables.

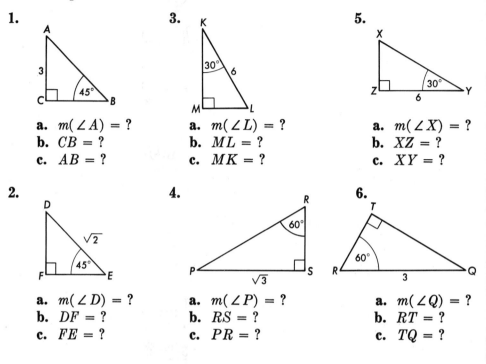

1.
a. $m(\angle A)$ = ?
b. CB = ?
c. AB = ?

3.
a. $m(\angle L)$ = ?
b. ML = ?
c. MK = ?

5.
a. $m(\angle X)$ = ?
b. XZ = ?
c. XY = ?

2.
a. $m(\angle D)$ = ?
b. DF = ?
c. FE = ?

4.
a. $m(\angle P)$ = ?
b. RS = ?
c. PR = ?

6.
a. $m(\angle Q)$ = ?
b. RT = ?
c. TQ = ?

VOCABULARY

Use each of the following correctly in a sentence. Numerals in the parentheses refer to pages where these words were used. If you are not sure of the meaning of any word, turn to the indicated page and refresh your memory.

acute angle (425)

adjacent (421)

complementary angles (425)

cosine (424)

cotangent (426)

hypotenuse (421)

leg (421)

opposite (421)

Pythagorean Relation (422)

reciprocal (426)

sextant (431)

similar triangles (434)

sine (424)

solving right triangles (429)

tangent (424)

trigonometric ratio (423)

trigonometry (421)

REVIEW EXERCISES

1. For the picture below, name each of the following:
   a. hypotenuse
   b. leg adjacent to A
   c. leg opposite to A
   d. leg adjacent to B
   e. leg opposite to B
   f. two acute angles
   g. right angle

2. Using the picture of the right triangle below, give each of the following:

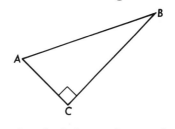

   a. $\sin(a)$
   b. $\cos(a)$
   c. $\tan(a)$
   d. $\cot(a)$

3. Using the picture of exercise **2,** prove that for the acute angle of degree-measure a.

   a. $\sin(a) = \cos[(90 - a)]$ **c.** $\tan(a) \cdot \cot(a) = 1$
   b. $\tan(a) = \cot[(90 - a)]$

4. One of two complementary angles is five times as large as the other. What is the measure of each of the two angles?

5. **a.** If $\sin(38°) \doteq .616$, what is $\cos(52°)$ equal to?
   b. If $\cot(9°) \doteq 6.31$, what is $\tan(81°)$ equal to?
   c. If $[\sin(a)]^2 + [\cos(a)]^2 = 1$, and $\sin(a) = \frac{1}{2}$, what is $\cos(a)$ equal to?

6. Using the table of trigonometric ratios on page 450 and, whenever necessary, an appropriate formula, give the following:

   a. $\sin(21°)$ **e.** $\tan(28°)$
   b. $\cos(42°)$ **f.** $\cot(11°)$
   c. $\sin(78°)$ **g.** $\tan(54°)$
   d. $\cos(89°)$ **h.** $\cot(75°)$

7. Use the table of trigonometric ratios on page 450 and supply the missing answers.

   a. If $\sin(x) \doteq .669$, then $x \doteq$?
   b. If $\cos(x) \doteq .993$, then $x \doteq$?
   c. If $\tan(x) \doteq .754$, then $x \doteq$?
   d. If $\cot(x) \doteq 8.14$, then $x \doteq$?

8. Solve each right triangle. Determine angle measures to the nearest whole degree and the measures of sides to two digits.

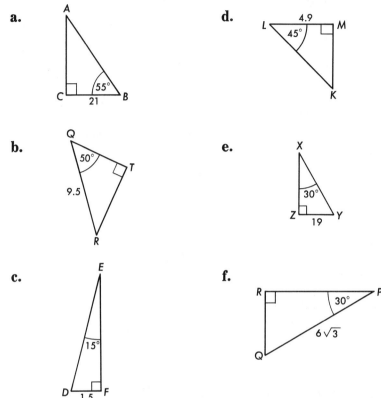

a.

b.

c.

d.

e.

f.

9. The top of a monument is sighted at the distance of 45 feet from the base of the monument. The angle between the horizontal line and the line from the eye to the top of the monument is 70°. Compute the height of the monument to the nearest foot. [Assume that the eye and the base of the monument are on the same level.]

10. Compute AB and BC to the nearest foot.

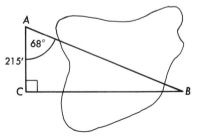

11. A ladder 20 ft. long is placed against a tree, so that the foot of the ladder is 10 ft. from the tree. Compute the measure of the angle between the ground and the ladder to the nearest whole degree.

12. Triangles ABC and $A'B'C'$ are similar. The pairs of corresponding angles are:

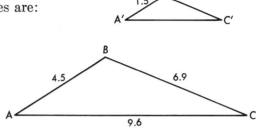

A and A',
B and B',
and C and C'.
Compute $B'C'$ and $A'C'$.

13. True or false?

a. If $m(\angle A) = 17°$ and $m(\angle B) = 163°$, then angles A and B are complementary angles.

Use the picture below for statements **b** through **n**.

b. $\sin(x) = \dfrac{b}{c}$

c. $\cos(y) = \dfrac{c}{b}$

d. $\dfrac{b}{a} = \tan(x)$

e. $\tan(x) = \dfrac{1}{\cot(x)}$

f. $\tan(x) = \cot(y)$

g. $a^2 + b^2 = c^2$

h. $a + b = c$

i. $c^2 - b^2 = a^2$

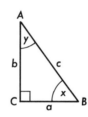

j. Angles A and B are complementary angles.

k. If $x > y$, then $\sin(x) > \sin(y)$.

l. If $x > y$, then $\cos(x) > \cos(y)$.

m. If $x > y$, then $\tan(x) > \cot(y)$.

n. If $x > y$, then $\cot(x) > \cot(y)$.

o. $\sin(45°) + \cos(45°) = 1$

p. $\sin(45°) = \cos(45°)$

q. For some x, $\tan(x) > 10^{20}$.

r. For some x, $\sin(x) > 10^{20}$.

s. $\cos(60°) = \dfrac{\sqrt{3}}{2}$

t. $\tan(45°) = 1$

u. $[\sin(30°)]^2 + [\cos(30°)]^2 = 1$

CHAPTER TEST

1. Using the given picture of the right triangle, tell the following:

   a. $\sin(x)$
   b. $\cos(x)$
   c. $\tan(x)$
   d. $\cot(x)$

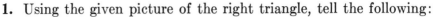

2. True or false?

   a. $\overline{AC}$ is adjacent to A
   b. $\overline{AC}$ is opposite to B
   c. $\overline{BC}$ is adjacent to A
   d. $\overline{BC}$ is opposite to A
   e. $m(\angle A) + m(\angle B) = 90°$
   f. $m(\angle C) < m(\angle B)$
   g. $(AC)^2 + (CB)^2 = (AB)^2$

   h. $\dfrac{BC}{AB} > 1$

   i. $\dfrac{AB}{AC} > 1$

3. True or false?

   a. $\dfrac{m}{r} = \sin(k)$

   b. $\sin(a) = \cos(k)$

   c. $\dfrac{r}{s} < 1$

   d. $\tan(k) \cdot \cot(a) = 1$
   e. $s + m = r$

   f. $\dfrac{\sin(k)}{\cos(k)} = \tan(k)$

   g. $\dfrac{\cos(a)}{\sin(a)} = \tan(a)$

   h. $a + k = 90$
   i. $[\sin(k)]^2 = 1 - [\cos(k)]^2$

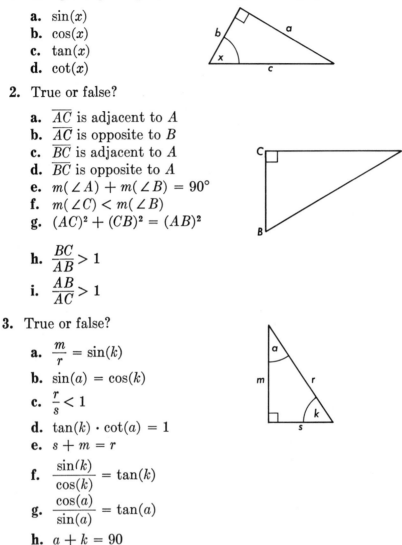

4. The sum of the measure of an angle and $\frac{1}{4}$ of the measure of its complementary angle is equal to $30°$. What is the measure of each angle?

5. In a right triangle the sum of $\frac{1}{5}$ of the measure of one acute angle and $\frac{1}{3}$ of the measure of the other acute angle is equal to $20°$. What is the measure of each angle?

6.   Solve each right triangle. Determine measures of angles to the nearest whole degree and the measures of sides to two digits.

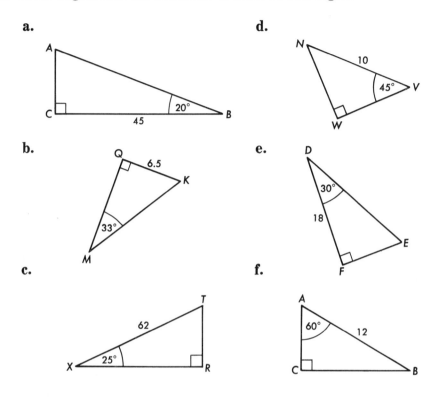

a.

b.

c.

d.

e.

f.

7.   The top of a building is sighted at the distance of 95 feet from the foundation. The angle between the horizontal line and the line from the eye to the top of the building is 50°. Compute the height of the building to the nearest foot. [Assume that the eye and the foundation of the building are on the same level.]

8. Triangle ABC is similar to triangle ADE. The pairs of corresponding angles are: $\angle C$ and $\angle E$, $\angle CAB$ and $\angle DAE$, and $\angle B$ and $\angle D$.

Compute each of the following:

a. $m(\angle CAB)$

b. $m(\angle D)$

c. $m(\angle DAE)$

d. AC

e. AB

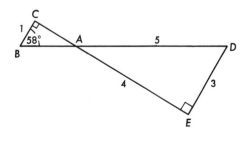

9. How high is a pole which casts a shadow 12 ft. long at the time a boy 5 ft. tall casts a shadow 6 ft. long?

10. True or false?

a. $\sin(45°) + \cos(45°) = \sqrt{2}$ **f.** $\tan(45°) \cdot \cot(45°) = 1$
b. $\sin(45°) \cdot \cos(45°) = \sqrt{2}$ **g.** $\tan(60°) > 1$
c. $\sin(30°) + \cos(30°) = 1$ **h.** $\cot(60°) > 1$
d. $\tan(60°) \cdot \cot(60°) = \sqrt{3}$ **i.** $\tan(30°) < 1$
e. $[\sin(60°)]^2 + [\cos(60°)]^2 = 1$ **j.** $\cot(30°) < 1$

CUMULATIVE REVIEW EXERCISES

These exercises are designed for your review of the basic ideas in Chapters 12 through 14.

1. Find the products.

a. $5(m + 3)$ **g.** $(2t + 1)(3t + 4)$
b. $-4(x - 2)$ **h.** $(3h - 2)(h + 4)$
c. $-5(-1 - m)$ **i.** $(2 - 5k)(2k + 6)$
d. $(x + 2)(x + 4)$ **j.** $(\frac{1}{2}x + 3)(\frac{1}{3}x - 2)$
e. $(y - 1)(y + 7)$ **k.** $(2.5s - 1)(2.5s + 1)$
f. $(2 - u)(3 + 2u)$ **l.** $(3 - 1.6n)(1.5n - 2)$

2. Factor.

a. $2m^2 + 8$ **f.** $4m^2 - 25k^2$
b. $6k^2 - 9k$ **g.** $8a^3 - 27b^3$
c. $u^2 + 4u + 4$ **h.** $6x^2 + 13x - 5$
d. $4n^2 - 12n + 9$ **i.** $-2y^2 - y + 6$
e. $c(a - b) + d(a - b)$ **j.** $2d^2 - 17d + 21$

3. Solve each quadratic equation by factoring.

a. $x^2 + 3x - 4 = 0$ **f.** $6x^2 - 11x - 10 = 0$
b. $x^2 + 11x + 24 = 0$ **g.** $3x^2 - 8x + 5 = 0$
c. $x^2 - 8x + 12 = 0$ **h.** $7x^2 + 33x - 10 = 0$
d. $2x^2 + x - 6 = 0$ **i.** $15x^2 + 23x + 4 = 0$
e. $9x^2 - 9x + 2 = 0$ **j.** $4x^2 - 4x + 1 = 0$

4. Solve each quadratic equation by the use of the quadratic formula.

a. $6x^2 - x - 1 = 0$ **d.** $-2x^2 + x + 2 = 0$
b. $x^2 + x - 4 = 0$ **e.** $x - 4 - 3x^2 = 0$
c. $3x^2 - 2x - 1 = 0$ **f.** $1 - x - x^2 = 0$

5. Compute the discriminant and for each equation tell whether it has two real roots, one real root, or no real roots.

a. $x^2 + 4x + 1 = 0$
b. $4x^2 - 12x + 9 = 0$
c. $x^2 + x + 1 = 0$

d. $4x^2 - 28x + 49 = 0$
e. $-2x^2 + x - 3 = 0$
f. $x^2 + 2x + 3 = 0$

6. Find equivalent expressions by factoring and simplifying.

a. $\dfrac{3n + 6}{12n + 18}$

b. $\dfrac{8 - 4k}{16k + 20}$

c. $\dfrac{5xy + 20y}{5y + 40xy}$

d. $\dfrac{a^2 + 4a + 3}{a^2 - a - 12}$

e. $\dfrac{2m^2 + 3m - 2}{4m^2 - 4m + 1}$

f. $\dfrac{ak + xk + a + x}{ax + x^2 - a - x}$

g. $\dfrac{2k^2 + 7k + 6}{2k^2 + 5k + 3}$

h. $\dfrac{2x - y - xy + 2}{2x - 3y - xy + 6}$

7. Given the polynomials

$$P(x) = 3x^4 - 10x^3 + 3x^2 + x - 3$$
$$Q(x) = x - 3$$

$$R(x) = x^3 - 3x^2 + 2x - 6$$
$$S(x) = x + 1$$

determine each of the following:

a. $P(0)$
b. $R(2)$
c. $S(-\sqrt{2})$
d. $Q(x) \cdot S(x)$
e. $\dfrac{P(x)}{Q(x)}$

f. $\dfrac{R(x)}{Q(x)}$

g. $R(x) \cdot S(x)$
h. $Q(0) \cdot S(0)$
i. $R(1) \cdot P(1)$
j. $P(0) \cdot Q(0) \cdot R(0) \cdot S(0)$

8. Solve each problem.

a. The product of twice a number and the number increased by 1 is equal to 60. What is the number? Are there two such numbers? If yes, what are they?

b. The measure of the base of a triangle is three times the measure of its corresponding altitude. Compute the measures of the base and altitude if the area of the triangle is equal to 24 sq. in.

*c. The sum of a number and its reciprocal is equal to $\dfrac{3\sqrt{3} + 1}{2}$. What is this number?

d. Compute the measure of a diagonal in a rectangle 10′ by 20′.

9. On a number line, graph the solution set of each of the following:

a. $3y + 7 > 1$ c. $|a| \geq 2$ e. $|2p + 1| \geq 5$
b. $2x - 1 \leq 0$ d. $|3t| < 9$ f. $|5u| \leq 0$

10. Given the universal set $U = \{-2, -1, 0, 1, 2\}$, list the ordered pairs which are members of the solution sets of the following:

a. $x = y$ c. $x < y$ e. $|x| = |y|$
b. $x > y$ d. $x \geq y$ f. $|x| < |y|$

11. Using the set of real numbers for the universal set, graph each of the following:

a. $\{(x, y) | y = 2x\}$ d. $\{(x, y) | y = 2x^2\}$ g. $\{(x, y) | |y| = x\}$
b. $\{(x, y) | y < 2x\}$ e. $\{(x, y) | y > 2x^2\}$ h. $\{(x, y) | |y| = |x|\}$
c. $\{(x, y) | y \geq 2x\}$ f. $\{(x, y) | y \leq 2x^2\}$

12. Graph each function and its inverse. Find the slope of each graph. The universal set is the set of real numbers.

a. $\{(x, y) | y = 3x - 2\}$ c. $\{(x, y) | y = -3x + 1\}$
b. $\{(x, y) | y = \frac{1}{3}x + 3\}$ d. $\{(x, y) | y = -\frac{1}{3}x - 4\}$

13. Which of the following are graphs of functions?

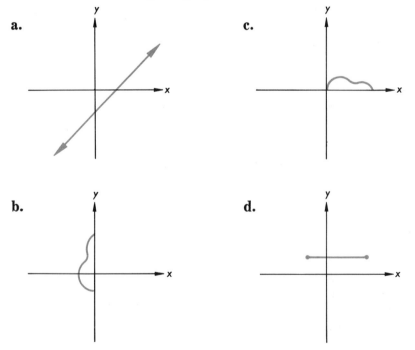

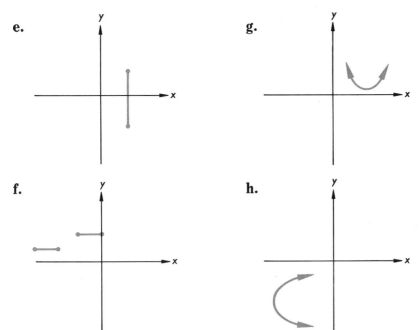

e.

g.

f.

h.

14. For each graph in exercise **13,** sketch the inverse of the relation. Tell whether the inverse is a function.

15. Compute BC and AB to the nearest whole foot.

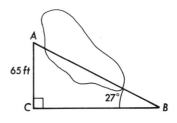

16. True or false?

a. $\sin(45°) = \cos(45°)$
b. $\tan(70°) > \tan(10°)$
c. $\cot(70°) > \cot(10°)$

d. $\cos(30°) = \dfrac{1}{\sin(30°)}$

e. $\cot(25°) = \dfrac{1}{\tan(25°)}$

f. If $\tan(38°) \doteq .781$, then $\cot(38°) \doteq .219$.

g. If $\tan(12°) \doteq .213$, then $\cot(78°) \doteq .213$.

h. $1 - [\sin(70°)]^2 = [\cos(70°)]^2$
i. If $a < b$, then $\sin(a) - \sin(b) > 0$.
j. If $a < b$, then $\cos(a) - \cos(b) > 0$.
k. If $a < b$, then $\tan(a) - \tan(b) > 0$.
l. If $a < b$, then $\cot(a) - \cot(b) > 0$.
m. $\tan(45°) + \cot(45°) = 2$
n. For some x,
$\tan(x) + \cot(x) > 5{,}000{,}000$.
o. For some x, $\sin(x) + \cos(x) > 2$.

BIBLIOGRAPHY

Hogben, L. *Mathematics for the Million*. New York: W. W. Norton and Company, Inc., 1951. Chapter 6.

Johnson, Donovan A., and Glenn, William H. *The World of Measurement*. St. Louis: Webster Publishing Company, 1961.

Moore, J. *Fundamental Principles of Mathematics*. New York: Rinehart and Company, Inc., 1960. pp. 105-125, 172-210.

Nichols, Eugene D. *Pre-Algebra Mathematics*. New York: Holt, Rinehart and Winston, Inc., 1965. Chapter 13.

Nichols, E. D.; Heimer, R. T.; and Garland, E. H. *Modern Intermediate Algebra*. New York: Holt, Rinehart and Winston, Inc., 1965. Chapters 13 and 14.

Ruchlis, Hy, and Engelhardt, Jack. *The Story of Mathematics*. Irvington-on-Hudson: F. E. Harvey, Inc., 1958.

Sawyer, W. W. *Mathematician's Delight*. Baltimore: Penguin Books, 1956. Chapter 13.

School Mathematics Study Group. *Mathematics Through Science*. Stanford: Stanford University Press, 1963. Part I, Measurement and Graphing.

Titchmarsh, E. C. *Mathematics for the General Reader*. New York: Doubleday & Company, Inc., 1959. pp. 126-139.

Whitehead, Alfred North. *An Introduction to Mathematics*. New York: Oxford University Press, 1958. pp. 128-143.

No.	Sq.	Sq. Root	Cube	Cu. Root	No.	Sq.	Sq. Root	Cube	Cu. Root
1	1	1.000	1	1.000	51	2,601	7.141	132,651	3.708
2	4	1.414	8	1.260	52	2,704	7.211	140,608	3.733
3	9	1.732	27	1.442	53	2,809	7.280	148,877	3.756
4	16	2.000	64	1.587	54	2,916	7.348	157,564	3.780
5	25	2.236	125	1.710	55	3,025	7.416	166,375	3.803
6	36	2.449	216	1.817	56	3,136	7.483	175,616	3.826
7	49	2.646	343	1.913	57	3,249	7.550	185,193	3.849
8	64	2.828	512	2.000	58	3,364	7.616	195,112	3.871
9	81	3.000	729	2.080	59	3,481	7.681	205,379	3.893
10	100	3.162	1,000	2.154	60	3,600	7.746	216,000	3.915
11	121	3.317	1,331	2.224	61	3,721	7.810	226,981	3.936
12	144	3.464	1,728	2.289	62	3,844	7.874	238,328	3.958
13	169	3.606	2,197	2.351	63	3,969	7.937	250,047	3.979
14	196	3.742	2,744	2.410	64	4,096	8.000	262,144	4.000
15	225	3.875	3,375	2.466	65	4,225	8.062	274,625	4.021
16	256	4.000	4,096	2.520	66	4,356	8.124	287,496	4.041
17	289	4.123	4,913	2.571	67	4,489	8.185	300,763	4.062
18	324	4.243	5,832	2.621	68	4,624	8.246	314,432	4.082
19	361	4.359	6,859	2.668	69	4,761	8.307	328,509	4.102
20	400	4.472	8,000	2.714	70	4,900	8.357	343,000	4.121
21	441	4.583	9,261	2.759	71	5,041	8.426	357,911	4.141
22	484	4.690	10,648	2.802	72	5,184	8.485	373,248	4.160
23	529	4.796	12,167	2.844	73	5,329	8.544	389,017	4.179
24	576	4.899	13,824	2.884	74	5,476	8.602	405,224	4.198
25	625	5.000	15,625	2.924	75	5,625	8.660	421,875	4.217
26	676	5.099	17,576	2.962	76	5,776	8.718	438,976	4.236
27	729	5.196	19,683	3.000	77	5,929	8.775	456,533	4.254
28	784	5.292	21,952	3.037	78	6,084	8.832	474,552	4.273
29	841	5.385	24,389	3.072	79	6,241	8.888	493,039	4.291
30	900	5.477	27,000	3.107	80	6,400	8.944	512,000	4.309
31	961	5.568	29,791	3.141	81	6,561	9.000	531,441	4.327
32	1,024	5.657	32,768	3.175	82	6,724	9.055	551,368	4.344
33	1,089	5.745	35,937	3.208	83	6,889	9.110	571,787	4.362
34	1,156	5.831	39,304	3.240	84	7,056	9.165	592,704	4.380
35	1,225	5.916	42,875	3.271	85	7,225	9.220	614,125	4.397
36	1,296	6.000	46,656	3.302	86	7,396	9.274	636,056	4.414
37	1,369	6.083	50,653	3.332	87	7,569	9.327	658,503	4.431
38	1,444	6.164	54,872	3.362	88	7,744	9.381	681,472	4.448
39	1,521	6.245	59,319	3.391	89	7,921	9.434	704,969	4.465
40	1,600	6.325	64,000	3.420	90	8,100	9.487	729,000	4.481
41	1,681	6.403	68,921	3.448	91	8,281	9.539	753,571	4.498
42	1,764	6.481	74,088	3.476	92	8,464	9.592	778,688	4.514
43	1,849	6.557	79,507	3.503	93	8,649	9.644	804,357	4.531
44	1,936	6.633	85,184	3.530	94	8,836	9.695	830,584	4.547
45	2,025	6.708	91,125	3.557	95	9,025	9.747	857,375	4.563
46	2,116	6.782	97,336	3.583	96	9,216	9.798	884,736	4.579
47	2,209	6.856	103,823	3.609	97	9,409	9.849	912,673	4.595
48	2,304	6.928	110,592	3.634	98	9,604	9.899	941,192	4.610
49	2,401	7.000	117,649	3.659	99	9,801	9.950	970,299	4.626
50	2,500	7.071	125,000	3.684	100	10,000	10.000	1,000,000	4.642

Table of Trigonometric Functions

Angle Measure	Sin	Cos	Angle Measure	Tan	Cot
1°	.017	1.000	1°	.017	57.3
2°	.035	.999	2°	.035	28.6
3°	.052	.999	3°	.052	19.1
4°	.070	.998	4°	.070	14.3
5°	.087	.996	5°	.087	11.4
6°	.105	.995	6°	.105	9.51
7°	.122	.993	7°	.123	8.14
8°	.139	.990	8°	.141	7.12
9°	.156	.988	9°	.158	6.31
10°	.174	.985	10°	.176	5.67
11°	.191	.982	11°	.194	5.15
12°	.208	.978	12°	.213	4.71
13°	.225	.974	13°	.231	4.33
14°	.242	.970	14°	.249	4.01
15°	.259	.966	15°	.268	3.73
16°	.276	.961	16°	.287	3.49
17°	.292	.956	17°	.306	3.27
18°	.309	.951	18°	.325	3.08
19°	.326	.946	19°	.344	2.90
20°	.342	.940	20°	.364	2.75
21°	.358	.934	21°	.384	2.61
22°	.375	.927	22°	.404	2.48
23°	.391	.921	23°	.424	2.36
24°	.407	.914	24°	.445	2.25
25°	.423	.906	25°	.466	2.15
26°	.438	.899	26°	.488	2.05
27°	.454	.891	27°	.510	1.96
28°	.469	.883	28°	.532	1.88
29°	.485	.875	29°	.554	1.80
30°	.500	.866	30°	.577	1.73
31°	.515	.857	31°	.601	1.66
32°	.530	.848	32°	.625	1.60
33°	.545	.839	33°	.649	1.54
34°	.559	.829	34°	.675	1.48
35°	.574	.819	35°	.700	1.43
36°	.588	.809	36°	.727	1.38
37°	.602	.799	37°	.754	1.33
38°	.616	.788	38°	.781	1.28
39°	.629	.777	39°	.810	1.23
40°	.643	.766	40°	.839	1.19
41°	.656	.755	41°	.869	1.15
42°	.669	.743	42°	.900	1.11
43°	.682	.731	43°	.933	1.07
44°	.695	.719	44°	.966	1.04
45°	.707	.707	45°	1.000	1.00

Glossary

This is a list of important terms used in this book. A brief description or an illustration, not necessarily a definition, is given for each term.

Abscissa. The first of the two coordinates of a point.

Absolute value (of a number). The absolute value of a non-negative number is that number, and the absolute value of a negative number is the opposite (additive inverse) of that number. $\forall_{x \geq 0}\ |x| = x$ and $\forall_{x < 0}\ |x| = -x$.

Acute angle. An angle with measure between $0°$ and $90°$.

Associative Property of Addition, APA. $\forall_x \forall_y \forall_z\ (x + y) + z = x + (y + z)$.

Associative Property of Multiplication, APM. $\forall_x \forall_y \forall_z\ (xy)z = x(yz)$.

Base. In 5^4, 5 is the base. More generally, in x^y, x is the base.

Binary operation. An operation which is performed on a pair of elements.

Binomial. A polynomial with two terms. Example: $2x - 13$.

Boolean Algebra. The algebra of sets developed by George Boole (1815–1864).

Braces, { }. Symbol used to denote a set, or as an inclusion symbol for punctuation.

Brackets, [ ]. Inclusion symbol used for punctuation.

Cartesian plane. A plane for which there is established a one-to-one correspondence between its points and the set of all ordered pairs of real numbers.

Cartesian set. A set of ordered pairs obtained by forming all possible ordered pairs from elements of two given sets. Example: If $A = \{1,\ 2\}$ and $B = \{1,\ 2,\ 3\}$, then the Cartesian set $A \times B = \{(1,\ 1),\ (1,\ 2),\ (1,\ 3),\ (2,\ 1),\ (2,\ 2),\ (2,\ 3)\}$.

Closure. A set has closure under a given operation if the result of operating on any members of a set belongs to the set. For example, the set of real numbers has closure under multiplication, since the product of any pair of real numbers is a real number.

Coefficient. In the polynomial $a_r x^r + a_{r-1} x^{r-1} + \ldots + a_1 x + a_0$, a_r, a_{r-1}, $\ldots$, a_1, a_0 are coefficients.

Commutative Property of Addition, CPA. $\forall_x \forall_y\ x + y = y + x$.

Commutative Property of Multiplication, CPM. $\forall_x \forall_y\ xy = yx$.

Complement (of a set). Set A is a complement of set B if and only if A consists of all elements of the universal set which are not in B. The symbol for the complement of B is $\overline{B}$.

Complementary angles. Two angles for which the sum of the measures is equal to $90°$.

Completing the square. Example: $x^2 + 4x + 1 = x^2 + 4x + 4 - 4 + 1 = (x^2 + 4x + 4) - 3 = (x + 2)^2 - 3$.

Complex fractional expression. An expression of the form $\dfrac{P}{Q}(Q \neq 0)$, where

451

at least one of P and Q is a fractional expression.

Composite number. A natural number (different from 1), which is not a prime number.

Coordinate. The first or second number in an ordered pair of numbers assigned to a point.

Coordinate plane. See Cartesian plane.

Cosine (of an angle measure). In a right triangle, the ratio of the measure of the leg adjacent to the angle to the measure of the hypotenuse.

Cotangent (of an angle measure). In a right triangle, the ratio of the measure of the leg opposite the angle to the measure of the other leg.

Counter-example. An example which contradicts a statement.

Degree of a polynomial (in one variable). The greatest exponent used with a variable whose coefficient is not zero.

Density. The property of a set of numbers in which there is a third number between any two given numbers. For example, the set of real numbers has the density property, or it is dense.

Dependent system (of linear equations in two variables). A system consisting of two equivalent equations.

Directed number. A positive or negative number.

Discriminant (of a quadratic equation). For the equation $ax^2 + bx + c = 0$, the discriminant is $b^2 - 4ac$.

Disjoint sets. Sets which have no common elements.

Distributive Property of Multiplication over Addition, DPMA.
$$\forall_x \forall_y \forall_z \; x(y + z) = (xy) + (xz).$$

Divisor (of a number). Natural number x is a divisor of natural number y if and only if $y \div x = z$, where z is a natural number.

Domain (of a relation). The set of all first members of all ordered pairs of a relation.

Element (of a set). A member of a set.

Empty set (ϕ). A set which has no members.

Equation. A sentence of the form $x = y$.

Equivalent equations. Equations which have the same solution set.

Equivalent expressions. Two expressions are equivalent if and only if for every set of the same replacements of the variable(s) they yield the same number. Example: $3(x - 4)$ and $3x - 12$ are equivalent expressions.

Euler circles. Circles used to illustrate the relations between sets.

Exponent. In 3^2, 2 is the exponent. More generally, in x^y, y is the exponent.

Factor. Examples: 2 and 3 are factors of 6, because $2 \times 3 = 6$; $x - 1$ and $x + 2$ are factors of $x^2 + x - 2$, because $(x - 1)(x + 2) = x^2 + x - 2$.

Field. A set of elements with two operations which possess eleven properties (See Pages 104 and 105 for the list of the eleven properties).

Finite set. A set is finite if the number of its elements can be expressed as a whole number.

First component. First element in an ordered pair.

Function. A set of ordered pairs in which no two pairs have the same first element.

Graph. A set of points shown in the Cartesian plane.

Hypotenuse. The side in a right triangle which is opposite the right angle.

Inconsistent system. A system of linear equations in two variables which has the empty set for its solution set.

Independent system. A system of linear equations in two variables which has an ordered pair of numbers for its solution.

Index. In $\sqrt[n]{x}$, n is the index.

Inequality. A sentence of the form $x < y$ or $x > y$.

Infinite set. A set which is not finite.

Integer. Any positive or negative whole number, or 0.

Intersection (of two sets). The set which consists of only those elements which belong to both of two given sets.

Inverse (of a function). The inverse of a given function F is the set of ordered pairs obtained by interchanging the first and the second element of each ordered pair in F. The symbol for the inverse of F is F'.

Inverse (operations). Example: addition and subtraction are inverse operations, because $\forall_x \forall_y \ (x + y) - y = x$ or $\forall_x \forall_y$, if $x + y = z$, then $z - y = x$.

Irrational number. A real number which has no name of the form $\dfrac{a}{b}(b \neq 0)$, a and b being whole numbers. Example: $\sqrt{3}$.

Is greater than, $>$. Example: $5 > 4$.

Is less than, $<$. Example: $1 < 2$.

Is not equal to, $\neq$. Example: $5 \neq 7$.

Is not greater than, $\not>$. Example: $5 \not> 7$.

Is not less than, $\not<$. Example: $3 \not< 1$.

Left Distributive Property of Multiplication over Addition, LDPMA.
$$\forall_x \forall_y \forall_z \ x(y + z) = (xy) + (xz).$$
Left Distributive Property of Multiplication over Subtraction, LDPMS.
$$\forall_x \forall_y \forall_z \ x(y - z) = (xy) - (xz).$$
Leg (of a right triangle). A side in a right triangle which is adjacent to the right angle.

Linear function. A set of ordered pairs (x, y), for which $y = ax + b$ (a and b are real numbers, $a \neq 0$).

Matching sets. Two sets between which there exists a one-to-one correspondence.

Member (of a set). A number or any other thing which belongs to the set.

Monomial. One term. Example: $9ax$.

Natural numbers. Counting numbers: 1, 2, 3, 4, 5, 6, ...

Negative number. A real number which is less than 0.

Non-terminating decimal. Examples: .367367367 . . ., 3.9356702 . . ., 27.01001000100001 . . ..

Null set. Empty set, that is, a set with no members.

Number line. A line for which there was established a one-to-one correspondence between the points and the set of real numbers.

Numeral. A name of a number.

One-to-one correspondence. A matching between two sets so that to each element of one set there is assigned exactly one element of the second set and vice versa.

Open expression. An expression containing at least one variable. Example: $5x + 9ab$.

Open rational expression. A quotient $\dfrac{P}{Q}$ of polynomials P and $Q(Q \neq 0)$ involving at least one variable.

Opposite (of a number). The opposite of a positive number is the negative number with the same absolute value. The opposite of a negative number is the positive number with the same absolute value. The opposite of 0 is 0. Also called *additive inverse*.

Ordinate. The second of the two co-ordinates of a point.

Origin. The point on the number line assigned to the number 0 or the point in the coordinate plane assigned to the pair (0, 0).

Parabola. The set of points described by $y = ax^2 + bx + c$, (a, b, $c \in R$, $a \neq 0$).

Parallel lines. Lines which do not intersect.

Parentheses, ( ). Inclusion symbols used for punctuation.

Perfect square (trinomial). A tri-nomial which results from squaring a binomial. Example: $x^2 - 2x + 1$ is a perfect square trinomial, because $x^2 - 2x + 1 = (x - 1)^2$.

Perimeter (of a polygon). The sum of the measures of all sides of a polygon.

Polynomial. Given the set consisting of all the real numbers and the variable x. Any element of this set or any expression which can be constructed from the elements of this set using only the operations of addition, subtraction, and multiplication is called a polynomial in x. Example: $5x^3 - 3x^2 + 5x - 9$.

Positive number. A real number which is greater than 0.

Power. $4^2 = 16$ means that 16 is the second power of 4; more generally x^n is the nth power of x.

Prime number. A natural number which has exactly two factors, 1 and the number itself.

Principal square root. The positive number whose square is equal to the given number. Example: 2 is the principal square root of 4, since $2 > 0$ and $2^2 = 4$.

Proof. An argument from an assump-tion to a conclusion in accordance with accepted rules of logic.

Proper subset (of a set). A is a proper subset of B if and only if A is a subset of B and A is not equal to B (see *subset*).

Pythagorean Property. In a right tri-angle, if a and b are measures of the two legs and c is the measure of the hypote-nuse, then $a^2 + b^2 = c^2$.

Quadrant. One of the four subsets of the coordinate plane into which the two axes separate the plane.

Quadratic equation. An equation of the form $ax^2 + bx + c = 0$.

Quadratic formula. For the equation $ax^2 + bx + c = 0$, $x = \dfrac{-b \pm \sqrt{b^2 - 4ac}}{2a}$ is the quadratic formula.

Quadratic function. A set of ordered pairs (x, y) for which $y = ax^2 + bx + c$ (a, b, c are real numbers and $a \neq 0$).

Radical. $\sqrt[n]{x}$ is a radical.

Radical equation. An equation which contains a variable under a radical sign.

Radical sign. $\sqrt[n]{}$ is a radical sign.

Radicand. In $\sqrt[n]{x}$, x is the radicand.

Range (of a relation). The set of all second members of all ordered pairs of a relation.

Rational number. A real number which has a name of the form $\dfrac{a}{b}$ ($b \neq 0$), a and b integers. Example: $\dfrac{-3}{11}$.

Real number. A rational or irra-tional number.

Reciprocal (of a number). Given any real number $x \neq 0$, y is the reciprocal of x if and only if $xy = 1$. Example: since $\frac{2}{5} \times \frac{5}{2} = 1$, $\frac{2}{5}$ and $\frac{5}{2}$ are reciprocals of each other. Also called *multiplicative inverse*.

Rectangular coordinate system (Cartesian coordinate system). See *Cartesian plane*.

Relation. A set of ordered pairs.

Remainder. In dividing 7 by 2, 3 is the quotient and 1 is the remainder, since $7 = 2 \times 3 + 1$. In dividing $x^3 + x^2 - x + 3$ by $x - 1$, $2x + 1$ is the quotient and $x + 4$ is the remainder, since $x^3 + x^2 - x + 3 = (x - 1)(2x + 1) + (x + 4)$.

Repeating decimal. Example: $.252525 \ldots$; also written $.\overline{25}$.

Right Distributive Property of Multiplication over Addition, RDPMA.
$$\forall_x \forall_y \forall_z \ (x + y)z = (xz) + (yz).$$

Right Distributive Property of Multiplication over Subtraction, RDPMS.
$$\forall_x \forall_y \forall_z \ (x - y)z = (xz) - (yz).$$

Right-hand Addition Property.
$\forall_x \forall_y \forall_z$, if $x = y$, then $x + z = y + z$.

Right-hand Multiplication Property.
$\forall_x \forall_y \forall_z$, if $x = y$, then $xz = yz$.

Root (of an equation). A number which satisfies the equation.

Scientific notation. If a number is shown as the product of a number between 1 and 10 and the appropriate integer power of 10, then it is said to be shown in scientific notation. Example: 267.9 shown in scientific notation is 2.679×10^2.

Second Component. Second element of an ordered pair.

Selector. An open sentence which selects the solution set from the universal set.

Set. A collection of things.

Sextant. An instrument used to sight angles.

Similar triangles. Triangles in which pairs of corresponding angles have the same measure and the ratio of the measures of corresponding sides is the same.

Sine (of an angle measure). In a right triangle, the ratio of the measure of the leg opposite the angle to the measure of the hypotenuse.

Slope (of a line). The number which a represents in $y = ax + b$. It determines the "steepness" of the graph of a line.

Solution set. A set of numbers which satisfy the given equation or inequality.

Solving a triangle. To solve a triangle means to determine all of its measures.

Square root (of a number). A number which when multiplied by itself results in that number. Example: $\sqrt{49} = 7$, because $7 \times 7 = 49$.

Standard form (of a linear equation in two variables). $Ax + By = C$.

Subset (of a set). A is a subset of B if and only if every element of A is also an element of B.

Symmetric Property of Equality.
$\forall_x \forall_y$, if $x = y$, then $y = x$.

System of equations. Two (or more) equations, the solution set for which is the solution set of the intersection of the equations.

Tangent (of an angle measure). In a right triangle, the ratio of the measure of the leg adjacent to the angle to the measure of the other leg.

Terminating decimal. A decimal which can be written with a finite number of digits. Example: .3965.

Theorem. A statement which has been proved.

Trigonometry. Triangle measurement.

Trinomial. A polynomial with three terms. Example: $3x + 4ab - 7m$.

Union (of two sets). The set consisting of the members which belong to one or the other of the two given sets (includes members belonging to both sets).

Universe. The set of all things which are chosen for a particular study (also called *universal set*).

Value of a function. A second member of a pair belonging to the function. Example: If $(2, 3) \in F$, then the value of F at 2 is 3.

Venn diagram. A pictorial representation of relations between sets, named after Venn, a British logician of the nineteenth century.

Vertical line test. A visual test which determines whether a relation is a function: Examine all lines parallel to the range axis. If no lines intersects the graph of the relation in more than one point, then the relation is a function.

x-axis. The horizontal line in the rectangular coordinate system.

x-intercept. The first coordinate of the point at which any non-horizontal line intersects the x-axis is called the x-intercept of the line.

y-axis. The vertical line in the rectangular coordinate system.

y-intercept. The second coordinate of the point at which any non-vertical line intersects the y-axis is called the y-intercept of the line.

Index

The figures in **bold-faced** type refer to the pages on which the words and expressions are described.